ACCIDENTAL EXPLOSIONS
Volume 2:
Types of Explosive Substances

ELLIS HORWOOD SERIES IN
APPLIED SCIENCE AND INDUSTRIAL TECHNOLOGY

Series Editor: Dr D. H. SHARP, OBE, former General Secretary, Society of Chemical Industry; formerly General Secretary, Institution of Chemical Engineers; and former Technical Director, Confederation of British Industry.

This collection of books is designed to meet the needs of technologists already working in fields to be covered, and for those new to the industries concerned. The series comprises valuable works of reference for scientists and engineers in many fields, with special usefulness to technologists and entrepreneurs in developing countries.

Students of chemical engineering, industrial and applied chemistry, and related fields, will also find these books of great use, with their emphasis on the practical technology as well as theory. The authors are highly qualified chemical engineers and industrial chemists with extensive experience, who write with the authority gained from their years in industry.

Published and in active publication

PRACTICAL USES OF DIAMONDS
A. BAKON, Research Centre of Geological Technique, Warsaw, and A. SZYMANSKI, Institute of Electronic Materials Technology, Warsaw
NATURAL GLASSES
V. BOUSKA, *et al.,* Czechoslovak Society for Mineralogy & Geology, Czechoslovakia
POTTERY SCIENCE: Materials, Processes and Products
A. DINSDALE, lately Director of Research, British Ceramic Research Association
MATCHMAKING: Science, Technology and Manufacture
C. A. FINCH, Managing Director, Pentafin Associates, Chemical, Technical and Media Consultants, Stoke Mandeville, and S. RAMACHANDRAN, Senior Consultant, United Nations Industrial Development Organisation for the Match Industry
OFFSHORE PETROLEUM TECHNOLOGY AND DRILLING EQUIPMENT
R. HOSIE, formerly of Robert Gordon's Institute of Technology, Aberdeen
MEASURING COLOUR
R. W. G. HUNT, Visiting Professor, The City University, London
MODERN APPLIED ENERGY CONSERVATION
Editor: K. JACQUES, University of Stirling, Scotland
CHARACTERIZATION OF FOSSIL FUEL LIQUIDS
D. W. JONES, University of Bristol
PAINT AND SURFACE COATINGS: Theory and Practice
Editor: R. LAMBOURNE, Technical Manager, INDCOLLAG (Industrial Colloid Advisory Group), Department of Physical Chemistry, University of Bristol
CROP PROTECTION CHEMICALS
B. G. LEVER, Development Manager, ICI plc Plant Protection Division
HANDBOOK OF MATERIALS HANDLING
Translated by R. G. T. LINDKVIST, MTG, Translation Editor: R. ROBINSON, Editor, *Materials Handling News*. Technical Editor: G. LUNDESJO, Rolatruc Limited
FERTILIZER TECHNOLOGY
G. C. LOWRISON, Consultant, Bradford
NON-WOVEN BONDED FABRICS
Editor: J. LUNENSCHLOSS, Institute of Textile Technology of the Rhenish-Westphalian Technical University, Aachen, and W. ALBRECHT, Wuppertal
PROFIT BY QUALITY: The Essentials of Industrial Survival
P. W. MOIR, Consultant, West Sussex
EFFICIENT BEYOND IMAGINING: CIM and Its Applications for Today's Industry
P. W. MOIR, Consultant, West Sussex
TRANSIENT SIMULATION METHODS FOR GAS NETWORKS
A. J. OSIADACZ, UMIST, Manchester
MECHANICS OF WOOL STRUCTURES
R. POSTLE, University of New South Wales, Sydney, Australia, G. A. CARNABY, Wool Research Organization of New Zealand, Lincoln, New Zealand, and S. de JONG, CSIRO, New South Wales, Australia
MICROCOMPUTERS IN THE PROCESS INDUSTRY
E. R. ROBINSON, Head of Chemical Engineering, North East London Polytechnic
BIOPROTEIN MANUFACTURE: A Critical Assessment
D. H. SHARP, OBE, former General Secretary, Society of Chemical Industry; formerly General Secretary, Institution of Chemical Engineers; and former Technical Director, Confederation of British Industry
QUALITY ASSURANCE: The Route to Efficiency and Competitiveness, Second Edition
L. STEBBING, Quality Management Consultant
QUALITY MANAGEMENT IN THE SERVICE INDUSTRY
L. STEBBING, Quality Management Consultant
INDUSTRIAL CHEMISTRY: Volumes 1 and 2
E. STOCCHI, Milan, with additions by K. A. K. LOTT and E. L. SHORT, Brunel

Series continued at back of book

ACCIDENTAL EXPLOSIONS
Volume 2:
Types of Explosive Substances

LOUIS A. MEDARD
formerly Head of the Laboratory
in the French Government Explosive Branch

Translator
PETER FAWCETT
Department of Modern Languages, University of Bradford

Translation Editor
V. C. MARSHALL
School of Industrial Technology, University of Bradford

ELLIS HORWOOD LIMITED
Publishers · Chichester

Halsted Press: a division of
JOHN WILEY & SONS
New York · Chichester · Brisbane · Toronto

This English edition first published in 1989 by
ELLIS HORWOOD LIMITED
Market Cross House, Cooper Street,
Chichester, West Sussex, PO19 1EB, England
The publisher's colophon is reproduced from James Gillison's drawing of the ancient Market Cross, Chichester.

Distributors:

Australia and New Zealand:
JACARANDA WILEY LIMITED
GPO Box 859, Brisbane, Queensland 4001, Australia

Canada:
JOHN WILEY & SONS CANADA LIMITED
22 Worcester Road, Rexdale, Ontario, Canada

Europe and Africa:
JOHN WILEY & SONS LIMITED
Baffins Lane, Chichester, West Sussex, England

North and South America and the rest of the world:
Halsted Press: a division of
JOHN WILEY & SONS
605 Third Avenue, New York, NY 10158, USA

This English edition is translated from the original French edition *Les Explosifs Occasionnels*, published in 1987 by Technique et Documentation, © the copyright holders.

© **1989 English Edition, Ellis Horwood Limited**

British Library Cataloguing in Publication Data
Medard, Louis A.
Accidental explosions.
Vol. 2
1. Explosions
I. Title
536'.41

Library of Congress Card No. 89–19866

ISBN 0–7458–0436–5 (Ellis Horwood Limited)
ISBN 0–470–21532–1 (Halsted Press)

Printed in Great Britain by Hartnolls, Bodmin

Table of contents Volume 1

Table of contents Volume 2

Preface

The present work is a unique and uniquely encycopaedic survey of a field of the utmost importance. Ranging widely over a vast array of well-documented sources, and moving with complete ease between theory and practice, the author brings together into' an erudite and critical whole an extensive body of knowledge covering the properties and causes of accidental and unwanted explosives. Although the references are there in great number to be followed up by those who need them, the author has done potential readers the service of bringing together the results of important experimental work which many would otherwise have access to only with considerable difficulty.

The first volume sketches in the necessary theoretical background in thermochemistry and kinetics before embarking upon a detailed study of the explosion and detonation properties (flammability limits, explosion temperatures, velocities, etc.) of substances in the gaseous, dense and powdered state, as well as providing extensive information and advice on causes such as hot spots and sparks and safety precautions such as vents and rupture disks.

The second volume is an intensive and extensive survey of a wide variety of substances in daily use in industry which can, in certain circumstances, give rise to accidental explosions. The properties and hazards are spelt out in detail, with the discussion describing and drawing on a long history of sometimes catastrophic accidents from which are derived vital safety measures to protect life and property. The author is always at pains to point out where our knowledge in these matters is still defective and to be critical of those who publish hasty, and sometimes even wrong, results.

This work will certainly be of interest to specialists working in laboratories, but also to industrial engineers and designers whose task it is to be aware of national and international standards, and to design industrial equipment and the layout of plant handling all substances which may, during treatment or storage, become explosive. It will be of interest to those involved with the road and rail transport of hazardous substances, and will also be of vital importance to safety experts and officers who have to be acquainted with government regulations and safety procedures, and train the workforce, sometimes in such simple, everyday matters as the proper type of clothing to be worn or the correct procedure for using an oxyacetylene blowpipe, since this work covers the problem of safety down to the slightest detail.

Finally, but by no means less importantly, this work is a reminder to the world community of the important pioneering work of French researchers in this field, from the early studies of Le Chatelier and Berthelot to the present day.

PART FOUR
Monographs on families
of explosives

17

Combustion supporters

17.1 COMBUSTION SUPPORTERS IN GENERAL

17.1.1 Definition of combustion supporters

Combustion supporters are
- either highly electronegative elements, such as oxygen and fluorine, which cause fuels to burn easily and *vigorously* with considerable release of heat,
- or compounds in which the electronegative elements are bonded only weakly with the result that the compounds may react *strongly* with fuels. Such are nitrogen dioxide NO_2 and chlorine trifluoride ClF_3 in which the bonds N–O and Cl–F have only a low energy, whereas in carbon dioxide CO_2 or aluminium fluoride AlF_3 the energies are much too high for these compounds to cause fuels to burn, so that CO_2 and AlF_3 are not combustion supporters.

Every combustion supporter is an oxidising agent but the two terms are not equivalent since an oxidising substance which cannot react strongly with fuels cannot be called a combustion supporter. This is the case with a solution of 3% hydrogen peroxide even though it has marked oxidising properties.

A solution of a fuel and a combustion supporter at a concentration between certain limits constitutes an explosive liquid. Mixtures of two solid phases or of a solid and a liquid phase, one of which is a fuel and the other a combustion supporter, are also capable of exploding, the violence of the explosion increasing with the degree of completeness of the mixture. In this respect, we need only remember that gunpowder, the oldest explosive and almost the only one to be used until the middle of the 19th century, is a mixture of a combustion supporter, saltpetre (potassium nitrate), with two fuels, sulphur and charcoal. Combustion-supporting liquids, such as nitrogen tetroxide N_2O_4 or concentrated nitric acid, which can be mixed with many liquid fuels, have been used to make powerful and sensitive intentional explosives such as panclastites (see 18.4.2) and Sprengel explosives (mixtures of strong nitric acid and a fuel such as carbon disulphide).

In some cases, simple contact between a fuel and a combustion supporter with no prior mixing of the two substances can give rise to a very strong deflagration. The two substances are then said to be *hypergolic* with respect to one another.

Some combustion supporters are explosive in themselves, either because they can dissociate exothermically with emission of gases, or through a more complex reaction involving a regrouping of atoms, as in the explosion of tetranitromethane.

The two notions of combustion supporter and fuel can be extended to groupings of atoms. In many definite compound explosives there are one or more combustible groups associated with combustion-supporting groups. A simple example is that of nitromethane which contains a combustible methyl group CH_3 and a combustion-supporting nitro group NO_2. In addition, various explosophore groups (see 2.8) are combustion-supporting groups or parts of such groups. Ion compounds often contain an oxidant anion (NO_3^- or ClO_4^-, for example) but there are also some combustion-supporting cations. When, in an ion compound, the anion and the cation are a combustion supporter and a fuel, the compound is generally explosive†, as is the case for example with ammonium perchlorate.

17.1.2 Brief overview of combustion supporters

Combustion supporters belong to various chemical families of which the following is a non-exhaustive list:
(a) oxygen itself and gases containing oxygen, such as the nitrogen oxides (see Chapter 18) and the halogen oxides (Chapter 19), fluorine and some of its gaseous compounds;
(b) oxygen-containing acids such as nitric acid (see 18.5) and perchloric acid (see 19.3);
(c) the salts of oxygen-containing acids, mainly the nitrates (see 17.4) and the chlorates and perchlorates (see 19.4). The sulphates themselves may sometimes act as combustion supporters since we know of a very violent explosion [1] which occurred when a molten mixture of aluminium and sodium sulphate was being heated to 800°C, with a probable reaction of

$$8Al(l) + 3Na_2SO_4(l) \rightarrow 4Al_2O_3 + 6Na(g) + 3/2S_2(g)$$

since sodium sulphide is dissociated at the very high temperature to which the products of the explosion are raised;
(d) various kinds of metal oxides, in particular the true peroxides (Chapter 20);
(e) some organic peroxides (Chapters 21 and 22) have combustion-supporting

---

† Such a compound might not be an explosive if none of the products of the reaction of the anion on the cation is gaseous or if the reaction is not sufficiently exothermic.

properties but it would be wrong to range them all with the combustion supporters.

17.1.3 Combustion-supporting metal oxides

The true peroxides, such as sodium peroxide Na_2O_2, have very strong oxidising properties, and the same is true of oxygen-rich oxides such as PbO_2, MnO_2, and CrO_3. Two accidents have been caused by the latter oxide. In the first, a warehouseman placed a funnel which had been used for transferring a lubricant oil on top of a drum of chromium trioxide (chromic anhydride) which had not been properly closed, whilst in the second, a laboratory chemist added chromium peroxide to pyridine. In both cases ignition was almost immediate.

It has been pointed out that although mixtures of magnesium and minium Pb_3O_4 (used as a tracer powder in pyrotechnics) are insensitive to a falling weight, they decrepitate when rubbed vigorously in a porcelain mortar. In a similar vein, we know of a case in 1920 of a very strong deflagration of a mixture containing the oxide Fe_3O_4, aluminium, and sulphur.

Even oxides in which the metal is in its normal valency, such as CuO and HgO, can support combustion. The oxides HgO and Ag_2O react almost explosively with the liquid alloy of sodium and potassium. A mixture of powdered aluminium and mercury oxide with a composition of $3HgO + 2Al$ is easily exploded by a detonator, whilst a mixture of the same oxide with sulphur deflagrates strongly when heated.

17.1.4 Combustion-supporting oxygenated salts

The oxygenated salts of chlorine are studied in Chapter 19, and ammonium nitrate, because of its importance, is covered in Chapters 23 to 25. The *nitrates* have long been known for their combustion-supporting properties ('they deflagrate on glowing coals'). Sodium nitrate and potassium nitrate, which melt respectively at 307°C and 334°C, give limpid liquids which are hardly decomposed up to 600°C but which, between 600 and 700°C, undergo the reversible reaction

$$NaNO_3 \rightleftarrows NaNO_2 + 1/2O_2.$$

A bath of molten nitrate is highly oxidising and many fuels thrown into it deflagrate strongly. When a mixture of sodium nitrate and sodium acetate or citrate is heated, an explosion occurs at around 350 or 400°C.

Molten mixtures of sodium nitrate and potassium nitrate† are used for the heat treatment of metal parts, and in particular aluminium alloy parts. This thermal treatment takes place at a temperature ranging from 150°C to more than 500°C, and it is not unusual for the operation to give rise to an explosion. This is sometimes the result of accidentally introducing water

---

† The most widely used composition is that of a eutectic mixture of $NaNO_3$ and KNO_3 with the addition of some 5% of $NaNO_2$. The presence of a small amount of nitrite ensures that the decomposition of the nitrates above 450°C does not produce free oxygen in the mixture which would increase its corrosive action on steel.

into the bath, but there are also cases of chemical explosions, some of
which are caused by the introduction of an organic substance into the bath,
whilst others are caused by the reaction of the metal immersed in the
nitrate. Examples of explosions caused by organic substances are the accidental introduction into the bath of bits of string, sacking, or rags.
There was also the case of the workman who topped up a bath with what he
thought was fresh nitrate but which was, in fact, cyanide, a compound in
use in the same factory. The heat-treated metal parts may cause explosions
for a number of reasons, the main ones being:
(a) too high a temperature in the bath, since at around 650°C molten
aluminium reacts strongly with nitrate;
(b) the formation of iron oxide which often accumulates as a mud at the
bottom of the hardening bath. If aluminium comes into contact with this
hot oxide, the resulting thermite reaction triggers an explosion of the
bath contents in the presence of the metal.

The measures to be taken to avoid these explosions are simple and
consist above all in properly maintaining equipment and ensuring that there
are no combustible substances in the vicinity of the baths. Electric heating is preferable to heating with a fuel since it gives greater control
over the temperature and prevents the formation of soots which might react
dangerously with the nitrate. All of these precautions, as well as those
against the risk of burns and poisoning (accidental release of nitrous
vapours in a fire) are set out in detail in a publication of the British
Health and Safety Executive [2].

Alloys containing more than 2% magnesium must not be treated in a
nitrate bath unless more specific precautions are taken.

Similar mixtures of molten nitrates† are also sometimes used as a heat
transfer medium in reactors used in the organic chemistry industry, in
particular in reactors with tube stacks. It has happened that a tube has
been pierced by corrosion with resulting contact between the reacting
mixture and the molten nitrate leading to a violent reaction and an explosion. Corrosion is rapid if the temperature locally happens to exceed
600°C. Such overheating can be detected by periodically analysing the
bath. If chromium from the stainless steel of the apparatus is found in
the bath, it indicates that corrosion has begun.

Sacks made of vegetable fibres which have contained sodium nitrate and
which have not been completely cleansed of the substance are liable to ignite very easily and burn very rapidly, as has been observed on many occasions. Accidents with sacks that have contained potassium nitrate are far
less frequently mentioned, probably because this nitrate, which is not
hygroscopic, does not impregnate sack fibres as sodium salts do. Some
cases are also known of spontaneous ignition, caused solely by the heat
from the sun's rays, of deposits containing sodium nitrate and very fine
wood dust. When these mixtures deflagrate in the open air, they have only
a weak explosive effect, but this is probably not the case under confinement.

When subjected to the lead block test, anhydrous calcium nitrate with
mineral oil added produces a non-negligible effect, but hydrated ordinary
calcium nitrate (about 14% water) is only a very weak combustion supporter,

---

† For example, the ternary mixture composed of 40 parts sodium nitrite to 3
parts sodium nitrate and 53 parts potassium nitrate.

unlike barium nitrate which does not form a hydrate. Magnesium nitrate, which is a hygroscopic and easily hydrolysed salt, makes vegetable fibres impregnated by the substance particularly flammable [3]. In this case, the nitric acid given off may play a part. A certain number of nitrates are found in class 5.1 of the R.I.D. regulations governing the transport of dangerous substances.

The nitrates of heavy metals (such as Cu, Ag, and Pb), which decompose more easily than the alkaline and the alkaline-earth nitrates, give more explosive mixtures with fuels. For example, the mixture of powdered magnesium and silver nitrate reacts by exploding when moistened with water. A nitrate of tin has been described as explosive, namely the basic nitrate $(NO_3)_2Sn.SnO$ which friction or heating to above $100^\circ C$ causes to explode with release of nitrous fumes.

No combustion-supporting activity has been found in the phosphates, arsenates, carbonates, or borates but the permanganates (see 19.6) are strong supporters of combustion. The chromates and dichromates are much less so, but the dichromates of sodium and potassium well mixed with saccharose or wood dust deflagrate if strongly ignited. In the open air, they are difficult to ignite and burn slowly. but similar mixtures with potassium permanganate ignite very easily. Mixtures of chromate or di-chromate with boron or strongly reducing metals (zinc, aluminium) react, especially when wet, but the explosive effect is weak.

It should be remembered that various combustion-supporting salts (nitrates, perchlorates, permanganates, etc.) have in their anhydrous form a relatively high degree of solubility in organic solvents such as acetone $CH_3 - CO - CH_3$, methyl sulphoxide $OS(CH_3)_2$, and dimethyl formamide $H - CO - N(CH_3)_2$ which are often used in organic chemistry as a reaction medium to cause a reaction in an oxidising salt, but that some of these solutions may explode more or less violently either at ordinary temperature after an induction period (see 3.11) or as a result of heating. An example of this is given in section 19.6.1. After the solvent has evaporated, the re-maining solid may be an addition compound with explosive properties. This is what happens with a solution of copper nitrate in benzonitrile which leaves behind the explosive compound $4Cu(NO_3)_2.C_6H_5 - CN$ discovered by Guntz and Martin [5]. By evaporating the water from an aqueous solution containing an oxidising salt and an organic substance, it is also possible to obtain a solid explosive addition compound such as $CO(NH_2)_2.NaNO_3.H_2O$ which deflagrates when heated.

17.1.5 Potential for the support of combustion

By this is meant the greater or lesser aptitude of a combustion-supporting substance to react strongly with fuels. The notion is vague and implies that if we have found given values of combustion-supporting potential for various combustion supporters with a given combustible substance, then we should find the same values with a different combustible substance. This is not usually the case and the rank order of a series of combustion sup-porters would not always remain the same when measured with a different standard fuel. Nonetheless, various attempts have been made to measure this potential†.

Kuchta, Furno, and Imhof [6] studied the problem at the Bureau of Mines

---

† In some reports, this potential is called oxidising capacity.

in the United States and devised a method for solid combustion supporters
and another for liquids. For solids the method consists in measuring the
rate at which combustion progresses through a layer of a mixture of the
combustion supporter and wood dust of red oak with a given granulometry.
The test is conducted by laying the mixture in a channel with a rectangular
cross section 50 mm wide and 25 mm deep. A number of percentages are
tested and the result is taken to be the maximum value observed, which
ranges from 6.9 cm/min for wood dust with no combustion supporter to 2160
cm/min for a mixture with sodium peroxide (30% wood dust to 70% Na_2O_2). In
this way, the following substances are classified by order of increasing
combustion-supporting potential:

potassium dichromate	potassium nitrate
lead nitrate	chromium trioxide
potassium permanganate	potassium bromate
sodium chlorate	sodium peroxide.

When the dimensions of the channel are changed, the results and even
the rank order of some of the combustion supporters analysed also change.
The results also vary with the granulometry of the combustion supporter,
which should in theory be as fine as the wood dust used in the test.

For liquid combustion supporters the method used by the Bureau of Mines
consists in injecting a small quantity of combustion supporter through a
syringe into a mass of wood dust previously heated to a given temperature
and observing the resulting temperature rise as well as the time taken for
the maximum temperature to be reached. No rules are given for deriving the
value of the combustion-supporting potential of these liquids, but those
which are tested can be compared with one another.

With ammonium nitrate and fertilisers with an ammonium nitrate base,
these tests do not give any useable results. Consequently, a number of
manufacturers working with the R.A.R.D.E. and the I.M.C.O. and later the
Government Arsenal at Woolwich devised a variation on the method of combustion in a channel and, after several years of testing, came to the
following conclusions:

(a) The test of combustion in a channel must be conducted in a nitrogen
atmosphere since the rate of combustion is altered by the oxygen present in
air.

(b) Of the various combustible substances tested (iron filings, carbon
black, animal black, wood dust; pure cellulose, etc.), the results which
were most easy to reproduce were given by a certain pure cellulose (a fine-
grained substance sold for use in chromatography).

(c) There are optimum dimensions for the channel used in the test.

Although research is continuing, it seems likely that a valid measure
of combustion-supporting potential can be made only by comparing entire
curves of rates of combustion as a function of the percentage of combustion
supporter in the mixture.

Consequently, there can be no hope of developing a single method for
comparing the 'combustion-supporting potentials' of all substances. A
given method provides reproducible results only when a large number of
conditions are strictly observed, and there is still discussion on how to
interpret the results in order to arrive at values which give a true
representation of combustion-supporting potential. However, test results
do have a useful qualitative value. It might have been easier to obtain a
numerical measurement of combustion-supporting potential by looking for the

minimum percentage of an inert substance such as talc which must be added
to a combustion supporter to prevent it from forming mixtures with a
typical combustible substance which are capable of propagating flame in a
given channel test.

The following remarks on combustion-supporting potential will serve as
a conclusion to this section: this potential is clearly unrelated to the
oxygen content (or the content of any other element supporting combustion)
of the substance under consideration, and neither does it have any direct
relation to the oxygen balance (o.b.) since lead nitrate (o.b. = 24 g per
100), for example, is certainly less of a combustion supporter than sodium
peroxide (o.b. = 20.5 g per 100). But the o.b. is involved in determining
which is the most powerful of various mixtures of a given combustion
supporter with a given fuel. We can see from Fig. 17.1, which shows how
the coefficient of mixtures of tetranitromethane and mononitrobenzene [7]
varies with concentration, that the maximum is indeed obtained with the
stoichiometric mixture (o.b. nil) with 23.1% nitrobenzene.

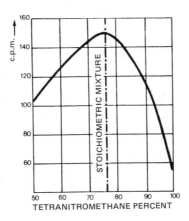

Fig. 17.1 – Variation of the coefficient in the lead block (c.p.u) of
mixtures of tetranitromethane and nitrobenzene.

17.1.6 Safety in handling, storing, and transporting combustion supporters

The basic rule in handling combustion-supporting substances is that, if
they are to be associated with combustible substances, it must be done in
strictly controlled conditions, so that any potentially explosive mixture
is not subjected to a shock or to heating. If a combustion-supporting
substance is to be crushed, then the apparatus used for this purpose must
be thoroughly cleaned and free from any residue from previously treated
substances, and lubricants (oil, fat) must not be allowed to contaminate
the product.

Combustion-supporting substances other than those which by themselves
have explosive properties are, when properly stored, only minimally
dangerous if a fire erupts in the vicinity. Heat may cause them to release
oxygen or other combustion-supporting gases which are liable to make the

fire burn more vigorously, but they can cause an explosion only if, as a result of the fire or through negligence, they should happen to mix with combustible substances. Of the latter, the most dangerous are those which are liquid or which melt easily and which can easily flow through capillary action into combustion-supporting substances in the form of powder, grains, or crystals.   Rules for keeping combustion-supporting and combustible substances apart must be observed on vehicles and ships.   A vehicle which has been used for the bulk transport of a solid combustion supporter must, after unloading, be thoroughly cleaned out if it is to be reloaded with a different substance.

If a fire reaches a combustion-supporting substance, the extinguishing agent used should preferably be water† which acts mainly by cooling down the substance.   Contrary to what happens with fuels, there is no point in trying to prevent air from reaching the product, for example by covering it with sand, since the product contains in itself the oxygen needed for combustion.

Containers for combustion supporters should, as far as possible, be made of unreactive materials, although paper or textile sacks and even wooden containers are suitable for some of them.   If a damaged container is losing its contents, the latter must be transferred to a *clean* container in good condition and the substance which has spilled onto the floor must be removed and destroyed.   Empty containers which previously held combustion supporters must not be stored in the same warehouse as those substances. Soiled packaging made of combustible substances can be destroyed by burning on the spot as long as appropriate precautions are taken: compact piles should not be allowed to form, other kinds of rubbish (acids, toxic bodies, etc.) should not be burned at the same time, and only limited quantities should be dealt with at any one time.

In the case of combustion-supporting substances which give off dust, the workforce must wear protective clothing: close-fitting headwear which covers the hair completely, aprons, and so on.   Work clothes must be washed frequently because when they are impregnated with sufficient quantities of a combustion supporter, they are liable to ignite easily and burn with considerable vigour.

Any substance containing oxygen (or an electronegative element) whose properties are not well known will have to be examined for any potential combustion-supporting properties before it is used in reactions involving combustible substances.

17.2 OXYGEN

17.2.1 Oxygen as a combustion supporter

Oxygen is an element which plays an important part in various types of explosion, since
(a) it is present in a variety of explosophore groups such as NO, $- NO_2$, $- O.NO_2$, $- ClO_3$, $- IO_2$, $Cl - O$, $Br - O$, etc.;
(b) it readily transforms organic compounds into explosive peroxides by

---

† Unless the combustion supporter in question is one which is decomposed by water with release of oxygen (for example, Na_2O_2).

self-oxidation (see 21.2);
(c) the mixtures it forms in the gaseous or liquid state with combustible substances are generally explosive.

Oxygen is the most widespread combustion supporter†. A large number of industrial combustions or processes use air which contains only 21% oxygen, but operations involving welding, scarfing, and metal cutting with a blowpipe require pure oxygen. In the chemical industry, oxygen is used in a variety of manufacturing processes, and the gas in its pure state or in the form of oxygen-enriched air is used in considerable quantities in the steel industry.

Pure oxygen has a much greater combustion-supporting potential than air, as is shown by the classic example of a stick of wood (a matchstick) which still has an incandescent spot and which flares up again immediately in pure oxygen, giving off a highly luminous flame. As we saw in Chapter 8, combustible gases have a much wider flammability range in oxygen than in air. The combustion-supporting potential of oxygen increases considerably when it is at a pressure higher than atmospheric, whilst that of compressed air is also higher than that of air at ordinary pressure because the partial pressure of the oxygen is increased.

The reactions which take place in oxygen at high pressure are deflagrations, which are often given the technical name 'flashes' because of their violence and brevity. Combustible substances which are absorbent, powdered, or porous form explosive mixtures with liquid oxygen, and intentional explosives with a liquid oxygen base were used in France mainly between 1920 and 1950. In some countries, such as India, they are still in use.

17.2.2 The danger of oxygen-enriched atmospheres

Combustions in pure oxygen at atmospheric pressure are different from combustions in air in the following ways:

1˙ The flame of a solid or liquid combustible substance in pure oxygen has a much higher temperature than that of the same substance in air. For example, a cotton fabric containing 10% hygroscopic water (the usual content) has a flame temperature of around 2900˙C when it burns in pure oxygen but only around 1750˙C in air. Because of this high temperature, these flames radiate with very high intensity and are thus liable to cause more serious burns than would a fire in air at the same distance.

2˙ It is much easier to ignite a substance in oxygen than in air. The minimum ignition temperatures (see 10.3.7) of gases are much lower in oxygen than in air. Solid substances such as leather, which it is virtually impossible to burn in air, ignite easily in pure oxygen.

3˙ Ignition propagates much more rapidly along a solid combustible surface in oxygen than in air, which is why, when an item of clothing catches fire in an oxygen atmosphere, the person is completely covered in flames in a very short space of time and thus suffers from extensive burns.

The oxidising capacity of air increases when it is enriched with

---

† There are certain vulgarisers of science who call oxygen a fuel and sometimes even an explosive!. Saacke [8] read in a magazine that oxygen is a more devastating explosive than nitroglycerine!

oxygen.   It was long believed that an O_2 content of 40 or 50% was needed for there to be a serious risk of danger, but this is not so, and there is already an appreciable level of danger in an atmosphere with a 25% content, in other words when 5 volumes of oxygen are added to 95 volumes of air. At 28% the danger becomes significant, and beyond 35% it can be considered to be very serious no matter where the oxygen content falls between 35 and 100%.   Various studies have been carried out on the combustion of fabrics in enriched air, and the following paragraphs des- cribe some of the main results.

Coleman [9] has studied the speed of ignition, in other words the rate of propagation of the flame, along strips of fabric placed vertically in a moderate current of over-oxygenated air containing up to 50% oxygen.   The rapidity of flame propagation varies considerably from one fabric to an- other.   Apart from specially fire-proofed fabrics, those which burn least rapidly are flannels of tightly-woven wool. For a given fabric, the speed increases in direct proportion to the oxygen content.   In general, when there is 35 to 40% oxygen in the atmosphere, the speed of combustion rises considerably.   Most fabrics fire-proofed with a borate- or phosphate-based solution, which burn very slowly in air, burn just as rapidly as fabrics with no fire-proofing in pure oxygen.

The ignition of fabrics by electrostatic sparks has been studied by Voigtsberger [10] who found that many fabrics are ignited by a spark of 45 millijoules.   Ignition is much easier when they are soiled with fatty substances.   Using a different operating mode, Purser [11] was able to ignite a number of fabrics with energies between 1 and 10 millijoules.

Fires resulting in lethal injuries to personnel have often broken out in workshops or low points (pits or trenches) with an oxygen-enriched atmosphere.   In many cases, the atmosphere contained the oxygen by acci- dent.   The following is a particularly instructive example.

In June 1960, in a Spanish factory, a worker was given the task, which was performed once a day, of purging the water which accumulated at the low points of the oxygen-carrying inlet and outlet pipes on a gasometer in- stalled in a pit.   The purge taps were at the bottom of a pit 4.5 m deep with a rectangular cross section (1 m by 1.1 m) which was accessed by a metal ladder sealed to the wall.   The entry to the pit was normally closed by full, tightly-fitting doors of sheet steel. When the workman, who was carrying no tools, reached the bottom of the pit and even before he had touched the valve, he saw that his trousers were on fire. He was able to climb the ladder out of the pit and be rescued. After the accident, it was found that one of the two oxygen valves at the foot of the gasometer was leaking, and ignition was almost certainly caused as follows: the workman was wearing *rubber-soled* sandals so that, as he walked and moved about, his clothes had become electrically charged. At some point, they had brushed against metal and discharged, giving a spark which, in a very oxygen-rich atmosphere, had set fire to the fabric.   This accident illustrates how easily an electrostatic spark can ignite fabric in pure oxygen, something which never happens in air.

It must always be assumed that any workplace and any pit or other space below ground level which houses oxygen containers or equipment is liable to have an oxygen-enriched atmosphere as a result of a possible leak.   Such places should be ventilated as much as possible before anybody enters them and smoking should be strictly forbidden.

The accidental oxygen enrichment of air can result from a leak at a tap or in a rubber pipe supplying oxygen.   Fires which break out during welding work inside a container or boiler are often attributed by operatives to the acetylene they use because they are often unaware of the properties of oxygen. All flexible pipes feeding gases into a container in which work has to be carried out must be in good condition and perfectly gas-tight.

People are also all too frequently unaware that the use of a cutting torch causes rapid oxygen enrichment of the surrounding atmosphere, since a good cut is obtained only by supplying the apparatus with a large surplus of oxygen in relation to what is consumed by combustion as Fe_3O_4 oxide as a result of the cut made in the metal. Consequently, the use of a cutting torch in a confined space or a pit exposes workers to serious risk if the workplace has not been thoroughly ventilated beforehand.

Other accidents have occurred because people have forgotten that an atmosphere might be very rich in oxygen. This was the case in July 1963 in a Belgian steelworks where arc welding was needed to modify a strut inside a pressure dome, which is a cylindrical metallic chamber 2.5 m in diameter and 3.5 m high with conical end sections used for suspending a fine powder of lime in oxygen. Two days previously, the foreman had ordered the modification of an identical dome which had not yet been put into service. He probably forgot that the second dome to be modified had already been put into operation and contained oxygen. He entered the dome through a manhole with another worker without taking any special precautions. As soon as the arc welder was lit, the clothes of both men caught fire and they burned to death inside the dome.

Finally, fires occur in containers which are known to contain oxygen but in which it is wrongly assumed that no ignition source is present. The following are just several examples:

(a) The accident on board the spaceship Apollo at Cape Kennedy on 27 January 1967 in which cosmonaut Grissom and his two companions perished. The atmosphere in the capsule was pure oxygen at a pressure of 1.12 bars. It is thought that one of the very many electric conductors in the capsule may have short-circuited, but the real cause may have been static electricity, since the people in the capsule were wearing spacesuits made of a material which easily developed static.

(b) The fire which broke out in 1973 during treatment of a convalescent patient to promote cicatrisation of wounds. This took place in a caisson with an atmosphere of oxygen at a gauge pressure of 2 bars. The patient's hair caught fire, and since his head was lying on a pillow filled with polyurethane foam, it is possible that ignition was caused by static electricity. Denison and his associates [12] have dealt with this problem of the risk of fire in hyperbaric chambers and have suggested improvements for such apparatuses which remove the risk of accidents. There are also codes of practice for the use of oxygen-rich atmospheres for medical purposes.

(c) The fire which broke out in a maternity hospital in the oxygen atmosphere inside an incubator containing a newborn child.

There have been other fires in hospitals caused by oxygen atmospheres, not to mention those started in oxygen tents by patients breaking the ban on smoking.

There is even a risk of an oxygen-rich atmosphere occurring in the open air, as is proven by the following accident: a worker was repairing a liquid oxygen tanker in a factory yard when a leak of *gaseous* oxygen occurred towards the back of the vehicle; for some reason which cannot be established with certainty (it is assumed that there may have been shock or friction caused by a tool during the operation), the worker's clothes caught fire and he was burned to death.

Finally, the following accident report illustrates how easy it is for oxygen to linger for a long time between layers of clothing. A worker went from one workplace in which containers of liquid oxygen were stored into another workshop to sharpen a tool on a grindstone. During grinding, a spark set fire to his clothes, which began to burn rapidly, and, in spite of prompt help, he suffered severe burns. There is also the case of an engineer who spent some time in a workshop in which there was an oxygen leak and then returned to his office where he tried to smoke a cigarette, but as soon as he lit it, it burned vigorously because of the oxygen he had brought back in his clothes.

Many other accidents could be mentioned, all of them having serious human consequences. They show widespread ignorance of the high risk of fire in oxygen-rich atmospheres, probably because it is possible to breathe oxygen easily for quite a long time without realising it. Because our sense of smell does not allow us to detect the presence of this gas when it has enriched air, it is insidious in the extreme. Consequently, an analysis must always be made when oxygen is or may be present in air at a content higher than 21%. Apparatuses exist which use the paramagnetism of oxygen to give an immediate measurement of its concentration in air, and there are also cheaper apparatuses based on the absorption of oxygen by specific reagents (alkaline solutions of pyrogallol, chromous chloride, or sodium dithionite, etc.). It has sometimes been suggested that the nature of an atmosphere in a tank or pit be tested with a piece of burning newspaper which falls and begins to burn very brightly when dropped into a container holding oxygen. However, the test is not very reliable, and, in addition, a container which has not been specially ventilated may have considerable differences in oxygen concentration from one place to another. We may quote the case of a tanker, which, after being emptied of the liquid oxygen it had carried, stood for three weeks with all openings and valves open, including the manhole cover. In the central region under the manhole, the 'newspaper' test had detected no oxygen enrichment, and yet when a worker went into the tank to clean it and lit a cigarette, his clothes caught fire when he went towards one end of the tanker. As we have already said (10.1.4), diffusion must not be relied upon to evacuate a gas from a container in which there are only weak convection currents.

17.2.3 Explosions caused by mixtures with liquid oxygen

In the liquid state at its normal boiling point (− 183.4°C), oxygen, which has a density of 1.14 g/cm³, is slightly blue. In this form it has considerable combustion-supporting potential, and porous or absorbent combustible solids impregnated with it are explosives whose power and sensitivity to mechanical effects, which depend on the ratio of the masses of oxidiser to fuel, can reach considerable values. A shock may also cause an explosion with solid bodies, such as leather or many plastic materials, which are non-porous but which may absorb liquid oxygen at the surface. It is advisable to assume that any solid substance liable to burn in gaseous oxygen may give rise to an explosion with liquid oxygen. The following are descriptions of various accidental explosions caused by liquid oxygen.

If, during the loading or unloading of a tanker, oxygen falls onto a porous asphalt floor, the latter is impregnated with oxygen and becomes sensitive to mechanical effects. There were several cases between 1945 and 1960 when a lorry was started up and the friction of its tyres on the gravel was enough to explode the underlying asphalt-oxygen mixture.   In another accident, the unloading of a tanker required the use of a long flexible hose made of two sections with a connecting piece which was leaking.   When the worker dropped his rather heavy hexagonal wrench, which he had used to disconnect the join, there was an explosion with flame which blinded him.   We even know the case of a person who caused a small explosion when walking on gravel on which liquid oxygen had been spilt some time before.   There have been similar incidents on wood-tiled floors.

As a result, since these accidents factories follow the rule of creating completely incombustible parking areas at points where liquid oxygen is loaded and unloaded.   A cement covering should not be used on a base of asphalt or hard core consisting of coal waste because of the possibility of cracks in the cement.   During transfer, metal buckets or bowls, which must be *clean*, are placed under joins and connexions to collect potential leaks.

The parking area should be built in such a way that if there is a heavy leak of liquid oxygen, it cannot get into drains and sewers.   Since it is heavier than water, it would fall to the bottom where it would undergo intense boiling, agitating the entire mass and producing an intimate mixture with the other substances present.

The sensitivity to mechanical effects of combustible solid substances impregnated with liquid oxygen is well illustrated by the following accident which took place in September 1960:   a worker was transferring liquid oxygen through a flexible hose from a large fixed tank into a small mobile tank of 200 litres mounted on a tipper.   Seeing from the start of the operation that the connexion in the tube on the mobile tank was leaking, he attempted to tighten the two bayonet-fitting sections making the connexion by hitting it with a hexagonal wrench held in his right hand whilst holding the join in his left hand after wrapping it with a cloth to protect himself from the cold liquid.   The result was a deflagration with flame which set fire to the clothes of the workman who, since he was in an oxygen-rich atmosphere, was burned to death.

The use of combustible materials must be avoided as much as possible in the construction of tankers for transporting oxygen.   Such materials must be used only in those parts of the vehicle where they cannot be affected by an oxygen leak.   Of course, the material used for thermally insulating the tankers must be incombustible.   It was the failure to observe this condition that led to a number of accidents in Germany around 1960 when a material made of flakes of urea-formaldehyde resin was used.   Comparable to this was the accident followed by a fire which occurred in March 1969 in an Australian port on board a ship fitted out for seismic prospecting at sea on the bridge of which was an 8000 litre tanker of liquid oxygen.   When an attempt was made to tighten a leaking valve, the flange on the valve stem snapped leading to a large leak, with the result that the steel bridge on the ship cracked because of the very low temperature to which the liquid oxygen had been cooled[†].   This liquid then soaked into a sound-proofing padding under the bridge made of highly porous and combustible material. The mixture of this material and the oxygen exploded, killing three operatives.

---

† Translator's note: Steel, unless specially alloyed, is extremely brittle at liquid oxygen temperatures.

Weber [13] has described the very serious accident in Dortmund in 1962 which caused the death of fifteen people. It happened when liquid oxygen was absorbed by beams made of spruce. Experiments conducted after this explosion showed that beechwood or deal may absorb around its own weight in liquid oxygen and that in this state it explodes violently when ignited with a No. 8 detonator.

Of the very few liquids which are miscible with oxygen we should mention methane, which mixes completely at - 183°C. A study [14] of these solutions has shown that they can explode at between 3-6% and 50-67% of CH_4, and the detonation velocity can reach 5000 m/s. The more common liquids are not really soluble in oxygen since they freeze in it, often forming very small crystals. The very small quantities of lubricating oil from air compressors which are found in liquid oxygen do not cause it to explode, unlike other impurities, in particular acetylene crystals. But when the oxygen vaporises, oil carried off as droplets has sometimes caused mists to explode in ducts, which is why producers use appropriate filters in an attempt to stop the oil before it gets into tanks of liquid oxygen.

There is one final and serious risk which must not be ignored: the atmosphere in the vicinity of any place in which liquid oxygen is being handled becomes oxygen-enriched, so the precautions listed above should be taken. When a large quantity of liquid is being poured off, oxygen enrichment may affect a comparatively large area in which the still cold vaporised oxygen causes the humidity in the atmosphere to condense into a white cloud. The air inside this cloud is heavily over-oxygenated, and we may, in this connexion, quote the accident which occurred in 1962 when such a cloud spread down the slight slope of the road to some 60 m away from a tank in which a false manoeuvre had caused a sizeable leak. A driver doing a U-turn drove one or two metres into the cloud and a fire broke out under the bonnet because the oily deposits on the hot engine were suddenly brought into contact with oxygen-enriched air.

17.2.4 Containers for transporting liquid oxygen

Initially, small quantities of liquid oxygen were transported in glass containers of the type devised by d'Arsonval (a container with two walls separated by a vacuum) and later perfected by Dewar (silver-plating of the walls in contact with the vacuum). Around 1910, brass containers appeared in the shape of a sphere, made by welding two hemispheres, with a long neck and a double wall with the inner container joined to the outer envelope near the top of the neck. In order to maintain a strong vacuum in spite of any slight intakes of air that might occur should the weld prove to be porous, granules of absorbent charcoal were placed in the space between the two walls, since at the temperature of liquid oxygen activated carbon has a very high absorbent capacity for the gases in air (up to 800 cm³ per gramme of carbon).

But there were some cases in which these liquid oxygen Dewar flask containers exploded, apparently spontaneously. Subsequent inquiries revealed that they were caused by liquid oxygen seeping into the double envelope because the inner sphere had lost its air-tightness and reacting violently with the charcoal which contained a small quantity of iron oxide. The conditions for this spontaneous exothermic reaction, which was all the more remarkable since it occurred at a very low temperature, have been studied by Wöhler [15] who brought out the role of ions of Fe^{3+} and showed that no such thing happens when the charcoal is impregnated with ZnO. Given that one can never be sure that charcoal is completely free of catalytic impurities, it was decided to replace the charcoal in such vessels with alumina gel.

The larger-volume mobile containers are also two-walled, of course. Around 1945-50, the intermediate space was filled with a powdered insulating material with a magnesium carbonate base. Since 1950-55, the thermal insulation of these containers is provided by multiple layers of sheets of a low-conductivity material in a vacuum.

It is important not to let any kind of absorbent combustible material into the double envelope of an apparatus intended to contain a liquid at a temperature which is equal to or less than $-183°C$, since any defect in the air-tightness of the outer envelope would lead to the condensation of oxygen-rich liquid in the space between the two walls given that the liquid phase which is in equilibrium with the air contains almost 40% oxygen.

BIBLIOGRAPHICAL REFERENCES

[1]   Kohlmeyer, E. J. (1942) *Aluminium* 24 361
[2]   Health and Safety Executive (1975) *Precautions in the Use of Nitrate Salt Baths*. (HSW 72) H.M.S.O., London
[3]   Van Hoogstraten, C. W. (1947) *Chem. Weekblad* 43 185
[4]   Guttmann, O. (1892) *J. Ch. Soc.* 11
[5]   Guntz, A. & Martin, F. (1910) *Bull. Soc. Ch. Fr.* [4] 7 313
[6]   Kuchta, J. M., Furno, A. L. & Imhof, A. C. (1972) *Report 7594* of the Bureau of Mines
[7]   Médard, L. (1947) *Lab. C.S.E.*
[8]   Saacke, F. C. (1959) *Nat. Safety Congress Trans.* 15 14
[9]   Coleman, E. H. (1959) *British Welding Journal*, p. 406
[10] Voigtsberger, P. (1961) *Arbeitschutz*, p. 72
[11] Purser, P. R. (1966) *The Lancet*, p. 1405
[12] Denison, D. M. *et al.* (1968) *Nature* (G.B.) 218 1110; (1966) *The Lancet*, p. 1404
[13] Weber, U. (1963) *Chimie et Ind.* 90 181
[14] Kirschenbaum, A. D. *et al.* (1957) *J. Am. Ch. Soc.* 79 6341, and (1959) *J. Ch. Eng. Data* 4 127
[15] Wöhler, L. (1918) *Z. Ges. Schiess-u. Sprengst.* 13 365

18

Nitrogen oxides and nitric acid

18.1 GENERAL OBSERVATIONS ON NITROGEN OXIDES

Nitrogen oxides, which have been known for a very long time, form the series:
- N_2O nitrous oxide
- NO nitric oxide,
- N_2O_3 dinitrogen trioxide,
- NO_2 nitrogen dioxide,
- N_2O_5 dinitrogen pentoxide.

They are all oxidising agents with a combustion supporting potential lower than that of pure oxygen in the case of N_2O and NO, but high in the case of the last two terms in the series. With the exception of the two lower oxides, they are easily liquefied. Table 18.1 gives a number of physical constants. It will be seen in particular that they are formed endothermically, which explains the explosive properties, albeit weak, of some of them.

18.2 NITROUS OXIDE

18.2.1 Physical properties and uses

Nitrous oxide is a colourless gas with a slight odour and a sweet taste and is slightly soluble in water (1 litre of gas per litre of water at 0°C) and four times more soluble in alcohol. Many of its physical constants (such as its critical temperature, density in the liquid state, etc.) are close to those of carbon dioxide. However, whereas the latter has a triple point at a pressure of 5.2 bars, that of N_2O is slightly below normal atmospheric pressure, which means that it can be observed in the liquid state at that

Table 18.1

Properties of nitrogen oxides and nitric acid

		N_2O	NO	N_2O_3	NO_2	N_2O_4	HNO_3
Heat of formation (at 25°C) of the gas	F_p (kJ/mol)	− 82	− 90.3	− 82	− 33	− 9	135
	F_v (kJ/mol)	− 83.3	− 90.3	− 85.8	− 34.3		131
Heat of formation (at 25°C) of the liquid	F_p (kJ/mol)	− 81.2	− 76 (a)	− 57		19.6	172
	F_v (kJ/mol)	− 84.9	− 79 (a)	− 63		12.1	165
Normal boiling point (°C)		− 88.5	− 151.7	+ 3.5	21.2		82.6
Critical temperature (°C)		36.41	− 93		158		
Critical pressure (bars)		72.4	65		101		

(a) values at a temperature of − 152°C

pressure over a narrow temperature range (from $-$ 90.8 to $-$ 88.5°C). The
vapour pressures of the liquid at 0°C and 20°C are respectively 31.3 and
50.6 bars.

The gas is used as a mild anaesthetic in dentistry and surgery, as a
propellant in aerosols, and as a foaming agent in edible creams. All these
uses require the gas to be extremely pure, which is why, after the reaction
from which it is obtained (see 23.4), the raw gas is chemically purified by
passing it through columns filled with Raschig rings where it is washed in
water and other appropriate solutions (caustic soda and sometimes aqueous
solutions of $KMnO_4$). It is then dried with alumina gel and stored under
refrigeration in the liquid state (at about $-$ 25°C at 18 bars).

Nitrous oxide is also used as a tracer gas for detecting leaks, especially in buried pipes, since its presence in air is very easy to detect,
even at a very low concentration, by an apparatus which absorbs infra-red.
By contrast, there has been no development of its use as a refrigerating
agent in cold rooms or as a constituent in bipropellants for rocket engines.

18.2.2. Stability and oxidising effect

Nitrous oxide is a robust compound which dissociates only at quite high
temperatures: at a pressure of 600 bars it remains undecomposed at 420°C
[6], whilst at atmospheric pressure it must be raised to more than 550°C
for an appreciable part of it to decompose in one hour, and at 625°C its
half life is still around 30 minutes. Decomposition in these conditions
and at this pressure is never explosive. Thus Destriau [13], following
Volmer (1930), found that the decomposition is a first-order reaction with
an activation energy of 222 kJ/mol. Various authors have studied this
decomposition in shock tubes and found values for the activation energy of
the order of 200 kJ/mol. Such a comparatively high value is typical of
substances where thermal decomposition is difficult.

Nitrous oxide has oxidising properties, but the reaction of a combustible substance with N_2O has a higher activation energy than that of the
same fuel with oxygen, with the result that this reaction is less easily
initiated than combustion with oxygen, which is why some substances, such
as sulphur, which burn very easily in oxygen, only burn in N_2O if they are
already burning well with a very bright flame. We also know the classic
demonstration that a match with an ignited point but no flame re-lights in
nitrous oxide and burns with a luminous flame.

Combustible gases with nitrous oxide have an upper flammability limit
situated between their upper limit in air and the same limit in oxygen.
For example, the upper limit in N_2O is 86 for hydrogen, 40.2 for methane,
and 21 for butane [18].

All of these facts together lead us to conclude that the oxidising
potential of nitrous oxide is higher than that of air but lower than that
of oxygen.

18.2.3 The explosion of nitrous oxide

A - *Theoretical values*. Since nitrous oxide is formed endothermically but
requires a high activation energy in order to decompose, it can only be
regarded as an explosive which is not easily initiated. For nitrous oxide

in the gaseous state, calculation of its explosive properties at constant
volume gives the following values:

$$Q_V = 83 \text{ kJ/mol} \qquad T_V = 2350°K \qquad \pi = 12.1.$$

In the gases from the explosion, there are 0.03 moles of NO per mole of
decomposed N_2O. For liquid nitrous oxide the values are:

$$Q_V = 1530 \text{ kJ/kg} \qquad T_V = 2020°K.$$

B – *Explosion by initiation.* In 1875, Berthelot [11] successfully
caused the sudden decomposition of 50 cm³ of gas by sudden compression (a
falling weight of 500 kg) reducing the volume to 0.1 cm³. There is certainly some considerable heating of the substance in such an experiment,
but in the process the container is deformed, making the experiment difficult to interpret. Maquenne [12] conducted an experiment in 1895 which
consisted in initiating gaseous nitrous oxide in a 1 litre balloon flask at
atmospheric pressure with a capsule of 1 decigramme of mercury fulminate.
He observed a total and violent explosion. However, the experiment gives
rise to the following objection: not only is the mass of the detonator 5%
of the mass of the excited gas, but also an explosion caused by mercury
fulminate produces carbon monoxide at a very high temperature which burns
in the nitrous oxide. Consequently, the energy of excitation was very high
compared with the energy released by the decomposition of nitrous oxide.
    Some highly convincing experiments were described by Rasch [28] in
1904. They were performed on N_2O placed under pressure in steel cylinders
of about 1 litre capacity. By putting either 0.6 g of nitrocellulose or a
detonator of 0.3 g of mercury fulminate in the cylinder before introducing
the gas and then raising the temperature by means of an alcohol flame, an
explosion of the donor is set at around 170°C and this explodes the gas in
the cylinder. When the loading density of the gas was less than 0.1 kg/l,
the pressure created by the explosion did not reach the value (which must
be situated between 700 and 750 bars) at which the cylinder breaks, so that
it was possible to analyse the products of the explosion and note that they
are indeed oxygen and nitrogen. At loading densities higher than 0.1 kg/l,
the explosion shattered the cylinder into fragments from the state of which
it was possible to declare with certainty that no detonation had taken
place, only a deflagration. In other experiments involving *external*
ignition by 100 g of dynamite of cylinders filled with N_2O at a loading
density of 0.72 kg/l, the contents were never seen to explode, whether they
were at 0°C or around 70°C. Similarly, firing bullets at a cylinder loaded
with N_2O never caused the gas to explode, even though the cylinder was
pierced in two opposite places.
    A variety of subsequent experiments [15] have been conducted on the gas
at a pressure higher than 1 bar or on the liquid. Melting caused by an
electric current flowing through a lead or tungsten wire 0.2 mm in diameter
and 15 mm long immersed in the liquid phase at around 10°C (the pressure
being close to 40 bars) causes nitrous oxide to explode, although it is not
a detonation since the metal container is only broken into a few pieces.
It should be noted that in these experiments the metal reacts with the
oxide as soon as the former is brought to its melting point, so that – as
in Maquenne's experiment quoted above – the energy created by this kind of
ignition is high, exceeding 50 joules. It has also proved possible to
cause an explosion by igniting the liquid phase with a spark of a few

joules between gold electrodes (so that there is no combustion of the metal).

Two researchers from the B.A.M. later made a systematic study of the explosion of gaseous nitrous oxide ignited by an electric spark. They found that the phenomenon depends to a considerable degree on the container and the type of electric discharge. If the oxide is mixed with 30% oxygen, nitrogen, or air, then explosion no longer occurs.

Other tests (over 10 000 of them) consisting in dropping from several metres a small vessel containing nitrous oxide and a piece of steel weighing 75 g with bevelled edges have all given negative results.

By melting a copper wire (measuring between 0.2 and 0.3 mm) with an electric current, Brandt and Rozlovsky [30] produced a deflagration in nitrous oxide in a tube 6 mm in diameter provided the pressure was above 1.6 bars. Later German experiments have shown that, in a spherical container with a capacity of 14 litres, N_2O can be exploded at atmospheric pressure by melting a platinum wire, with the measured pressure rising to 9 bars.

Finally, Bollinger and his associates [29] conducted an important series of experiments in which the gas was ignited by melting a copper wire (0.12 mm in diameter) at various temperatures and pressures. They were thus able to draw the curve in Fig. 18.1. By using white-hot platinum wire as the ignition source, they obtained more complex results giving two arcs of a curve and an area of erratic results which are difficult to explain.

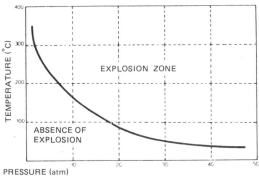

Fig. 18.1 - Explosion of nitrous oxide (initiation by melting copper wire).

It can be concluded from these experiments that nitrous oxide is highly insensitive to impact and it can be deflagrated only by applying a fairly high impact of energy. Bringing together the results of various researchers shows that the pressure at which explosions can be observed are lower as the dimensions of the container are greater. Furthermore, this pressure is lower when the initial temperature of the gas rises. In none of these experiments was detonation observed. Indeed, one might ask, given the weak combustion-supporting potential of nitrous oxide, if the compound is in fact capable of detonating.

C - *Homogeneous explosion* (by spontaneous ignition). The earliest observations on the spontaneous explosion of nitrous oxide were made by Zeldovich and Jacovlev [14] using a tube 25 mm in diameter and 18 cm long. An explosion accompanied by a blue flame was observed when the gas was allowed into the container at a temperature decreasing from 1285 to 1100°K as the pressure rose from 170 to 590 mm of mercury. Destriau and Navailles

[25], working with a container 18 mm in diameter, obtained ignition at 900°C (1170°K) at 500 mm of mercury. The results obtained by the two Russian researchers may be connected to those found by French experimenters by the constancy of the product of the limit pressure by the diameter at each temperature.

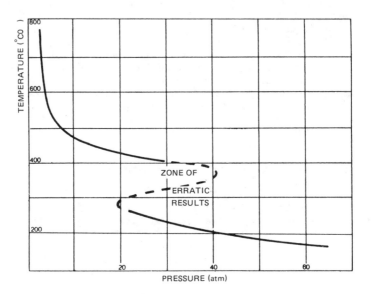

Fig. 18.2 – Explosion of nitrous oxide (ignition by melting platinum wire). The curve in dotted lines is hypothetical.

In some of his experiments Bollinger [29] observed the spontaneous ignition with a delay of less than one second of N_2O placed in a container at 760°C and a pressure of 3.7 bars.

18.2.4 Accidental explosions of nitrous oxide

Explosions which may occur during the manufacture of nitrous oxide are described in Chapter 23. Cases of accidental explosion of a container housing the liquefied gas are very rare. Lange [27] relates an accident which occurred in August 1900 in Berlin during transfer of N_2O from one gas cylinder to another. The cylinder to be emptied was being heated by a low flame (reducing flame) of gas being moved about its surface. An explosion occurred without it being possible to say if the content had been raised to a high temperature.

In December 1945 in Boulogne-sur-Seine the nitrous oxide contained in a steel cylinder also exploded during heating, but in this case we know that as a result of negligence the flame was applied for several minutes to the same spot. It was the flame of a blowpipe working on town gas, and the explosion caused the container to shatter and throw off several large splinters.

There was a third case in April 1967. During unloading of a lorry, a
50 litre cylinder containing only 3 to 4 kg of nitrous oxide exploded,
throwing several large and very hot fragments over some distance. The
likely cause of the explosion was the presence in the cylinder of a piece
of steel which had broken off a dip tube and which must have caused fric-
tion† on the wall. A particle of steel raised to white heat may have
served as initiator.

18.2.5 Safety of use, storage, and transport of nitrous oxide

The physiological properties of nitrous oxide must never be forgotten.
Though it supports combustion, it does not support life and, from this
point of view, presents dangers very similar to those of nitrogen. Work-
places in which it is manufactured, stored, or used must consequently be
well ventilated.

If, in theory, N_2O is explosive, *from the practical point of view* we
are justified, as with ammonium nitrate, in not classifying it with the
explosives since its potential is very low and its sensitivity very weak.
This gas is handled in thousands of tons every year throughout the world,
but no explosion has been observed‡ *when it is on its own.* Kirk–Othmer
[17], in comparing N_2O with other anaesthetics, is perfectly justified in
referring to its inexplodability and safety.

Since, however, it is an oxidising agent, nitrous oxide must be stored
with combustible substances only with the utmost circumspection. It is
compatible with edible creams, which are products containing an appreciable
percentage of water, at least up to a pressure of 15 bars. With flammable,
compressed liquids, an explosion cannot be ruled out. One occurred in
January 1969 in the United States when methanol was being saturated with
N_2O at 11 bars in a closed vessel. We should also mention an explosion
which occurred in 1973 in an industrial apparatus when an attempt was made
to substitute nitrous oxide for carbon dioxide, which was the gas normally
used at a pressure of 30 to 40 bars to treat certain mixtures of water and
food products. Amongst the components fitted inside the apparatus was an
insulating unit made of plastic (polyester). This reacted strongly with
the nitrous oxide, which decomposed explosively, raising the pressure
beyond what the apparatus could withstand. This oxidising capacity of
nitrous oxide must not be forgotten when choosing and maintaining equipment, especially pumps. Any contact with an oily lubricant must be avoided
and the pipes, valves, and fittings with which it comes into contact must
be degreased before use. The pumps should be lubricated with fluorocarbon
oils. Finally, there must be no smoking in workshops which house nitrous
oxide.

Because of its low critical temperature (36.4°C), a temperature to

---

† However (see 18.2.3), experiments attempting to reproduce what may have
happened in a cylinder containing a loose metallic mass have given only
negative results.
‡ The cases mentioned in section 18.2.4 are the only ones about which we
have been able to find any information in as complete a survey as possible.
Two of them were the result of a mistake: the application of a flame to
the gas cylinder containing the nitrous oxide.

which containers may easily be raised in summer, the authorised filling
ratios for N_2O depend on the resistance of the container. For cylinders
which have been subjected to a hydraulic test at 250 bars, the filling
level which has been in use in France for quite a long time is 0.75 kg per
litre of water capacity. At this level the contents are entirely liquid
and fill the container completely between 24°C and the critical temperature. The pressure exerted by the fluid (equal to its vapour pressure
below 24°C) at this filling density of 0.75 is

31.2 bars at 0°C	81 bars at 30°C
40 bars at 10°C	123 bars at 40°C
50.5 bars at 20°C	165 bars at 50°C
54.9 bars at 24°C	207 bars at 60°C.

As with all liquefied gases it is important not to exceed the maximum
degree of filling allowed, otherwise the container will be subjected in hot
weather to very high pressures which may rupture it.

We may conclude from the accident which occurred in 1967 (see 18.2.4)
that dip tubes should not be fitted to cylinders containing nitrous oxide
unless they are made of copper and are checked at regular intervals to
ensure that they are still fixed to the cylinder valve†. The other accidents show that a cylinder of nitrous oxide should not be heated with a
naked flame‡. If heating is necessary, it must be achieved by plunging the
cylinder into a bath of water at a temperature no higher than 50°C.

Valves on cylinders of nitrous oxide should not be covered with any
kind of oily lubricant (which would, in any case, be dissolved by the
oxide) since the cylinders, when used in anaesthesia, must be fitted with a
pressure reducing valve into which the gas might carry oily droplets that
could cause an explosion in the valve.

18.3 NITRIC OXIDE

18.3.1 General properties

Nitric oxide is a colourless gas which is barely soluble in water and is
obtained easily from various reactions. One which gives a very pure gas
consists in reducing sodium nitrite with an acid solution of ferrous
sulphide. In the open air at ordinary temperature it oxidises into red
nitrogen dioxide NO_2. In the presence of an alkaline solution oxidation
gives a nitrite:

$$2NO + 1/2O_2 + 2NaOH = 2NaNO_2 + H_2O,$$

but in the absence of oxygen the reaction of NO with alkaline solutions
follows a different course:

---

† The handling of gas cylinders subjects the dip tube mounting to repeated
stresses until it is ultimately no longer able to withstand sharp pressure
applied at right angles to it.
‡ Using a naked flame to heat a gas cylinder, whatever its contents, is
clearly a primitive act completely at odds with the rules of the craft.

$$4NO + 2NaOH \rightarrow 2NaNO_2 + N_2O + H_2O.$$

This latter reaction, which, at ordinary temperature, takes months to complete with soda, is more rapid (a few days) with potash. Above 120°C nitric oxide also reacts with mercury.

18.3.2 The oxidising property of nitric oxide

At ordinary pressure and temperature the NO oxide has only weak oxidising properties: mixtures of the gas with hydrogen or carbon monoxide cannot be ignited [7]. Bonnefois and Destriau [19] consider that H_2–NO mixtures can be thermally exploded only at a high temperature (above 900°C) and at a pressure higher than standard atmospheric pressure. However, a strong electric spark does explode the equimolar H_2–NO mixture. At initial pressures of less than 10 bars initiation is difficult, whilst at between 10 and 30 bars detonation in a tube preceded by a deflagrating phase is not always stable. All this can be explained by the relative slowness of the rate of reaction between NO and hydrogen.

Wolfhard and Burgess [8] have found that it is very difficult to ignite mixtures of methane and nitric oxide with a pilot light. Mixtures of a combustible gas and NO, passing through a ceramic tube at a speed of 50 cm/s, ignite at very high temperatures [9]: 1045°C for C_2H_4–NO mixtures and 1320°C for H_2–NO mixtures. Whereas mixtures of CS_2 vapour and oxygen have an ignition temperature below 100°C, the same vapour mixed with NO only ignites above 900°C. Nitric oxide is a weak oxidising agent only if it is pure, however: if it contains NO_2 as a result of decomposition, it may react more vigorously with combustible substances (see 18.3.5).

18.3.3 The stability of nitric oxide

At ordinary temperature and pressure the oxide NO is stable and no sign of decomposition was seen after forty years in nitrogen oxide contained in a sealed bulb [10], but at high pressure it decomposes slowly at ordinary temperature, as Briner and Wroczynski observed as early as 1909. More detailed research [4] led Briner to conclude that at 350 bars at ordinary temperature (15 to 20°C) after six months NO changes† almost completely into a dark–blue liquid which he took to be dinitrogen trioxide containing N_2O and NO in solution. Melia [1] made a more accurate study of the decomposition and established that at 30°C it is well represented by the equation

$$3NO \rightarrow N_2O + NO_2 \qquad (18.1)$$

which implies a law of the third order

$$- d[NO]/dt = k[NO]^3$$

---

† Richter and Sage [21] found that, at 7°C and 330 bars, in a metal apparatus, more than 10% of NO decomposes in the first hour.

where the velocity constant k, which varies with temperature, equals $2.7.10^{-5}$ (litre/mol.hour)^2 between 30 and 50°C.

At high temperatures and under pressure decomposition is more rapid and gives a small quantity of nitrogen. Thus, when NO was put in Melia's test bomb tube at 210°C and 200 bars, after 65 hours the gas contained 4.5% N_2O to 8% NO_2 and 9% N_2. According to Richter and Sage [21], decomposition at 150°C and high pressure is represented overall by

$$4NO = 2NO_2 + N_2.$$

Although these decomposition reactions are exothermic, they are very slow even at 250°C. At ordinary pressure nitric oxide begins to decompose only at about 500°C, giving N_2O. The reaction is facilitated by catalysts (CaO, Al_2O_3, etc.).

When it is adsorbed by chabazite – and probably also by an artificial zeolite – nitric oxide undergoes reaction (18.1) at ordinary temperature, and when the gas is desorbed by gradual heating, it first gives off N_2O, then NO from 150°C, and finally NO_2 at around 200°C. Clearly, the effect of adsorption is to condense NO, in which state it decomposes as rapidly as it does at high pressure.

18.3.4 The explosion of nitric oxide

In the gaseous state at ordinary pressure the NO oxide can be exposed to a flame or electric sparks without exploding. Berthelot [6] caused it to explode only by priming it with mercury fulminate. An explosion could probably be initiated more easily at a pressure of several bars. It can be shown by calculation that the detonation of the gas must follow the equation

$$NO \rightarrow 0.46N_2 + 0.46O_2 + 0.08NO, \qquad\qquad (18.2)$$

which gives off 83 kJ and raises the products of the explosion to around 3100°C.

Miller [3] has carried out experiments on the detonation of liquid NO at a temperature close to its normal boiling point. In a vertical tube 52 mm in diameter using 135 g of cyclonite (RDX) as a booster, velocities of 5100 m/s and 5460 m/s were recorded (in the second of these experiments the NO was partly solid at the bottom of the tube). The explosion is highly destructive but the NO is not decomposed completely since after the detonation red nitrous fumes from oxidation in air of the undecomposed NO are observed. This was confirmed by experiments conducted eight years later by two Americans [49] following an explosion which occurred during an operation to distil liquid oxide at a low temperature.

In a theoretical study on the propagation of flames, Henkel and his associates [20] applied their theory to the case of NO and came to the conclusion that a flame (deflagration) of gaseous nitric oxide is not possible unless the gas has been well heated beforehand and even then only very high energy sparks would be able to initiate deflagration.

18.3.5 Accidental explosions of nitric oxide - safety measures

In 1967, when nitric oxide was being compressed in a duct by a dry compressor, an explosion occurred at a pressure of 40 bars, causing the pipe
to tear open in several places. An inquiry revealed that there was a small
amount of lubricating oil in the dead end of the duct and that the gas
being treated had been kept in a container at 50 bars for over six months
and must have been rather impure. Melia [1] had already warned against the
use of NO which, when it has been stored for too long in the compressed
state, contains NO_2, causing it to react strongly with a number of substances and in particular with hydrocarbons.

For safety purposes, then, nitric oxide should be allowed into pipes
and apparatuses only when they are free from oxidisable lubricants. If a
vacuum pump is to be used (for example a pump with blades immersed in oil),
check valves and filters must be used to hold in droplets of oil.   In
general, NO should be treated in very clean apparatuses, and if it has to
be liquefied, it must not be forgotten that it is then a powerful, albeit
not very sensitive, explosive (2550 kJ/kg). For purposes of storage and
transport, nitric oxide should be housed in steel cylinders at a pressure
no greater than 50 bars in order to limit the gradual decomposition that it
will undergo.

18.4 NITROGEN DIOXIDE

18.4.1 General properties

Nitrogen dioxide† in the solid state is white and melts at $-11.2°C$ when it
consists almost entirely of the dimer N_2O_4 (dinitrogen tetroxide). The
liquid, which is pale yellow, boils at $21.2°C$, giving off a red vapour
composed of a mixture of the two species NO_2 and N_2O_4 in an equilibrium
which varies with temperature and pressure.   At standard atmospheric
pressure the percentages of NO_2 at 21.2, 37, and $79°C$ are respectively 16,
30, and 75%. It is this monomer which gives its red colour to the gas.
The vapour pressure of the liquid (a balanced mixture of NO_2 and N_2O_4)
reaches 3.48 bars at $50°C$ and 5.11 bars at $60°C$.

The brightly coloured NO_2 monomer is the nitryl radical in the free
state.   The N_2O_4 dimer may be thought of as nitrosyl nitrate $NO - NO_3$,
given some of its reactions‡. Nitrogen dioxide (a mixture of NO_2 and N_2O_4)
reacts readily and rapidly with water to give a mixture of $NO_3H + NO_2H$ in
solution. It is not explosive in itself, indeed in the gaseous state its
formation is only weakly exothermic.   At temperatures above $150°C$ NO_2
begins to dissociate into NO and oxygen, and the dissociation is almost
total at around $550°C$. Nitrogen dioxide may be stored in carbon steel
containers, but it should be known that steel pipes, whether ordinary steel
or stainless steel, fix the traces of nitrous fumes from the gases which

---

† We should no longer call this nitrogen peroxide, reserving that term for
compounds containing the bond $- O - O -$.
‡ For example, with dry potassium iodide it produces the reaction

$$KI + NO.NO_3 = KNO_3 + NO + 1/2I_2.$$

flow through them.

Vapours of NO_2 + N_2O_4 attack mercury at ordinary temperature, the reaction being

$$2NO_2 + 4Hg = N_2 + 4HgO.$$

For the physical and chemical properties of the NO_2 – N_2O_4 system, the reader is referred to a monograph by Gray and Yoffe [26].

18.4.2 Oxidising properties of nitrogen dioxide

This substance is a powerful oxidising agent. Any substance which can burn in oxygen burns even more vigorously in NO_2. It can ignite many combustible substances, such as aniline, even at ordinary temperature. Combustible liquids with which it can be mixed without excessive heating form explosive mixtures, the use of which under the name of panclastites [46] was recommended by E. Turpin in 1881. These mixtures are highly sensitive and quite dangerous explosives. A recent study by Kristoff [50] of mixtures of liquid tetroxide with nitrobenzene or mononitrotoluene has confirmed this extreme sensitivity to impact. Those which are at the stoichiometric mixture seem to be sensitive enough to detonate under the effect of a sudden rise in pressure of the order of 100 bars of the kind that may occur when a valve is rapidly closed on a pipe along which the liquid is flowing. This would give a good explanation of some accidental explosions which have occurred with spent acids from the mononitration of aromatic hydrocarbons. N_2O_4 reacts very strongly with double bonded hydrocarbons. When solidified N_2O_4 and an ethylenic hydrocarbon (such as isobutylene, butylene, or cyclohexene) are combined at the temperature of liquid nitrogen (– 195°C), a strong explosive reaction is initiated during heating at a temperature between – 75 and – 40°C.

Halogenated solvents, such as dichloromethane and trichloromethane, are miscible with N_2O_4 and form explosive mixtures [22]. Those which contain a double bond, such as trichloroethylene, are more sensitive and may give rise to explosive reactions which occur spontaneously.

The numerous molecular combinations which N_2O_4 forms easily with many organic substances, such as dioxane $C_4H_8O_2.N_2O_4$, are explosive. Addition compounds with perchlorates, like crystallised solid $LiClO_4.N_2O_4$, have been proposed as oxidising agents for rocket propellants.

18.4.3 The dangers of nitrogen dioxide

It must be remembered that nitrogen dioxide is a highly toxic substance belonging to the asphyxiators. Anyone handling it in the liquid state must wear leather gloves and protect the respiratory tract. It is the main constituent in the nitrous fumes given off by many chemical reactions and it cannot be stressed too strongly that operatives should be protected from their effects, which are insidious and are often not felt until several hours after inhalation. A person who has inhaled nitrous fumes must be laid out on a stretcher at once and left to rest with a blanket over him to prevent him from getting cold. Artificial respiration must *not* be given unless the victim has stopped breathing. If his breathing is laboured, however, he may be given a little oxygen. He should remain under medical supervision for forty eight hours and the doctor must be told that the person has been poisoned by nitrous fumes.

Nitrogen dioxide also forms dangerous explosives when mixed with many combustible substances. It is necessary, therefore, not only to handle it in clean apparatuses but also to ensure that there is no possibility of it being mixed with a combustible substance during handling. There were serious explosions [23] in Zachornewitz in 1917 and Bodio in 1921 in some tubular heat exchangers in which NO_2 vapours were being condensed. The refrigerating liquid circulating around the outside of the tubes was benzol in one case and toluene in the other. Cracks in the tubes [24] allowed the combustible liquid to react with the NO_2.

Alumina gel easily adsorbs nitrogen dioxide, changing colour, so the gas must not be allowed to come into contact with any gel which might have fixed combustible vapours or droplets of lubricant.

For purposes of storage and transport, nitrogen dioxide is housed in steel cylinders which are required by the R.I.D. to have a hydraulic test pressure of at least 10 bars. It should be noted that as the temperature rises from 50 to 60°C the vapour pressure increases by 46% (whereas for butane the increase is only 26%). In large quantities it is transported in stainless steel containers with joints made of polytetrafluoroethylene or polychlorotrifluoroethylene. Equipment used with nitrogen dioxide must be lubricated only with substances which are incombustible, such as polytetra-fluoroethylene, or which are not easy to ignite, such as graphite.

18.5 NITRIC ACID

18.5.1 General properties of nitric acid

One hundred percent pure nitric acid is an almost colourless liquid when it has just been distilled with a relative density at 15°C of 1.522 g/cm³ and a normal boiling point of 84°C. With water it gives an azeotropic mixture which boils at 121.8°C and contains 68.8% HNO_3. This mixture used to be called quadrihydrated nitric acid because its composition is very close to $N_2O_5.4H_2O$. Its usual commercial grades are the following:

Percentage of HNO_3	Boiling point	Density at 20°C	Former name
94		1.5	acid at 48° Baumé
68	122	1.41	" " 42° "
61.9	121	1.38	" " 40° "
52.8	118	1.33	" " 36° "

The name white fuming nitric acid is given to a product which contains at least 97.5% HNO_3 and less than 0.5% NO_2, the rest being water. Indeed, all products which contain at least 70% HNO_3 fume in the open air. The highly concentrated acid can dissolve quite large quantities of nitrogen dioxide. The name red fuming nitric acid is given to a solution containing from 13 to 15% N_2O_4 and 1.5 to 2.5% water with a density of around 1.55.

Nitric acid decomposes slowly in the light and more rapidly if it is heated. Its vapour is almost completely decomposed at 260°C into

$$2HNO_3 \rightarrow 2NO_2 + H_2O + 1/2O_2.$$

At lower temperatures the vapour contains other nitrogen oxides. It is a
highly corrosive liquid on most metals, but when it is mixed with a small
quantity of hydrofluoric acid, the latter forms a protective layer of
fluoride on the metal wall and corrosion is halted. It is manufactured in
very large quantities to make nitrates, and it is used in nitration or in
nitric esterification and to produce various oxidations (such as, for
example, the oxidation of iodine into iodic acid). It also has various
uses as a pickling solution.

18.5.2 The oxidising properties of nitric acid

It has long been known that nitric acid is a very powerful oxidising agent,
which is understandable given the ease with which it decomposes. It used
to be stored in carboys wrapped in straw, and very often when the container
cracked, the straw would catch fire. To see this in action, one simply has
to put 200 g of a 94% acid solution (density 1.5) in a 1 litre beaker and
add 40 g of straw cut into well-packed sprigs measuring 6 to 8 cm. The
bottom of the container heats up, leading to an emission of white smoke,
quickly followed by a flame in the upper part where convection provides a
constantly renewed supply of air, while the straw, brought to glowing heat
in the lower part, burns in the HNO_3 vapour and its decomposition products.
The phenomenon is very different from the combustion of straw in air.

Sawdust is also liable to ignite when it is brought into contact with
concentrated acid, and it is likely that the wood is not only oxidised but
also, in part at least, nitrated. In the old timber frame workshops where
nitric acid was used, the vapours from the acid, together with the vapours
of NO_2 which it produces when it is used in nitration, gradually attacked
the wood – both by oxidation and nitration – which became highly flammable.
There is even a case on record of a wooden beam spontaneously catching fire
on a very hot summer's day.

Thin strips of wood, commonly called wood shavings, are often used as a
packing material to provide a cushion around glass containers in a parcel.
With nitric acid there is a considerable risk of the wood igniting if the
glass breaks, even when the acid is at a concentration between 40 and 60%.
Experiment shows that strips of wood bathed in acid undergo an exothermic
decomposition which increases the temperature to around 100°C and give off
nitrous fumes which, when they come into contact with wood not soaked in
acid, react so strongly that the material is raised to a temperature which
is higher as the concentration of the acid increases. If air is present
when the wood has been heated to over 180°C, it will ignite. This can
happen with 50% and even 40% acid solutions if both acid and wood are at an
initial temperature of 50°C.

All kinds of cellulosic organic materials react strongly in this way
with nitric acid (see the Reinsdorf accident described in 26.4.3), whilst
non-cellulosic organic materials can also undergo the oxidising action of
nitric acid. The case has been quoted [31] of resins exchanging anions
which react at a temperature of 50°C with acid at medium concentration and
which have given rise to an explosion.

Very many organic liquids ignite immediately or after a short time when
they come into contact with white fuming nitric acid. The action is even
more violent with red fuming nitric acid. When ignition at ordinary temperature occurs within a fraction of a second, the liquid is said to be
hypergolic in relation to the acid, a property which is put to use in jet

engines using liquid propellants.   Amongst the hypergolic liquids are
methylaniline, the methylhydrazines, vinyl oxide and other vinyl compounds,
furaldehyde, mercaptans, etc.   The reaction is particularly violent with
unsaturated substances such as compounds containing one or more double
bonds.   By contrast, the saturated hydrocarbons, such as decane, withstand
the action of 97% solutions of acid when cold.   Explosions can be caused by
combining concentrated nitric acid with burning hydrocarbons (see the
Traskwood accident described in 24.2.11).

Many powdered metals react very strongly with nitric acid, but some may
react very dangerously even when they are in bulk form.   Cases have been
quoted [32] of titanium steel 'exploding' when brought into contact with
nitric acid.

Using nitric acid to produce oxidation in organic chemistry is not
without risk.   An explosion occurred during the oxidation of mesitylene
into 3,5-dimethylbenzoic acid in a pressurised autoclave at around 115°C
[33].   There have also been explosions in the manufacture of mellitic acid
$(C_6(Cu_2H)_6$ by oxidising charcoal with diluted nitric acid [45].

18.5.3 Solutions with a nitric acid base

Nitric acid is a good solvent for a large number of solid or liquid organic
substances.   With substances which dissolve in the acid without undergoing
any change, thus forming a true solution, mixtures are obtained which are
stable but which have explosive properties since the oxidising agent and
the fuel are juxtaposed in them at the molecular level.   Formerly, these
solutions were recommended for use as intentional explosives.   They are
generally very sensitive to ignition and quite sensitive to impact and can
admit a certain percentage of water without splitting into two phases, but
that reduces their sensitivity.

A serious explosion occurred in Klingsport in the U.S.A. in a tank
containing nitrobenzene mixed with concentrated nitric acid.   Van Dolah and
his associates [43] made a study of the explodability of the ternary system
$C_6H_5NO_2$ - HNO_3 - H_2O, mixtures of which are homogeneous only in a certain
range.   Using a booster of 50 g of compressed tetryl, they found that
mixtures over most of this range are likely to detonate (Fig. 18.3).   Card
gap tests (see 15.3.7) have shown the very high sensitivity of these
mixtures.   For example, it takes a thickness of more than 12 cm of cards to
stop ignition of the anhydrous mixture $C_6H_5NO_2$ + $5HNO_3$.   The study also
showed that if the temperature is raised from 25 to 80°C, there is an
appreciable increase in the range of detonability.   In that part of the
range where mixing does not occur, well-dispersed emulsions of the two
phases are still liable to detonate†.

Some mixtures of nitric acid and organic substances react slowly at
first, and then more and more rapidly as the mixture heats up, culminating
in an explosion.   This was the case with a mixture of some ten cubic
centimetres of nitric acid and formic acid, both in 99.5-100% solutions,
which, after an induction period lasting about five minutes, heated and
deflagrated.   We also know of a case [51] of the spontaneous explosion of a

---

† Similarly, emulsions of nitroglycerine and water (50% in mass) detonate
easily when ignited with 50 g of P.E.T.N. [35].

scaling solution composed of nitric acid and formalin (an aqueous solution
of formaldehyde with a small quantity of methanol).

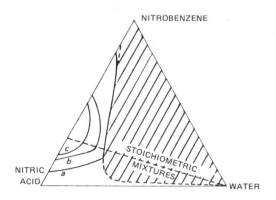

Fig. 18.3 - Results of card gap tests on mixtures of nitric acid, nitrobenzene, and water [43].   Thickness of cards still giving rise to an
explosion: curve a – 0; curve b – 25 mm; curve c – 50 mm. The range of
mixtures forming two phases at 25°C is shown by the hatched area.

    Nitric acid enters into the composition of various solutions used in
metallography to attack the surface of metals and alloys or for the
chemical polishing of metals.   For example, to attack nickel a mixture is
used of equal volumes of acetone, concentrated nitric acid, and acetic acid
(a 75% solution), which has given rise to explosions [36].   The same is
true of a solution containing ethyl alcohol and 15% NO_3H used to attack
bismuth [37].   A solution of lactic acid, nitric acid (39% solution), and
hydrofluoric acid (7.5%) used for the chemical polishing of zirconium is
unstable.   In the space of a few hours it heats up gradually and then
decomposes suddenly [38].   A similar mixture [39] of 50% glycerol†, 25%
nitric acid, and 25% hydrofluoric acid – to which water was later to be
added – exploded four hours after it was prepared.   Many other cases of
explosions of these solutions containing an organic substance with nitric
acid have occurred in laboratories.   Workers should therefore be on their
guard in this respect, especially since spontaneous heating and explosive
decomposition occur only after an induction period which may exceed twelve
hours.   Consequently, when these solutions are being prepared, the constituents should be added in the correct order, an intermediate mixture
should not be abandoned, and the quantity must be limited to only that
which is needed.   It is advisable to get rid of any unused reagent by
diluting it in large quantities of water.

18.5.4 Acetyl nitrate

Acetyl nitrate is a compound related to nitric acid.   It is prepared by the

_____

† Lactic acid or glycerol is added to make the solutions viscous.

action of dinitrogen pentoxide on acetic anhydride and can be thought of as

$$O \begin{matrix} \diagup^{NO_2} \\ \diagdown_{CO - CH_3} \end{matrix}$$

the mixed nitric-acetic anhydride, and since the molecule combines an oxidising group and a combustible group, it is a potential explosive. It has been known for a long time that when it is heated to more than 100°C, it explodes after giving off nitrous fumes. Spontaneous explosions have also been reported at ordinary temperature after several days' storage [40]. It is therefore advisable to use it immediately after preparation and to limit the amount being treated. Benzoyl nitrate, $NO_2 - O - CO - C_6H_5$, which is a viscous liquid, is also suspect.

It is highly likely that acetyl nitrate occurs in mixtures of acetic anhydride and nitric acid which have sometimes been used in nitration. Brown and Watt [42] have pointed out the danger of these mixtures, which are sensitive to impact and to friction, and suggested that the cooled and stirred reagents be mixed in the following way: when the mixture contains less than 55% nitric acid, this should be added gradually to the acetic anhydride, but to make a mixture with 85% HNO_3, the acetic anhydride should be poured into the acid. Dubar and Calzia [41] have studied the explosive properties of ternary mixtures of the two substances with water and found that the most sensitive to initiation is that which contains 60% HNO_3 and 40% $(CH_3CO)_2O$, whilst mixtures close to this composition deflagrate strongly when raised to 145°C (a test described in 16.1.4).

Acetyl pernitrate, $NO_2 - O - O - CO - CH_3$, is an organic peroxide of acetyl and nitryl which explodes very easily, especially when concentrated in gas column chromatography during analysis of the impurities which pollute the air [47], since it is formed in polluted air by the union of nitrogen trioxide (pernitric anhydride) and the acetyl radical.

18.5.5 Mixed nitric and sulphuric acids

Mixtures of nitric acid and sulphuric acid, for which the technical term is mixed acids, are commonly used in nitration and have oxidising properties which are all the more marked as the HNO_3 content is higher. Médard and Aunis [34] have carried out systematic tests in which 200 g of warm (50°C) pitchpine dust were thrown into 50 ml of acid. In some cases, a white-hot region is formed in the combustible substance over which one simply has to blow a light air current to produce a flame which burns until combustion is complete. The tests also showed the importance of temperature: sawdust which ignites easily at 50°C with a given mixture may not react quite so strongly with the same mixture at 40°C.

As a result of these tests, it was possible to draw on a triangular diagram (Fig. 18.4) for $H_2SO_4 - HNO_3 - H_2O$ the range of mixtures which give rise to ignition. Just 22% of HNO_3 causes a strong reaction with ignition. If the mixture also contains sulphuric acid, which is known to have a strong dehydrating effect on organic substances, the oxidising property of the nitric acid is enhanced. This test, like all such empirical tests, is somewhat arbitrary, and the choice of a different combustible substance and a different operating mode might have produced a different limiting curve.

In particular, tests on larger masses, which would lose less heat, would probably produce a wider ignition range than that in Fig. 18.4, although the latter does give a good idea of the oxidising effect of mixed acids and was at one time used to define such mixtures from the point of view of transport regulations (roughly speaking, the regulated mixtures were those in the quadrilateral A'-M-B'-HNO$_3$).

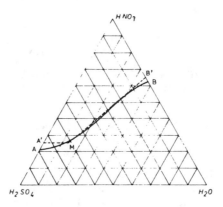

Fig. 18.4 – Range of oxidising properties of mixed acids, from tests by Médard and Aunis [34].

18.5.6 Safety measures in the use of nitric acid

Although the oxidising properties of nitric acid have been known for a long time, there have still been accidental explosions in the use or transport of the substance. The following are just five examples:

   (a) Explosions have occurred in a centrifugal pump circulating nitric acid.   Subsequent inquiry revealed that the reaction took place in the asbestos–based gland packing which contained cotton threads.

   (b) An explosion occurred in a compartment of a transport tanker which had been loaded with a 98% solution of nitric acid.   The vehicle had previously been used to carry toluene and had not been cleaned, contrary to statements made by the transporter.

   (c) A road haulage tanker which had been used to transport ethanol was carefully washed out with water, but unfortunately a small amount of alcohol was left in a space in the valve which the water did not reach. The vehicle was then used to transport a 70% solution of nitric acid, and when the valve was opened to empty the contents, an explosion occurred which cracked the pipe and spilled a large quantity of acid onto the ground.   Clearly, the acid and the alcohol had reacted very strongly (oxidation and also, perhaps, nitration).   It is therefore advisable to fit tankers with valves designed in such a way that they can be properly rinsed out with water.

   (d) When a small quantity of a 64% solution of nitric acid was poured into a tanker which still contained a certain amount of alcohol, the latter was quite quickly oxidised into acetaldehyde which escaped as a vapour through a vent with a whistling noise.   The large release of heat produced a hot spot which exploded the mixture of air and vapours of alcohol and acetaldehyde in the tanker.

(e) A serious accident happened in a laboratory in Paris around 1961 when a small quantity of a mixture of nitric and sulphuric acids was poured into a sink in the trap of which there was still some methanol which had been poured away shortly before and which reacted explosively with the mixture, shattering the trap and causing considerable damage and leaving one person injured. This accident shows that if one wants to pour a small quantity of nitric acid down a sink, one must first flush a large amount of water down it to clean out whatever might be in the trap, and then pour the acid away slowly with the tap still running.

In the chemical industry, then, nitric acid, even when it is in low concentrations, should not be allowed to come into contact with organic substances other than those with which it is intended to react. After a reaction carried out in controlled and reliable conditions, it sometimes happens that the compound obtained is still wet with residual acid and thus constitutes a dangerous mixture. Mention should be made in this respect of a study [44] of the butyl ester of the dinitrate of tartaric acid

$$C_4H_9.O.CO - CH(NO_3) - CH(NO_3) - CO - O - C_4H_9$$

steeped in nitric acid.

In metallography laboratories precautions should be taken with the various nitric acid-based solutions used, and finally it should be remembered that nitric acid is also dangerous because of its corrosive effect on skin and eyes, and the ease with which it gives off toxic nitrous fumes in a fire (see 18.4.3).

Nitric acid is stored in large quantities in metal tanks which should be located in a fund. When the acid is housed in carboys or other kinds of fragile container, the latter should preferably be located in the open air on grassless ground or better still on clinkers. Carboys should be arranged in relatively small, isolated groups, and, of course, stored well away from any kind of combustible substance. If nitric acid is stored in a warehouse, the latter should be well ventilated, and if it has a wooden framework, the beams must be covered with a layer of plaster 2 to 3 cm thick (with imbedded wire netting).

BIBLIOGRAPHICAL REFERENCES

[1]   Melia, T. P. (1965) *J. Inorg. Nucl. Chem.* **27** 95
[2]   Briner, E. & Wroczynski, A. (1909) *Compt. Rend.* **149** 1372
[3]   Miller, R. O. (1968) *Ind. Eng. Chem. Process Design and Div.* **7** 590
[4]   Briner, E. & Boubnoff, N. (1913) *J. Chimie phys.* **11** 597
[5]   Noyes, W. A. (1931) *J. Am. Ch. Soc.* **53** 514
[6]   Berthelot, M. (1883) *La force des matières explosives.* 3rd edition, Paris, pp. 106 & 293
[7]   Berthelot, M. (1880) *Ann. Chimie* [5] **20** 258
[8]   Wolfhard, H. G. & Burgess, D. S. (1958) *Comb. and Flame* **2** 3
[9]   Wolfhard, H. G. & Strasser, R. (1958) *J. Chem. Physics* **28** 172
[10] Howard, C. S. & Daniels, F. (1958) *J. Phys. Chem.* **62** 360
[11] Berthelot, M. (1875) *Ann. Chimie Phys.* [5] **4** 415
[12] Maquenne, L. (1895) *Compt. Rend.* **121** 424
[13] Destriau, M. (1962) *Comb. and Flame* **6** 347; Destriau, M. & Heleschewitz (1965) *Compt. Rend.* **261** 4101

[14]   Zeldovich, J. B. & Jacovlev, B. I. (1938) *Doklady Ac. Sc. USSR* **19** 699
[15]   Perraudin, R. & Rigolet (1965) *Laboratoire de l'air liquide*
[16]   Briner, E. & Wroczynski, A. (1910) *Compt. Rend.* **150** 1325
[17]   Kirk-Othmer (1963) *Encyclopedia of Chemical Technology.* 2nd edition,
       Vol. 2, p. 396
[18]   Pannetier, G. & Sicard, A. (1954) *Compt. Rend.* **238** 1516
[19]   Bonnefois, J. & Destriau, M. (1967) *Compt. Rend.* Série C **265** 983
[20]   Henkel, M. J., Hummel, H. & Spaulding, W. P. (1949) *3rd Symposium on
       Combustion*, p. 135
[21]   Richter, G. N. & Sage, B. H. (1959) *J. Chem. Eng. Data* 4 36
[22]   Turley, R. E. (23 Nov. 1964) *Chem. Eng. News* **42** 53; Benson, S. W.
       (21 Dec. 1964) *Chem. Eng. News*, p. 4
[23]   Raschig, F. (1922) *Angew. Chem.* **35** 117
[24]   Schaarschmidt, A. (1923) *Angew. Chem.* **36** 565
[25]   Destriau, M. & Navailles, J.-Cl. (1965) *Compt. Rend.* **260** 3661
[26]   Gray, P. & Yoffe, A. D. (1955) *Quarterly Rev.* 9 362
[27]   Lange, A. (1902) *Angew. Chem.* **15** 725
[28]   Rasch, H. (1904) *Z. für kompr. und flüss. Gase* 7 169
[29]   Krisjansons, J. O., Bollinger, L. E. & Edse, R. (Sept. 1962) *A.R.L.
       Rapport 62-431*
[30]   Brandt, D. B. & Rozlovsky, A. I. (1960) *Doklady Akad. Nauk. SSSR*
       132 1129
[31]   Molen, G. F. (1965) *Chem. Abstracts* **63** 16545h
[32]   Gilbert & Finck (1956) *Metal Prog.* **70** 93
[33]   Wilms, H. & Dorlars, A. (1961) *Angew. Chem.* **74** 465
[34]   Médard, L. & Aunis, G. (1941) *Lab. C.S.E.*
[35]   Médard, L. (1953) *Mém. Poudres* **35** 59
[36]   Trant, M. S. (1960) *Chem. Eng. News* **38** 56
[37]   Fawcett, H. (1949) *Chem. Eng. News* **27** 1396
[38]   Bubar, S. F. & Vermilyea, D. A. (1966) *J. Electrochem. Soc.* **113** 519
[38]   Buck, R. H. (1966) *J. Electrochem. Soc.* **113** 1352
[40]   Konig, W. (1955) *Angew. Chem.* **67** 157
[41]   Dubar, J. & Calzia, J. (1968) *Compt. Rend.* C **266** 1114
[42]   Brown, T. A. & Watt, J. A. (1967) *Chem. Brit.* 3 504
[43]   Mason, C. M., Van Dolah, R. W. & Ribovich, J. (1965) *J. Chem. Eng.
       Data* **10** 173
[44]   Mason, C. M. (1961) *Report 3846*, Bureau of Mines
[45]   Chaigneau, M. (1951) *Compt. Rend.* **233** 657 & 692
[46]   Calzia, J. (1959) *Les substances explosives et leurs nuisances.*
       Paris. p. 155
[47]   Chovin, P. (1968) *Bull. Soc. Chim. Fr.*, p. 2202
[48]   Conrad, D. & Dietlen, S. (1983) *Amt. Bull. B.A.M.* **13** 19
[49]   Ramsay, J. B. & Chiles. W. C. (1976) *Los Alamos Lab. Rep. (C.A.
       87 142218s)
[50]   Kristoff, F. T., Griffith, M. L. & Bolleter, W. T (1983) *J. of
       Hazardous Mat.* 7 199
[51]   Pirie, C. J. (1979) *Chem. in Britain* **15** 11

19

Oxygenated compounds of halogens and manganese

19.1 GENERAL OBSERVATIONS

19.1.1 Oxides and oxysalts of halogens and heptavalent manganese

The oxygenated compounds formed by halogens are all to a degree oxidising agents. Some of them have appreciable oxidising properties, and some of them are explosives. We shall also discuss highly oxygenated compounds of manganese in this same chapter since, like the halogens, with which it is classified in column VII of the Periodic Table, it forms highly oxidising or explosive oxygenated compounds in which it is heptavalent.

19.2 COMPOUNDS OF OXYGEN AND THE HALOGENS

19.2.1 Oxygen fluorides

There are a number of oxygen fluorides known to chemists, and a study of them can be found in a monograph by Allamagny [4]. The most stable is the difluoride OF_2 discovered in 1927 by Lebeau and Damiens. It is a gas which liquefies at $-145°C$ at atmospheric pressure and has a critical temperature of $-58°C$. Its formation is weakly endothermic [47]:

$$F_p = -25 \text{ kJ/mol}, \qquad F_v = -26 \text{ kJ/mol}.$$

However, it has not been seen to explode, even at a pressure of 10 bars, when electric sparks are applied to it, and it is quite stable to heat, at least up to 200°C. Because of its very strong oxidising properties it is able to form explosive mixtures not only with combustible gases and vapours but even with chlorine or water vapour. A spark ignited in wet oxygen difluoride triggers an explosion through the reaction†

$$OF_2 + H_2O(g) = O_2 + 2HF$$

which releases 330 kJ (at constant volume).

Silica gel which has adsorbed OF_2 explodes easily under impact since the reaction

$$SiO_2 + 2OF_2 = 2O_2 + SiF_4$$

is strongly exothermic (757 kJ at constant volume). Substances liable to react strongly with fluorine also react strongly with OF_2, but with the latter the initiation of the reaction involves a higher activation energy than with free fluorine, so that from the practical point of view OF_2 can be thought of as a more workable form of fluorine than elementary fluorine itself. Indeed, it has been suggested for use as an oxidising agent with rocket propellants.

19.2.2 Oxides of chlorine

The two most stable chlorine oxides are the monoxide Cl_2O and the heptoxide Cl_2O_7 (perchloric anhydride) which may be stored at ordinary temperature since their thermal decomposition becomes measurable only above 100°C. They are both endothermic and easy to explode, and the same is true of the dioxide ClO_2, which has become an important industrial substance. For the properties of the chlorine oxides, the reader is referred to the monograph by Masschelein [49].

Chlorine monoxide is a gas which dissolves quite easily in water and liquefies at around 2°C at atmospheric pressure. Given its heat of formation ($F_p = - 87$ kJ/mol), when it explodes at constant volume and an initial pressure of one atmosphere, gases are formed at around 1900°K and 10 atms. According to experiments by Pannetier and Lecamp [57], the lower limit pressure of chlorine monoxide must be extremely low since it is always exploded by an electric spark at the lowest pressures at which observation is possible.

Its explosion by an electric spark when diluted with oxygen has been studied by Cady and Brown [3] who found that mixtures containing more than 30% Cl_2O give rise to a violent explosion with an orange-coloured flame. Between 23.5 and 25% the explosion is very weak and produces no visible flame. Calculation shows that at this lower limit of 23.5% the gases after the explosion are raised to no more than some 650°C, and the mixture is an explosive with only a low calorific value (of the order of 420 kJ/kg). This limit of 23.5% is also given for mixtures of air and chlorine monoxide by Russian authors [58] who consider that in these conditions the oxide could be used instead of the dioxide in bleaching.

---

† This reaction raises the gases formed to more than 4000°K and the pressure rise factor is about 20, whereas the explosive dissociation of OF_2 raises the gases to only 1005°K (π factor = 5.1).

19.2.3 Chlorine dioxide

Chlorine dioxide ClO_2 is a greenish-yellow gas which condenses at $11°C$ into a highly dangerous liquid, since it is exploded easily by a variety of stimuli.   Gray and Ip [14], whose experiments were disrupted by two unexpected explosions in spite of the meticulous precautions they took, have confirmed that this dioxide is liable to be explosively decomposed by light, by an electric discharge, or by a rise in temperature, and that it is even more dangerous when mixed with hydrocarbons.   It is a strongly endothermic substance (F_p = 105 kJ/mol) with an explosion temperature† higher than $2100°K$ and a pressure rise factor of the order of 12.

It is unstable to heat and undergoes a heterogeneous decomposition at around 40-50°C, which does not, however, prevent it from being used in industry to bleach wood pulp when it is diluted with an inert gas to reduce its content to between 5 and 10% and when it is left in darkness, since light causes it to explode at ordinary temperatures, or when it is used in an aqueous solution. According to a study by Booth and Bowen [5], dry ClO_2 diluted in an equal volume of CO_2 can be stored in the dark for several hours at 85°C without decomposing. Nitrous oxide is even better than CO_2 for inhibiting the decomposition of chlorine dioxide.

The detonation velocity of ClO_2, initially studied by Dixon in 1896, was the object of an important research programme undertaken by Ben Caid in 1965 [6].   Taken at an initial pressure of 200 to 400 mm of mercury, the gas has a detonation velocity close to 1300 m/s, which is, to within 1 or 2%, the velocity as calculated by the Chapman-Jouguet theory.   It is interesting to note that, for a given tube diameter, there is a limit pressure below which the explosion is no longer a detonation but a deflagration, and that pressure is

Diameter (cm)	0.78	1.06	1.45	2.8	infinite
Limit pressure (mm of mercury)	49	39	30	19	7.5.

As for deflagration, Gray [14] states that at temperatures between 42 and 80°C, it only ceases to occur at pressures below 1 mm of mercury, so that in practice there is always a danger that chlorine dioxide will explode at the temperatures normally encountered in daily use. When it is diluted to 10% in an inert gas, the explosion assumes the form of a deflagration which is sufficiently slow for it to be possible to fit reactors and other equipment with vents consisting of large panels which lift up under pressure.

19.2.4 Various halogen oxides

Perchloryl fluoride ClO_3F, discovered in 1951 by Bode and Klesper [44], can be obtained by the action of fluorine on potassium chlorate. It is a toxic

---

† This explosion temperature varies appreciably with the initial pressure because of the variation in the rate of dissociation of Cl_2 into monatomic Cl at a high temperature.

colourless gas which liquefies at – 47°C at atmospheric pressure and has a vapour pressure of around 21 bars at 50°C.   Its critical temperature and pressure are 95°C and 53.7 bars.   Its formation is exothermic (F_p = 21.3 kJ/mol) and it is stable to heat, beginning to decompose only above 400°C. It is not decomposed by water, at least as long as the temperature does not exceed 120°C.

It is a powerful oxidising agent, and mixtures of the substance in the liquid state with absorbent combustible materials such as sawdust are explosives comparable to the liquid oxygen explosives.   With some substances, such as hydrazine or activated carbon, it reacts strongly and causes ignition.   It has been used in organic chemistry either to introduce the perchloryl radical into a molecule† or to produce oxidation or fluorination reactions which are difficult to achieve with other reagents.   But using it in the presence of certain substances is not without danger; during a reaction in which methanol was being used as a solvent, a gaseous mixture of ClO_3F and CH_3OH vapour exploded [23], whilst in other cases oxidation is so violent that it also leads to an explosion.

It is stored in ordinary or stainless steel cylinders, the valves of which must never in any circumstance be lubricated with grease.   In this respect, the same precautions must be taken as with oxygen.

Chloryl fluoride ClO_2F is prepared, amongst other methods, by the direct union of fluorine and ClO_2 at a low temperature.   It is a gas which liquefies at around – 5°C, is easily hydrolysed, and is dissociated by heating into F_2 and ClO_2 without explosion.   It reacts very strongly with many combustible substances;   fats in particular give rise to explosions.

Fluorine perchlorate ClO_4F is a gas which liquefies at – 16°C and which explodes easily.   It has no application and must be handled only with the utmost care in the laboratory.

19.3 PERCHLORIC ACID

19.3.1 Explosive and oxidising properties of perchloric acid

Perchloric acid, which, until 1938, was used only in laboratories mainly for analysis, has become an industrial product with various applications. It occurs either as an acid with 64–65% $HClO_4$ or as an acid at 70–72% strength, a concentration close to that of the azeotropic mixture which boils at 203°C and contains 72.4% $HClO_4$.

The anhydrous acid is a colourless mixture which freezes at – 112°C and is prepared simply and safely according to Smith [33] by the distillation at low pressure of a mixture of oleum and a 72% solution of perchloric acid.   It can be stored in the solid state at the temperature of liquid nitrogen, but at ordinary temperatures it gradually decomposes and after thirty days generally explodes spontaneously.   Gradual decomposition gives it an amber colour which serves as a warning that it should be destroyed, which is easily done by diluting it in water.   The monohydrate, which melts at 50°C and contains 84.8% $HClO_4$, is thought of as hydronium perchlorate $(OH_3)ClO_4$.

---

† It should be pointed out that perchlorylated organic compounds such as $C_6H_5(ClO_3)$ and $C_5H_4(NO_2)(ClO_3)$ are highly dangerous explosives because of their high sensitivity to impact and mechanical effects.

It is stable at ordinary temperature, as are less concentrated solutions [7].

The anhydrous acid, the monohydrated acid, and even mixtures containing up to 23% water have vigorous oxidising properties at ordinary temperature. Many organic substances explode on contact with them and they easily form explosive mixtures. By contrast, mixtures containing 72% $HClO_4$ at most are highly stable and practically devoid of oxidising properties *at ordinary temperature*. They act like a strong acid. However, they may have an oxidising effect at a temperature generally higher than 100°C.

The action of perchloric acid at 40, 60, and 70% $HClO_4$ on various combustible substances has been studied by Elliot and Brown [43]. By progressively heating a mixture of acid and fuel, they observed a strong reaction (ignition, deflagration, or vigorous explosion) with various substances (paper, wood shavings, sawdust, cotton, tar, rubber, sugar) at a temperature between 160 and 200°C. The concentration of acid used has only a minor influence on the temperature of the strong reaction. Strangely enough, sulphur did not ignite: in experiments on a mass of 50 g heated at a point (by a white-hot metal wire), there is weak deflagration at low confinement and a stronger explosion when the confinement is sufficiently high.

The authors initiated a mixture of sawdust and a 60% solution of perchloric acid with a No. 8 detonator and easily obtained a detonation with a velocity of about 3000 m/s (the density was not specified but was probably between 1 and 1.2).

The preceding observations justify the R.I.D. transport rulings: acid at concentrations between 40 and 72.5% is placed in class 5.1 (oxidising substances); containers must be firmly wedged in their outer packing using incombustible absorbent materials. It is forbidden to transport acid at concentrations of more than 72.5%.

19.3.2 Precautions in the use of perchloric acid in chemical analysis

We are talking here of an acid no stronger than 72%. Care must be taken not to drop fragments of easily flammable materials into perchloric acid. The reagent must be stored in containers with glass stoppers. Any spilt acid must be mopped up with a woollen cloth, and certainly *not* with cotton or any other cellulosic material which could esterify into a dangerous organic perchlorate.

It is advisable to carry out all operations under a well-ventilated hood and to wear a face mask or a good pair of goggles. Where perchloric acid is used regularly, care must be taken to ensure that the vapours given off do not attack any wooden parts in the vicinity, which might become highly flammable over a period of time.

One of the analytical uses of perchloric acid is in the analysis of alloys, in particular for the titration of chromium, when the effect of the acid has frequently been to cause an explosion. Dietz [34], who has studied the problem, has shown that this is because hydrogen is formed when steel is attacked by the acid and mixes with $HClO_4$ to form a highly sensitive explosive gas mixture which can explode spontaneously even at a temperature as low as 215°C when it comes into contact with steel chips. Explosions are avoided by using a sufficiently diluted acid which boils without emitting fumes of $HClO_4$. This is the case with 60% solutions of acid which boil at around 150-160°C. Explosions have also been observed since 1923 when hot perchloric acid attacks bismuth or bismuth-rich alloys, producing a surface layer of an explosive brown substance the nature of which has yet to be discovered [35]. Care must be taken not to expose bismuth to the effects of perchloric acid.

In the detection and titration of potassium using the method proposed by Serullas in 1831, perchloric acid is added to the solution under study in the presence of a 95% solution of ethyl alcohol in which potassium perchlorate does not readily dissolve. On numerous occasions an explosion has occurred when attempts were then made to eliminate the alcohol by heating the solution. Some researchers have tried to explain these explosions by the formation of ethyl chlorate, which is indeed a highly sensitive explosive ester, but it is more likely that they are caused by the extremely violent oxidation of the alcohol by the $HClO_4$. Around 1930, in a laboratory where potassium titration was constantly carried out, the alcohol used to wash the perchlorate was put to one side so that the alcohol could later be recovered by distillation after the liquid had been neutralised with lime. One day the neutralisation process was omitted and during distillation an explosion occurred which caused considerable damage. It is, in fact, better not to heat these filtrates but to destroy them as soon as possible by diluting them in large quantities of water.

Attack by perchloric acid in a 65-68% solution (density 1.6 to 1.65) is a powerful method for 'mineralising' organic and biological substances, but it has frequently led to explosions. Kahane [36], who has studied this use of perchloric acid in analysis, recommends that such disintegrative operations begin with treatment by nitric acid which will destroy the most oxidisable part, with perchloric acid then being used to complete the process. The initial attack using nitric acid must be taken as far as possible. Even so, the operation is still a delicate one, with Moureu and Munsch [1] quoting two cases of explosion in their laboratory in Paris even though the recommended operating mode had been followed scrupulously, and another case being quoted of a serious explosion in a laboratory in the United States [2].

Finally, one should preferably not mix sulphuric acid (and even less so phosphorus pentoxide) with perchloric acid since to do so gives mixtures in which $HClO_4$ is in a highly oxidisable covalent form. Equally dangerous are perchlorates with an organic base (see 30.2.4).

19.3.3 Mixtures used for electrolytic polishing

It was Jacquet [37] in 1937 who pointed out the method of electropolishing various metals by using an electrolyte composed of a mixture of perchloric acid with acetic acid or acetic anhydride, sometimes with alcohol also added. However, accidents have occurred either during the preparation of such mixtures or during the process of electrolysis.

Bartlett and Turner [39] have described the accident in a university laboratory which blinded a student who had attempted to make such a mixture by adding ice to acetic anhydride and then pouring in perchloric acid with a density of 1.6. After 30 ml had been added, there was an extremely violent explosion. The authors have established that if perchloric acid (with a density of between 1.2 and 1.6) is poured drop by drop into acetic anhydride whilst stirring well, there is immediate hydration of the acetic anhydride with release of heat, and the operation can be carried out without danger if it is done slowly enough to prevent the temperature going above 40°C. Jacquet and Rocquet [40] state quite rightly that the mixture should be prepared by pouring 765 ml of pure acetic anhydride slowly and in small quantities into a chilled vessel containing 185 ml of perchloric acid in a 65-66% solution and only then adding 50 ml of water. The explosion we have just described was caused by mixing the ice and the acetic anhydride, which react only after some time. It seems preferable, however, in the first phase of the operation to pour the perchloric acid into the acetic anhydride rather than the other way round, because in the latter case there comes a moment when one reaches the stoichiometric mixture (93 ml of acetic anhydride to 185 ml of perchloric acid) which is extremely sensitive.

Kuney [38] describes the explosion which occurred on 20 February 1947 in a tank containing 600 l of an aceto-perchloric mixture in a Los Angeles workshop carrying out electrolytic polishing. The accident killed 17 people and caused very heavy damage. The mixture was composed of 1 part acetic anhydride to 3 parts of a 72% solution of perchloric acid.

A study was made in 1947 at the C.S.E. Laboratory [41] of ternary aceto-perchloric mixtures. The mixtures shown in Fig. 19.1 by the points inside curve S are liable to detonate under the effect of a generally weak initiation source. For the mixtures at points B and D detonation is normally low regime (see 14.4.7) with velocities between 1000 and 1600 m/s. The mixture at point B, composed of

$$HClO_4 : 47.5 - CH_3CO_2H : 28.5 - H_2O : 24,$$

has a calorific value of about 4000 kJ/kg and a c.p.u. equal to 85, and in the Sevran drop-weight test it is exploded by impacts with an E_{50} energy equal to 14 joules. It is therefore a dangerous mixture.

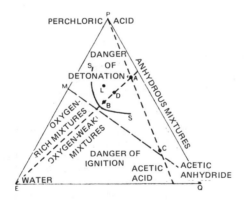

Fig. 19.1 - Risk of detonation in aceto-perchloric mixtures.

The mixture represented by point A, which is liable to explode according to the equation

$$HClO_4 + CH_3CO_2H \rightarrow HCl + 2CO_2 + 2H_2O$$

and which has a calorific value of almost 5500 kJ/kg, has an explosion temperature of the order of 2500°C and must detonate at a velocity greater than 5000 m/s.

One practical consequence to be derived from the diagram thus established is that mixtures obtained with acetic anhydride and perchloric acid with 57% $HClO_4$ at most (an acid with a density of less than 1.5), which are those in the triangle MEQ, are free from the risk of detonation, although some of them can be ignited [42]. However, the mixture used in Los Angeles (point L on the diagram) was most definitely a detonable mixture.

19.3.4 Safety in the industrial use of perchloric acid

The acid which is most commonly used in industry has a strength of 72%. Higher-strength acids should not be prepared without good reason because they are dangerous. Consequently, care must be taken not to mix the acid with strongly dehydrating agents (concentrated phosphoric or sulphuric acid, active alumina, etc.). Even the perchlorate of magnesium anhydride should not be allowed to come into contact with perchloric acid.

With the acid at 72% maximum the most frequent accidents are caused by accidental mixing with combustible substances. During storage, then, the acid must be kept away from anything combustible. Carboys, or other glass recipients containing the acid, must be stored in cement basins.

The periodic acid $HIO_4.2H_2O$ (or H_5IO_6), which is used as an oxidising agent in organic chemistry, can give rise to explosions when it is in solution with certain solvents such as dimethyl sulphoxide [60, 64].

19.4 THE OXYGENATED SALTS OF HALOGENS

19.4.1 The hypochlorites

The hypochlorites of sodium and potassium are used only in solution and present no risk of explosion. Calcium hypochlorite is solid. The product known as bleaching powder which is generally given the formula $CaOCl_2$ is really a mixture of hypochlorite $Ca(ClO)_2$ and a compound $CaCl_2.Ca(OH)_2.H_2O$ with small quantities of lime and calcium chlorite. Since around 1925, products called high-content hypochlorites have been manufactured. They are made of almost pure $Ca(ClO)_2$ and keep better than ordinary bleaching powder. However, during storage they still undergo gradual loss of active chlorine and the decomposition is exothermic (around 85 kJ/mol). Japanese researchers [59] have applied the Frank–Kamenetskii theory (see 3.9) to the self-heating of calcium hypochlorite in the commercial containers used for the product in Japan, which are cardboard drums 38 cm in diameter. The critical temperature found by calculation is 75°C, which is in agreement with results obtained by experiment.

One sometimes finds references to explosions of bleaching powder. What in fact happens is that air-tight containers burst under the pressure of the gases gradually released by the substance, since the latter slowly gives off oxygen from ordinary temperature upwards. However, accidentally mixing calcium hypochlorite with its decomposition catalysts (cobalt salt or iron or manganese oxides, for example) could in certain conditions result in an explosive reaction.

The oxidising effect of calcium hypochlorite, which is generally carried out with more or less diluted solutions, may lead to explosions when the reagents are solid. Thus, we have a report of an explosion [31] caused by transferring calcium hypochlorite from a clean metal container into a drum which had not been properly cleaned after being used to store resinous soap.

Hypochlorites other than those of alkaline and alkaline-earth metals are of no industrial importance and very little is known about them. It is likely that some of them are explosive.

19.4.2 Sodium chlorite

Sodium chlorite $NaClO_2$ is a non-hygroscopic, crystalline substance. Although it has been known for more than a century, industrial manufacture only began in the 1940s. It is used mainly in the bleaching of textile fibres. It crystallises out of aqueous solutions in the anhydrous form above $38°C$ or in the hydrate form $NaClO_2.3H_2O$ at ordinary temperature. Neutral aqueous solutions of the substance are stable up to at least $150°C$, but the alkaline solution is changed by heating into a chlorate. The industrial product often contains only 80% $NaClO_2$ because, in addition to small amounts of chlorate and carbonate, it contains about 15% chloride. The pure salt can be obtained in the laboratory by preparing the inter-mediate substance lead chloride, which is insoluble in water, and reacting it with sodium carbonate.

Sodium chlorite is an oxidising agent which is not so strong as the chlorate but is equally capable of forming explosives by mixture with combustible substances. Sulphur and rubber react strongly in this way, whilst cloth which is impregnated with chlorite dust presents the same dangers as when it is impregnated with chlorate.

The heat of formation of $NaClO_2$, as well as that of various salts which contain halogens, are given in Table 19.1. Sodium chlorite decomposes at a relatively low temperature (from $175°C$). The process is strongly exo-thermic, with the main reaction being

$$3NaClO_2 \rightarrow 2NaClO_3 + NaCl + 218kJ \text{ (constant pressure)},$$

but some 5% of the chlorite undergoes the reaction

$$NaClO_2 \rightarrow NaCl + O_2 + 107kJ \text{ (constant pressure)},$$

both reactions causing a deflagration which raises the products formed to around $350°C$. The deflagration temperature with no delay of sodium chlorite is about $275°C$ [21b].

Anhydrous chlorite – or the high-content industrial product (90% $NaClO_2$) – is highly insensitive to impact. According to Taylor [51], provided care is taken to make sure that there are no traces of organic matter in the apparatus, it does not explode in the drop-weight test, but mixtures with 10% sawdust are sensitive to approximately the same degree as TNT [21b].

Mixtures based on $NaClO_2$, an organic anhydride, and a diluent have been proposed as a convenient way of preparing gaseous ClO_2 in small quantities simply by adding water. However, some of these mixtures are not safe and can give rise to explosions.

Chlorite spilt on the ground can easily be destroyed by neutralising it with a solution of sodium sulphite and then washing the floor with plenty of water. It should be remembered that sodium chlorite is no less toxic than the chlorate.

Table 19.1

Heats of formation at constant pressure
of various salts containing halogens
(Values in brackets are estimated rather than measured).

Salt (crystallised)	F_p (kJ/mol)
LiCl	(408)
LiClO$_3$	(389)
LiClO$_4$	380
LiBrO$_3$	356.5
LiBr	351
NaCl	411
NaClO$_2$	303.7
NaClO$_3$	358.6
NaClO$_4$	382.8
NaBrO$_3$	342.7
NaBr	361
KCl	436.7
KClO$_3$	391.2
KClO$_4$	430
KBrO$_3$	361.5
KBr	393.7
KIO$_3$	508.3
NH$_4$Cl	315.5
NH$_4$ClO$_4$	295.8
Ca(ClO$_3$)$_2$	(695)
Ca(ClO$_4$)$_2$	(728)
Ba(ClO$_3$)$_2$	760
Ba(ClO$_4$)$_2$	807
Mg(ClO$_3$)$_2$	(520)
Mg(ClO$_4$)$_2$	(565)
Pb(ClO$_4$)$_2$	(196)
AgCl	127
AgClO$_3$	25.1
AgClO$_4$	31.6
AgIO$_3$	171.5
NOClO$_4$	174.9

19.4.3 Various chlorites

Chlorites of heavy metals which are hardly or not at all soluble in water
can be easily obtained from NaClO$_2$ by double decomposition reactions.
Chlorites of alkaline-earth metals are less stable than alkaline chlorites.
Thus, Ba(ClO$_2$) heated gently to around 130–150°C decomposes into chlorate
and chloride, and if it is heated to 200°C, it explodes. The same is true
of lead chlorite at around 112°C [48] and silver chlorite at around 100°C.
Copper chlorite Cu(ClO$_2$) is a brown powder that is exploded by an impact or

by sudden heating [50].

19.4.4 Potassium chlorate

Known for almost two hundred years and used on a large scale, potassium chlorate has often been wrongly classified as an explosive. The main reason for this is that until around 1930 the product was almost always kept in wooden containers and a fire in these during storage or transport would very often end in an explosion. One accident which is still remembered is that of a fire followed by an explosion in Saint Helens (Great Britain) in 1899 in a warehouse containing 150 tons of potassium chlorate.

The chlorate $KClO_3$, which is a colourless salt with a density of 2.32 g/cm^3, undergoes a polymorphic transformation at 250°C, and then, if its temperature is raised above 460°C, it melts and undergoes pyrolysis by two simultaneous reactions†:

$$4KClO_3 = 3KClO_4 + KCl + 161kJ \qquad\qquad (19.1)$$

$$KClO_3 = KCl + 3/2O_2 + 45kJ \qquad\qquad (19.2)$$

This decomposition has long been used to prepare oxygen, and it is known that MnO_2 acts as a catalyst in the second of these two reactions, which may take place at around 290–300°C.

To find out whether potassium chlorate can be detonated would require an experiment of which only a very small part has actually been carried out. In a thick steel tube 50 mm in diameter and with strong ignition, it seems that an overdriven detonation occurs in the chlorate which propagates only over a short distance [9]. The energy released by reaction (19.2) above is not enough to maintain a stable detonation. Nor is any explosion observed when the pure, unconfined chlorate is heated unless it is raised to a very high temperature in a very short space of time as when a small amount of molten chlorate is dropped into a red-hot steel capsule, in which case the release of oxygen becomes very rapid and a small deflagration is observed.

From the practical point of view this salt must be considered to be non-explosive, but it gives rise to explosive reactions with a large number of substances. In theory, any mixture of potassium chlorate and a combustible substance in suitable proportions is an explosive. Even a relatively small percentage of combustible substance gives a sensitive mixture, whilst mixtures of $KClO_3$ and red phosporus‡ have a sensitivity to impact which is surpassed only by that of nitrogen iodide. One of the most typical binary mixtures in this respect is the mixture of sulphur and potassium chlorate, which is highly sensitive to impact and also explodes by heating at around 160°C [8]. A drop of sulphuric acid falling onto a mixture of sulphur and $KClO_3$ ignites the substance after a short time. According to Taradoire [8], the mechanism is as follows: the acid acting

---

† The heats of which in the above equations are given at 25°C for the salts in the solid state.
‡ Mixtures with red phosphorus were once used to make small fireworks.

on the chlorate liberates chlorine dioxide which reacts exothermically with the sulphur to ignite it. Sulphur dioxide can also ignite the mixture.

Finally, there have been various references† to the spontaneous explosion several months after preparation of mixtures of sulphur and $KClO_3$ stored in containers. It may be either that the sulphur used contained acid products or that it formed SO_2 with air and that ignited the mixture. Consequently, mixtures of sulphur and potassium chlorate‡ should only be prepared shortly before they are to be used and must not be stored.

By mixing potassium chlorate with lactose and organic colouring substances, pyrotechnic compounds are created which are used to make coloured smoke. These compounds, which burn very steadily when the smoke created can escape easily, may, when confined (see 14.2.1), deflagrate very vigorously and even detonate.

In spite of the oxidising properties of potassium chlorate, it is capable, when in the form of a fine powder, of extinguishing a flame of CH_4 or CO, as Dufraisse and Germain [11] have shown. $KClO_3$ dust even puts out such flames more easily than does $NaHCO_3$. This specific extinguishing potential is related to the anti-oxygen catalysis by K^+ ions.

19.4.5 Various inorganic chlorates

Sodium chlorate, which is now produced in even larger quantities than potassium chlorate, has oxidising properties similar to the latter. It is a hygroscopic salt which is much more soluble in water than potassium chlorate and which melts at 248°C. When it is heated to between 400 and 500°C, it is possible to change it into perchlorate:

$$4NaClO_3 \rightarrow 3NaClO_4 + NaCl \tag{19.3}$$

without any appreciable release of oxygen. At higher temperatures, the perchlorate decomposes and oxygen is liberated.

Sodium chlorate is normally transported in metal containers, but it is also possible to use paper bags lined with aluminium sheet on both the inside and the outside. Experiments were conducted in 1966 to observe the behaviour of a pile of these sacks in the open air leaning against a brightly burning wood brazier. The chlorate does not react with the sack, but the latter opens under the pressure of the oxygen released and the molten chlorate mixed with chloride is shed.

The chlorates of alkaline-earth metals have applications in pyrotechnics because they decompose at lower temperatures. $Ba(ClO_3)_2$ begins to decompose at 400°C, whilst the chlorates of heavy metals are even more easily decomposed by heat. The decomposition of lead chlorate raised to around 200°C becomes rapid after a rather long induction period.

Some compounds, such as hydrated chlorate $Mn(ClO_3)_2.6H_2O$, which is

---

† One case of such an explosion occurred just before 1939 in the chemistry laboratory of a school in Paris.
‡ The only application for these mixtures nowadays is in chemistry lessons to illustrate the extreme sensitivity to impact of chlorate mixtures. At the beginning of the 19th century, they were used in the manufacture of some types of matches, which caused accidents.

obtained by double decomposition between solutions of $MnSO_4$ and $Ba(ClO_3)_2$, are even explosives at quite low temperatures.

Mixtures of sulphur with lead, silver, and barium chlorate ignite respectively [8] at around 65, 75, and 100°C, values which are to be compared with that for the mixture of sulphur and $KClO_3$ (160°C).

19.4.6 Safety in the use of chlorates

Chlorates cause accidents because of their oxidising properties. Mixtures of the salts with combustible substances are extremely sensitive to impact and to flame. They are especially dangerous when they are in the form of a fine powder. In a workshop in which dry sodium chlorate was being reduced to a powder in a ball-mill, the leather belts driving the apparatus became impregnated with chlorate dust, at surface level at least, to the point where they exploded with a sharp cracking sound. In this workshop it was necessary to replace the thick grease in the gearing at frequent intervals because the chlorate dust was forming explosive compounds with dirty grease.

Fires which were sometimes followed by an explosion were caused mainly by the wooden barrels which were the normal form of packing for potassium chlorate over twenty years ago, since wood, especially when it is wet, becomes impregnated with chlorate and can thus be ignited by simple friction. In a factory using chlorates a worker wearing wooden clogs saw them catch fire while he was walking. During the unloading of inert substances from a railway carriage, the floor of which had become impregnated with sodium chlorate because of a leaking container from a previous journey, the wood of the floor ignited under the feet of the workers and spread so rapidly that three people, unable to escape quickly enough from the vehicle, were badly burned.

In 1903 on a Marseilles dock 13 tons of fine potassium chlorate, waiting to be loaded and stored in wooden barrels and boxes, were the seat of a fire which was probably caused by friction on some chlorate which had seeped out of a barrel and mixed with combustible dusts. Although the fire burnt strongly, there was no explosion, only a rapid release of oxygen inside the barrels as they were heated from the outside, causing the staves to shatter. Some of the barrels were even recovered almost intact.

A serious fire on May 12 1899 in a factory in England [10] was caused by friction when two empty barrels which had contained potassium chlorate rubbed against one another. The fire spread to the roof of the warehouse, which contained 143 tons of chlorate. After ten minutes there was an explosion which made a large hole in the ground. The inquiry established that the warehouse had been built on ground filled in with alkali wastes from the manufacture of soda by the Leblanc process. The explosion was caused by molten chlorate mixing with residues of sodium sulphide.

Explosions have occurred during the pharmaceutical preparation of mixtures of chlorate with lactose or liquorice extract when the mixture was being worked without enough water having been added.

In 1954, there was an explosion during the handling of barrels of sodium dithionite $Na_2S_2O_4$ (sodium hydrosulphite). The inquiry proved that extreme negligence had led to the dithionite being housed in metal barrels which still contained chlorate residues. Because of the well-known exothermic reaction between water and dithionite, a few drops of water on a mixture of $Na_2S_2O_4$ and $NaClO_3$ cause heating which initiates the explosive reaction

$$3Na_2S_2O_4 + 2NaClO_3 \rightarrow 3Na_2SO_4 + 2NaCl + 3SO_2.$$

Of the dangerous mixtures, mention must be made of that of potassium chlorate with powdered aluminium. When ignited, it is changed almost at once into a very high explosive. The mixture $KClO_3 + 2Al$ releases on explosion 4200 kJ/kg and produces KCl and Al_2O_3 (partially dissociated into AlO_2 and AlO) as vapours which condense rapidly, so that the power of this mixture is low, but its high sensitivity to flame makes it very dangerous, and it has caused accidents during demonstrations in chemistry lessons[†]. It was also the cause of a bizarre accident in Aubervilliers in 1913: a mixture of equal masses of $KClO_3$ and aluminium having been declared unsafe, workers were assigned to bury it, but when the ground was subsequently watered, an explosion occurred which claimed several victims.

These accidents, like many others we could describe, prove that the precautions listed in 17.1.6 to be taken with all oxidising agents are absolutely necessary in the case of the chlorates. When they are being treated, strict attention must be paid to the cleanliness of containers and all apparatuses (grinders, etc.) in which they are placed. Workers exposed to chlorate dusts must leave all their work clothes and underclothes in a cloakroom adjoining the workshop, and it is advisable for them to be able to take a shower on the spot before changing back into their own clothes.

The chlorates themselves must be kept away from strong acids which would cause them to decompose and give off chlorine dioxide, and during transport they must be kept separate from all combustible substances, as stipulated by the regulations. In 1971, an explosion completely destroyed an entire ship carrying a variety of merchandise including a cargo of sodium chlorate and vegetable oil which had been stowed too close to one another, with the result that when a fire broke out, the fuel mixed with the chlorate to form a mixture which exploded.

19.4.7 Potassium perchlorate

Potassium perchlorate $KClO_4$, known since 1816, has been manufactured on an industrial scale since around 1895. Although it has become less important since 1945, being replaced by ammonium perchlorate, it is still widely used in industry. Its manufacture and its properties are described in a work by Schumacher [26].

It is a crystalline substance with a relative density equal to 2.53 g/cm³; it is not very soluble in water and even less soluble in alcohol. Unlike $KClO_3$ it does not give off chlorine dioxide from cold under the effect of sulphuric acid. It is stable over a wide temperature range and in general reacts less strongly than potassium chlorate. Thus, mixtures of solid organic substances with potassium perchlorate ignite when heated at a temperature some 100 to 120°C higher than that at which similar mixtures with potassium chlorate catch fire [61].

When it is subjected to thermal analysis, it is seen to undergo a polymorphic transformation at around 310°C, changing from orthorhombic to

---

† One such accident occurred in 1938 in Le Raincy (Seine-Saint-Denis).

cubic. When heated at a rate of 2.5°C per minute, it begins to decompose, giving off oxygen, at around 530°C, although certain impurities, such as MgO, may lower its decomposition temperature by 50°C. Decomposition does not leave behind only chloride, but rather a liquid mixture containing KCl, $KClO_4$, and $KClO_3$. Pure $KClO_4$ has never been seen to decompose, since, of the two reactions

$$KClO_4 = KClO_3 + 1/2O_2 \qquad\qquad (19.4)$$

$$KClO_4 = KCl + 2O_2, \qquad\qquad (19.5)$$

the first is endothermic and the second is only weakly exothermic (about 6 kJ/mol at constant pressure).

Although potassium perchlorate is richer in oxygen than potassium chlorate, it has long been known that it is a less powerful oxidising agent. According to Smith [7], for example, a mixture of sulphur and potassium perchlorate can safely be crushed, whereas the same operation on a mixture of sulphur and potassium chlorate is not without a real danger of explosion. However, some mixtures of perchlorate with 3 or 4% organic substances are sensitive to friction, whilst mixtures with solid or finely powdered combustible substances may deflagrate very strongly when a flame is applied.

The safety measures to be followed with potassium chlorate apply equally well to the perchlorate. In particular, there should be no wood in the workshops where it is treated. A case has been reported of a wooden ventilator hood deflagrating after long exposure to perchlorate dusts.

19.4.8 Other inorganic perchlorates

Sodium perchlorate, a hygroscopic salt forming a hydrate $NaClO_4.H_2O$, has properties similar to the potassium salt. Its decomposition with release of oxygen begins 30 to 40°C lower than that of $KClO_4$. Mixtures with a sodium perchlorate base have been manufactured for use as elements to heat liquid carbon dioxide in Cardox shells which are used for blasting coal and other substances which break up easily. The following is an example of such mixtures:

sodium perchlorate	78
powdered aluminium	15
powdered charcoal	7

which is usually loaded into cardboard tubes 20 mm in diameter. Ordinary ignition causes it to deflagrate strongly – especially when under pressure in a Cardox tube – but cannot detonate it since its critical detonation diameter is very wide. Similar mixtures containing $NaClO_4$ or $KClO_4$ and very finely powdered sulphur deflagrate even more strongly.

Anhydrous lithium perchlorate melts at 247°C without decomposing. It releases oxygen only at around 400°C. The commonest form is a trihydrate $LiClO_4.3H_2O$ which can be totally dehydrated only with great difficulty.

Calcium perchlorate decomposes in a similar way to potassium perchlorate. The bivalent metal perchlorates decompose at lower temperatures than the alkaline perchlorates. Heated barium perchlorate decomposes from around 400°C into chloride and oxygen with the formation of a small quantity of chlorate.

Perchlorates of magnesium and zinc give a mixture of chloride and oxide, and the gases contain oxygen and chlorine. All these salts are powerful oxidising agents. Some substances, such as the chromates, catalyse the decomposition of anhydrous zinc perchlorate, which may then take place at around 300°C.

Amongst the heavy metal perchlorates, there are some which are capable of decomposing exothermically into chloride and oxygen. One example is $AgClO_4$, a dense salt which is highly soluble in water and also soluble in organic solvents (toluene, for example). Hein [28] observed an explosion of a mass of pure silver perchlorate which was being crushed in a mortar. Naturally, silver perchlorate which, after crystallisation and drying, contains a certain quantity of solvent (benzene), explodes even more violently, as Brinkley [29] observed in one particular case.

Magnesium perchlorate, which, in its common form, is a hexahydrate $Mg(ClO_4)_2.6H_2O$, is very stable up to around 300°C. One may continue to heat it without it melting or exploding. It leaves a residue of magnesia. The anhydrous perchlorate soaks up large quantities of water [27] which it fixes by successively forming hydrates with $2H_2O$, $4H_2O$, and $6H_2O$ and giving off a considerable quantity of heat (137 kJ to change one mole of $Mg(ClO_4)_2$ into its hexahydrate), a fact which explains its use in laboratories as a desiccant. It is also capable of fixing ammonia and various vapours (methanol, acetone, etc.), but there is a clear possibility of an explosive mixture being formed and, indeed, explosions have been reported when argon containing combustible vapours has been passed through a tower of magnesium perchlorate, or when unsaturated hydrocarbons have been dried at around 200°C [30]. Barium perchlorate has drying properties similar to those of magnesium perchlorate.

Anhydrous lead perchlorate may be explosive, and, in any case, a solution of the substance in methanol is liable to explode. Very little is known of the explosive nature or otherwise of the other metal perchlorates. Caution should be exercised if they are to be prepared.

Nitrosyl perchlorate, an ionic compound $(NO)^+(ClO_4)^-$, is a crystalline substance which begins to decompose when heated at less than 80°C with release of gases (oxygen and oxides of chlorine and nitrogen). Weak explosions of the substance have been observed [56] at around 120°C. If this is not due to the presence of impurities or the effect of humidity, then it is a surprising fact given the very high value of its heat of formation. Nitryl perchlorate NO_2ClO_4, a crystalline endothermic compound which fumes in air, is not prone to explosion. These two perchlorates have intense oxidising properties.

19.4.9 Chlorate candles

In countries where it is difficult to maintain a supply of oxygen in cylinders of compressed gas, it has long been the practice to decompose alkaline chlorates by heat, using compressed cylindrical blocks called *candles*, which most commonly contain sodium chlorate with 2.5% charcoal and 4% manganese dioxide. The heat of oxidation of the carbon makes the decomposition of the chlorate self-sustaining, whilst the purpose of the MnO_2 is to make the reaction steady. These candles are placed in a closed metal cylinder in an oxygen generator; the reaction is ignited at one end by external heating and propagates by degrees along the cartridge (candle),

the density of which, together with the granulometry of the chlorate, have
been determined in such a way that the deflagration thus produced maintains
a moderate velocity. The oxygen released, which contains a small amount of
chlorine, is purified by an appropriate solution and accumulated at a
pressure of some 15 bars in the gasometer part of the apparatus. Only
candles whose composition has been tested should be used in this apparatus.
In 1957 in Brazil, during an improvised test in which the standard candles
were replaced by cartridges in which the charcoal had been replaced by 4%
powdered aluminium, the initial deflagration gave way at one point to a
detonation, or at least to a much faster rate of propagation, which damaged
the apparatus and injured the operator.

Around 1935, attempts were made to manufacture candles giving off a
breathable gas, in other words one which did not contain chlorine, to be
used in underground shelters or on board submarines. The small percentage
of fuel they contain must be something other than charcoal; it may be a
metal such as steel wool, powdered iron, or powdered manganese. Candles
made in this way are lit by means of a small quantity of a special compound
which can be ignited by a firing pin. They work at a pressure close to
atmospheric, and can supply an individual breathing mask in an emergency on
an aeroplane.

Lithium perchlorate, a compound rich in oxygen (60%), has been studied
[12] with a view to being used in breathable chlorate candles, in which
case the temperature in the reaction zone must be around 500°C compared
with only 375-400°C in sodium chlorate-based candles.

The most difficult problem in developing these various kinds of candle
is that of obtaining a steady decomposition in the conditions (pressure,
confinement, external cooling, etc.) in which such devices must work.

19.4.10 Bromates, iodates, and periodates

Bromates have greater oxidising properties than the chlorates. When heated
to around 300-400°C, alkaline bromates decompose into bromide and oxygen,
whilst zinc and aluminium bromates decompose into oxide and bromine.
However, these reactions, which are only weakly exothermic, are not
explosive, unlike the reaction of barium bromate which begins slowly
between 265 and 300°C and becomes explosive above 300°C [45]. It is not
surprising, then, that various mixtures of bromate and combustible
substances are sensitive explosives which need no heating in order to
react. All it takes is a drop of water on an intimate mixture of $KBrO_3$ and
sulphur to initiate a reaction which, if the mass is large and confined,
leads to a strong explosion. The following accident is an example of what
may happen.

In order to clean a mill in which $NaBrO_3$ had been treated [13], the
shaft was dismantled together with its bearings so that it could be placed
in a degreasing apparatus. Then, while it was still hot (125°C), an
attempt was made to separate one of the bearings from the shaft by striking
it with a lead mallet, causing an explosion which hurled out flying metal
splinters. The felt in the joint had become impregnated with bromate and
lubricant (mineral oil), leading to an accident similar in every way to
that caused by dirty chlorate grease (see 19.4.6). Therefore, in mills or
other apparatuses (kneaders, mixers, etc.) in which an oxidising salt can
over a period of time come into contact with a joint on a shaft, it is
important to make the joint out of an incombustible material (asbestos

tape, for example) and to inspect it at frequent intervals and clean away
any particles of oxidising agent which have been deposited on it and which
might mix with the lubricant in the bearings.

Fatal accidents [46] have occurred during the preparation of lead
bromate by double decomposition between potassium bromate and lead acetate.
In a mixture of the two salts the combustible acetate anion is in the
presence of the oxidising bromate anion, and lead bromate is highly
sensitive to friction. Accidents of this kind can be avoided by making the
double decomposition between $KBrO_3$ and an organic lead salt such as the
nitrate.

Iodates are more stable than chlorates, and yet they are powerful
enough oxidising agents to form explosive mixtures with many fuels.
Indeed, iodine pentoxide I_2O_5 explosively oxidises some substances, such as
sulphur†.

19.5 AMMONIUM PERCHLORATE

19.5.1 General observations

Ammonium perchlorate is an oxygen-rich compound which, in itself, has
mediocre explosive properties, but can be added to combustible substances
to produce explosives [15]. Perchlorate-based explosives were manufactured
around 1912 in Belgium under the name of yonckites. But it was the
development of solid rocket propellants which has led since 1945 to the
manufacture of ever increasing quantities of ammonium perchlorate, which is
normally obtained by double decomposition between sodium perchlorate and
ammonium chloride. Since then the substance has been the subject of as
many research papers as were written on the nitro-celluloses between 1890
and 1930.

19.5.2 Physical properties of ammonium perchlorate

Ammonium perchlorate is a non-hygroscopic white salt with a density of 1.95
g/cm³. At ordinary temperature it is orthorhombic, but when heated it
changes at around 240°C by heat absorption (9.6 kJ/mol) into cubic form
with a density of 1.76 g/cm³. At higher temperatures it has measurable
volatility since at 110°C in the open air it undergoes a loss of mass of
0.3% in 20 days [16]. This is caused by sublimation, as was demonstrated
by Dodé [17]. As with the other ammonium salts, this sublimation is
accompanied by the dissociation of the salt into acid and ammonia

$$NH_4ClO_4(cr) \rightarrow HClO_4(v) + NH_3(g). \tag{19.6}$$

This process is strongly endothermic (243 kJ/mol), but the vapour pressure
of NH_4ClO_4 is 10 to 50 times less than that of NH_4NO_3.

---

† It should be pointed out in this respect that the heat of formation of
I_2O_5 (F_V = 171.5 kJ/mol, or, in terms of an I atom, 85.5 kJ/mol) is
considerably lower than that of the oxides of the more common combustible
elements (C, H, S, etc.).

19.5.3 The decomposition of ammonium perchlorate by heat

When it is heated, ammonium perchlorate undergoes a series of quite complex decompositions in the temperature range 200 to 400°C, and at about 430°C it deflagrates with mechanical effects, giving off a bright orange light. But if a fair-sized quantity, such as a long trail, is heated when it is not confined, then deflagration in the heated part does not spread to the rest of the mass.

As Dodé [17] found and as others [24] who later studied the matter have confirmed, the thermal decomposition of ammonium perchlorate occurs in two different ways:

- between 150°C, the temperature below which decomposition is negligible, and around 325°C, there is, in addition to the dissociation into NH_3 and $HClO_4$, a slow decomposition which may be represented approximately by the equation

$$2NH_4ClO_4 \rightarrow Cl_2 + 4H_2O(g) + N_2O + 1.5O_2, \qquad (19.7)$$

although, in fact, a small quantity of nitrogen and chlorine oxide are given off;

- around 380 to 400°C the decomposition, which is accompanied by many reactions in the gas phase, no longer gives nitrous oxide N_2O but nitric oxide with nitrogen dioxide, which Dodé represents by the equation

$$2NH_4ClO_4 \rightarrow 4H_2O + Cl_2 + (O_2, N_2, NO, NO_2). \qquad (19.8)$$

Bircumshaw and Newman [24], who have studied the thermal decomposition, have found that, as with ammonium nitrate, the presence of nitric acid suppresses the induction period preceding decomposition. By contrast, in an ammonia atmosphere at temperatures from 200 to 370°C, decomposition is slowed down considerably.

When ammonium perchlorate is dried in a drying tunnel by circulating it against the current of a mixture of hot gases, which are usually the flue gases from some form of combustion, thermal decomposition may be initiated if the temperature is too high. Since reaction (19.7) is exothermic (about 147 kJ per mol of NH_4ClO_4), it raises the temperature, with the result that decomposition very quickly takes place as in equation (19.8), which is even more exothermic, releasing a large volume of red nitrous fumes.

The several hundred studies which have been made of the thermal decomposition of ammonium perchlorate have been critically examined in a work to which the reader is referred [19]. The chemical mechanism of the decomposition is highly complex. After sublimation accompanied by dissociation, the products of the decomposition of perchloric acid vapour themselves react with ammonia. One remarkable and virtually unparalleled feature of the decomposition at low temperature (not more than 300°C) is that it stops at atmospheric pressure when 30% of the product has decomposed, and the residue has a particular structure. By contrast, decomposition at high temperature reaches completion.

Quite a large number of metallic compounds, and in particular transition metal oxides (ZnO, CuO, Cr_2O_3, etc.), act as catalysts to the decomposition at low temperature, making it faster and modifying the nature of the products of the reaction.

19.5.4 Deflagration of ammonium perchlorate

Pure ammonium perchlorate deflagrates, after an induction period, at temperatures above 420°C. The presence of the catalysts mentioned above may lower this deflagration point to as little as 225°C. At atmospheric pressure deflagration affects only the heated part, but when the pressure is high enough, propagation occurs, in other words the product becomes the seat of a self-sustained combustion wave. Experiments by Watt and Peterson [18] have established that the minimum pressures for self-sustained combustion are 22 and 15 bars approximately for pure perchlorate at 0°C and 70°C respectively . The presence of catalysts in sufficient quantity lowers this limit pressure, sometimes even down to atmospheric pressure. The velocity of the combustion front is less than 1 cm/s.

19.5.5 The explosive nature of ammonium perchlorate

When ammonium perchlorate is ground with a pestle in a porcelain mortar, small crackling sounds are heard. It is also sensitive to impact, as has been shown by experiments by Aufschläger [25] and Médard [21b]. Their results are in agreement in establishing at about 1.2 kgm the energy of impact which gives 50% explosions in a test with a small falling weight. However, these explosions are accompanied by a noise which is not very loud, whilst in tests with a large weight (see 15.2.5.5), only part of the charge usually explodes.

Sensitivity to ignition is not very high. Lheure [15] found that a No. 8 detonator does not cause the perchlorate to explode in the open air, although explosion does occur in the lead block with stemming.

Ammonium perchlorate can be detonated, but its critical diameter is quite large. Using tests in an elongated box (see 15.3.2), Vieille [10] observed detonation with a critical diameter of 15 cm at a density of 1.05 g/cm³ and 22 cm at a density of 1.2 g/cm³. When it is loaded into thick steel tubes, perchlorate can be detonated at a diameter of 35 mm by strong ignition at a density of 1.2 g/cm³.

Measurements of the detonation velocity were made by Aufschläger [25] in steel tubes 40 cm long and several millimetres thick. With the perchlorate at a density of 1.1 g/cm³, he obtained the following values:

> 2 460 m/s in a tube 20 mm in diameter
> 3 150 m/s in a tube 35 mm in diameter
> 3 805 m/s in a tube 60 mm in diameter.

Because of the effect of confinement created by the 8 mm wall, the last value listed above is very close to the limit velocity which, according to formulae supplied in 1969 by American authors [22], is 3050, 3700, and 4850 m/s at densities of 0.75, 1, and 1.58 g/cm³ respectively.

Pure ammonium perchlorate is thus an explosive which is only moderately sensitive to ignition, but given that it is an oxygen-rich compound, it needs only a small percentage of combustible substance to be added to make it detonate more easily. However, when the density exceeds 70% of the real density of the mixture, detonation still requires a sizeable critical dimension of the order of 7 cm for a mixture with 5% powdered aluminium to 95% ammonium perchlorate. The chemical equation for the decomposition of ammonium perchlorate when it detonates, giving gases at high pressure, is approximately

$$4NH_4ClO_4 = 6H_2O + O_2 + 4HCl + 2N_2,$$

but in deflagration at relatively low pressure, the gases produced contain chlorine.

19.5.6 Safety in the storage and transport of ammonium perchlorate

From what has been said above, the dangers posed by ammonium perchlorate can be evaluated as follows: it is an explosive which is not easily detonated but which is less insensitive to impact and friction than ammonium nitrate. When it is not under confinement, an impact causes an explosion which remains strictly localised.

In a fire, still assuming no confinement, ammonium perchlorate does not explode. This was proved by an accident which took place in the railway station in Hirson in 1925 when a railway truck containing 5500 kg of ammonium perchlorate stored in wooden barrels with an internal lining of strong paper was the seat of a fire which burned so strongly that it lasted no more than ten minutes and destroyed the entire superstructure of the truck. The apparently spontaneous ignition can probably be explained by the fact that the truck had been moved and shunted half an hour before the accident, and that may have caused a small amount of perchlorate to leak from one of the barrels onto the wooden floor of the vehicle where it was subjected to friction, thus setting fire to the vehicle and the barrels. The fire must have smouldered for some time before workers in the vicinity saw it flare up.

Ammonium perchlorate should be stored in metal containers with lids which yield easily to low internal pressure (a few bars, for example). Warehouses must be kept clean and no combustible materials should be stored close by. When perchlorate is being handled, care must be taken to prevent it being contaminated by foreign bodies, whether they be organic compounds or metal derivatives.

Ammonium perchlorate is now officially classified as an oxidising agent.

19.6 COMPOUNDS OF Mn^{7-}

19.6.1 Oxygenated compounds of manganese

The oxidising action of the permanganates is well known in chemistry, which uses acidic or alkaline solutions of potassium permanganate $KMnO_4$. The heated crystals of the salt decompose without melting, whilst oxygen begins to be released at around 200°C. The complex reaction which it undergoes is exothermic at around 275–300°C. In the solid state this permanganate reacts with various combustible liquids, releasing so much heat that ignition often occurs. The reaction of glycerol when in contact with permanganate was observed in 1902. Rathsburg and Gawlick [53] have made a systematic study of ignition caused by placing $KMnO_4$ in contact with organic substances. The strongest reactions occur with the polyalcohols (glycol, etc.), the sugars (fructose, saccharose, etc.), the aldehydes, and formamide. The accumulation of the groups OH or CO in a molecule make it highly active with potassium permanganate.   In 1937 in France, when a carboy of triethanolamine broke during transport, the spilt liquid came into contact with a neighbouring sack containing potassium permanganate and ignited. The fire spread very rapidly.

Potassium permanganate is quite soluble in acetone and other organic solvents.   Some of these solutions are stable, at least at ordinary temperature, but others are liable to become the seat of a strongly exothermic reaction after a certain induction period (see 3.11). Finlay [62] describes the following accident: 20 g of potassium permanganate had been added to 100 g of perfectly pure dimethylformamide, $H - CO - N(CH_3)_2$, in a flask which was shaken for a few moments by hand in order to speed up dissolution and then set down on the laboratory bench.   Three to four minutes later the contents of the flask exploded violently.

Calcium permanganate has even more marked oxidising properties than the potassium salt, probably because its very high solubility in water allows it to act in the form of an extremely concentrated solution.   There is a report [55] of zinc permanganate exploding in contact with filter paper. Silver permanganate begins to give off oxygen from $160°C$.

Permanganic acid $HMnO_4$ has not been isolated and is known only in solution, but its anhydride Mn_2O_7, manganese heptoxide, is easily obtained by treating crystals of pure potassium permanganate with concentrated sulphuric acid [52].   It is a dark-green liquid which solidifies at around $6°C$, gives off purple vapours, loses oxygen at around $60°C$, and explodes at around $70°C$ [52, 54].   The reaction

$$Mn_2O_7(l) \rightarrow 2MnO_2(s) + 3/2O_2(g)$$

releases 230 kJ at constant pressure.   This liquid is dangerous to handle since particles of solid combustible substances, such as cork or paper, oxidise so violently when they come into contact with it that they cause it to explode.   There has even been a report of a case of spontaneous explosion of Mn_2O_7 at ordinary temperature several hours after it was prepared.

The green liquid obtained by triturating sulphuric acid with potassium permanganate is probably permanganyl sulphate $(MnO_3)_2SO_4$, which is a highly oxidising compound.

Just as $KClO_4$ gives perchloryl fluoride (19.2.4) under the action of fluorosulphuric acid, $KMnO_4$ with the same acid forms [32] permanganyl fluoride MnO_3F, a rather volatile dark-green liquid which is liable to explode spontaneously in moist air:

$$2MnO_3F \rightarrow MnF_2 + MnO_2 + 2O_2.$$

In summary, permanganates in the undissolved state are powerful oxidising agents which must be used with caution.   When treated with concentrated acids, they form explosive compounds, such as Mn_2O_7 and others, which are dangerous because of their very poor stability.

BIBLIOGRAPHICAL REFERENCES

[1]   Moureu, H. & Munsch, H. (1951) *Arch. Maladies Prof.* 12 157
[2]   Muse, L. A. (1973) *Ch. Eng. News*, p. 29
[3]   Cady, G. H. & Brown, R. E. (1945) *J. Am. Ch. Soc.* 67 1614

[4]   Allamagny, P. (1969) *Les fluorures d'oxygène*. Gauthier-Villars, Paris
[5]   Booth, H. & Bowen, E. J. (1925) *J. Chem. Soc.* **127** 510
[6]   Ben Caid, M., Hajal, J. & Combourieu, J. (1965) *Bull. Soc. Chim.*,
        p. 2908
[7]   Smith, C. F. (1955) *The Analyst* **80** 16
[8]   Taradoire, F. (1942) *Bull. Soc. Chim. Fr.* [5] **9** 610, 615
[9]   Burlot, E. (1918) *Lab. de la C.S.E.*
[10]   Ford, A. (1899) *Mém. Poudres* **10** 271
[11]   Dufraisse, C. & Germain, M. (1938) *Compt. Rend.* **207** 1221
[12]   Markowitz, M., Boryta, D. & Stewart, H. (1964) *Prod. Res. and
        Develop.* **3** 321
[13]   Mason, W. A. (1964) *Safety in Air and Ammonia Plants* **6** 45
[14]   Gray, P. & Ip, J. K. K. (1972) *Comb. and Flame* **18** 361
[15]   Lheure, L. (1903) *Mém. Poudres* **12** 7
[16]   Dautriche, H. (1908) *Mém. Poudres* **14** 211
[17]   Dodé, M. (a) (1934) *Compt. Rend.* **200** 63;   (b) (1938) *Bull. Soc. Chim.*
        [5] **5** 170
[18]   Watt, D. M. Jr. & Peterson, E. E. (1969) *J. Chem. Physics* **50** 2196
[19]   Jacobs, P. W. M. & Whitehead, H. M. (1969) *Chem. Rev.* **69** 551
[20]   Vieille, P. (1917) *Lab. C.S.E.*
[21]   Médard, L. *Lab. C.S.E.* (a) 1941;   (b) 1946-47
[22]   Price, D. *et al.* (1969) *Comb. and Flame* **13** 104
[23]   Papesch, V. (1959) *Chem. Eng. News* **37** No. 13, 60
[24]   Bircumshaw, L. L. & Newman, H. (1954) *Proc. Roy. Soc.* A **227** 115;
        (1957) *J. Am. Ch. Soc.* **79** 4741
[25]   Naoum, P. & Aufschläger, R. (1924) *Z. Ges. Sch. Sprengst.* **19** 121
[26]   Schumacher, J. C. (1960) *Perchlorates, their Properties, Manufacture
        and Use*. Reinhold Public. Corp., New York
[27]   Willard, H. H. & Smith, G. F. (1922) *J. Am. Ch. Soc.* **44** 2255
[28]   Hein, F. (1957) *Chem. Tech.* **9** 97
[29]   Brinkley, S. R. (1940) *J. Am. Ch. Soc.* **62** 3524
[30]   Heertjes, P. M. & Houtman, J. P. (1941) *Chem. Weekblad* **38** 85
[31]   Weichherz (1928) *Chem. Ztg.* **52** 729
[32]   Engelbrecht, A. & Grosse, A. V. (1954) *J. Am. Ch. Soc.* **76** 2042
[33]   Smith, G. F. (1953) *J. Am. Ch. Soc.* **75** 184
[34]   Dietz, W. (1939) *Angew. Chem.* **52** 616
[35]   Nicholson, D. G. & Reedy, J. H. (1935) *J. Am. Ch. Soc.* **57** 817
[36]   Kahane, E. (1934) *Action de l'acide perchlorique sur les matières
        combustibles*. Hermann, Paris
[37]   Jacquet, P. A. (1937) *Compt. Rend.* **205** 1232
[38]   Kuney, J. H. (1947) *Chem. Eng. News* **25** 1658
[39]   Bartlett, R. K. & Turner, H. S. (1965) *Chem. and Ind.*, p. 1933
[40]   Jacquet, P. & Rocquet, P. (1939) *Compt. Rend.* **208** 1012
[41]   Médard, L. & Sartorius, R. (1950) *Mém. Poudres* **32** 179
[42]   Médard, L., Jacquet, P. A. & Sartorius, R. (1949) *Rev. Métal.* **46** 549
[43]   Elliott, M. A. & Brown, F. W. (1948) *Report 4169*, Bureau of Mines
[44]   Bode, H. & Klesper, E. (1951) *Z. Anorg. Ch.* **266** 275
[45]   Hackspill, L. & Winterer (1930) *Compt. Rend.* **191** 663
[46]   *Jahresbericht IV of the C.T.R.* (1924-25), p. 71
[47]   King, R. C. & Armstrong, G. T. (1968) *J. Res. Nat. Bureau Standards*
        A **72** 113
[48]   Solymosi, F. & Bansagi, T. (1968) *Acta Chim. Ac. Sc. Hung.* **56** 251
[49]   Masschelein, W. (1969) *Les oxydes de chlore et le chlorite de sodium*.
        Dunod, Paris

[50] Levi, G. & Cipollone, C. (1923) *Gazz. Chim. Ital.* 35 200
[51] Taylor, M. C. *et al.* (1940) *Ind. Eng. Ch.* **32** 899
[52] Durand, J. F. (1924) *Compt. Rend.* **178** 1193, 1822
[53] Rathsburg, H. & Gawlick, H. (1941) *Chem. Ztg.* **65** 426
[54] Glemser, O. & Schroeder, H. (1953) *Z. Anorg. Ch.* **271** 293
[55] Svergel, U. (1960) *Pharm. Praxis*, p. 30
[56] Gerding, H. & Haak, W. F. (1956) *Chem. Weekblad* **52** 282
[57] Pannetier, G. & Lecamp, M. (1954) *Bull. Soc. Chim.*, p. 1068
[58] Zharova, N. N. *et al.* (1981) *C. A.* **95** 172024
[59] Uehara *et al.* (1977) *Anzen Kogaku* **16** 1538
[60] Cookson, R. L. (1979) *Chem. in Britain* **15** 329
[61] Patai, S. & Hoffmann, E. (1952) *J. Applied Chem.* **2** 8
[62] Finlay, J. B. (1980) *Chem Eng. News* **58** No. 38, 65
[63] Anon. (1952) *Chem. Eng. News* **30** 3210
[64] Rowe, J. J. M. *et al.* (1968) *J. Am. Ch. Soc.* **90** 1924

20

Peroxidised inorganic compounds

20.1 GENERAL OBSERVATIONS

This chapter gathers together under the name peroxidised compounds the
following substances:
1˙ Inorganic substances containing a peroxy group $- O - O -$, the prototype
of which is hydrogen peroxide H_2O_2 with the structural formula

$$H - O - O - H.$$

The most important of these substances, apart from H_2O_2, are the metallic
peroxides with a formula M_2O_2 or MO_2 depending on whether the metal† is
monovalent or bivalent, and the peroxy acids whose formula derives from $H -
O - O - H$ by substitution of the Ac radical (from the acid Ac OH) for the
hydrogen. These peroxy acids are often formed by the action of hydrogen
peroxide on the acid following the reversible reaction

$$Ac\ OH + H - O - O - H \rightleftarrows Ac - O - O - H + H_2O.$$

These peroxy acids contain hydrogen for which metals can be substituted.
The salts thus obtained are often called persalts. It has not been
possible to isolate some of the peroxy acids, and they are known only
through their persalts. It should also be noted that the H atoms in
hydrogen peroxide have a somewhat acidic character. We know of some

---

† However, MO_2 compounds are not all peroxides since they may contain the
two oxygen atoms in a group other than $- O - O -$ (for example, PbO_2 has the
structure $O = Pb = O$).

hydroperoxides such as K – O – O – H,   but they have no real practical
importance. X-ray crystallography has brought out the presence of bivalent
$O_2^=$ ions in true metallic peroxides.

2° Compounds containing the monovalent O_2^- ion, for example potassium
hyperperoxide KO_2.

3° Compounds containing the O_3^- ion, called ozonides.

4° Molecular addition compounds in which are found one or more molecules of
hydrogen peroxide. They are generally salts which retain crystallisation
molecules of H_2O_2 and are often incorrectly called persalts in industry.
In an aqueous solution they are apparently completely dissociated into
their constituent molecules.

All these substances are, to very varying degrees, oxidising agents.
Many of them are powerful combustion-supporters, and some are explosives.
There are very many of these compounds, and their composition is not always
known with certainty. In particular, it is sometimes difficult to decide
whether one is dealing with a true hydrated persalt or the corresponding
salt with crystallised H_2O_2, for example

$$NaAcO_2.H_2O \qquad or \qquad NaAcO.H_2O_2.$$

20.2 HYDROGEN PEROXIDE

20.2.1 History and manufacture

Hydrogen peroxide, which was known as *oxygenated water* throughout the 19th
century, was obtained in 1818 by Thenard by the action of acids on barium
peroxide.   It was from this compound of barium that it was manufactured
industrially from 1870 to around 1910, giving a 3% solution (called
oxygenated water at 10-12 volumes), or sometimes a 5% solution.   Around
1909, the electrolytic processes appeared using perdisulphuric acid, which
had been discovered by Berthelot in 1878, or its salts of ammonium or
potassium.   These processes include the following stages: oxidation by
electrolysis of aqueous solutions of sulphuric acid or of ammonium or
potassium hydrogen sulphate;   hydrolysis by water vapour of the compound
thus formed;   finally,   concentration in a rectifying column at reduced
pressure.   This method was commonly used around 1925 to obtain a product
containing 30%, 35%, or 40% hydrogen peroxide†.

Since 1962, these processes have been replaced almost everywhere by
more economical techniques based on the oxy-reduction of an appropriate
organic substance, a reaction discovered in 1934 by Walter and Fison.   In
practice, the substances which lend themselves best to these reactions
belong to the anthrahydroquinone group. They are oxidised by oxygen from
the air and then returned to their initial state by hydrogenation in a
suitable organic solvent, and thus undergo the reaction

$$quinone + H_2 \xrightarrow{catalyst} hydroquinone$$

$$hydroquinone + air \rightarrow quinone + H_2O_2.$$

---

† The 30% solution had already been put on sale just before 1914 by the
German firm Merck under the brand name 'perhydrol'.

Washing with water extracts the peroxide from the organic solution, and the aqueous solution obtained in this way is purified and then concentrated by distillation.

In other words, the peroxide H_2O_2 is obtained as an aqueous solution from hydrogen and the oxygen in the air. It is purified nowadays in a highly efficient apparatus which gives a very pure product. For safety reasons, concentration by distillation is generally limited to a value such as 70 or 85% in mass production. Any need for a more concentrated hydrogen peroxide is met by installations in which distillation is carried out in a pyrex apparatus to give an 85–90% solution from which hydrogen peroxide at 98–99% can be obtained by fractional crystallisation, since the diagram for the liquefaction of the H_2O_2 – H_2O system shows that solutions with more than 62% H_2O_2 deposit on cooling a solid phase containing two or three times less water than the liquid with which it is in equilibrium. A series of crystallisation operations are carried out on a semi-industrial scale in an apparatus containing a tube stack. They yield a very pure product since most of the impurities existing in the dissolved state in the raw material remain in the diluted liquids which are discarded.

90% peroxide has been a commercial product in the United States since 1945, while 70% peroxide has been common in France since 1960. 99% peroxide has been on sale in the United States since 1956 and is now also produced in France.

Low-concentration solutions of hydrogen peroxide are used mainly in bleaching natural or artificial materials such as textile fibres or wood pulps as well as for removing the colour from panels of reconstituted wood. They have been used for purifying the cyanated waste water [1] from electro-plating workshops and for eliminating bad smells released by the activity of micro-organisms in sewage works. The main use of H_2O_2 is in the manufacture of persalts such as sodium perborate and organic and inorganic peroxides. It is also used in various oxidation reactions in organic chemistry.

High-concentration solutions of 85 or 90% are used as a constituent in rocket engine propellants, the other constituent being the hydrocarbon kerosene. These engines are used in aeroplane propulsion for acceleration during take-off or for launching satellites. Concentrated peroxide can also be used as a monopropellant to fuel small gas turbines being used as auxiliary engines. It has also been used for rocket propulsion in engines in which it reacted with an aqueous solution of calcium permanganate. The heat of the reaction vaporised all the water present.

20.2.2 General physical and chemical properties of hydrogen peroxide

Hydrogen peroxide in the pure state is a colourless liquid slightly more viscous than water with a specific gravity equal to 1.45 g/cm^3 at 18°C. When cooled, it readily remains in a state of supercooling. Its crystals, with a density equal to 1.71 g/cm^3, melt at $-$ 0.45°C. It boils at standard atmospheric pressure at 150.2°C. It mixes with water in any proportions, and it has been and still is often the commercial practice to define an aqueous solution of hydrogen peroxide by the ratio of the volume of gaseous oxygen which it can liberate in the reaction of decomposition

$$H_2O_2(l) \ = \ H_2O(l) + 1/2O_2(g) \hspace{3cm} (20.1)$$

to the volume of the solution itself, the gas volume being corrected for
0°C and 760 mm of mercury[†]. Table 20.1 gives this volume of oxygen as a
function of the mass percentage t of H_2O_2 in the solution, as well as the
mole fraction of the solution and its specific gravity at 18°C. The
transition from t to the mole fraction x of H_2O_2 in the solution and vice
versa from x to t is achieved by the relations

$$x = t/(188.81 - 0.8881t) \qquad\qquad t = 100x/(0.5296 + 0.4704x).$$

Table 20.1

Properties of aqueous solutions of hydrogen peroxide

Strength in H_2O_2 (%)	Specific gravity at 18°C (g/cm³)	Volume of oxygen per volume of solution	Mole fraction
5	1.016	16.7	0.02712
10	1.036	34.1	0.05558
20	1.073	70.7	0.11693
30	1.111	110	0.18499
40	1.153	152	0.26095
50	1.197	197	0.34625
60	1.242	245	0.44273
65	1.266	271	0.49587
70	1.290	297	0.55273
75	1.315	325	0.61374
80	1.341	353	0.67934
85	1.367	383	0.75008
90	1.394	413	0.82659
95	1.422	445	0.90961
100	1.450	477	1.00000

Aqueous solutions of H_2O_2 are acidic in nature, the pH of 50 to 70%
solutions of peroxide being about 4.5

Decomposition reaction (20.1) above, as well as the reaction

$$H_2O_2(l) = H_2O(v) + 1/2O_2(g), \qquad\qquad\qquad (20.2)$$

are readily produced in the liquid by a variety of catalysts, including

---

[†] To be precise, the temperature of the solution must also be fixed. The
values in Table 20.1 assume this temperature to be 18°C.

alkalis, the ions of various metals with a valency which might have two or more values (Fe, Cu, V, Cr, Mo, Pb), many metal oxides, and various metals, especially silver. Some salts, like potassium permanganate and potassium dichromate, decompose H_2O_2 and at the same time undergo decomposition themselves. Reaction (20.2), which produces a large quantity of gas, can be so rapid that it is really an explosion.

Hydrogen peroxide is a powerful oxidising agent. The very high combustion supporting potential of its concentrated solutions has been known for a very long time as a result of laboratory observations. Since solutions at more than 30% have been on the market, there have been accidental fires, especially when the solutions were stored in carboys, which are fragile containers. When they break, the spilt liquid may come into contact with wood, straw, or rags, which ignite because of the temperature rise they undergo when reacting with H_2O_2. The concentration above which the product sets fire to these combustible materials depends to some extent on external conditions, but when the latter are favourable, in other words when the ambient temperature is higher than 25°C and the air is not humid, it can be assumed that solutions at 32% and are supporters of combustion.

20.2.3 Thermochemical data and theoretical explosive properties

The most reliable thermochemical data on hydrogen peroxide are based on the determination by Giguère and his associates [2] of the variation in enthalpy of reaction (20.1), which they found to be equal to - 98 kJ/mol at 25°C. On the other hand, the heat of vaporisation of H_2O_2 at 25°C is equal to 51.6 kJ/mol. From this, the following values at 25°C are deduced:

H_2O_2 liq. F_p = 188 F_v = 183⎤

H_2O_2 vap. F_p = 136 F_v = 134⎦

The dissolution of hydrogen peroxide in water is exothermic. The heat of mixing of x moles of H_2O_2 and $(1 - x)$ moles of H_2O can be represented, with deviations not exceeding 2%, by the formula

$$Q_{mix.} = 4.1x(1 - x) \text{ kJ},$$

so that the heat of formation of one mole of mixture at 25°C

$$F_p(\text{mixture}) = xF_p(H_2O_2) + (1 - x)F_p(H_2O) + Q_{mix.}$$

is expressed as a function of x by

$$F_p(\text{mixture}) = 285.8 - 93.7x - 4.1x^2.$$

From the above data it is a simple matter to calculate the explosion temperature at constant pressure (equal to standard atmospheric pressure) of a 100% solution of hydrogen peroxide: T_p = 1270°K. The lower calorific value is 1686 kJ/kg and the higher calorific value is 2916 kJ/kg. The gas volume of explosion at N.T.P. (see 14.2.3) is quite high at 988 dm³/kg, but two thirds of it is water vapour which condenses when cooling of the gases brings them to below 100°C. The explosion temperature in a closed vessel would reach T_v = 1570°K.

The decomposition of aqueous solutions assumes various forms, depending on the composition:

(a) With sufficiently weak solutions the heat from the decomposition of the H_2O_2 they contain is low enough for there to be only insignificant vaporisation of water. Thus, the decomposition of these solutions gives moist oxygen and liquid water at a temperature below 100°C. This is what happens with solutions with a mole fraction lower than 0.0622, in other words at less than 11.8% H_2O_2.

(b) For solutions with a higher mole fraction, but one which does not exceed 0.497 (65.1% solution), vaporisation of the water cannot be total. Thus, decomposition gives gases composed of oxygen and water vapour, and leaves a liquid residue of water, the latter being, like the gases, at a temperature of 100°C. Such a decomposition may, if produced with the help of a catalyst, be strong enough to be considered as a deflagration.

(c) The heat of decomposition of solutions at more than 65.1%† allows all the water to vaporise. The gas formed is at a temperature which rises with the percentage of H_2O_2 in the solution according to a law which is not very different from a linear law.

20.2.4   Explosions of hydrogen peroxide and its concentrated aqueous solutions

It was formerly observed that during concentration by distillation at reduced pressure, sudden decomposition of an explosive nature sometimes occurred. Matheson and Maas [14] noted in 1929 that with a 99% solution of peroxide decomposition into water and oxygen became explosive at around 150°C. This happened with impure products since the pure and stable hydrogen peroxide which we are able to manufacture nowadays can be distilled without decomposition at reduced pressure. Calculation has shown that hydrogen peroxide is a poor explosive. It is therefore not surprising that it is difficult to detonate, although it can be made to deflagrate with ease.

A. – Detonation of liquid hydrogen peroxide

In 1946, Médard [11] detonated hydrogen peroxide at 99.6% H_2O_2 in a steel tube with a wall 3 mm thick and an internal diameter of 34 mm using a 50 g booster of P.E.T.N. as detonator. The container was reduced to small fragments. Similar tests show that the 95% solution detonates, but with an aqueous solution at 92% detonation occurs only over a length equal to about three times the diameter of the tube (overdriven detonation). In less severe conditions of confinement, for example in an aluminium tube which has the same diameter but is not very thick (0.3 mm), hydrogen peroxide does not detonate. Tests carried out by the Bureau of Mines [24] in 1967

---

† These concentrations (11.8 and 65.1%), which correspond to decomposition with production of liquid or vaporised water at 100°C, assume that the initial temperature is 18°C. If it is higher, the above concentrations are reduced and become, at 25°C for example, about 11 and 64.5%.

found that the detonation velocity is 5500 to 6000 m/s.

B. - *Detonation of solid hydrogen peroxide*

Other experiments [25] were conducted on the crystallised peroxide kept at
- 5°C (a substance with a strength of only 95%). It is easy to detonate
when loaded at a density of 0.85 in a tube with a diameter of 30 mm using
15 g of P.E.T.N. as booster. By contrast, crystals packed at a density of
1.4 can be detonated only by 30 g of P.E.T.N. Thus, the sensitivity to
priming of crystallised H_2O_2 decreases as the density increases, following
a fairly general rule for solid explosives, but it is quite low, which
suggests that the crystals can withstand fairly strong mechanical impacts
without exploding.

C. - *Detonation of hydrogen peroxide in vapour*

Extremely difficult experiments were conducted by Monger and his associates
[12] on a mixture of vapours of H_2O and H_2O_2 created by boiling a 90%
solution of peroxide at various pressures. At pressures of 0.2 and 0.45
bars, when the mole fraction of H_2O_2 in the vapour was close to 0.55 and
0.4 respectively, initiation caused deflagration but no detonation. By
contrast, at atmospheric pressure detonations with a velocity of 1500 to
1600 m/s were obtained when the mole fraction exceeded 0.33. When it is
lower, explosions propagate in the vapour at a velocity higher than that of
sound (450 m/s) but lower than that of the regular detonation. Thus, the
detonations are not stable.

D. - *Deflagration of liquid hydrogen peroxide*

What were once thought to be explosions of liquid peroxide during
distillation were in reality only explosions of its vapour. No case is
known of an explosion in the vapour being transmitted to the liquid, even
when the explosion was very strong and shattered the apparatus [13].
Neither intense mechanical impacts (high-velocity machine gun bullets) nor
sudden compression to 140 bars [15] cause hydrogen peroxide to deflagrate,
whatever the strength of the solution. However, catalysts, of which the
most active is powdered manganese dioxide, do produce such a violent
decomposition of hydrogen peroxide that even in a wide-open container
deflagration takes place, at a speed which naturally increases with the
strength of the solution. In a closed vessel the pressure may rise to a
very high value. In a small bomb with a capacity of 25 cm³, 95% peroxide
at a loading density of 0.38 g/cm³ was made to deflagrate by a small pellet
of MnO_2, taking the pressure to more than 2000 bars in 55 milliseconds
[16].

E. - *Deflagration in vapour*

Hart [13] demonstrated in 1949 that a metal wire raised to red heat ignites
a flame in a current of H_2O_2 vapour diluted with water vapour at a low
pressure of the order of 0.1 bar. At atmospheric pressure the vapour from

98% peroxide deflagrates with great violence. Monger and his associates [17] measured the pressures at which deflagration is possible as a function of the mole fraction of H_2O_2 in the vapour phase, whilst Marshall [18] measured the values of minimum ignition energies and quenching distances (see 6.5.2). They fall between those of mixtures of methane and air and acetylene and air and thus point to a gas mixture which deflagrates with ease.

20.2.5 The kinetic stability of hydrogen peroxide

Aqueous solutions of hydrogen peroxide were for a long time thought to be intrinsically unstable because experimenters did not prepare them with reagents that were as pure as possible, unlike Thenard who was thus able to obtain a solution at more than 95% strength which was stable enough for him to study its properties.

When hydrogen peroxide is decomposed slowly enough for the liquid not to heat, the process follows equation (20.1). If the product is totally free of any impurities which have a catalytic effect, the decomposition of even highly concentrated solutions is very slow at ordinary temperatures. According to various experimenters, the thermal coefficient of the rate of decomposition (see 3.5) is between 1.9 and 2.2 at temperatures ranging from 40 to 100°C. But the rate of the reaction is very strongly influenced by catalysts, being subject on the one hand to homogeneous catalysis by certain impurities in solution in the liquid, bases in particular, and on the other hand to heterogeneous catalysis both by solid particles in suspension in the liquid and by the walls of the container holding it. The stability of the product can be improved by rendering the walls inactive (passivation of the wall) or by adding stabilisers to the liquid, the two most frequently used being:

(a) Sodium pyrophosphate, which acts mainly by taking up the Fe^+ ions present in the solution and incorporating them into a complex. The action of sodium pyrophosphate is weak since the $(P_2O_7)^{4-}$ ions are gradually hydrolysed into fairly inactive $(PO_4)^{3-}$. In addition, it has no effect on the heterogeneous catalysts.

(b) Sodium stannate $Na_2SnO_3.3H_2O$ used in a dose of 5 millionths, which creates a colloidal stannic hydroxide which gradually absorbs the metal ions present and suppresses their catalytic activity.

Around 1910, a common commercial product was considered to decompose at ordinary temperature at a rate of 10% a year. Nowadays a high-strength product (70% and over) decomposes in moderate climates at a rate of barely 0.1% a year in large tanks made of pure aluminium, which has the weakest catalysing action of all metals both on the liquid and on the vapour above it. In tanks of stainless steel the loss of active oxygen is slightly greater since the alloy is not perfectly inert with H_2O_2. It seems that for the very pure products which we are able to manufacture nowadays, decomposition takes place mainly on contact with the wall, so that it is greater in small tanks than in large ones, since the latter have a lower surface to volume ratio.

There is reason to believe that pure peroxide (100%) completely free of dissolved impurities could be stored indefinitely with no noticeable decomposition at ordinary temperature if it could be kept in a container with a wall that is totally inert with H_2O_2.

Tests to measure the stability of high-strength hydrogen peroxide are based on the measurement of the quantity of product which decomposes in water and oxygen when heated to 100°C over a given length of time. One operating mode consists in heating for 15 hours in a water bath 100 cm³ of the product being studied in a balloon flask surmounted by a reflux condenser. After heating, the strength is measured by the potassium permanganate method. In another, more rapid, operating mode, called the gasometric test, 25 cm³ of liquid are heated in a container surmounted by a reflux condenser with its top connected to a set of gas burettes. A direct measurement is made of the volume of oxygen released during heating. All these methods require the use of glassware made of very clean borosilicated glass which must be washed before use with hot nitric acid and then rinsed with demineralised water.

With the very pure 98% hydrogen peroxide which is manufactured nowadays, the fall in strength at 100°C is of the order of 2% in 24 hours.

It is obvious that these stability tests cannot measure the intrinsic stability of peroxide, but only its stability in the presence of walls of borosilicate glass.

20.2.6 Precautions for storing hydrogen peroxide at less than 70% strength

Hydrogen peroxide in limited quantities is often stored in glass or polyethylene containers which are also used to transport it. Ordinary glass, which has an alkaline reaction, decomposes hydrogen peroxide, but in borosilicated glass (pyrex) the substance keeps well. Before using a pyrex container, it is better to give it an initial treatment by leaving some hydrogen peroxide in it for some time and then throwing it away. If the stock is kept in the open air or under a simple canopy, the ground must not be made of clinkers since they contain combustible materials. A case has been reported in which a polyethylene conduit carrying hydrogen peroxide, which was buried not far below the surface of a layer of clinkers, was burst by frost at one point, and the peroxide oozing into the ground began to react and produce a considerable quantity of heat which caused the pipe to soften and open up over a long section.

The stock must be kept in a place which is not exposed to dust from nearby installations, and it must be kept away from combustible materials. If it is kept inside, the building should be made without wood and must not be used to store combustible materials. If it is used to store chemical products, the latter must not react with hydrogen peroxide, and it must not be forgotten that powdered substances do react with it. Containers should preferably be stood in a concreted zone, and water hoses should be placed in the storehouse so that any liquid from a leak can be heavily diluted.

Hydrogen peroxide in large quantities should be stored in metal tanks, the most suitable material being one that contains at least 99.5% aluminium, although for reasons of mechanical resistance an 18/8 stainless steel with molybdenum is sometimes preferred for large constructions. Metal sheets should be assembled by arc welding with argon, since this is the best way of ensuring that the weld lines are not contaminated with metals which might cause the peroxide to decompose. For the same reason, if the sheets are to be be ground after welding, then a corundum grinding stone must be used, and if they are to be brushed with a metal brush, the wires should be made of stainless steel. In fitting out these tanks, great care must be exercised in the choice of materials. Transfer valves and pumps should be made of stainless steel or plastic, and the pipes should be made of pure aluminium, polyvinyl chloride, or polyethylene.

20.2.7 Precautions in the use and storage of high-strength hydrogen peroxide

By high-strength peroxide we mean solutions containing at least 70% of H_2O_2. It must not be forgotten that they are explosive substances. They are highly unlikely to detonate in the conditions in which they are treated, but they may deflagrate strongly with violent effects if they are in a closed vessel. Consequently, safety measures are absolutely necessary when using and storing them. These measures come under three headings.

1° The substance must not be mixed, or even allowed into contact, with combustible materials, except, of course, in deliberate reactions, and even then only in conditions which have been checked for safety by a series of experiments on small quantities. The only combustible substances which are, in very small quantities, compatible with high-strength peroxide are some plastic materials such as polyethylene which are useful for making leakproof joints. No lubricant should be used on the walls of an apparatus, such as a centrifugal pump, which comes into contact with peroxide.

2° High-strength peroxide should be stored and used in tanks, containers, and apparatuses made of a material that causes little or no decomposition by heterogeneous catalysis. The safest materials in this respect are pure aluminium and pyrex glass, followed by polyethylene, polyvinyl chloride, and austenitic steel with molybdenum. Some stainless steels in contact with high-strength hydrogen peroxide undergo very slow but detectable corrosion, since after a few months' storage Cr^{3+} ions are found in the liquid, whilst even aluminium is not completely inert. This corrosive activity can be much reduced by adding a few millionths of ammonium nitrate to the high-strength peroxide.

3° Any contamination by impurities, even in minute quantities, must be avoided. It needs only a few decigrammes of rust or some sealing lead to fall into the liquid to trigger an extremely violent decomposition. The product must be transferred to very clean containers and any unused residue must not be poured back into the storage tank.

The following precautions can also be taken:

It is advisable to place near workstations and storage sites sufficient quantities of water to dilute the peroxide rapidly if decomposition is initiated by accident. Water is also necessary for first aid to anybody splashed by the liquid.

For long term storage, containers of several dozens or hundreds of litres should not be closed, but should rather have stoppers fitted with vents which allow the release of oxygen formed by decomposition of the peroxide. There have been explosions in stainless steel barrels on which the vents, which were in any case too small, became blocked after an 85% solution of peroxide had been stored for several months. The initial stability of the liquid had not been perfectly satisfactory since it released 35 cm^3 of oxygen a minute in the 'gasometric' test. For a period of time of not more than one week, for example during transport, high-strength peroxide can be housed in a completely sealed aluminium container provided it is no more than three-quarters full to prevent an appreciable build-up of pressure when oxygen is liberated.

Large storage tanks of stainless steel or high-grade aluminium must, before being brought into service, be very carefully washed and degreased, and then subjected to passivation treatment with diluted nitric acid [19] followed if need be by passivation by a 35% or stronger solution of H_2O_2. Precautions must be taken during construction of these tanks to ensure that the welds contain no harmful impurities. The wall must be smooth and polished.

In case of accidental spillage the liquid must not be allowed to flow into the drains before it has first been diluted with at least three times its volume in water. An explosion occurred when high-strength peroxide was allowed to flow into a gutter which was also taking in, amongst other effluents, flammable liquids.

Tanks must have vents which release into the air the small amount of oxygen that hydrogen peroxide normally gives off slowly, and these vents must be designed to keep out dust. Tanks must also be fitted with a discharge system for a situation, which is fortunately most unlikely, in which the contents should decompose rapidly. This system may consist, for example, of an ejectable cap with its base resting on a neck of polyvinyl chloride and kept in place by aluminium wires with a small enough diameter for them to be sheared when subjected to only a weak force.

It must not be possible during use for liquid flowing through a particular circuit to become 'trapped' between two valves with no safety valve or rupture disk to release into the atmosphere any oxygen given off by decomposition. This precaution is similar to the one that has to be taken in pipes containing liquefied gases. Dead ends should be avoided in all circuits, and the pipes should be laid out in a way that makes it easy to wash them. Further details on all these precautions will be found in the user manuals produced by manufacturers. When using hydrogen peroxide to oxidise organic compounds, special attention should be paid to the choice of the solvent to be used as a medium for the reaction (see 21.3.1).

20.2.8 Safety in the transport of hydrogen peroxide

Glass containers are now used only for low-strength solutions (10%) since the use of fragile carboys to transport 35% solutions was once the cause of frequent fires, because liquid leaking from a broken container and coming into contact with straw or some other flammable material would set fire to it. For these solutions and for those containing no more than 60% hydrogen peroxide, polyethylene containers are suitable. Grey polyethylene is used with a filler (2 to 3%) of carbon black which gives the contents good protection from the effects of the sun's rays. Such containers should not be placed inside protective cardboard wrapping since there have been cases in which the cardboard has been splashed with a 35% solution and has heated up and caught fire, leading to the destruction of the entire load.

For solutions stronger than 60% the use of polyethylene containers is not advised, for should any accidental cause of any kind whatever initiate decomposition in the container, the high temperature of the gases released would soften or melt the polyethylene, which might then react dangerously. High-strength solutions (70 and 85%) are thus housed in drums made of pure aluminium (99.5% at least). Such metal containers should, like those made of polyethylene, be fitted with vents designed to release any oxygen given off by the solution whilst preventing dust from getting inside.

For safety during transport these containers should not be able to fall over, otherwise the liquid might come into contact with combustible

materials and set fire to them.   There have been several examples of this
involving lorries or wagons with a wooden floor.   During hot summers in
particular, when the wood is very dry, it can be ignited by just a few
drops of a 35% solution.   To guard against such accidents, trailers have
been designed with the bottom and the side walls up to a height of one
metre encased in a continuous covering of aluminium made from welded
sheets.

On vehicles being used to transport these containers, the rules for
separating oxidising agents from fuels must be followed to the letter, and
there should be no wooden cases or any unusual object.   In 1970, during
transport of a 70% solution in a trailer, car parts (gears, etc.) in a
crate had been stored alongside polyethylene containers.   Along the way the
heavy parts fell onto one of the containers and damaged it, and the contact
between the lubricant on the parts and the high-strength peroxide caused a
strong fire together with several deflagrations.

For the transport of large masses (20 tons and over) of 70% solutions,
use is made of rail tankers made of 99.7% aluminium and road haulage
tankers made of stainless steel.   As far as possible, the latter should be
used exclusively for hydrogen peroxide or for the transport of nitric acid.
A highly spectacular accident occurred in 1960 in a stainless steel road
tanker which had been used to transport washing soda and which had not been
perfectly cleaned afterwards.   One hour after it was loaded with a 70%
solution of hydrogen peroxide, the decomposition which was initiated on the
bottom of the tank around a deposit of NaOH hurled jets of gas, vapour, and
liquid like a geyser through the tank opening which had been left
uncovered.

20.2.9 Explosive liquid mixtures with a hydrogen peroxide base

Various organic liquids can be mixed in any proportions with hydrogen
peroxide and water, forming solutions which can be stored for a long time
at ordinary temperatures with no noticeable decomposition provided they
contain no substances which catalyse the decomposition of H_2O_2.   Médard
[11] made a brief study in 1946 of mixtures of methanol and 85% hydrogen
peroxide.   They are highly sensitive to ignition, and the stoichiometric
mixture

$$H_2O_2: 67 \qquad CH_3OH: 21.2 \qquad H_2O: 11.8$$

housed in a glass tube with a diameter of 29 mm detonates at a velocity of
6720 m/s.   Kurbangalina [20], using another stoichiometric ternary mixture
that was richer in water (18%), measured a detonation velocity of 6400 m/s
in a 20 mm glass tube.   He also found the critical diameter of detonation
(see 14.4.4) of the mixture to be 3 mm.   But at diameters of between 3 and
16 mm he observed a low velocity regime of detonation (see 14.4.6) equal to
2000 m/s, so that the true critical diameter would be 16 mm.

Since propellants composed of ethanol and hydrogen peroxide have been
envisaged for auto-propulsion, there have been studies of the conditions in
which these mixtures explode.   Shanley and Greenspan [21] used a No. 6
detonator to ignite 10 ml of the solution in a 15 mm test tube placed
inside a lead tube 6 mm thick.   They evaluated the result of each test by
the noise it made – a somewhat uncertain criterion – and by the appearance
of the lead tube.   The result on a triangular diagram (Fig. 20.1) is curve

3 which marks out the range of compositions of the mixtures which exploded.

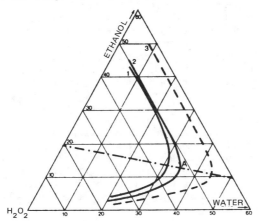

Fig. 20.1 – Liability to explode of mixtures of hydrogen peroxide,
ethanol, and water. The chain-dotted straight line represents the
balanced mixtures. Curves 1 and 2 are from Dutour and Fossat. Curve 3 is
from Shanley and Greenspan.

Tests by Dutour and Fossat [22], in which a No. 8 detonator was used to
initiate 350 ml of the mixture in a steel tube 3 mm thick and with a
diameter of 34 mm, produced curve 1, whilst 50 g of compressed P.E.T.N. as
a booster gave curve 2. When the calorific values of the mixtures on curve
2 are calculated, values are found which range from 1340 kJ/kg to 3000
kJ/kg, the latter value being for the stoichiometric mixture (point A on
the diagram).
        Shanley and Perrin [23] have stated an empirical rule to establish a
limit formed by two straight lines RS and ST (Fig. 20.2) enclosing the
curve which resulted from their tests. According to them it is the
locus of the points for which the enthalpy of the oxidation of ethanol by
the H_2O_2 present in the solution has a value of 0.9 kcal/g or 3.8 kJ/g,
this enthalpy being calculated in the following conventional manner:
ethanol is burnt into CO_2 and H_2O by the active oxygen in H_2O_2, with any
excess ethanol remaining unchanged.

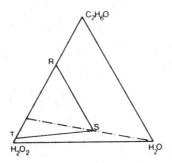

Fig. 20.2 – Application of the Shanley-Perrin rule.

Monger and his associates [12], who have studied the systems formed by various organic compounds such as 2-propanol, formaldehyde, acetaldehyde, etc. with H_2O_2 and H_2O, calculate the energy liberated in a different way and set at 0.45 kcal/g (1.9 kJ/g) the limit of the explosive range as given by tests in a given type of drop-weight apparatus. In the case of mixtures in which the combustible constituent is formic acid or acetic acid, they found a clearly increased liability to explode when there was a gap of several hours between preparation of the mixture and ignition. This is due to a partial transformation of the organic acid into a per-acid (formic or acetic). For such mixtures, which now contain not three but four constituents, the rule given above no longer applies. The authors conclude that ageing can turn an apparently non-explosive mixture into a powerful explosive, but it would be more accurate to say that ageing turns it into a sensitive explosive, because the chemical changes which have taken place in it do not increase its strength. In any event, one must subscribe to their conclusion that detailed experiment must be carried out before mixing hydrogen peroxide and organic substances or before using such a mixture.

20.3 PEROXIDISED METAL COMPOUNDS

20.3.1 Sodium peroxide

Sodium peroxide, sometimes called sodium dioxide, is the most important of the metal peroxides. It is manufactured industrially by heating molten sodium at around 450°C in a current of air (or oxygen-enriched air). It is a solid body with a density of 2.8 which, when heated, begins to lose oxygen above 400°C before melting at 460°C. It dissolves in iced water with release of heat according to the reaction

$$Na_2O_2 + 2H_2O \rightarrow 2NaOH(dis) + H_2O_2,$$

and if the temperature is raised, the hydrogen peroxide formed decomposes, liberating oxygen, with further release of heat. Aqueous solutions of Na_2O_2 are decomposed by the salts of heavy metals (Cu, Ni, etc.). Sixty years ago, sodium peroxide with added traces of copper salt was used under the trade name of oxylith. An explosion which occurred when oxygen was being prepared from oxylith was attributed to the presence of free sodium in the peroxide leading to the formation of a mixture of hydrogen and oxygen.

The correct quantity of peroxidic oxygen, which is also called active oxygen (one of the two O of the group – O – O –), in sodium peroxide, as also in the other metal peroxides, is obtained quite easily by dissolving them in a diluted acid and then titrating them with an acid solution of potassium permanganate as in the case of hydrogen peroxide.

Sodium peroxide is a powerful oxidising agent. When there is the slightest trace of humidity, it ignites cotton, charcoal, and numerous combustible substances. Various cases are known of this substance causing a fire during transport. In particular, a serious accident occurred in Hamburg in April 1960 when barrels of sodium peroxide were being loaded onto a ship. One of the barrels was leaking and started a fire in a hold. When firemen attempted to fight the fire with water, they simply made it worse since the strongly exothermic reaction of water on sodium peroxide

liberates oxygen.   The result was a series of explosions.   The correct
extinguishing agents to use on a fire caused by sodium peroxide are dry
sodium carbonate or sand.

20.3.2 Other metal peroxides

Applications may be found in the future for lithium peroxide, since its
active oxygen content is very high (41%) and it has excellent stability.
      Barium peroxide (formerly called barium dioxide), which was used before
1900 to extract oxygen from the atmosphere by the Brin process, has lost
its industrial importance since hydrogen peroxide ceased to be manufactured
by the old Thenard process.   Although less active than sodium peroxide, it
is still liable to give rise to deflagrations under the effect of friction
or impact when mixed in powder form with fine sawdust.   The mixture of 80%
BaO_2 to 20% powdered aluminium, which is used to ignite thermite, is
sensitive and may give rise to an explosion when under confinement.
      The CaO_2 and SrO_2 oxides, which are less stable than BaO_2, have never
had any commercial importance.
      The action of hydrogen peroxide on the oxides of magnesium and zinc are
used to manufacture magnesium and zinc peroxide, which are used in pharmacy
as disinfectants.   Commercial products contain only 60% MgO_2 and 70% ZnO_2
and are only very weak oxidising agents.   Their stability to heat is lower
than that of the alkaline-earth peroxides.   Magnesium peroxide readily
loses its active oxygen at around 300°C, whilst zinc peroxide loses it at
around 110°C.
      The other metal peroxides are of purely scientific interest.   Mention
should be made of mercury peroxide Hg_2O_2, which comes in two forms, both
highly sensitive to impact and to heat, so that there is some risk of
explosion when hydrogen peroxide is added to a reactive medium containing
mercury salts.

20.3.3 Potassium hyperoxide (superoxide)

When molten potassium is heated in the presence of oxygen, oxidation does
not, as in the case of sodium, stop at the peroxide K_2O_2, but goes further
to form a compound richer in oxygen, KO_2, the official name for which is
potassium hyperoxide but which is more commonly known as potassium
superoxide.   It is an orange-coloured substance which can be heated in an
oxygen atmosphere to 600°C without decomposing.   Its heat of formation F_p
is 284 kJ/mol.   It is manufactured industrially for use in self-contained
breathing apparatuses because it transforms into carbonate the CO_2 present
in exhaled air and reacts with water vapour by releasing oxygen.   Its use
quite clearly requires that it should not be allowed to come into contact
with combustible materials (oil, lubricant, various dusts, etc.).   It has
highly energetic oxidising properties but excellent stability when pure.
      It forms gradually on the surface of potassium exposed to air.   Small
flashes of light are frequently observed when potassium is cut with a
knife, but this cannot be caused by iron oxide, since the phenomenon occurs
even when a stainless steel knife is used.   It is caused by contact between
a surface of fresh potassium and the superoxide KO_2 which has formed on the
surface.   The reaction $KO_2 + 3K = 2K_2O$ is strongly exothermic, and when a
large amount of superoxide is present, there may be an explosion with

projection of droplets of molten potassium. There was a remarkable case of such an explosion in 1930 in a stock of 1 ton of potassium in the form of briquettes which had been in store for several years and on the surface of which had formed an oxidised crust several millimetres thick. It is advisable, therefore, to take care when handling potassium which has taken on a yellowish tinge on the surface, and not to use it when it is encrusted in this way, but rather to destroy it by burning by scattering it on a bed of burning wood chips in the open air. There is no danger of this kind of accident with sodium since surface oxidation of this substance does not go so far as to form NaO_2.

Mellor [10] describes a case of an accidental explosion of a mixture of powdered graphite and a residue of an Na-K alloy which had changed into superoxide. The explosion was violent.

Sodium hyperoxide NaO_2 is not manufactured industrially although we know it is possible to obtain it by the action of oxygen at around 300°C and a pressure of more than 200 bars on the peroxide Na_2O_2. Tests have also been conducted with the aim of obtaining NaO_2 by auto-oxidation reactions in an alkaline medium in the presence of oxy-reducible organic compounds. Unfortunately, it is very difficult to remove all traces of organic matter from the superoxide thus obtained, and the impure product is liable to explode spontaneously.

Calcium hyperoxide CaO_4 is not manufactured, although the substance has been the object of a fair number of studies published in the chemical literature.

The structure, the hydration states, and the ranges of thermal stability of the peroxides and hyperoxides of alkaline and alkaline-earth metals have been studied by Allamagny [26].

20.3.4 The ozonides

The ozonide ion O_3^- contains on the one hand an O – O bond similar to that of the peroxides, and on the other a bond between two atoms of the kind found in the hyperoxides. The compound KO_3 (F_p = 259 kJ/mol) is formed easily by the action of ozonised oxygen on potassium dissolved in anhydrous ammonia [9]. It is also formed by the action of ozone on completely dehydrated potassium hydroxide, but on ordinary potassium the formation of hyperoxide turns the surface yellow:

$$O_3 + 2KOH \rightarrow 2KO_2 + H_2O.$$

The compound KO_3, which, at ordinary temperature, gradually loses oxygen to leave the hyperoxide KO_2, reacts very strongly with water, giving off very strong heat and light. Its presence in a warehouse constitutes a serious danger in case of fire. Its extremely violent reaction with organic compounds is frequently explosive.

Some interest has been shown in the alkali metal ozonides since they would provide a useful source of oxygen for a number of applications.

20.4 PERSULPHURIC ACIDS AND THEIR SALTS

20.4.1 Overall view

Two per-acids are derived from sulphuric acid (I):   peroxymonosulphuric acid (II) and peroxydisulphuric acid (III), both of which are diacids. Diperoxymonosulphuric acid (IV) is not known.

$$O_2S\begin{cases}/OH \\ \backslash OH\end{cases}\qquad O_2S\begin{cases}/O-OH \\ \backslash OH\end{cases}\qquad \begin{matrix}O-SO_2-OH \\ | \\ O-SO_2-OH\end{matrix}\qquad O_2S\begin{cases}/O-OH \\ \backslash O-OH\end{cases}$$

$$(I)\qquad\qquad (II)\qquad\qquad (III)\qquad\qquad (IV)$$

20.4.2 Peroxydisulphuric acid

In 1878, Berthelot obtained an oxide of crystallised sulphur with the formula S_2O_7 which reacted with water to give peroxydisulphuric acid $H_2S_2O_8$. The name is often simplified to perdisulphuric acid. It is manufactured as an aqueous solution by the electrolysis of hydrogen peroxide. In the pure state it is a crystallised substance which melts at around 65°C, but which already decomposes at that temperature, although aqueous solutions of the substance are relatively stable at ordinary temperatures, However, peroxydisulphuric acid is not a commercial product, unlike two of its salts, potassium and ammonium, which are normally called persulphates.

Ammonium persulphate is obtained in solution by electrolysing a solution of ammonium hydrogen sulphate at an appropriate current density. The process is called the anodic oxidation of the sulphate, but it may be thought of as the polymerisation of two sulphate ions with loss of electric charges

$$2SO_4{}^{2-} = S_2O_8{}^{2-} + 2e^-.$$

20.4.3 Ammonium peroxydisulphate

This salt, which is commonly called ammonium persulphate, is found commercially in a crystallised state with a low humidity content (0.5 to 0.8%). It is slightly hygroscopic and must be prevented from absorbing more moisture since water is detrimental to good storage. In the dry state (less than 0.8% water), it remains undecomposed up to around 100°C, but at 120°C it loses oxygen at a rate of 0.5 g per 100 g of persulphate per day. When it is wet, and a fortiori when it is in an aqueous solution, its loss of weight is even more rapid. The reaction, which is weakly exothermic (100 kJ approximately), has the equation

$$(NH_4)_2S_2O_8 + H_2O \rightarrow 2H(NH_4)SO_4 + 0.5O_2.$$

From the variation in the rate of this reaction it has been possible to calculate its activation energy, which is 120 to 125 kJ/mol. The solid salt heated to over 150°C undergoes a more complete decomposition with release of gases (oxygen, water vapour, sulphur dioxide, and ammonia) and leaves no residue at 400°C. Mixtures with highly oxidisable substances, such as powdered aluminium, give rise, when exposed to humidity, to a strongly exothermic reaction which may raise the products to white heat.

Experiments on piles of some 50 kg have shown that ammonium persulphate in contact with a heated metal wall begins to decompose quite vigorously

when its temperature reaches 100 to 150˚C. It gives off gases composed of
water vapour, sulphur dioxide, and nitrogen, as well as a liquid composed
of water containing dissolved ammonium salts. The decomposition propagates
in the mass at a rate of 2.5 to 3 cm per minute, and the temperature at the
front of the decomposition is 280˚C. The phenomenon is similar to that of
the self-sustained decomposition of complex fertilisers (see 25.4.4).

The question has been raised of whether heating in the lower part of a
large pile of the product in bulk form may take on a rate such that the
decomposition would propagate and produce a large quantity of vapour.
Applying the Frank–Kamenetskii theory (see 3.9) shows that this can happen
only if the critical dimension of the pile (distance of the furthest point
from the surface) exceeds 2 to 3 m. It should also be pointed out that
there can be no talk of an explosion since the phenomenon is extremely slow
and, in addition, raises the products formed only to a moderate temperature
lower than 300˚C. There is no flame, only the release of hot (around
250˚C) irritant gases.

Ammonium persulphate is used, like organic peroxides, to initiate
certain polymerisation processes.

20.4.4 Potassium peroxydisulphate

Potassium peroxydisulphate $K_2S_2O_8$, which is known commercially as potassium
persulphate, is obtained by a process of double decomposition between
ammonium persulphate and a soluble salt of potassium, usually hydrogen
sulphate. Potassium persulphate, which is hardly soluble when cold (5% at
around 20˚C) precipitates in a fairly pure state containing 5.85% active
oxygen. It is a salt which is stable in air, and has a heat of formation
of 1910 kJ/mol [6]. Its pyrolysis follows the simple equation

$$K_2S_2O_8(cr) \;\rightarrow\; K_2S_2O_7(cr) + 0.5O_2(g)$$

and leaves a residue of potassium pyrosulphate. It is a fairly slow
deflagration which, at atmospheric pressure, only raises the products to a
temperature of 320˚C†

A case has been reported of a fire in a stock of 20 tons of potassium
persulphate housed in cardboard packages in a warehouse. The cardboard
burned and gave off dense smoke but at no time did the rate of propagation
of the fire accelerate.

A series of tests [5] led their author to conclude that the danger of
persulphates exploding has been wrongly overestimated, since Agde and
Alberti were unable to produce an explosion by either impact or heating in
potassium or ammonium persulphates with combustible sweepings added.

20.4.5 Peroxymonosulphuric acid

Peroxymonosulphuric acid H_2SO_5, which is commonly called peroxysulphuric

---

† This value is calculated from the following values at constant pressure:
- heat of reaction 75 kJ/mol,
- specific heat of pyrosulphate 217 J/˚C mol,
- specific heat of oxygen 16.7 J/˚C mol.

acid or Caro's acid, after the name of the chemist who discovered it in 1898, can be obtained in the pure state by the reaction of hydrogen peroxide on chlorosulphuric acid.

$$SO_2\begin{array}{c}/OH\\\\\backslash Cl\end{array} + H_2O_2 \rightarrow SO_2\begin{array}{c}/OH\\\\\backslash O-OH\end{array} + HCl.$$

It is a highly hygroscopic crystalline substance which melts at 45°C. Although it has better chemical stability than peroxydisulphuric acid, it gradually loses oxygen at ordinary temperature and turns into sulphuric acid. Its decomposition may be explosive. In the accident described by Edwards [8] 7 ml of the product in a 95% solution exploded at 0°C in a test tube closed with a wad of glass wool. The explosion may have been caused by fragments of the glass wool falling into the substance.

It is found commercially as an aqueous solution containing between 200 and 400 g of H_2SO_5 per litre, and it is usually manufactured by using sulphuric acid to slowly hydrolyse ammonium persulphate into an aqueous solution at around 60°C

$$(NH_4)_2S_2O_8 + H_2O \rightarrow (NH_4)_2SO_4 + H_2SO_5$$

and then neutralising excess sulphuric acid at least in part. This process works more easily than the action of highly concentrated hydrogen peroxide on sulphuric acid or even on oleum with 20% SO_3, which is capable of giving a product containing more than 60% H_2SO_5 and free of ammonium salt.

These aqueous solutions lose their active oxygen only slowly, but if the liquid is contaminated by substances such as those which decompose hydrogen peroxide (salts of heavy metals such as Cu, Mn, Pb, etc.), then decomposition becomes vigorous, although there is no explosion when the concentration is not higher than 400 g per litre. The SO_5^{2-} ion has more marked oxidising properties than the $S_2O_8^{2-}$ ion.

The main outlet for Caro's acid is in the industrial treatment of wool. When it reacts with organic compounds, it acts both as an oxidising agent and a desiccant. It can be used to oxidise the ketones and the secondary and tertiary alcohols, but using too concentrated an acid, even when chilled, leads to explosions [7]. By acting on organic acids, it can form organic per-acids. These reactions involving concentrated Caro's acid are delicate operations because they must be carried out over a narrow temperature range. If the temperature is too low, the reaction does not take place, and if it exceeds another value, between 15 and 20°C higher than the previous one, the reaction runs away. These conditions are reminiscent of those pertaining to the nitric esterification of glycerol.

An important use has been found for Caro's acid in the destruction of $(CN)^-$ ions in waste water:

$$CN^- + H_2SO_5 \rightarrow CNO^- + H_2SO_4.$$

Using an excess of H_2SO_5 even leads to complete oxidation of the cyanate ion in carbonate and nitrogen.

Monopotassic peroxymonosulphate $KHSO_5$ (sometimes given the commercial name of potassium caroate) has a number of applications. It is a substance which melts and decomposes at around 100°C and reacts very vigorously with organic compounds, sometimes exploding.

20.5 VARIOUS PERSALTS

20.5.1 The perborates

The true perborates, KBO_3 and NH_4BO_3, in anhydrous form can be prepared in
the laboratory, but they are not manufactured industrially. Commercial
'sodium perborate', a compound which is very important in industry, was
first thought to be the hydrate $NaBO_3.4H_2O$, but subsequently, given that,
unlike the peroxysulphates, it reacts in the same way as hydrogen peroxide
on the acid solution of potassium permanganate, it was assigned the formula

$NaBO_2.H_2O_2.3H_2O$.

But Hansson [3] concluded, after a study with X-rays, that this 'perborate'
in the crystalline state does in fact contain peroxyborate ions with the
bonds $B - O - O - B$. This peroxyborate ion is hydrolysed much more rapidly
than the peroxydisulphate ion, which explains the immediate reaction with
permanganate.

Sodium perborate contains 10.4% active oxygen. It melts at around 63°C
with decomposition. By dehydrating it with care, the monohydrate $NaBO_3.H_2O$
can be formed, which is very stable up to 60°C at least and contains 15.4%
active oxygen.

Sodium perborate was discovered in 1898 by Tanatar and became an
industrial product at the beginning of the 20th century. It is most
commonly manufactured by the action of a 70% solution of hydrogen peroxide
on a solution of sodium metaborate obtained by adding caustic soda in the
form of crystals or of a concentrated solution to pentahydrated borax
$Na_2B_4O_7.5H_2O$. The latter is used in preference to dehydrated natural borax
which generally contains troublesome impurities. The reaction precipitates
sodium perborate, which dissolves only with difficulty. It is then dried
carefully at a temperature no higher than 55°C. A good commercial product
contains 10.3 to 10.4% active oxygen.

It is a very stable substance which, in the right storage conditions,
loses less than 0.5% of its active oxygen in a year. It has very mild
oxidising properties. An accident led to the hypothesis that this
perborate could, when mixed with combustible substances, give rise to
strong, not to say explosive, reactions, but experiments have shown this is
by no means the case. Mixtures of lubricating oil and perborate are
completely insensitive to impact [4] and display no reaction even at 100°C,
and neither can 'monohydrated perborate' be made to react by impact or heat
with the lubricant. Comments to be found in a certain work on the dangers
involved in handling the perborates seem to be exaggerated. Sodium
perborate is quite rightly not classified by transport regulations as a
dangerous merchandise.

20.5.2 The percarbonates

Low-temperature electrolysis of solutions of potassium carbonate or the
action of CO_2 on potassium peroxide gives a peroxydicarbonate $K_2C_2O_6$. A
peroxymonocarbonate $KHCO_4$ is also known. These substances, like similar

sodium compounds, are not manufactured industrially, but a sodium percarbonate is found commercially, and is manufactured from carbonate in a very similar way to the perborate. In the pure state this product would have a composition corresponding to the formula

$$Na_2CO_3.1.5H_2O_2,$$

but it is not known if this is a combination of H_2O_2 and carbonate or a true peroxycarbonate. It is a white powder soluble in water, containing about 14% active oxygen (the pure product would contain 15.2%). It keeps well at temperatures no higher than 50°C.

20.5.3 The peroxyphosphates

We know of a peroxymonophosphoric acid H_3PO_5 with the structure

$$H - O - O - PO(OH)_2$$

which reacts very strongly with organic substances, and which seems to be similar to Caro's acid. By electrolysing solutions of potassium phosphates, anodic oxidation leads to the formation of the relatively stable peroxydiphosphate $K_4P_2O_8$, but these substances are not manufactured industrially, and neither are the products obtained by adding H_2O_2 to the pyrophosphates.

20.5.4 The perhydrates

When an aqueous solution of salt to which is added hydrogen peroxide is evaporated, it often happens that what crystallises is a molecular combination of H_2O_2 and the salt, such as, for example, $KF.H_2O_2$. These addition compounds are normally called perhydrates. They resemble a hydrated salt, but they may be dangerous because those with a high H_2O_2 content can react very strongly on certain combustible substances. The H_2O_2 in these hydrates, of which there are very many, is held by hydrogen bonds of the same kind as those which come from H_2O.

Organic compounds (such as acetamide and erythritol) can also give addition compounds with H_2O_2. The best known is the compound with urea, $CO(NH_2)_2.H_2O_2$, which is sold commercially under the name of 'solid oxygenated water'.

Any crystalline substance derived from a mother liquor containing hydrogen peroxide must be regarded with suspicion as long as it is not known whether it is a mild oxidising agent or not.

BIBLIOGRAPHICAL REFERENCES

[1] Zumbrunn, J. P. (1970) *Traitments de surfaces*, No. 97, p. 3
[2] Giguère, P. A. & Morissette, B. G. (1955) *Canad. J. Chem.* 33 804
[3] Hansson, A. (1961) *Acta Chim. Scand.* 15 934
[4] Forestier, H. (1964) *Rapport d'expertise*
[5] Roth, W. (1928) *Ind. Eng. Chem. News Ed.* 6 5
[6] Stull, D. R. quoted by Hu T., & Hepler, L. G. (1962) *J. Chem. Eng.*

Data 7 58
[7]   Toennies, G. (1937) *J. Am. Ch. Soc.* **59** 552
[8]   Edwards, J. O. (1955) *Chem. Eng. News* **33** 3336
[9]   Kraus (1934) *J. Am. Ch. Soc.* **56** 2384
[10]   Mellor, D. P. (1965) *Chem. and Ind.*, p. 723
[11]   Médard, L. (1946) *Compt. Rend.* **222** 1491
[12]   Monger, J. M. *et al.* (1964) *J. Ch. Eng. Data* **9** 124
[13]   Hart, A. B. (1949) *Nature* (G.B.) **163** 876
[14]   Matheson, G. L. & Maass, O. (1929) *J. Am. Ch. Soc.* **51** 674
[15]   Bellinger, F., Friedman, H. B. & Bauer, W. H. (1946) *Ind. Eng. Ch.* **38** 310
[16]   Médard, L. (1949) *Mém. Poudres* **31** 273
[17]   Monger, J. M., Baumgartner, H. J., Hood, G. C. & Sanborn, C. E. (1964) *J. Chem. Eng. Data* **9** 119
[18]   Marshall, J. G. (1959) *Trans. Faraday Soc.* **55** 288
[19]   Girard, R. (1966) *XXVIème Congrès Chim. Ind.* S.16, p. 544
[20]   Kurbangalina, R. K. (1948) *Zh. Fiz. Khim.* **22** 49
[21]   Shanley, E. S. & Greenspan, F. P. (1947) *Ind. Eng. Ch.* **39** 1536
[22]   Dutour, M. & Fossat, R. (1947-48) *Lab. C.S.E.*
[23]   Shanley, E. S. & Perrin, J. R. (1958) *Jet Propulsion*, p. 382
[24]   Bureau of Mines (1967) Circ. 8387
[25]   Médard, L. & Gignier, J. (1950) *Lab. C.S.E.*
[26]   Allamagny, P. (1965) *Rev. Chim. Minérale* **2** 645

21

Organic peroxides

21.1 GENERAL OBSERVATIONS

21.1.1. Definition

Organic peroxides are substances which derive formally from hydrogen peroxide, $H - O - O - H$, by replacement of one (or two) hydrogen atoms by one (or two) organic residues R. A distinction is made between the hydroperoxides (I) and the peroxides (II)

$$R - O - OH \text{ (I)} \qquad R - O - O - R' \text{ (II)},$$

but the two residues R and R' may themselves come from peroxides. It is thus possible to have diperoxides, triperoxides, hydroperoxy-peroxides, etc. Acyl hydroperoxides are usually called peroxy-acids or per-acids (for example, peracetic acid $CH_3 - CO - O - OH$).

Peroxides and hydroperoxides do not derive only formally from hydrogen peroxide H_2O_2. In many cases, the latter is actually the raw material from which they are manufactured. In particular, it is from the direct reaction of H_2O_2 that are obtained alkyl peroxides and hydroperoxides, such as tertiary butyl hydroperoxide $(CH_3)_3C - O - OH$, and alkylidene peroxides deriving from ketones, which are often polyperoxidised compounds (see 21.2.6).

Quite frequently, the action of hydrogen peroxide on an organic body produces a number of peroxidised compounds at the same time. With ketones and aldehydes there may also be condensation of two or three molecules, possibly with cyclisation (see 21.3.1).

Products sold under a name such as 'methyl ethyl ketone peroxide' are actually mixtures and may, therefore, depending on the manufacturing process, contain different proportions of the various peroxides formed by the action of H_2O_2 and thus have different properties of stability and sensitivity.

21.1.2 Auto-oxidation

Auto-oxidations are reactions in which molecular oxygen O_2 is introduced, either at ordinary or some higher temperature, into an organic molecule to form a peroxide or a hydroperoxide. Unlike strong combustions, which are highly exothermic and split the organic molecule to form CO_2 and H_2O at a high temperature, auto-oxidations occur in relatively mild conditions. A large number of liquid organic compounds are susceptible to auto-oxidation, which takes place by means of a chemical chain reaction involving free radicals. For example, in the case of 1,2,3,4-tetrahydronaphthalene (tetralin), the oxidation chain is initiated by the formation of a hydro-carbon radical (III) by means of initiating substances or the action of photons, and proceeds to the fixation of oxygen, giving a peroxidised radical (IV) which, in turn, reacts with the hydrocarbon to form a hydro-peroxide (V) and regenerate the radical (III).

The reaction [1] is very fast, so the rate of the oxidation process is governed by the spread of oxygen in the liquid. In the example just given, the hydroperoxide may be separated from non-oxidised tetrahydronaphthalene. It is a solid which melts at 56°C.

Auto-oxidation in a liquid may be prevented by dissolving in it a small quantity of a substance which has the property to interrupt a chain by reaction (addition, donation) on the RO_2^* radical. These substances, such as phenols or amines, are called *anti-oxidants*†. They are not catalysts in the proper sense of the term, since the auto-oxidation process may resume when they are used up in the reaction. Conversely, traces of heavy metal ions may promote auto-oxidation, and the process may also be initiated by the addition of a small quantity of a peroxide from another preparation.

Auto-oxidation of saturated aliphatic hydrocarbons takes place only at a temperature higher than 180°C, but it occurs readily, and often at ordinary temperature, with double-bonded compounds. It takes place only

---

† Moureu and Dufraisse, who discovered this inhibiting property, called these substances 'anti-oxygens', which seems to be a better term than anti-oxidant since it reminds us that their action is part of a reaction involving the oxygen molecule rather than any oxidising agent.

with difficulty on primary carbon atoms, but more readily on secondary
carbon atoms, and even more easily on tertiary carbons. For example, the
action of oxygen on toluene, even in the best conditions, gives only a very
small amount of benzyl hydroperoxide, whilst its action on ethylbenzene
secondary carbon gives a small quantity of 1-phenylethyl hydroperoxide, and
the auto-oxidation of isopropylbenzene (cumene) provides a fair quantity of
2-hydroperoxy-2-phenyl propane (cumyl hydroperoxide) (IV).   It is thus
possible to manufacture industrially the hydroperoxides of pinane (VII) and
p-menthane (VIII).   Benzene cannot be oxidised in this way, and indeed
there is no known case of a hydroperoxide or a peroxide with an − 0 − 0 −
group fixed directly onto the benzene nucleus.

   Auto-oxidation reactions play an important role in many natural
processes (the process whereby fatty substances become rancid) and many
industrial processes (the drying property of oils).   They are sometimes
undesirable, since they can lead to explosions (see 21.3) In industrial
processes in which dangerous peroxides can form, either accidentally or
normally (as in parasite reactions accompanying a main reaction), they
should be destroyed as they form.   Thus, in the manufacture of acetic acid
by oxidation of compressed acetaldehyde, 0.1 to 0.2% manganous acetate is
added to the reactive medium so that the Mn^{2+} ion will catalyse the
decomposition of peracetic acid as it is formed.

21.1.3 General properties of organic peroxides

The main property of the peroxides (including the hydroperoxides) is that
they readily decompose into radicals according to a first order reaction

   $$R − 0 − 0 − R' \rightarrow R.O^* + R'.O^*.$$

In the case of many peroxides, this decomposition is noticeable at ordinary
temperature or at temperatures below 80°C.   It is the *thermal decomposition*
of the peroxide, the kinetics of which always has as its initial phase the
breaking of an 0 − 0 bond.   The radicals created by this initial phase may
react with one another, or on still undecomposed peroxide, or on the
solvent when there is one.   For example, it has been possible to prove [1]
that with methyl peroxide on its own in a gas phase, the methoxy radicals
created by the splitting of the molecule undergo the reactions

   $$CH_3O^* + CH_3O^* \rightarrow CH_3OH + H_2CO$$
   $$CH_3O^* + H_2CO \rightarrow CH_3OH + HCO^*$$
   $$CH_3O^* + HCO^* \rightarrow CH_3OH + CO,$$

so that the equation for the full reaction of thermal decomposition is

   $$2CH_3 − 0 − 0 − CH_3 \rightarrow 3CH_3OH + CO. \tag{21.2}$$

   These reactions which form free radicals are the basis for the main use
of the peroxides in initiating polymerisation reactions.   They catalyse
both condensation polymerisation (in other words, reactions accompanied by
the elimination of a simple molecule, such as H_2O, between two monomer
molecules), as in the formation of the phenol-formaldehyde resins, and
addition polymerisation, examples of which are unsaturated compounds,
ethylene, and vinyl compounds.

The thermal stability of these substances varies quite considerably. Thus, trifluoromethyl peroxide $CF_3 - O - O - CF_3$ is a gas (b.p. $- 37°C$) which begins to decompose appreciably only at around $220°C$. Some peroxides can be distilled or sublimed at low pressure (1/4 or 1/10 of a bar) between 25 and $80°C$, but other peroxides are stable only below $- 80°C$.

This decomposition can be conveniently studied in the laboratory by heating a diluted solution of peroxide in an inert solvent, in other words one which has no effect on the products of the thermolysis of the peroxide. It is found to be a first order reaction and it is therefore possible to define the thermal stability of a peroxide at a given temperature by its half life (see 3.7) at that temperature.   In practice, however, it is scarcely possible to make measurements with highly diluted solutions, and there is no such thing as an absolutely inert solvent, so that normally a 5% solution is used in benzene, toluene, or chlorobenzene, and in addition to the simple reaction of the peroxide splitting there are decomposition reactions (sometimes called induced decompositions) involving the molecules of the solvent.   The order of these reactions is higher than unity, and they have the effect that what is measured under the name of half life is a shorter time span than the real half life of the peroxide. They are still extremely useful, however (Table 21.1), and the values can also be used to determine at what temperature a peroxide has a half life of a given duration, such as one hour (Table 21.2).   The values in these tables are accurate to only ± 10% because experimental measurements are made on products of varying degrees of purity.   They are especially useful for comparing two peroxides.

Thermal decomposition of the peroxides in the pure state is generally more complex than in a diluted solution. By using quasi-isothermal tests of spontaneous heating (see 16.3.3) or differential thermal analysis, it is possible to determine an instability temperature, that is a temperature above which it is possible to detect the decomposition of the peroxide by the test used.   The 'instability threshold' is not a precisely defined temperature. since it varies a little from one test method to another, but rather a range of temperatures extending over ten degrees or so.   When this 'threshold' is around $60-70°C$, the peroxide still decomposes quite appreciably, although very slowly, at temperatures 30 to $40°C$ lower, as can be seen from the decrease in the active oxygen content after a few months or years.

We know the heat of activation, which is situated between 125 and 160 kJ/mol, with the latter value being characteristic of tertiary butyl peroxide.   This activation energy is generally identified with the energy of dissociation D (RO — OR'), which thus has a value only marginally dependent on the nature of the radicals R and R'.

Catalysts such as $AlCl_3$, iron salts, etc. can make decomposition of a peroxide possible at a temperature far below that of its decomposition threshold.

Organic peroxides are oxidising agents.   Some, the per-acids in particular, are highly energetic, whilst others are hardly energetic at all.   Their reactivity is often considerable.   Organic peroxides have a great propensity to react with the most varied substances and thus lend themselves to oxidation reactions in organic chemistry.   For the general chemical properties of organic peroxides, the reader is referred to the specialist literature quoted in reference [20].

Finally, decomposition of the peroxides, which always evolves gas products, can be strong enough to constitute an explosion.   Here again, the

Table 21.1

Half life (in hours) of organic peroxides
in an approximately 5% solution with hydrocarbon

NB – These values are for products of standard technical purity

A. – Peroxides with relatively high thermal stability

	100°C	110°C	120°C	130°C	140°C	150°C
3,3,6,6,9,9-hexamethyl-1,2,4,5-tetraoxacyclononane	–	–	67	21	7	2.5
2,5-dimethyl-2,5-di(tertiobutylperoxy)-3-hexyne	–	90	27	8	1.7	0.9
Tertiary butyl peroxide	–	75	22	6	1.4	0.6
Tertiary butyl hydroperoxide	165	42	12	3.2	1	0.3
Cumene hydroperoxide	115	42	13	4.8	2	0.8
Cumene peroxide	100	25	6.6	1.7	0.5	0.1
Tertiary butyl perbenzoate	30	7.8	2.2	0.6	0.2	–

Table 21.1 ctd.

B. – Peroxides with average thermal stability

	60°C	70°C	80°C	90°C	100°C	110°C
Tertiary butyl perisononanoate	–	–	215	58	15	4.2
Tertiary butyl peracetate	–	–	165	43	11	3.3
Tertiary butyl perisobutyrate	120	28	6.7	1,8	0.5	0.1
Tertiary butyl peroctoate	140	28	5.7	1.4	0.4	0.1
Benzoyl peroxide	45	13	3.7	1.2	0.4	0.1
Acetyl peroxide	30	8	2.2	0.6	0.2	–
Propionyl peroxide	17	4.5	1.2	0.4	0.1	–
Lauroyl peroxide	14	3.7	1	0.3	–	–

C. – Peroxides with poor thermal stability

	30°C	40°C	50°C	60°C	70°C	80°C
Tertiary butyl perpivalate	–	83	23	6	1.9	0.6
Tertiary butyl perneodecanoate	130	30	7	1.8	0.5	–
Isopropyl percarbonate	56	12	2.4	0.5	0.1	–
Acetyl cyclohexane sulphonyl peroxide	11	2.4	0.5	0.1	–	–

Table 21.2

Temperatures at which organic peroxides have a half life of one hour

NB - Values are for technical products in solution

	°C
t-butyl monoperoxyphthalate	175
3,3,6,6,9,9-hexamethyl-1,2,4,5-tetraoxacyclononane	160
2,5-dimethyl-2,5-di(tertiobutylperoxy)-3-hexyne	150
Tertiary butyl peroxide	147
Cumene hydroperoxide	147
Tertiary butyl hydroperoxide	140
Methyl ethyl ketone peroxide (a)	134
Tertiary butyl perbenzoate	125
Tertiary butyl perisononanoate	122
Tertiary butyl peracetate	120
Cyclohexanone peroxide (a)	115
Tertiary butyl permaleate	104
Tertiary butyl perisobutyrate	95
Tertiary butyl peroctoate	92
Benzoyl peroxide	92
Acetyl peroxide	87
Lauroyl peroxide	80
Tertiary butyl perpivalate	74
Tertiary butyl perneodecanoate	64
Isopropyl percarbonate	55
Acetyl cyclohexane sulphonyl peroxide	46

(a) Value somewhat variable depending on the proportions of the constituents in the mixture.

explosive property shows great diversity.

21.1.4 Thermochemistry of organic peroxides

There is very little experimental data on the heats of formation of the organic peroxides. Some of the most reliable values are collected in Table 21.3. Their degree of uncertainty is between 5 and 10 kJ/mol. For some peroxides other than those quoted, an approximate calculation can be made

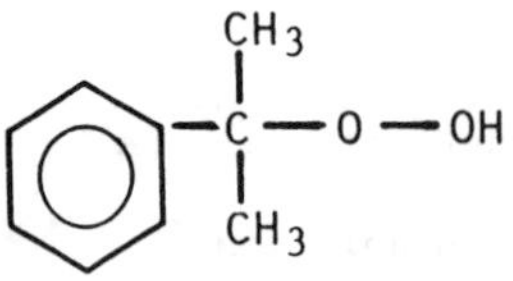

VI

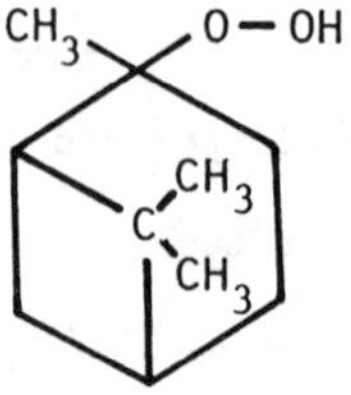

VII

VIII

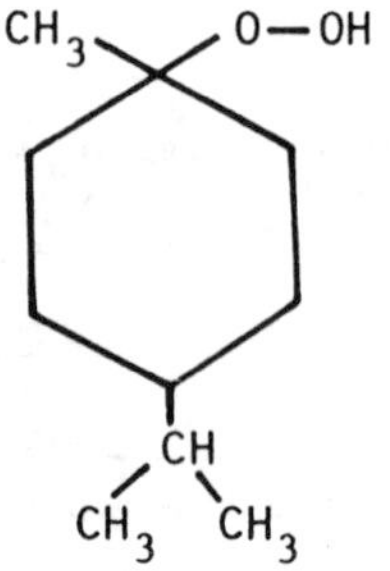

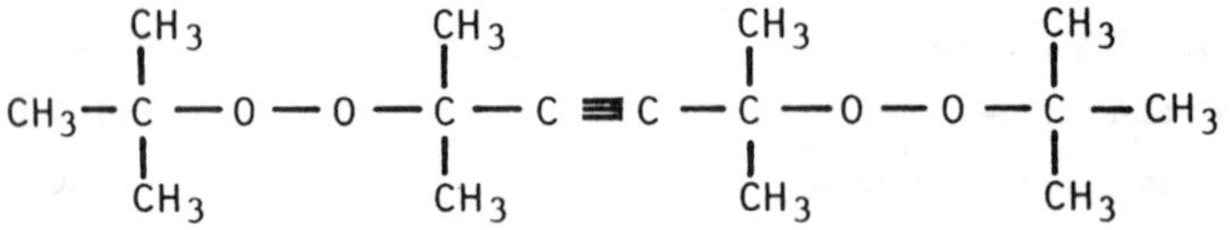

IX

X

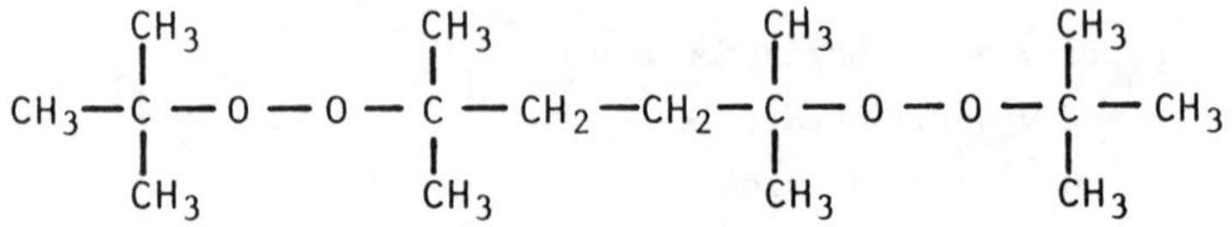

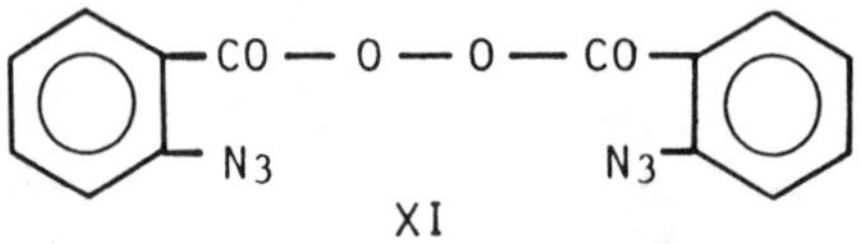

XI

XIII

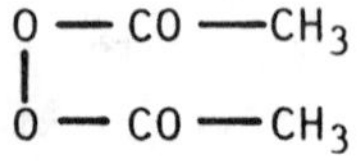

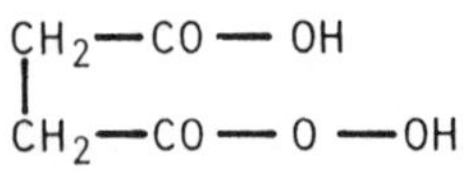

XII

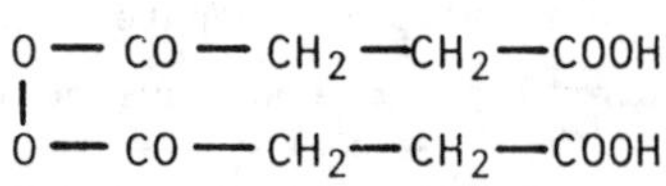

XIV

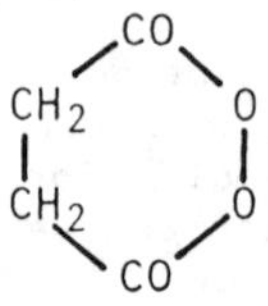

XV

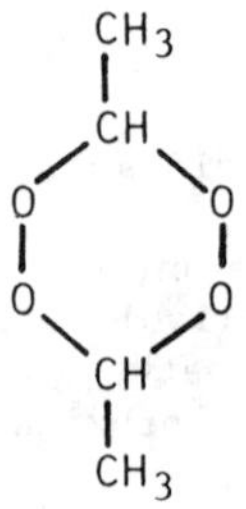

XVI

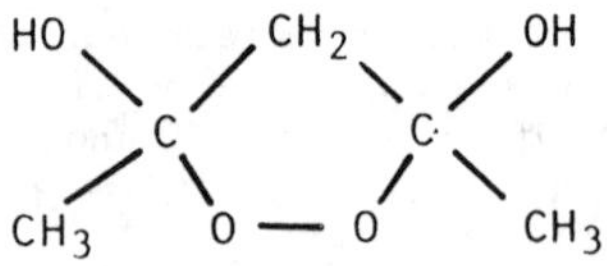

XVII

using the system of values in Table 2.3. It can be seen that the heat of
formation of a peroxide is lower than that of the corresponding merely
oxygenated compound taken in the same liquid or gaseous state†.

Table 21.3

Heats of formation of several organic peroxides

Peroxide	F_p (kJ/mol)	F_v (kJ/mol)	Reference
Methyl hydroperoxide (liq)	163	159	
Tertiary butyl hydroperoxide (liq)	268	253	[24]
Tertiary butyl hydroperoxide (gas)	220	207	
1-hydroperoxy-1,2,3,4-tetrahydro-			
naphthalene (cryst)	125	109	[33]
Methyl peroxide (gas)	125	118	[35]
Ethyl peroxide (liq)	224	209	[35]
Ethyl peroxide (gas)	192	180	[35]
Tertiary butyl peroxide (liq)	381	356	[35]
Tertiary butyl peroxide (gas)	339	318	[35]
Acetyl peroxide (liq)	535	523	[26]
Benzoyl peroxide (solid)	369	352	[29]

Using these values, it is possible to calculate the thermal properties
of explosions or thermal decompositions of peroxides where the chemical
reaction is known. The following are a few examples.

Thermal decomposition of methyl peroxide – Equation (21.2) above leads
easily to the value

$$Q'_p = (201 \times 3) + 110.5 - (125 \times 2) = 463.5 \text{ kJ/mol,}$$

or 232 kJ for one mole of peroxide. At this point, a general observation
may be made: the overall reaction of thermal decomposition in which an
organic peroxide deteriorates may be different from the reaction involved
in its explosion, since the temperature of the latter generally exceeds
several hundred degrees Celsius. However, the enthalpy of this reaction of
deterioration is always of the same order of magnitude as that of the
explosion, ranging from 130 to 290 kJ per mole of peroxide.

_____

† For example, we have the following values:
liquid tertiary butyl alcohol: F_v = 339 kJ/mol
tertiary butyl hydroperoxide: F_v = 253 kJ/mol
liquid propionic anhydride: F_v = 649 kJ/mol
liquid propionyl peroxide: F_v = 603 kJ/mol.

Explosion of liquid performic acid – This substance, $H.CO_3H$, which is a stoichiometric compound, has a value $F_v = 343$ kJ/mol. It occurs only in a 90% or more aqueous solution. The equation for the explosion of the 77.5% solution is

$$HCO_3H(1) + H_2O(1) = CO_2(g) + 2H_2O(g),$$

and the method expounded in Chapter 14 allows easy calculation of

$$Q'_v = 249 \text{ kJ/mol}$$
$$T_v = 2400°C \text{ approximately.}$$

Explosion of liquid methyl hydroperoxide – This substance decomposes at around 300°C according more or less to the equation

$$CH_3 - O - OH = H.CHO + H_2O,$$

which has a calorific value (condensed water) of 234 kJ/mol (4870 kJ/kg). This reaction in uncontrolled conditions leads to a very high explosion temperature, but in that case the equation for the decomposition, which certainly takes on the characteristics of a detonation, is that of a slightly oxygen-deficient explosive. The method in 14.2.6 leads to the following products:

$$0.88(CO + H_2O) + 0.12CO_2 + 1.12H_2$$

with $Q'_v = 192$ kJ/mol, $T_v = 2500°K$ and a calorific value (condensed water) of 4770 kJ/kg, which makes methyl hydroperoxide an explosive very much comparable to picric acid.

Explosion of solid benzoyl peroxide – The elementary reactions by which benzoyl peroxide decomposes are well known. They are an initial splitting of the molecule

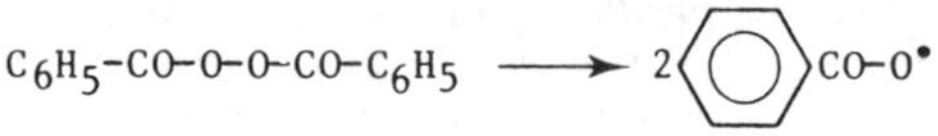

$$C_6H_5-CO-O-O-CO-C_6H_5 \longrightarrow 2\ C_6H_5\langle\bigcirc\rangle CO-O^\bullet$$

followed by

$$\langle\bigcirc\rangle CO-O^\bullet \longrightarrow CO_2 + \langle\bigcirc\rangle^\bullet$$

and recombination of radicals

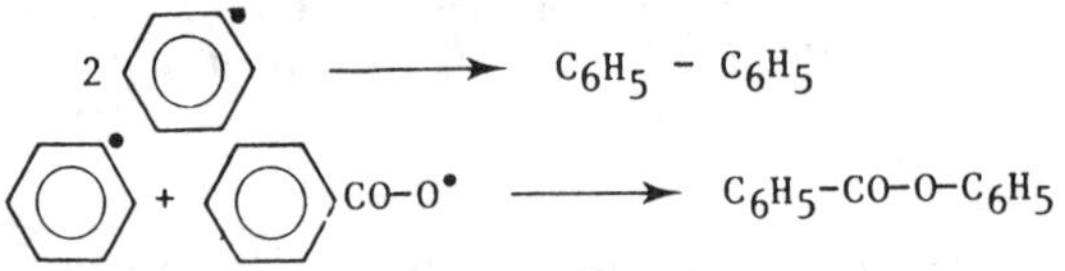

$$2\ \langle\bigcirc\rangle^\bullet \longrightarrow C_6H_5 - C_6H_5$$

$$\langle\bigcirc\rangle^\bullet + \langle\bigcirc\rangle CO-O^\bullet \longrightarrow C_6H_5-CO-O-C_6H_5$$

The two following overall reactions thus represent the explosion of solid benzoyl peroxide:

$$C_{14}H_{10}O_4(s) = C_6H_5 - C_6H_5(v) = 2CO_2(g)$$
$$C_{14}H_{10}O_4(s) = C_6H_5 - CO.O.C_6H_5(v) + CO_2(g),$$

with the one which gives diphenyl occurring for 20% of the mass exploding. Calculation gives for this reaction

$$Q'_V = 243 \text{ kJ/mol } (= 1004 \text{ kJ/kg})$$
$$T_V = 986\,^{\circ}C,$$

whilst the reaction which forms phenyl benzoate has the values

$$Q'_V = 182 \text{ kJ/mol } (= 749 \text{ kJ/kg})$$
$$T_V = 811\,^{\circ}K.$$

Thus, there are gaseous products at around $600\,^{\circ}C$, but the volume of these gases (corrected for $0\,^{\circ}C$ and 1 atm) is scarcely more than 200 litres per kg, which is three or four times less than with the classic explosives. Furthermore, in a closed vessel the vapours of diphenyl and phenyl benzoate condense very soon after the explosion. When the explosion takes place in the open air, the gases mix with the air and there may then be a secondary explosion from the combustion of these gases which is much more exothermic than the primary explosive reaction (up to 25000 kJ per kg of benzoyl peroxide).

Tertiary butyl peroxide and hydroperoxide – The vapour of tertiary butyl hydroperoxide decomposes in part according to the equation

$$(CH_3)_3C - O - OH \rightarrow CH_3 - CO - CH_3 + CH_3OH,$$

and in part according to more complex products (CH_4, HCHO, etc.). For the above equation calculation gives

$$Q'_V = 201 \text{ kJ/mol } (2218 \text{ kJ/kg}).$$

If the calorific capacity of the products formed is calculated at $230 \text{ J/}^{\circ}C$, the explosion temperature will be $890\,^{\circ}C$, but for the more complex reaction calculation leads to a value of around $800\,^{\circ}C$. For vaporised peroxide decomposing according to the equation

$$(C_4H_9)_2O_2 \rightarrow C_2H_6 + 2CH_3 - CO - CH_3,$$

with a calorific value of 1234 kJ/kg, the explosion temperature is around $700\,^{\circ}C$.

21.1.5 Explosive properties of organic peroxides

The observations made in this section and the following one apply to pure organic peroxides, since, when the latter are put into mixtures in the form of commercial 'preparations' (see 22.1.1), their explosive properties are more or less attenuated.

Almost all organic peroxides have explosive properties in the pure state. However, when the molecule containing a peroxy group $- O - O -$ also contains a great number of hydrocarbon groups, the explosive property, as in the case of stearoyl peroxide, may become practically nil. We can say as an almost general statement that the peroxides as explosives are low-power but have a relatively high sensitivity to mechanical actions and to heat, which is why they have never been used as intentional explosives.

Three authors [36] have tried to establish correlations between the numerical values found in practical explosion tests conducted on six organic peroxides and the parameters for the criteria used in the CHETAH programme (see 2.11); they estimate that their attempt 'met with moderate success'.

Peroxides have only weak 'power' because their composition is almost always very far from being the stoichiometric mixture, and because their decomposition (21.1.4) gives off gases at a fairly low temperature and in small quantities. This has been verified experimentally by Guillet and Meyer [9] in explosion experiments in a manometric bomb of tertiary butyl peroxide and perbenzoate. Judging from the pressures that were engendered, the explosion temperatures were of the order of 700°C, and analysis of the gases after the explosion gives a composition very close to that of the gases which are released in the thermal decomposition of the same peroxides at a lower temperature (150 to 250°C).

By contrast, organic peroxides are generally fairly sensitive to impact. Some of them are even more sensitive than the classic primary explosives such as mercury fulminate. Usually, their thermal stability is poor, and heating beyond 100°C explodes most peroxides. It has been noted that their sensitivity to impact increases appreciably when the temperature rises.

When accidents have occurred during the manipulation of organic per-oxides in the laboratory, surprise has often been expressed at their shattering properties. However, brisance is only very partially dependent on power. Indeed, it was once proposed to use a peroxide† derived from hexamethylenetetramine as a primary explosive in the manufacture of deton-ators.

Some peroxides, when suitably ignited, are liable to detonate, but most of them can only deflagrate, and often only weakly.

Table 21.4 compares the explosive properties of benzoyl peroxide, which is a typical peroxide, with those of picric acid, which is, in France, the usual comparator from the classic explosives.

Organic peroxides with a molecule which contains other explosophore groups in addition to the peroxy group – O – O – may, of course, show more marked explosive properties, and in this respect it is interesting to compare (Table 21.5) the properties of the two following liquid peroxides for which applications have been found in Germany:

– 2,5-dimethyl-2,5-di(tertiobutylperoxy)-3-hexyne   (IX)
– 2,5-dimethyl-2,5-di(tertiobutylperoxy)-hexane.   (X)

---

† This peroxide, called hexamethylenetriperoxydiamine, the formula for which has not been established with certainty, suffers from a number of disadvantages: high sensitivity to impact and liberation of ammonia, which corrodes the detonator caps during slow decomposition. Tests carried out with a view to using it in 1943 did not find a practical solution.

Table 21.4

Comparative explosive properties of benzoyl peroxide and picric acid

Property	Benzoyl peroxide	Picric acid
Explosive calorific value (kJ/kg)	710	3 225
Gas volume at N.T.P. (litre/kg)	200	700
Power (c.p.u.)	16	100
Sensitivity to the Sevran drop weight (daJ for 50% explosion)	1.2	6
Deflagration point	105°C	>300°C
Limit diameter in the steel tube with nozzle plates (mm)	8	4

Table 21.5

Comparison of the explosive properties and thermal stability of two peroxides

Property	Peroxide (IX)	Peroxide (X)
Sensitivity to impact (daJ)	0.4	1.5
Deflagration point	160°C	>200°C
Expansion of the lead block (cm^3 per 10 g)	36	25
Limit diameter in the steel tube with nozzle plates (mm) (Koenen tube)	3.5	1.5
Half life at 120°C (in hours)	28	9

The presence of some explosophore groups may make a substance highly sensitive. Such a one is o-azidobenzoyl peroxide (XI) which, during handling, exploded when touched with a spatula.

There is no parallelism between sensitivity to mechanical actions (impact, friction) on the one hand and chemical stability on the other. For example, the dimer ethylidene peroxide (see 21.2.6) is extremely sensitive to impact but has good chemical stability. Another example is provided by the two peroxides in Table 21.5, where it can be seen that the more explosive substance has better thermal stability than the other.

21.1.6 Active oxygen in peroxides

In the − O − O − group which is to be found in all the peroxides and hydroperoxides, one of the two oxygen atoms may oxidise other substances, so that an important characteristic of a peroxide or of a mixture which contains one or more peroxides is its active oxygen content, which is a measure of its oxidising capacity (or oxidising potential) and is also proportional to the total number of free radicals which can be produced by the substance. However, the active oxygen content must not be confused with what is normally called the 'activity'† of the peroxide, which is linked to the comparative rapidity with which it decomposes and produces radicals. The degree of 'activity' of a peroxide in initiating polymerisations does not depend solely on the concentration of radicals RO* which it provides, but also on the *nature* of those radicals.

Table 21.6 gives some values of active oxygen content. The most dangerous peroxides have a high content (12 to 25%), whilst, conversely, when the content is low (less than 5%), the peroxide has little tendency to explode. However, this property can in no way be used to classify the peroxides from the point of view of comparative danger since some peroxides with a relatively high active oxygen content are scarcely dangerous. At best it allows comparisons to be made in a series of homologues in which the very first terms are often explosives, with the degree of danger falling as one goes up through the series. It can, however, be accepted that peroxides with an active oxygen content of less than 5% present no serious risk of explosion.

The most frequently used method for measuring the active oxygen in a peroxide is based on the oxidation of potassium or sodium iodide

$$R − O − O − R' + 2KI + H_2O = R − O − R' + 2KOH + I_2,$$

the liberated iodine being titrated by the thiosulphate solution. There are a number of variations on this method, depending on the solvent used (acetone, alcohol, acetic acid, etc.) and the temperature or duration of the action. The operating mode described by Nozalki [22] is particularly suitable for a large number of peroxides. It is described in the following paragraph.

To the sample is added 5 to 10 ml of acetic anhydride and 1 g of powdered sodium iodide. The mixture is stirred to dissolve the iodide and then left to rest for 15 minutes. 50 to 75 ml of water are added, the mixture is stirred vigorously, and then the liberated iodine is titrated with sodium thiosulphate in the presence of starch as an indicator.

The iodide method may give a result which contains an error by default when the mixture to titrate contains an unsaturated body, since the iodine then fixes on to the double bonds. In that case, reduction by As_2O_3 can be used, as was done by Siggia [25]. The iodide method is also defective with some highly resistant peroxides such as the cyclic peroxides of acetone (see 21.3.1). The great variety of organic peroxides has made it necessary to develop a number of analytical techniques.

---

† This is not activity in the meaning used in chemical thermodynamics, although there is a certain relationship between the two.

Table 21.6

Active oxygen content of pure organic peroxides

NB - Roman numerals refer to formulae

Peroxide		Active oxygen content (%)
Tertiary butyl hydroperoxide		17.7
Cumene hydroperoxide	(VI)	10.5
p-menthane hydroperoxide	(VIII)	9.3
Tetralin hydroperoxide	(V)	9.7
Cyclohexanone hydroperoxy-peroxide	(L)	13
Methyl ethyl ketone hydroperoxide	(XLV)	15.2
Peracetic acid		21
Monoperoxyphthalic acid	(XXXV)	8.8
Acetyl peroxide	(XIII)	13.5
Propionyl peroxide		10.9
Isononanoyl peroxide		4.67
Decanoyl peroxide		4.3
Lauroyl peroxide		4
Benzoyl peroxide		6.6
Acetyl and benzoyl peroxide		8.8
Acetyl and cyclohexane sulphonyl peroxide	(XXXVI)	7.2
Tertiary butyl peroxide		10.9
Cumene peroxide	(XXXII)	5.9
Tertiary butyl peracetate		12.1
Tertiary butyl perpivalate	(XXXVII)	9.8
Tertiary butyl perbenzoate		8.2
Tertiary butyl permaleate		8.5
Tertiary butyl perisononanoate		6.55
Tertiary butyl peroctoate	(XXXVIII)	6.95
Isopropyl percarbonate	(XLII)	7.75
Cyclohexyl percarbonate	(XLIII)	5.6
2-ethylhexyl percarbonate		4.5
Cetyl percarbonate		2.8
3,3,6,6,9,9-hexamethyl-1,2,4,5-tetraoxacyclononane	(XXXIV)	14.6
Methyl ethyl ketone peroxide	(XLV)	15.2
1-hydroxy-1'-hydroperoxycyclohexyl peroxide	(L)	13

21.1.7 Biological action of organic peroxides

Although the main purpose of this work is to deal with explosions, mention must be made of the important biological risks posed by the peroxides. Their general toxicity is low, with the lethal dose 50% usually being more than 1 g/kg, but most of them cause serious damage to the integuments (skin, mucous membranes, eyes) both in the liquid and the vapour state. A small group, including in particular the peroxides of lauroyl, benzoyl, and tertiary butyl as well as tertiary butyl perbenzoate, have no more than

a passing irritant effect on the eyes, but the other peroxides go more
deeply and cause irreversible damage to the cornea. Particularly dangerous
are the peroxides derived from ketones and hydroperoxides, which, even in
low-concentration solutions, can cause loss of sight in a fairly short
space of time. The same peroxides kill skin cells, causing damage that
heals only very slowly.

Consequently, when handling organic peroxides, great precautions must
be taken (wearing goggles, etc.). Should the body be splashed with them,
the affected parts must be washed with soap without delay, and the eyes in
particular must be washed rapidly and at length (for at least fifteen
minutes) with pure water, or better still with a 2% solution of sodium
bicarbonate.

21.2 THE PRINCIPAL FAMILIES OF ORGANIC PEROXIDES

21.2.1 Nomenclature of the organic peroxides

If one wishes to conform with the official nomenclature of organic
chemistry†, some peroxides would have to be given long and complicated
names. For such substances industry generally uses abbreviated names which
are simpler and more easily understood, but which are not always free of
ambiguity. In this chapter and the next one we shall occasionally make use
of these abbreviated terms marked with an asterisk. A table at the end of
the chapter shows the correspondences between these abridged names and the
correct official names.

21.2.2 Hydroperoxides and peroxides of alkyls and aralkyls

These substances have the formulae (I) and (II) given in 21.1.1, with R
being an alkyl, cycloalkyl, or aralkyl radical. In the hydroperoxides of
the alkyls the hydrogen in the functional group has acidic properties, and
these hydroperoxides can form salts, of which those of barium, lead, and
mercury are often sensitive explosives. Of the primary hydroperoxides of
the alkyls, the first two terms (methyl and ethyl) are volatile liquids,
miscible with water, and strongly explosive (see 21.1.4 for the case of
methyl hydroperoxide $CH_3 - O - OH$).

The mobility of the hydroxyl of the tertiary alcohols, of which the
simplest is tertiary butyl alcohol $(CH_3)_3C - OH$, means that it is an easy
matter to use H_2O_2 in the presence of soda to make hydroperoxides which are
more stable than those of the primary and secondary alkyls. This explains
why only tertiary hydroperoxides are manufactured industrially.

Tertiary butyl hydroperoxide $(CH_3)_3C - O - OH$, prepared in 1938 by
Milas and Harris [21], is a colourless liquid with a strong odour and a
specific gravity equal to about 0.92 g/cm³, which crystallises at $-3°C$ and
is slightly soluble in water. It is very stable at ordinary temperature

---

† One can apply to the organic peroxides either the *substitutive* nomenclature (prefixes: peroxy, hydroperoxy), or the *functional* nomenclature
(- peroxide), or the *replacement* nomenclature (using dioxa, tetraoxa,
etc.).

and easy to distil at reduced pressure (17 mm of mercury at 35°C). At around 95–105°C the vapour of tertiary butyl hydroperoxide begins to decompose in a rather simple way into oxygen and tertiary butyl alcohol. At 190°C the rate of decomposition is still moderate, but at a higher temperature, over 200°C, the products of the decomposition are more complex (methanol, formaldehyde, acetone, methane, etc.). Decomposition is never explosive unless the hydroperoxide is heated in a resistant closed vessel.

By using acyl chlorides on tertiary butyl hydroperoxide in the presence of soda, peroxyesters, such as those mentioned in 22.3.4, are easily obtained.

Of the simple peroxides, methyl peroxide $CH_3 - O - O - CH_3$, which is gaseous at ordinary temperatures (b.p. 14°C), is a highly dangerous substance to manipulate because of its sensitivity to mechanical actions and heat. Liquid ethyl peroxide (b.p. 65°C), although less explosive, is still quite dangerous.

As with the hydroperoxides, it is the tertiary alkyl radicals which give the most stable peroxides. Tertiary butyl peroxide, which has been known since 1945, has only a weak oxidising effect and does not undergo any decomposition up to 80°C. It is a liquid which is insoluble in water, more volatile than the corresponding hydroperoxide, and so stable that it is possible, although not advisable†, to distil it at standard atmospheric pressure at 110°C. It is practically insensitive to impact but ignites easily (flash point 19°C).

21.2.3 The peroxy-acids

Peroxy-acids, or per-acids, are acyl hydroperoxides. Their acid strength is weaker than that of the corresponding organic acids and their oxidising potential is quite strong. The simplest of these per-acids is performic acid $H - CO - O - OH$ which has never been isolated in the pure state and which occurs only in an aqueous solution. It is a liquid which is highly sensitive to impact, even in 75% aqueous solution, and with explosive properties comparable to those of nitroglycerine. It has poor thermal stability and a 75% aqueous solution loses some of its active oxygen in a few hours at ordinary temperature. Solutions over 50% may even explode spontaneously.

The next term is peracetic acid, discovered by D'Ans in 1912, which is formed, at the same time as acetyl peroxide, easily and rapidly by the action of high-strength hydrogen peroxide on acetic anhydride, giving a mixture in which acetic acid, peracetic acid, acetyl peroxide, H_2O_2, and H_2O coexist in chemical equilibrium. A high pH favours the production of acetyl peroxide. In the absence of a strong acid, the equilibrium is reached only after about ten hours.

Pure peracetic acid, a liquid which crystallises at around 0°C, is an explosive substance. Even when cooled to − 20°C, friction will cause it to explode [30]. Two Czech researchers [28] experimenting on a 97.3% solution of acid found that the detonation velocity is 5100 m/s and that in the lead block test (with 10 g) there is an expansion of 215 cm³, which is typical

---

† To avoid any violent decomposition, it is preferable to distil it at reduced pressure: at 200 mm of mercury it distils at around 70°C.

of an explosive of average power. Solutions at more than 80% gradually decompose with release of CO_2, and for safety reasons it is transported only in 40% solutions at most. At this degree of dilution the solution cannot be exploded by a No. 8 detonator. At a concentration of 70% it cannot be heated, even in small quantities in an open vessel, without deflagrating and breaking the container [27].

Perbenzoic acid C_6H_5 – CO – O – OH is a white powder which melts at around 42°C and has several applications in analytical chemistry, but it is highly flammable and must be handled with the same precautions that apply to dry benzoyl peroxide. It has no industrial applications because of its poor thermal stability. We should mention that the auto-oxidation in air of benzaldehyde produces perbenzoic acid and a small amount of benzoyl peroxide, just as the auto-oxidation of furaldehyde produces peroxyfuroic acid (C_4H_3O) – CO – O – OH and furoyl peroxide (C_4H_3O) – CO – O – O – CO – (C_4H_3O).

The diacids generally give only substances with a single hydroperoxide function, such as the one which is derived from succinic acid. This monoperoxysuccinic acid (XII) decomposes quite rapidly at its melting point of 107°C.

21.2.4 Acyl peroxides

Acyl peroxides are to acid anhydrides what per-acids are to organic acids. They can sometimes be obtained by treating the anhydride with H_2O_2, as is the case with acetyl peroxide (XIII), a solid body which melts at 28°C, is highly sensitive to all mechanical actions, and explodes when heated. Its homologues, liquid propionyl peroxide and butyryl peroxide, obtained by the action of acid chlorides on a 10% solution of hydrogen peroxide in the presence of soda, are less dangerous to handle. The higher terms, such as palmitoyl peroxide (melting point 71.5°C) and stearoyl peroxide (melting point 77°C), are practically devoid of explosive properties. Benzoyl peroxide (see 22.3.4) is especially important from both the historical and practical point of view. Acyl peroxides liberate the iodine in potassium iodide and, when cold, take the colour out of acid solutions of potassium permanganate.

A diacid may give two peroxides. For example, from succinic acid are derived peroxydisuccinic acid (XIV), a solid which melts at around 130°C, and acyclic peroxide (XV), which explodes with shattering effects when heated to around 100°C.

21.2.5 Peroxy esters and peroxy carbonates

The general formula for peroxy esters (per-esters) is

R – CO – O – O – R'.

They cannot be obtained by esterifying the per-acid R – CO – O – OH with R'OH, but they are made easily by the reaction between the acid chloride R – CO – Cl and the hydroperoxide R' – O – OH, which is comparable to a Schotten–Baumann reaction.

The reaction in the presence of soda between chloroformates and hydrogen peroxide or hydroperoxides gives two kinds of peroxidised

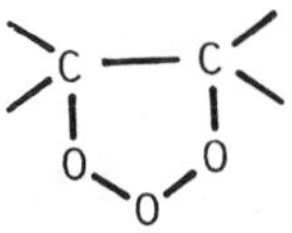

XVIII

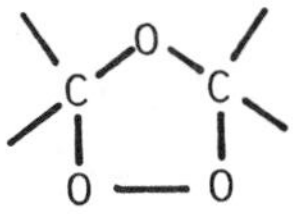

XIX

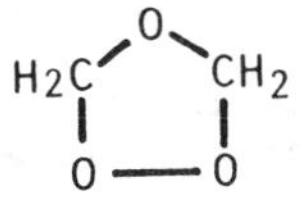

XX

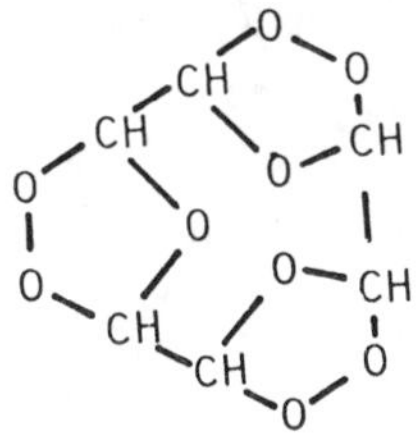

XXI

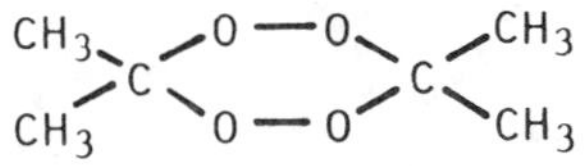

XXII

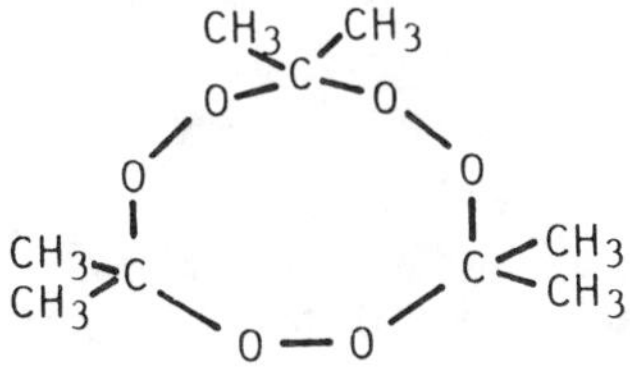

$$CH_3-C\overset{\displaystyle O-O}{\underset{\displaystyle O-O}{}}C\overset{\displaystyle CH_3}{\underset{\displaystyle CH_3}{}}$$

XXIII

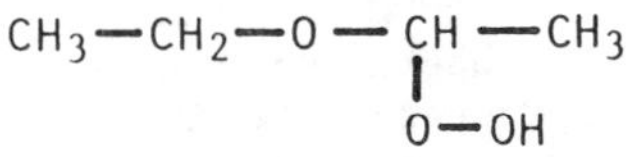

$$CH_3-CH_2-O-\underset{\underset{\displaystyle O-OH}{|}}{CH}-CH_3$$

XXIV

$$CH_3-\underset{\underset{\displaystyle O-OH}{|}}{\overset{\overset{\displaystyle CH_3}{|}}{C}}-O-\underset{\underset{\displaystyle O-OH}{|}}{\overset{\overset{\displaystyle CH_3}{|}}{C}}-CH_3$$

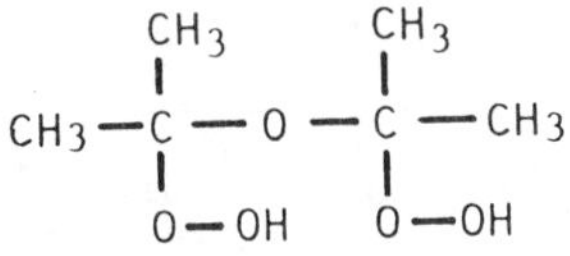

XXV

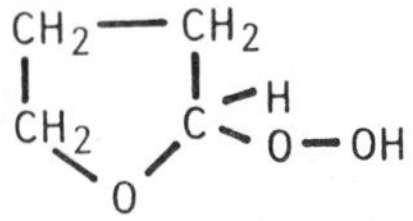

XXVI

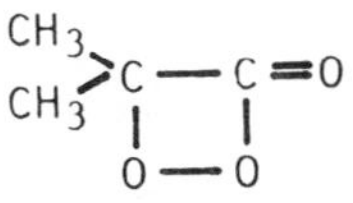

XXVII

derivatives of carbonic acid:

- peroxydicarbonates RO – CO – O – O – CO – OR,
- peroxymonocarbonates R – O – O – CO – OR',

whose acids correspond respectively to peroxydisulphuric acid and peroxy-monosulphuric acid (see 20.2).

Ethyl peroxydicarbonate was obtained in this way in 1925 from ethyl chloroformate. These peroxydicarbonates generally have very poor chemical stability at ordinary temperatures. The peroxymonocarbonates are more stable, such as, for example, isopropyl peroxytertiobutyl carbonate

$$(CH_3)_3C - O - O - CO - O - CH \begin{matrix} \diagup CH_3 \\ \diagdown CH_3 \end{matrix}$$

which can withstand being heated up to 60°C.

21.2.6 Peroxides derived from aldehydes and ketones

An aldehyde reacting with H_2O_2 may, depending on the conditions of the reaction and the proportions of the reagents, give quite a number of peroxidised products, including

- a hydroxy hydroperoxide
- a hydroxy hydroperoxy peroxide
- a dihydroperoxy peroxide
- cyclic diperoxides and triperoxides
- polymers with – O – O – bridges and – OH and – O – OH terminal groups.

For example, H_2O_2 reacting on acetaldehyde in the presence of dehydrating agents forms the dimer ethylidene peroxide (XVI), a solid which melts at 63°C and whose thermal stability depends on the hexagonal ring which it contains.

The simple addition product of a mole of H_2O_2 and a mole of ketone R – CO – R' is an α–hydroxy hydroperoxide

$$\begin{matrix} R \diagdown \diagup OH \\ C \\ \diagup \diagdown \\ R' \quad O - OH \end{matrix}$$

which is practically impossible to isolate since it reacts immediately with the ketone to give

$$\begin{matrix} R \diagdown \diagup O \text{————} O \diagdown \diagup R \\ C \qquad\qquad\qquad C \\ \diagup \diagdown \qquad\qquad \diagup \diagdown \\ R' \quad O - OH \; HO - O \quad R' \end{matrix}$$

which reacts in its turn. Many products are obtained in this way, some of which have a ring structure (see 21.3.1). Acetylacetone* peroxide (XVII), a very stable compound, is easily derived from pentane-2,4-dione by the action of hydrogen peroxide.

21.2.7 The ozonides

The action of ozone (ozonised air or oxygen) at a low temperature on ethylene compounds R – CH = CH – R' dissolved in an anhydrous solvent gives substances which, following Harries (1904), have been called ozonides. They were thought to have an – O – O – O – chain (XVIII). Since the work done by Staudinger (1925) and Griegel, we know that they are epoxydised compounds of peroxides (XIX) and are therefore true peroxides. Their formation is quantitative. The action of hot water, alcohols, and alkalis splits them into molecules of aldehyde, ketone, and acid. The explosive properties of ozonides have been known since they were discovered, but in the pure state they are often less sensitive than had previously been reported, since some of them can be distilled without decomposing. It would seem that certain raw ozonides had been made sensitive by impurities, possibly alkylidene peroxides.

Ethylene ozonide (1,2,4-trioxolan) (XX) is a liquid. The ozonide of maleic anhydride is stable only at around – 60°C and decomposes explosively at higher temperatures. The ozonide derived from benzene (XXI) is an explosive substance which is sensitive to friction and easily hydrolysed into glyoxal. There are also polymer ozonides, of which those with a high molecular weight are insoluble.

On various occasions, in laboratory experiments during which ozonides have formed as intermediate substances, spontaneous explosions have occurred at ordinary temperature. Thus, reactions involving ozone and organic substances must be conducted with great caution.

21.3 ACCIDENTAL AND UNWANTED EXPLOSIONS OF ORGANIC PEROXIDES IN THE LABORATORY

21.3.1 Particularly dangerous peroxides

1° *Acetyl peroxide* $(CH_3 – CO – O)_2$, a solid which is sensitive to impact and melts at 27°C, has been the cause of numerous accidents in laboratories when used in highly concentrated form. Kuhn [23] reports a spontaneous explosion of 5 g of crystallised peroxide which led the chemist who had just taken the flask containing the peroxide from the refrigerator to lose both hands. We know of an accident in which serious injuries were caused by the same peroxide in a laboratory in Paris in 1942. It is a highly sensitive substance which explodes with considerable destructive effect, and yet its calorific value is only average (about 2000 kJ/kg) and its explosion temperature at constant volume is of the order of 1400°C. The R.I.D. allows this peroxide to be transported only in a mixture with at least 75% phlegmatiser.

2° *Acetone peroxides* – Since the work of Wolfenstein (1895) and Baeyer and Villiger (1900), we know that acetone can form, in addition to other products, cyclic peroxides. The dimer peroxide (XXII) melts at 132°C and the trimer (XXIII) at 98°C. They are crystalline substances which are insoluble in water, slightly soluble in alcohol, and soluble in acetone, and they explode violently under the effect of impact or of sudden heating. According to Rieche and Koch [34] the dimer is more sensitive than the trimer. When they are dry, their sensitivity to impact is greater than that of mercury fulminate, and even when wet, with 25% water, they can still be exploded by a sufficiently violent impact. Tests [19] have shown that the trimer, with a density of 0.7 g/cm^3, detonates with a velocity of 3060 m/s.

These peroxides are formed by the action of H_2O_2 or peroxymonosulphuric acid on acetone. They are resistant to potassium iodide and to the other agents which normally destroy the peroxides, a fact which makes them especially dangerous. The dimer peroxide, which is more robust than the trimer, can be subjected to the action of boiling sulphuric acid diluted to 10% without being destroyed.

In his work [20, p. 74), Davies states quite correctly that one should never follow the frequently given instruction to use acetone as a solvent in a reaction involving hydrogen peroxide. We know of a laboratory accident which occurred in Aubervilliers in 1964 during preparation of pyruvic acid by oxidation of acetone using H_2O_2. The oxidation itself, carried out in a large surplus of acetone, went off without incident. It was during the final operation of distillation in a balloon flask heated by a bath of oil to extract the product of the reaction that the acetone peroxide (or peroxides) exploded in the flask.

A later accident, which caused serious injuries, occurred in Finland in 1977 during oxidation of an organic substance placed in an acetone solution using hydrogen peroxide. Naponen [37], who describes it, explains how it was possible to prove that the trimer acetone peroxide (XXIII) had formed during the operation. This substance, which forms very easily and which is highly sensitive to both heat and friction, has been the cause of many other accidental explosions.

3* When conducting research on a new peroxide of which the properties are not yet known, the normal precautions in research on explosives must be taken. The initial tests to prepare the substance should involve only a few grammes, since, even if there is reason to believe that the peroxide being studied has no explosive properties, intermediate reactions during preparation may well form highly unstable peroxides liable to decompose violently. It must not be forgotten that some peroxides are comparable to the primary explosives as regards their sensitivity to friction.

A peroxide should be dried completely only if it is absolutely necessary, since it is often when the substance is very dry that conditions arise, such as the formation of static electricity, which ignite an explosion.

When it is intended to purify a solid peroxide by recrystallisation, taking advantage of its greater solubility at temperatures of 50 to 70°C, one must exercise circumspection in the choice of the solvent, which must be as unreactive as possible. Rather than purifying a peroxide by recrystallisation in a hot solvent, it is preferable, whenever possible, to dissolve the peroxide at ordinary temperature in a suitable solvent and then to precipitate it by addition of another liquid. Thus, Rieche and Schulz [10] obtained pure benzoyl peroxide by precipitation by methanol in a chloroformic solution.

An organic peroxide should be distilled in the laboratory only after making sure that it has adequate stability at the temperature at which one is expecting to work. The operation should be carried out at reduced pressure on only a small quantity of the substance, and the operative should be protected by a good Plexiglas screen.

21.3.2 Explosions caused by ether (ethyl oxide)

21.3.2.1 Preliminary observations

We are not concerned here with gas mixtures of vapours of ethyl oxide (ordinary ether) and air, but with the formation of dangerous peroxides in ether by auto-oxidation, a phenomenon first observed by Schönbein in 1851. When this impure ether is evaporated, there is a concentration of one or more impurities and the residue is liable to explode. Because of the widespread use of ether in extraction (of fats, for example), there have been many cases of explosions in laboratories either during distillation or at the end of evaporation.

21.3.2.2 Conditions of formation of ether peroxide

According to experiments by Perkins and Clover [4] in bottles two-thirds filled, peroxides form in ether exposed to light at an increasing rate, and after several months one may find several units per hundred of peroxide. Light plays an important part in the preliminary stage, but peroxide also forms, albeit less rapidly, in liquid sheltered from light. Indeed, it seems that some peroxides are actually destroyed by light, with the result that the percentage of peroxide in glass containers remains limited.

The reactions which take place are quite complex. Various compounds are formed, none of which is true ethyl peroxide. Clover [4] had the idea, which was confirmed by later research, that the first substance to form is a hydroperoxide (XXIV) with no real explosive properties. Rieche [5] has explained how this substance, through various reactions, forms polymerised alkylidene peroxides, in addition to acetaldehyde and H_2O_2. According to Rieche, the dimer (XVI) in particular is the most sensitive to friction and impact of all the peroxides he has prepared. When the peroxides reach a sufficient level of concentration in the ether, the liquid may explode violently, causing damage to equipment and injuries to people. These explosions occur in particular when ether is heated, after an extraction or a reaction in which it is used as a solvent, in order to remove it by distillation. The explosion occurs at around 90°C. The effect of heating is to transform moderately sensitive hydroperoxide into highly sensitive alkylidene peroxide.

21.3.2.3 Detecting and titrating peroxides in ether

In addition to the general reaction of liberating iodine from iodides and colouring with titanium sulphate, we have at our disposal several highly sensitive reactions for detecting the presence of peroxides in ether. Here are just two of them:
(a) According to O'Brien [2], the reaction with ferric thiocyanate can be conducted as follows: ferrous sulphate and potassium thiocyanate (formerly called sulphocyanide) are dissolved in water. Just before using it, the substance is made colourless by adding a small amount of powdered zinc. When it is added to ether, the solution takes on a pink or red colour of varying intensity depending on the quantity of peroxide present.

(b) Rieche [5] recommends the formation of benzidine blue: to 5 ml of a
cold, saturated solution of benzidine are added 5 ml of a saturated
solution of NaCl and a few drops of a diluted solution of ferrous sulphate
(a pin-head sized crystal in 5 ml of water). Adding one or two drops of
ether containing peroxides gives a distinct blue colour after a few
minutes, or immediately if a large amount of peroxide is present.

Measuring the precise amount of peroxides in ether is difficult for a
number of reasons. With the iodide method, iodine is liberated only quite
slowly, so that, according to Nozalki, the quantity of iodine released
should be measured only after several hours (12, for example). King [12]
has proposed the following method: 5 to 10 ml of the ether to be tested
are added to 50 ml of more or less normal sulphuric acid together with a
few crystals of $MnSO_4$. A well-stirred solution of decinormal permanganate
is then slowly added. Titration is finished when a pink colour persists
for at least 10 seconds after adding two drops of permanganate.

21.3.3 Auto-oxidation of isopropyl oxide

Isopropyl ether, which has the formula $(CH_3)_2CH - O - CH(CH_3)_2$, is a liquid
(b.p. 66.7°C) lighter than water which has been manufactured industrially
since 1930. It has given rise to frequent explosions because of peroxides
which are formed even more readily and rapidly than those in ethyl oxide.
The product to form first is a dihydroperoxide (XXV) which is relatively
stable and can be heated to around 150°C without exploding, but which is
gradually transformed into cyclic peroxides of acetone from which can be
extracted crystals of the dimer peroxide (melting point 132°C) and the
trimer peroxide (melting point 98°C). Two serious explosions have been
reported by Morgan and Pickard [6] who analysed the product and found that
it contained up to 8% peroxide. Rieche and Koch [34] found 15% by weight
of peroxide in isopropyl oxide that had been stored for eight years in a
tin drum.

Hunter and Downing [8] have established that the auto-oxidation of
isopropyl oxide occurs just as readily in darkness as in light. Hamstead
and Van Delinder [11] have found that the substance can be stabilised by a
variety of anti-oxidants (ethylenediamine, morpholine, etc.) and recommend
in particular the use of N-benzyl paraminophenol.

21.3.4 Auto-oxidation of various ether oxides

It seems to be generally the case that all ether oxides, acyclic or cyclic,
aldehyde acetals $R(OR')_2$, and ketone acetals $RR'(OR'')_2$ are prone to
auto-oxidation. Schenck [14] has shown that cold oxygen can transform
furan into a peroxide, $C_8H_8O_4$, which decomposes at around 100°C, whilst
tetrahydrofuran readily produces a hydroperoxide (XXVI) which has been
isolated by Robertson [15] and is a viscous liquid decomposed by heating
from around 70-80°C. It forms so readily that it can be detected in
freshly distilled tetrahydrofuran after only a few hours using ordinary
reagents with peroxides. Rein [16] has reported the case of an explosion
of a still hot residue left behind in a balloon flask after distillation of

tetrahydrofuran. Criegee [17] suggests that prolonged heating transformed the hydroperoxide into a highly explosive polymer alkylidene peroxide.

An accident occurred in a laboratory in Paris in September 1951 during purification of 400 ml of tetrahydrofuran placed in a 500 ml balloon flask surmounted by a rectifying column and heated in a water bath. After heating, some 40 ml of liquid remained in the flask. Five to ten minutes later the flask filled with smoke in less than one second, and then there was an explosion. At no time had the temperature of the water bath risen above 70°C.

As with ordinary ether, it is at the end of distillation that the unstable substance explodes spontaneously. It is therefore advisable to take the same precautions with tetrahydrofuran as with ether. Any hydroperoxide present in the substance can be easily destroyed by the action on the solvent of a solution of ferrous sulphate or soda. Given that tetrahydrofuran is often used as a solvent and that peroxides readily initiate violent reactions with the reagents, it is advisable, when using the substance, to cleanse it completely of all peroxide. Failure to take this precaution caused an accident in 1971.

Methyl tetrahydrofuran (b.p. 78°C) gives an explosive hydroperoxide even more readily than tetrahydrofuran. After several months the peroxide content in the solvent may be as much as 20% [18]. According to two Russian authors [31], auto-oxidation of dioxane at 25°C gives a solution of hydroperoxide which, if left to itself, is transformed into a dimer, and at 50°C a dihydroperoxide. Although in normal conditions these peroxides are formed only in limited quantities, with equilibrium being reached rapidly according to Macfarlane and Fuoss [32], they are still undesirable because they may cause an explosion, and in any case the presence of peroxide should be avoided since it may disturb a reaction taking place in dioxane being used as a solvent.

Since peroxides may be present in ether and similar oxides, a suitable desiccating agent should be used to dehydrate them. Lithium aluminium hydride should not be used.

The danger posed by the presence of peroxides in ethers led to the adoption by the R.I.D. in 1954 of a regulation which limits to 0.3% (measured as H_2O_2) the maximum level of peroxides permitted to be present in a flammable liquid, since a fire during transport might heat the contents of a tank to produce a kind of fractional distillation leaving behind a peroxide-rich, explosive residue.

21.3.5 Preventing the formation of and destroying peroxides in solvents

It is difficult to prevent the auto-oxidation of ether oxides and other solvents, but it can be slowed down and reduced by a variety of means:

1° In the first place, it is advisable not to keep for too long flasks containing only a small residue of liquid in the presence of a large quantity of air. Ether should be kept in containers filled to leave only the minimal margin (ullage) compatible with the need to allow a gaseous volume to exist at the highest temperature likely to be reached. If possible, the liquid should be put in a nitrogen atmosphere. Opaque containers are preferable, since peroxides often form much less rapidly in vessels made of brown-coloured glass than in those made of clear glass.

2° If it is not inconvenient for the intended use, it is possible to add anti-oxygens to the ether. Pyrogallol has been recommended for this purpose [1] since, at a strength of 0.1 mg per 100 ml, it considerably retards the formation of peroxides as well as other phenols (hydroquinone, naphthols) and diphenylamine.   Soda also acts as a stabiliser;   ether stored over sodium does not peroxidise.

MacCullough [7] observed that the formation of peroxide in a flask can be avoided if a copper wire is placed in the container. This has been denied by a number of authors, including Hunter and Downing [8], although the latter have found that iron filings do prevent formation of peroxides, and it does seem that only small amounts of peroxide form in ether stored in steel tanks.

3° Many methods have been proposed for removing peroxides from a solvent:

(a) the liquid is left to digest on a mixture of powdered potassium hydroxide and permanganate and is then distilled;

(b) the liquid is agitated with a solution of potassium iodide, which provides good elimination of the hydroperoxides;

(c) the liquid is agitated with a solution of ferrous salt which acts as a decomposing catalyst on peroxides; in the case of ether, this stirring may make the liquid boil because of the heat released by decomposition of the peroxides;

(d) many other procedures have been proposed: agitation with a solution of thiosulphate, digestion on cerous hydroxide, etc.

However, cyclic peroxides which are polymers of aldehydes and ketones often withstand these reagents. Criegee says that prolonged agitation with a solution of ferrous sulphate in 50% sulphuric acid is more effective.

An interesting procedure, since it introduces no water into an anhydrous solvent, is passage through a column of alumina gel which retains peroxides [13]. Silica gel has also been proposed.

Finally, peroxide-free solvents remain in that state as long as they are stored on a bed of sodium threads.

As has already been said, the peroxides present in a liquid normally explode at the end of distillation, which is why Williams [3] quite rightly states as a rule that ether should never be distilled until dry. It is advisable to follow this rule whenever one is distilling a solvent which is likely to contain peroxides. On this subject, it should not be thought that the explosive decomposition of peroxides can be avoided by carrying out distillation at a reduced pressure, and therefore at a temperature lower than at ordinary pressure. The opposite may happen. For example, when tetrahydronaphthalene (tetralin) is being distilled at atmospheric pressure, the liquid must be raised to 208°C so that any small quantities of peroxides it might contain are destroyed by heating at around 200°C. If distillation is carried out at around 80°C at a pressure of 12 mm of mercury, any peroxides present remain in the liquid and explode at the end of the operation. If it is thought useful to create a slow bubbling in the liquid to regularise distillation, argon or nitrogen rather than air should be injected through a capillary tube, since an explosion has been reported during distillation with a vacuum water pump of tetralin which had been checked before the operation and found to be free of peroxides. However, the flask was fitted with a capillary letting air into the apparatus, and that caused the heated hydrocarbon to auto-oxidise.

If one has to distil a volatile solvent, or a mixture after a reaction, which is suspected of containing dangerous peroxides, one can add to the liquid before the operation a fair quantity, for example an equal volume, of a hydrocarbon with a high boiling point which will retain the peroxides in a diluted solution at the end of distillation when most of the volatile constituents have been removed. Care must be taken not to heat the liquid too much at the end of the operation.

21.3.6 Auto-oxidation of various compounds

Many substances other than the ether oxides may undergo auto-oxidation in air leading to the creation of explosive peroxides. This is the case with most ethylene compounds. For example, vinylidene chloride $CH_2 = CCl_2$ stored in the presence of air peroxidises if a stabiliser has not been added. Acyclic olefins oxidise in this way all the more readily as they are more branched. Cyclic olefins (for example, cyclohexene) also give peroxides in air, as do diolefins. Special mention must be made of dienes with conjugated double bonds which in the presence of oxygen give rise to copolymerisation, producing the polymers

$$- M - O - O - M - O - O - M -$$
or $$- M - M - O - O - M - M - O - O -,$$

where M designates the monomer unit. Butadiene in particular gives rise to a peroxide in this way because it is insoluble in the hydrocarbon from which it is derived, separates out in solid form, and is highly sensitive to impact. Adding anti-oxygens, such as phenols, prevents this process of auto-oxidation-polymerisation (see 27.4.2).

Aromatic hydrocarbons (xylene and cumene but not benzene) or hydro-aromatic hydrocarbons (decalin, tetralin, etc.) oxidise in the same way. The case has been quoted of an accident caused by leaving a layer of tetralin on the bottom of an apparatus. The substance peroxidised and then exploded when the apparatus was used subsequently.

Although less prone to auto-oxidation than ethers, alcohols, especially the secondary and tertiary alcohols, may, after long storage, contain peroxides if no special precaution has been taken (such as storing it in a nitrogen atmosphere) to protect them completely from the action of oxygen in the air. A case has been reported [38] of an explosion that occurred during distillation at ordinary pressure of 2-butanol (secondary butyl alcohol with a boiling point of 99.6°C). Measurements made after the accident showed that the contents of the storage tank from which the alcohol came contained 12% peroxide.

Ketocetenes also auto-oxidise readily to produce dangerous substances such as dimethylcetene peroxide (XXVII).

Table 21.7

Commercial or abbreviated names of organic peroxides

Commercial Name	Designation in the nomenclature of organic chemistry
Acetylacetone (peroxide)	3,5-dimethyl-3,5-dihydroxy-1,2-dioxolan
Caprylyl (peroxide)	Octanoyl peroxide
Cetyl (percarbonate)	Hexadecyl peroxydicarbonate
Cumene (hydroperoxide)	2-hydroperoxy-2-phenylpropane
Cumyl (hydroperoxide)	"
Cumene (peroxide)	2,5-dimethyl-2,5-diphenyl-3,4-dioxahexane
Cumyl (peroxide)	"
Isononanoyl (peroxide)	3,5,5-trimethylhexanoyl peroxide
Metadiisopropylbenzene (hydroperoxide)	2-hydroperoxy-2(3-isopropylphenyl)propane
Myristyl (percarbonate)	Tetradecyl peroxydicarbonate
Paramenthane (hydroperoxide)	8-paramenthanyl hydroperoxide
Pelargonyl (peroxide)	Nonanoyl peroxide
Percarbonates	Peroxydicarbonates
t-butyl perethylhexanoate	t-butyl-2-ethylperhexanoate
t-butyl perisononanoate	t-butyl 3,5,5-trimethylperoxyhexanoate
t-butyl permaleate	t-butyl monoperoxymaleate
t-butyl perneodecanoate	mixture of per-esters with the formulae $$(CH_3)_3C - O - O - CO - \overset{R_1}{\underset{R_2}{C}} - CH_3$$ with $R_1 + R_2 = C_7H_{15}$
t-butyl peroctoate	t-butyl 2-ethylperhexanoate
Succinyl (peroxide)	Peroxydisuccinic acid
Stearyl (percarbonate)	Octodecyl peroxydicarbonate
Tetralin (hydroperoxide)	1-hydroperoxy-1,2,3,4-tetrahydronaphthalene
Diacetone alcohol (peroxide)	2-hydroperoxy-4-methyl-2,4-pentanediol (main component)
Phthalide (peroxide)	Phenyl phthalide tertiary butyl peroxide

BIBLIOGRAPHICAL REFERENCES

[1]   Roy, A. (1955) J. Appl. Chem. 5 188
[2]   O'Brien, J. L. (1955) Chem. Eng. News 33 2008
[3]   Williams, E. C. (1936) J. Soc. Chem. Ind. 55 580
[4]   Clover, A. M. (1922) J. Am. Ch. Soc. 44 1107
[5]   Rieche, A. (1931) Ang. Chem. 44 896
[6]   Morgan, G. T. & Pickard, R. H. (1936) Chem. and Ind. 55 421
[7]   MacCullough, A. F. (1936) Chem. and Ind. 14 964
[8]   Hunter, W. & Downing, J. (1949) J. Soc. Chem. Ind. 68 362
[9]   Guillet, J. E. & Meyer, M. F. (1962) Ind. Eng. Ch. Prod. Research
       Develop. 1 226
[10]   Rieche, A. & Schulz, M. (1959) Chem. Tech. 11 264
[11]   Hamstead, A. C. & Van Delinder, L. S. (1960) J. Chem. Eng. Data 5 383
[12]   King, H. (1929) J. Chem. Soc., p. 738
[13]   Dasler, W. & Bauer, C. D. (1946) Analyt. Chem. 18 52
[14]   Schenck, G. O. (1943) Naturwiss. 31 387
[15]   Robertson, A. (1948) Nature 162 153
[16]   Rein, A. (1950) Angew. Chem. 62 120
[17]   Criegee, R. (1950) Angew. Chem. 62 120
[18]   Société des Usines de Melle, personal communication
[19]   Rohrlich, M. & Sauermilch, W. (1943) Z. Ges. Schiess u. Sprengst.
       38 97
[20]   Karnojitzki, V. (1958) Les peroxydes organiques. Hermann, Paris;
       Hawkins, E. G. C. (1961) Organic Peroxides. E. & F. Spon Ltd., London
       Davies, A. G. (1961) Organic Peroxides. Butterworth, London
[21]   Milas, N. A. & Harris, S. A. (1938) J. Am. Ch. Soc. 60 2434
[22]   Nozalki, K. (1946) Analyt. Chem. 18 583
[23]   Kuhn, L. P. (1948) Chem. Eng. News 26 3197
[24]   Bell, E. R., Dickey, F. H. et al. (1949) Ind. Eng. Ch. 41 2597
[25]   Siggia, S. (1947) Analyt. Chem. 19 872
[26]   Jaffe, L, Prosen, E. J. & Szwarc, M. (1957) J. Chem. Physics 27 416
[27]   Hackel, J., Kutkiewic, M. & Kuboscek, R. (1964) Przemysl. Chem.
       43 262
[28]   Havel, S. & Greshner, J. (1966) Chem. Prum. 16 203
[29]   Carson, A. S., Laye, P. G. & Morris, H. (1975) J. Chem.
       Thermodynamics 7 993
[30]   Leadbeater, R. J. (1956) Bull. Soc. Chim. Fr., p. 1285
[31]   Varfolomeeva, E. K. & Zolotova, Z. G. (1960) C.A. 54 14254
[32]   Macfarlane, R. & Fuoss, R. (1955) J. Am. Ch. Soc. 77 2194
[33]   Hock, H. & Knauek, G. (1951) Ber. 84 1
[34]   Rieche, A. & Koch, K. (1942) Ber. 75 1016
[35]   Baker, G. et al. (1965) J. Ch. Soc., p. 6970
[36]   Mohan, V. K., Becker, K. R. & Hay, J. E. (1982) J. of Hazardous mat.
       5 197
[37]   Naponen, A. (1977) Chem. Eng. News 55 No. 8, 5
[38]   Peterson, D. (1981) Chem. Eng. News 59 No. 19, 3

22

Commercial organic peroxides

22.1 GENERAL OBSERVATIONS ON COMMERCIAL PEROXIDES

22.1.1 Introductory observations

Of the thousands of organic peroxides known, most have no industrial application, either because their cost price is too high, or because they do not readily lend themselves to the reactions for which peroxides are generally used, or because manufacturing and handling them would be too dangerous since they are sensitive explosives lacking in thermal stability. This latter property, however, is not an insuperable disadvantage. Since 1960, peroxides have been sold which would decompose rapidly, not to say dangerously, at ordinary temperatures, but which are stored at a low enough temperature for decomposition to be unnoticeable.

Some peroxides are put on the market just as they are immediately after manufacture, since the uses to which they will be put do not require prior purification. They are called 'technical grade products' and their purity rarely reaches 98%. Indeed, they sometimes contain as much as 10 to 25% of the raw material from which they are made or of the intermediate product (see 22.3.1.2. for the case of cumene hydroperoxide*). In this form, many peroxides pose risks which it is thought necessary to reduce by dilution with another substance, giving more manageable substances which are known as 'preparations' and which may be one of the following:
- a solution in a solvent (hydrocarbon or other) with a boiling point below 150°C and a flash point generally below 55°C;
- a mixture with a liquid with a high boiling point called a *phlegmatiser* because it reduces the sensitivity of the product to impact;
- a mixture with a solid substance in powdered form which is chemically inert, such as calcium carbonate or finely-powdered silica, or with a soft substance which gives a good covering (stearic acid, for example);

- the peroxide mixed with a certain quantity of water, but never too much since beyond a certain point the mixture obtained is not homogeneous.

The first peroxide to be manufactured industrially was benzoyl peroxide in 1900.   It was then used mainly to bleach oils and flours.   Peroxides developed only after 1930 and in particular after 1945.   Quite a large number of peroxides or peroxide preparations are needed to satisfy a wide range of needs, since the nature of the radical supplied by a peroxide plays a part in polymerisation processes.   There are some fifty peroxides on the market, with sales of several thousand tons a year, to which must be added the very large quantities of substances manufactured for on-the-spot transformation, such as cumene hydroperoxide*.

Organic peroxides are used mainly as catalysts† in the polymerisation of compounds with ethylene bonds or of other substances which can be polymerised in the plastics and synthetic resins industry.   When used in the manufacture of objects made of polyester resin, they are called 'hardeners'.   However, peroxides are also used to bleach natural or artificial textiles, and also for epoxidation or oxidation reactions in organic chemistry, for example in the manufacture of diphenic acid from anthracene.

A large number of monomers are used to produce plastic materials or 'prepolymerised' substances used to make resins, and each monomer or mixture of monomers requires appropriate conditions for polymerisation which also depend on the use to which the end product will be put.   This explains the need for 'catalysts' with a wide variety of activities and properties, something which can be achieved easily thanks to the large number of organic peroxides which can be manufactured nowadays, and to the various diluents or phlegmatisers which can be used in varying percentages to obtain commercial products adapted to all needs.   Use has also been made of 'preparations' containing two peroxides: the first, which is present in small quantities and has a low decomposition temperature (10 to 30°C), starts the polymerisation process which is then continued, as the temperature rises, by the other peroxide which has a higher decomposition temperature (over 50°C).   One example of such a preparation is that which brings together lauroyl peroxide and acetyl sulphonyl cyclohexane peroxide or isopropyl peroxydicarbonate, which combines the advantages of the two 'catalysts' in the mixture.

22.1.2 Phlegmatisers and solvents used with peroxides

Table 22.1 lists a number of properties of the main phlegmatisers used in the organic peroxide industry.   The R.I.D. accepts as phlegmatisers only liquids with a flash point of at least 100°C and a boiling point higher than 150°C.   It is useful to have a variety of phlegmatisers in order to be able to choose one which meets the requirements in each particular case.

Adding a phlegmatiser to a peroxide gives a solution which is less sensitive to mechanical action and which has a lower vapour pressure and,

---

† It is standard practice to call peroxides 'catalysts' when they are used in polymerisation, but the term is not strictly accurate, since the reaction involves the R − O − O − R peroxide, leaving R − O residues in the end product of the polymerisation.

Table 22.1

Phlegmatisers for organic peroxides

Substance	Formula	Specific gravity at 20°C (g/cm³)	Normal boiling point (°C)	Flash point (c) (°C)
Methyl phthalate	$C_6H_4(CO_2CH_3)_2$	1.19	282	150
Ethyl phthalate	$C_6H_4(CO_2C_2H_5)_2$	1.11	296	160
Butyl phthalate	$C_6H_4(CO_2C_4H_9)_2$	1.05	app. 365	165
2-ethyl hexyl phthalate (a)	$C_6H_4(CO_2C_8H_{17})_2$	0.98	app. 385	270 app.
Triethyl phosphate	$PO_4(C_2H_5)_3$	1.07	app. 212	115
Tributyl phosphate	$PO_4(C_4H_9)_3$	0.973	app. 293	140
Tricresyl phosphate (b)	$PO_4(C_6H_4 - CH_3)_3$	1.2	app. 410	240
Butyl maleate	$(CH - CO - O - C_4H_9)_2$	1	app. 280	140

(a) In commerce, this product is often called octyl phthalate (or secondary octyl phthalate).
(b) This product is a mixture of the isomers obtained from the three cresol isomers.
(c) Values of flash points to ± 5°C.

therefore, a much higher flash point. However, the presence of a phlegmatiser has only a negligible effect on the chemical stability of the peroxide. If a stabilised peroxide decomposes, the pressure produced in a closed container is lower than that which would be produced by the crude product, and the rate of deflagration is also reduced.

Thus, a phlegmatiser is not a stabiliser. Organic peroxides, like blowing agents (see 29.3.4), are different from other unwanted explosives in that their instability forms the very basis of their use, so that a peroxide should not be stabilised chemically as is done with intentional explosives (nitrocellulose powder) or with other unwanted explosives.

A solvent with a boiling point below 150°C is not a phlegmatiser. Such a solvent, also called a diluent, must be chemically inert in relation to the peroxide to which it is added and must be only moderately volatile in order to prevent the solution from becoming rich in peroxide through loss of solvent by evaporation in ordinary conditions of storage.

The nature of the solvent or the phlegmatiser in which a peroxide is dissolved has considerable influence on the rate of decomposition by heating, as is seen in tests in the covered Dutch container. For example, propionyl peroxide in a 25% solution with hexane (b.p. 68°C) breaks the disk with a 15 mm aperture, whereas in a 25% solution in a hydrocarbon which boils at over 100°C , the disk does not break with a 1 mm aperture. Similar observations are made with solutions of peroxy-esters in benzene, where decomposition is violent, and in a mineral oil with a high boiling point, where decomposition is calm. These differences in behaviour arise from the fact that heating rapidly expels volatile solvent, leaving peroxide in a strong concentration. By contrast, in a less volatile solvent heated peroxide is in a diluted state and decomposes more calmly.

It is sometimes believed that adding a phlegmatiser which boils at around 300°C gives greater safety than adding the same concentration of a solvent which boils between 80 and 150°C and is chemically inert in relation to the peroxide. This is not always the case, and there may be some advantage in dissolving a peroxide which decomposes at an appreciable but still relatively moderate rate at a given temperature θ in a solvent with a normal boiling point close to θ, since, if decomposition is initiated by accident (for example, as the result of a metallic impurity falling into the solution) when the peroxide is not under confinement (a container which is open or which gives way at low pressure), the rise in temperature as the decomposition accelerates will evaporate the solvent, and this vaporisation will become considerable when the boiling point of the solvent is reached. At that point the decomposition of the peroxide stops accelerating, and a state is established in which there is compensation between the endothermic phenomenon of the vaporisation of the solvent and the exothermic reaction of the decomposition of the peroxide. Such a state is similar to that which is observed in the decomposition of constant pressure of molten ammonium nitrate (see 23.2.5). Thus, the choice of an appropriate solvent and a suitable concentration makes it possible to remove the risk of an explosion.

The following example will make this point clear. Suppose a peroxide with a molar mass of 180 and a heat of decomposition equal to 170 kJ/mol is placed in a 25% solution with heptane, a hydrocarbon with a molar mass of 100 and a normal boiling point of 98°C. The solution contains 5.4 moles of C_7H_{16} per mole of peroxide. Thermal decomposition of the peroxide produces gases which carry off heptane vapour and liquids which remain dissolved and which, being in small quantity, change the boiling point only slightly.

When boiling point is reached, since the heat of vaporisation of heptane is 32.6 kJ/mol, each mole of peroxide in decomposing causes the vaporisation of 170/32.6 = 5.2 moles of heptane, a value which is lower than the ratio of 5.4 given above, which means that decomposition can continue until all the peroxide has disappeared without the temperature ever rising above that of the boiling point of the solvent. At such a temperature the process does not become explosive.

It is possible to determine the percentage of phlegmatiser or solvent necessary to reduce the sensitivity to impact of a peroxide in a given ratio. Guillet and Meyer [4] have used an apparatus designed by themselves (see 15.2.5) to test various peroxides with inert liquids added by subjecting the mixture to the impact of a 6.8 kg weight falling from 0.75 m and measuring the volume of gases produced by the explosion. This volume compared with that produced by pure peroxide gives a measure of the rate of decomposition. Fig. 22.1 shows how this volume varies as a function of concentration in the case of tertiary butyl peracetate with benzene added. It can be seen that as the concentration in peroxide rises from 60 to 70%, the rate of decomposition rises from 10 to 75%.

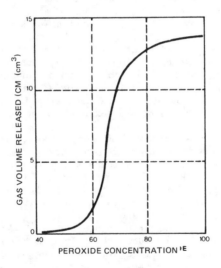

Fig. 22.1 – Rate of decomposition under impact of tertiary butyl peracetate with benzene added.

22.1.3 Peroxides wetted with water

As with other unwanted explosives, adding water reduces the sensitivity to impact of peroxides and slows down the spread of decomposition in a fire. However, only a limited amount of water can be added to a solid peroxide, since beyond a certain percentage there is sedimentation of the solid and formation of a layer of water above it, which is scarcely useful. The quantity of water that can be retained by a peroxide varies with the fineness of the grains but rarely exceeds 25%. Fortunately, however, a relatively low water content reduces the risks considerably. For example, cyclohexanone peroxide* containing 5 to 10% water is no longer liable to explode in a fire when it is in unconfined packing. Benzoyl peroxide wetted with 10% water explodes in the Sevran drop weight test only under the effect of an impact energy ten times greater than is required for the dry product. According to experiments by Chester et al. [6], this peroxide with 3% water decomposes only slowly in a closed vessel when it is ignited by melting a nichrome wire, whilst with 5% water the same source is unable to ignite it. Thus, from the safety point of view, adding water is highly effective, but unfortunately the presence of water in a peroxide is often incompatible with its uses.

Solid peroxides can also be mixed with a viscous liquid to form a paste which burns less rapidly in a fire than pure peroxide. Such pastes are made with phthalates, tricresyl phosphates, alkyl phosphates, or silicone oil.

22.1.4 ACCELERATORS AND INHIBITORS

In the manufacture of plastics and artificial resins, the name *accelerator* or *activator* is given to catalysts which accelerate the decomposition of peroxides into radicals by reducing the activation energy of the reaction of decomposition. Peroxides which normally decompose only at temperatures between 60 and 120°C can be used at ordinary temperature with such accelerators. The most commonly used belong to two groups:

1° Salts of iron, nickel, or cobalt which are soluble in organic solvents, such as cobalt napththenate or octoate† in a 1 to 6% solution in xylene or styrene; these solutions are used especially with methyl ethyl ketone peroxide and other ketone peroxides to achieve cold setting of certain resins.

2° Arylamines, such as dimethylaniline, in solution in phthalate or styrene; they are used in particular with benzoyl peroxide. Alkylamines and heterocyclic amines such as piperidine are also used.

Activators do not work with all peroxides. Thus, cobalt salts are practically without effect on acyl peroxides, although the latter react rapidly with tertiary amines. The chemical mechanisms of activation are, in effect, different from one class of activator to another.

In some industrial polymerisation processes involving peroxides, use is made of an *inhibitor* which slows down the polymerisation of the monomer (or of the mixture of monomers) and so lengthens the setting time, which is often an advantage. Indeed, commercial unsaturated resins for polyesters generally contain a small amount of inhibitor without which they would slowly polymerise during storage. Phenols and quinones constitute good inhibitors.

22.1.5 Peroxides with poor stability at ordinary temperature

Peroxide producers have tried to offer users 'catalysts' able to trigger a polymerisation reaction without the need to heat the reactive mixture. Such

---

† Octoate is the term often used commercially to designate the salt of 2-ethyl hexanoic acid.

'catalysts', which must be active between 10 and 25°C, are often peroxides having poor stability at these temperatures.   However, the commercial importance of these unstable peroxides, called 'low-temperature peroxides' in industry, has increased considerably since 1960.   They must be stored and transported at suitably low temperatures.   Since this low temperature needed to prevent dangerous decomposition must be constantly controlled, which means, if it is achieved by an appropriate refrigerating system, that the regulating mechanism must be faultless, it is called the 'control temperature'.   Table 22.2 lists those peroxides which require a control temperature and the value below which it must be kept.

For many of them it is important to ensure that cooling is not so great that it produces fractional crystallisation of the peroxide dissolved in a solvent or a phlegmatiser, since such crystals, which would separate out, are much more sensitive to mechanical effects than the solution from which they come, and it would be quite difficult to re-dissolve them.   With these products, then, there is a minimum temperature below which they must not be taken.   For example, technically pure tertiary butyl perpivalate must be stored between 0 and 25°C since it freezes at around – 10°C.   A 25% solution of the same peroxide in a hydrocarbon begins to crystallise only at around – 20°C.   Acetyl peroxide in a 25% solution in phthalate must not be cooled to below – 10°C, otherwise it deposits highly sensitive crystals of pure peroxide.

The transport of peroxides unstable at ordinary temperatures requires the use either of refrigerated vehicles or of containers surrounded by a refrigerant mixture.   They must be stored in warehouses maintained at a low temperature and organised in such a way that, if refrigeration should be interrupted for several hours, the stored products are only slightly heated, allowing time for emergency intervention using liquid nitrogen or dry ice.

22.1.6 Thermal stability tests for commercial organic peroxides

The practical question to which thermal stability tests must give an answer can be expressed as follows: what is the value of the ambient temperature which must not be exceeded during storage or transport in order to prevent the dangerous decomposition of a peroxide or a peroxide preparation?

From what has been said in Chapter 3 and in 16.3.3, there can be no valid unqualified answer to this question.   A temperature not to be exceeded can be fixed only for a *given mass* of substance housed in a *given container* which is itself placed in a given environment (for example, in an external protective packing) which more or less opposes dissipation to the external medium of the heat released by decomposition of the peroxide. Although it is not always stated explicitly, what is intended is a mass of 10 to 40 kg of peroxide in a commercial-style packing.

A test [2] has been used in the United States since 1964 to determine what has been called the 'self-accelerating decomposition temperature' or S.A.D.T., which is the lowest temperature at which a peroxide in its packing can decompose.   This test is carried out on the largest type of commercial packing that is actually intended to be used for the transport of the peroxide under consideration.   It is placed with its normal contents in an oven set to a given temperature and left for seven days, unless the peroxide decomposes beforehand, in which case another test is conducted at

Table 22.2

Self-accelerating decomposition temperatures of various commercial organic peroxides

	Decomposition temperature S.A.D.T. (°C)	Control temperature must not exceed (°C)
3,3,6,6,9,9-hexamethyl-1,2,4,5-tetraoxacyclononane	140	(a)
Tertiary butyl peroxide	> 110	(a)
Benzoyl peroxide	88	(a)
Lauroyl peroxide	55	(a)
Isononanoyl peroxide* (80% solution)	20	0
Octanoyl peroxide	25	+ 10
Propionyl peroxide (75% solution)	20	+ 2
Acetyl cyclohexane sulphonyl peroxide	15 to 20	- 5
Tertiary butyl perbenzoate	60	(a)
Tertiary butyl perisononanoate*	60	(a)
Tertiary butyl peroctoate*	35	20
Tertiary butyl perpivalate	25	- 5
Tertiary butyl hydroperoxide	88	(a)
Cumene hydroperoxide*	> 80	(a)
Cetyl percarbonate*	40	30
Cyclohexyl percarbonate*	30	15
2-ethylhexyl percarbonate	0	- 15
Isopropyl percarbonate*	10	- 18

(a) With these peroxides there is no risk that ordinary storage temperatures will cause dangerous decomposition.

a lower temperature. Thermocouples record the temperature both in the peroxide and in the oven, where the temperature is kept as uniform as possible by means of good external heat insulation and a small fan moving the air on the inside. Dangerous decomposition is considered not to have occurred if, during the test, the temperature of the peroxide remains the same as that of the oven or is only a few degrees higher. Just two tests are sufficient if the peroxide withstands heating at the lower temperature but decomposes at the higher and the difference between the two temperatures is no greater than 10°C. A note is made of the violence of the decomposition observed, which may consist of ignition followed by combustion, a relatively calm but persistent release of gases, or a violent decomposition which damages the packing and often also the oven.

Like all full-scale tests, this S.A.D.T. test has the advantage of putting the product being tested in exactly the same conditions it will be in during transport or storage, and in particular leaves it in contact with the material of the container in which it will be kept, whereas in the laboratory tests described above it is placed in a Pyrex container. But the test is not without risk and may be quite costly, with the result that in Europe laboratory tests are preferred which are carried out on moderate quantities of substance and so designed that the results can be used to draw valid conclusions for the practical problem under consideration.

Wandrey at the B.A.M. tests the thermal stability of peroxides by heating 400 ml of substance in a Dewar vessel (see 16.3.3.2), but takes care to select from a commercial batch of Dewar vessels of given dimensions those with a quality of vacuum which gives thermal insulation comparable to that of the packing of the peroxide under consideration. The thermal insulation of two containers, such as a Dewar vessel and some kind of packing, is the same if, when they are filled with a liquid at a temperature such as 80°C and left to cool at the same ambient temperature (20°C, for example), the law of the decrease in temperature of their contents as a function of time is the same†. The tests are carried out at temperatures which are multiples of 10°C up to 40°C, or at multiples of 5°C from 45°C and above. In this way, an exothermic decomposition temperature is determined in a test in which the temperatures recorded give a graph of the kind in Fig. 16.5C.

The Cerchar laboratory in France performs the self-heating test described in 16.3.3.3, which has the advantage of taking less time than the test just described. It also gives two temperatures, with 5°C difference between them, one of which is the minimum self-heating temperature T_1 (in the operating mode used in the test), and the other is a temperature without heating.

The exothermic decomposition temperature as found by the B.A.M. is equal to within 5 or 7°C to the self-accelerating decomposition temperature (the American S.A.D.T.). According to the rules adopted by a Group of Experts from the UNO, to obtain the maximum control temperature one has to

---

† In practice, the time is plotted along the x-axis and log $(T-T_0)$ is plotted along the y-axis, where T is the temperature of the liquid and T_0 that of the ambient medium. By virtue of Newton's law of cooling, the points form a straight line whose slope is the cooling factor. Two containers have the same thermal insulation if the corresponding straight lines have the same slope.

subtract from the S.A.D.T.

- 10°C when the S.A.D.T. is greater than 35°C,
- 15°C when it is higher than 20°C but not higher than 35°C,
- 20°C when it is equal to or less than 20°C.

From the minimal self-heating temperatures measured by the Cerchar method one would have to subtract respectively 30, 35, and 40°C to arrive at the maximum control temperature.

Table 22.2 gathers together some values of S.A.D.T. for various peroxides, values which are known only to within 5 to 7°C, and the maximum control temperature which must not be exceeded.

The validity of these limits imposed on the control temperature can be seen from experiments which show that they include a sufficiently wide margin of safety for peroxides in the common commercial containers, and probably more than sufficient for containers with a capacity of around 1 litre which are not thermally insulated. By contrast, they may not apply to tanks with a capacity of several cubic metres or to road tankers.

22.2 REGULATING AND CLASSIFYING ORGANIC PEROXIDES

22.2.1 Evolving regulations

The word peroxide in this section designates both pure, or technically pure, organic peroxides and preparations containing a peroxide.

The first regulation covering organic peroxides was concerned with transport and for a long time applied only to benzoyl peroxide which was the only peroxide manufactured industrially at the time. Before 1940, the R.I.D. made it illegal to transport benzoyl peroxide wetted with less than 10% water and placed the wettest product in the same class as solid flammable substances. In 1956, this peroxide was transferred to the class of the explosives, and in 1959 a special class was created covering some fifteen organic peroxides.

Any classification of dangerous substances must group them according to the nature of the dangers they pose and, for each danger, according to the degree of hazard. Faced with the organic peroxides, the regulations have shown some hesitation in making these choices. All those who have been involved in classifying these substances are agreed on the difficulty of the problem and on the need to modify some test methods to adapt them to the peroxides. They consider that a classification can be set up only on the basis of several different tests.

One of the first to have attempted to classify the peroxides, Siemens [11], based his results on the following tests: flash point (flammability), test in a silvered vessel (16.3.3.1), sensitivity to impact and friction, and explosion test in a closed vessel with calibrated aperture (16.2.4), but he stated no rules for the classification of the hazards. Noller [2] uses the same tests, but replaces the silvered vessel test by the self-accelerating decomposition temperature (22.1.6). The result of these tests is noted according to a scale specific to each one of them: strong, medium, weak, negligible. In addition, he performs an explosion test in a lead tube (15.3.3b), and, on the basis of all these tests, classifies the peroxides into five danger groups which he calls:

- detonation hazard group†
- deflagration hazard group
- fire hazard group
- moderate fire hazard group
- weak or negligible fire hazard group.

Some commercial peroxides might be classified as explosives because of their sensitivity to impact or friction. However, they are different from ordinary explosives in having a very much lower thermal stability than the latter. Some liquid peroxides have a flash point which makes them resemble flammable liquids, but whilst the latter can burn only in air, peroxides when not phlegmatised contain enough active oxygen for them to burn in the absence of air, and although the combustion is incomplete, it is still very dangerous.

The organic peroxides are particularly dangerous because of their thermal instability coupled with the fact that they contain active oxygen, which is why, when they are involved in a fire, they actively participate in fuelling it. In conditions of sufficient confinement the fire may even culminate in an explosion.

These considerations justify the inclusion in the regulations covering the transport of hazardous substances of a class specifically for organic peroxides as well as a specific rubric in the classification of hazardous installations. But it should not be forgotten that the large family of commercial peroxides presents just as wide a variety of risks as the classic explosives.

22.2.2. Selecting the criteria for classification

Which of the many possible tests should be used and how are their results to be interpreted? This difficult question has been analysed with much perspicacity by Clancey, Owen, and Taylor [3], who observe that the accidents to which peroxides are exposed during transport are linked essentially to fire and that what is important is to know if the fire can lead to an explosion or not. This leads them to select the following tests: firing in a ballistic pendulum, heating in a case with a calibrated opening, heating in a pressure bomb, and sensitivity to impact.

A study made in 1974 by the Cerchar explosives laboratory at the request of the French authorities was used in drawing up a law defining the classificational criteria for peroxides and grouping them into three classes as a function of the quantities held. The criteria used are:
(a) the power, compared with that of picric acid equal to 100, measured in the explosive pendulum mortar (ballistic mortar);
(b) the result of the test of heating in a case with calibrated opening;
(c) sensitivity to the falling weight;
(d) behaviour on contact with a flame.
As an example, Table 22.3 gives a number of results for commercial peroxides.

Some Japanese authors [11] have proposed a system for evaluating the

---

† The word detonation should not be taken here in its strict meaning. We should rather say risk of a strong explosion, with the deflagration hazard group corresponding here to a risk of moderate explosion.

Table 22.3
Results of tests on various commercial organic peroxides

	Limit diameter of the calibrated opening (mm)	Power	
		in the lead block (ml/dag)	in the ballistic mortar (picric acid = 100)
Benzoyl peroxide (+ 10% water)	10		14
Acetyl peroxide 10% solution	1.5	14	
Cumyl peroxide*	< 1	16	
Isononanoyl peroxide* 25% solution in a solvent	< 1		< 1
Tertiary butyl peroxide	< 1		14
Tertiary butyl perbenzoate 88% solution	4	25	
Tertiary butyl perpivalate 75% solution	1.5		10.5
Tertiary butyl peroctoate (technical)	2	28	7.5
Normal butyl percarbonate* 50% solution	< 1	22	
Cetyl percarbonate* 90% solution	< 1	14	
3,3,6,6,9,9-hexamethyl-1,2,4,5-tetraoxacyclo-nonane (technical)	2.5	73	
Cyclohexanone peroxide with 5% water	8	50	22
Methyl ethyl ketone peroxide (phlegmatised, 50% solution)	6		42

explosive properties of organic peroxides from the results of tests in the
pendulum mortar using different conditions which, according to them, give a
numerical measurement of (a) sensitivity to ignition, (b) aptitude to
propagate an ignited explosion, and (c) power. However, these properties
do not seem to take account of all those which must be known in order to
describe the risks that a peroxide presents in practice.

22.3 MONOGRAPH ON THE PRINCIPAL COMMERCIAL ORGANIC PEROXIDES

22.3.1 Hydroperoxides

22.3.1.1 Some hydroperoxides are manufactured in the liquid phase by
auto-oxidation of a hydrocarbon with air or air enriched with oxygen at a
suitable temperature, for example 120°C for diisopropyl benzene or
130-135°C for p-menthane, a saturated cyclic hydrocarbon produced by
hydrogenating dipentene (or 1,8-p-menthadiene). The reaction is stopped
when the peroxide content is between 8 and 15%, after which a part of the
untransformed hydrocarbon is expelled by distillation in a vacuum. The
commercial product is thus a mixture of hydroperoxide with other oxidation
products (alcohols, ketones, etc.) and untransformed hydrocarbon. The
following products are sold in this form:
- p-menthane hydroperoxide* (VIII) containing about 50% hydroperoxide,
- m-diisopropyl benzene hydroperoxide (XXVIII) containing about 55%,
- tetralin hydroperoxide* (V).
These technical products, which are completely insensitive to impact, have
very weak explosive properties and are low-risk.

*22.3.1.2 Cumene hydroperoxide** (VI), which is obtained by auto-oxidation
like the substances above, has greater industrial importance. It is a
colourless liquid which is insoluble in water, has low volatility, is
scarcely sensitive to impact (at ordinary temperatures), and cannot be
detonated, although it can be decomposed explosively by heating at around
140 to 150°C. The capacity to explode of industrial products (containing
95%, 91%, 86%, and 82% hydroperoxide) has been studied experimentally by Le
Roux [5]. Decomposition begins at around 140-150°C and gives, in addition
to liquids in vapour form (acetone, etc.), gases (H_2, CH_4, CO, CO_2) which
are released at a rate of 180 litres per kg of hydroperoxide, a fact which
explains the high pressures created in a closed vessel by the deflagration
of this substance.

The product sold under the name of cumene hydroperoxide contains 75 to
80% cumyl hydroperoxide*, cumene or related aromatic hydrocarbons, and
dimethylbenzyl alcohol. This solution, which is more volatile than pure
cumene hydroperoxide, has a flash point of 70-80°C. It is stable up to
about 110°C but sensitive to acids. The presence of acids can produce a
violent exothermic decomposition into acetone and phenol. This splitting
of cumene hydroperoxide, discovered by Hoeck and Lang,

$$C_6H_5 - \overset{\overset{\displaystyle CH_3}{|}}{\underset{\underset{\displaystyle CH_3}{|}}{C}} - O - OH \;\rightarrow\; C_6H_5{>}OH + CH_3 - CO - CH_3,$$

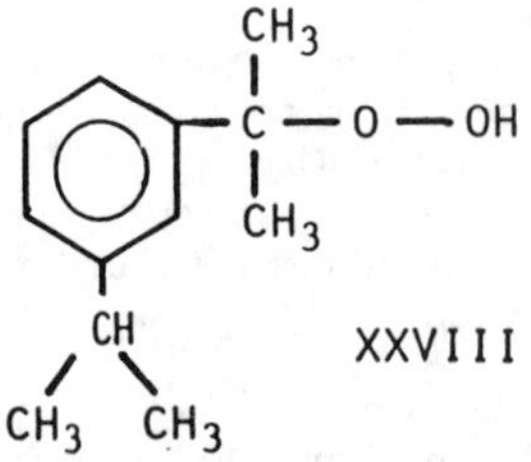

XXVIII

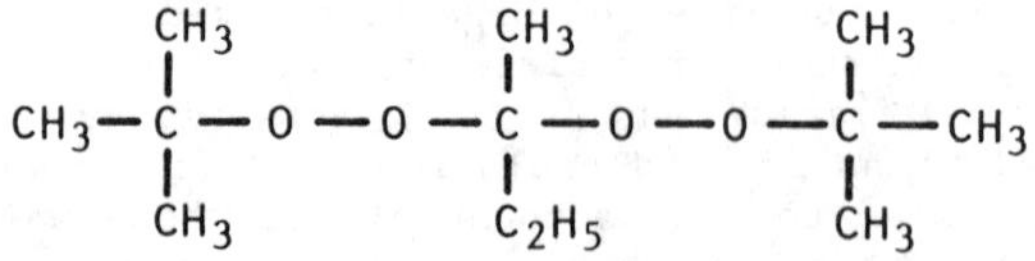

XXIX

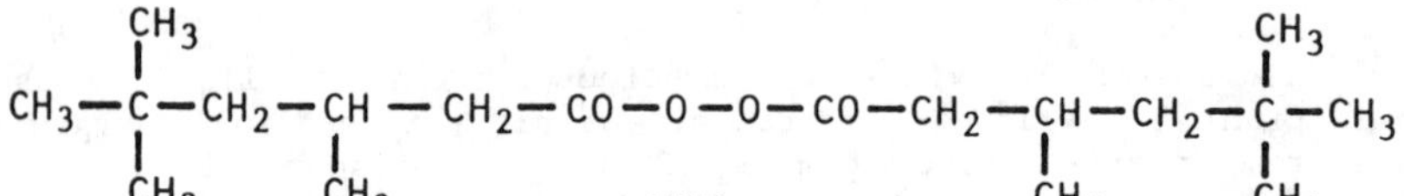

XXX

$$CH_3-(CH_2)_{10}-CO-O-O-CO-(CH_2)_{10}-CH_3$$

XXXI

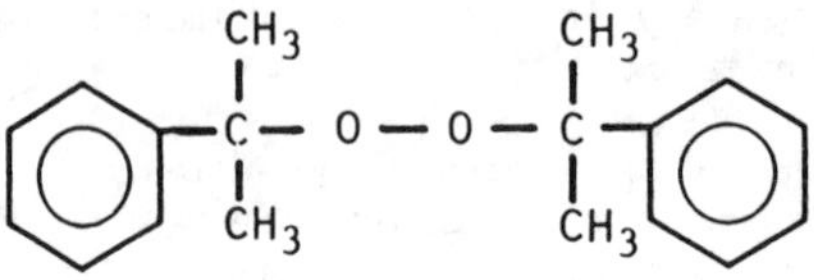

XXXII

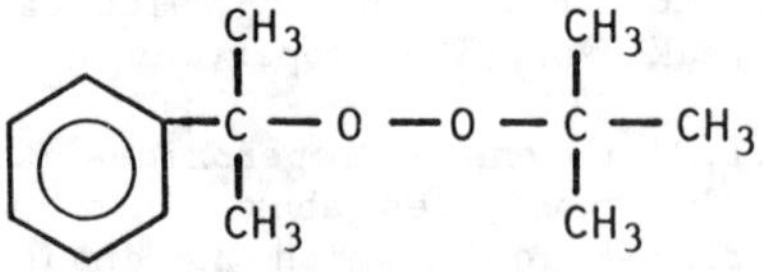

XXXIII

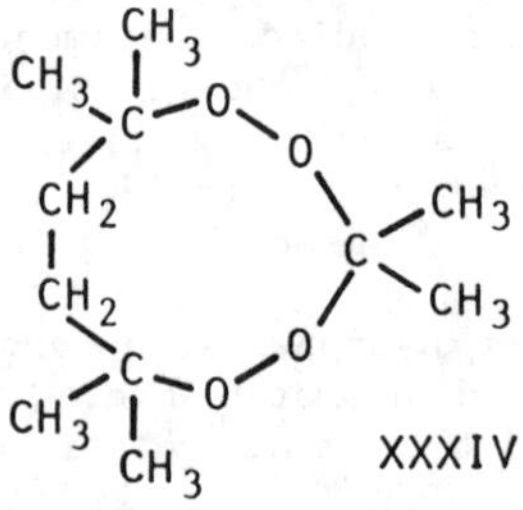

XXXIV

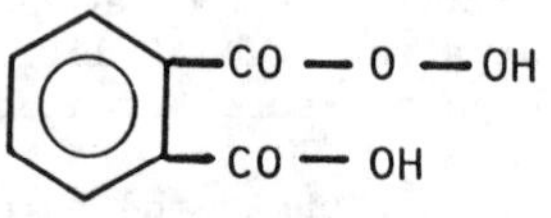

XXXV

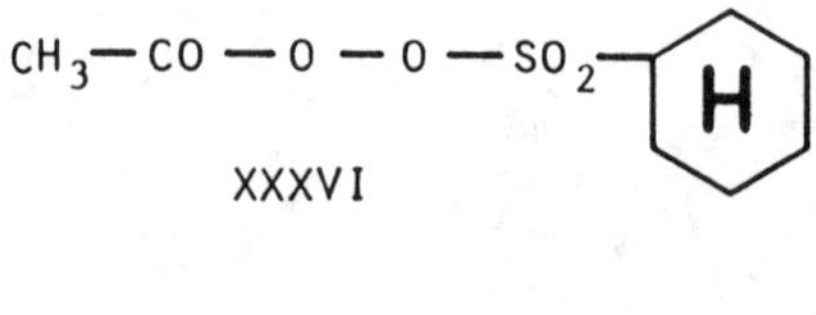

$$CH_3-CO-O-O-SO_2-\boxed{H}$$

XXXVI

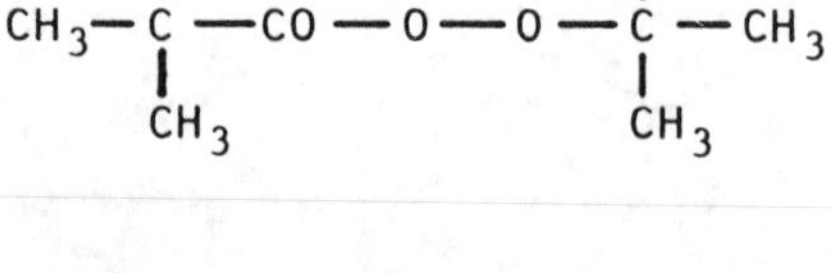

XXXVII

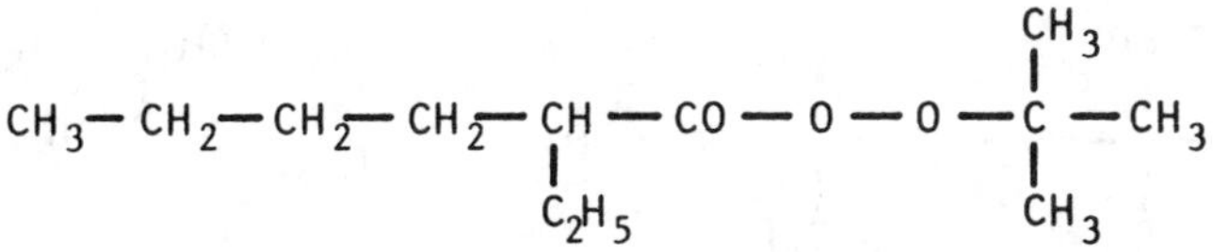

$$CH_3-CH_2-CH_2-CH_2-\underset{\underset{\displaystyle C_2H_5}{|}}{CH}-CO-O-O-\underset{\underset{\displaystyle CH_3}{|}}{\overset{\overset{\displaystyle CH_3}{|}}{C}}-CH_3$$

XXXVIII

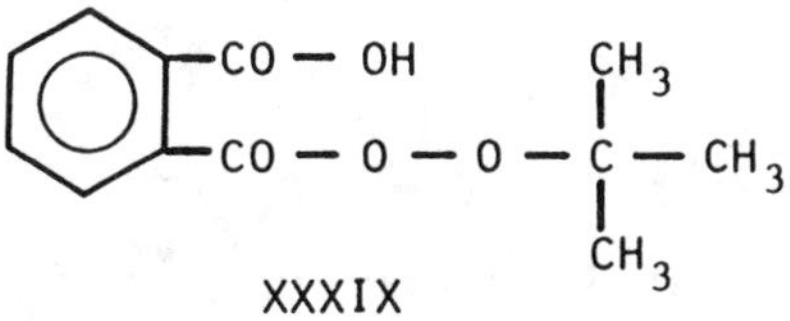

XXXIX

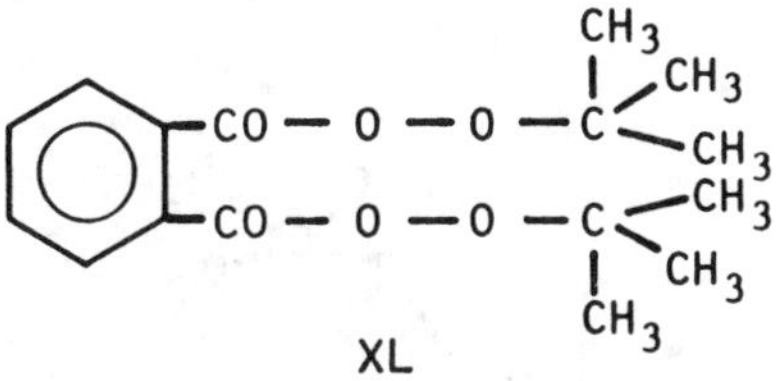

XL

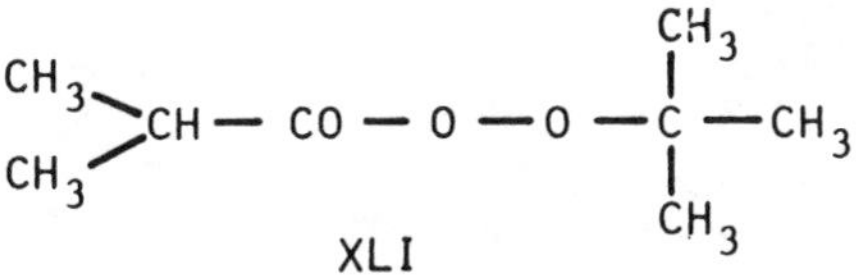

$$\underset{\displaystyle CH_3}{\overset{\displaystyle CH_3}{>}}CH-CO-O-O-\underset{\underset{\displaystyle CH_3}{|}}{\overset{\overset{\displaystyle CH_3}{|}}{C}}-CH_3$$

XLI

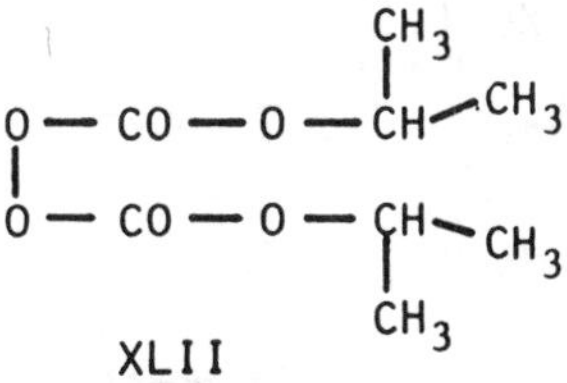

XLII

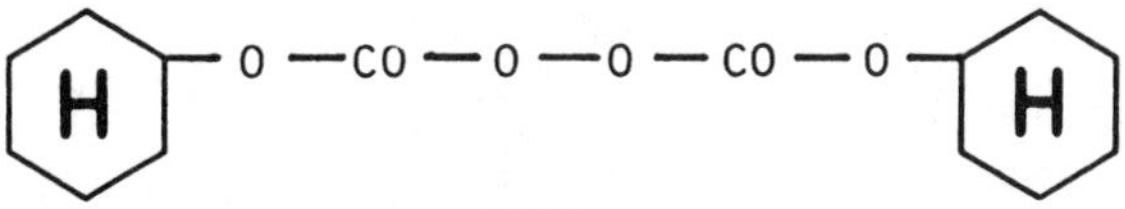

XLIII

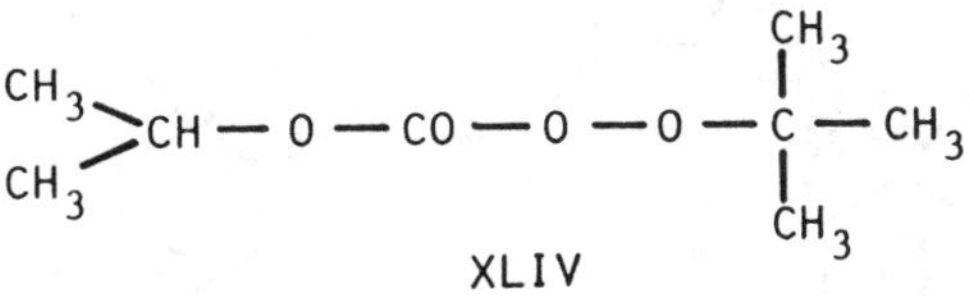

$$\underset{\displaystyle CH_3}{\overset{\displaystyle CH_3}{>}}CH-O-CO-O-O-\underset{\underset{\displaystyle CH_3}{|}}{\overset{\overset{\displaystyle CH_3}{|}}{C}}-CH_3$$

XLIV

$$HO-O-\underset{\underset{\displaystyle C_2H_5}{|}}{\overset{\overset{\displaystyle CH_3}{|}}{C}}-O-O-\underset{\underset{\displaystyle C_2H_5}{|}}{\overset{\overset{\displaystyle CH_3}{|}}{C}}-O-OH$$

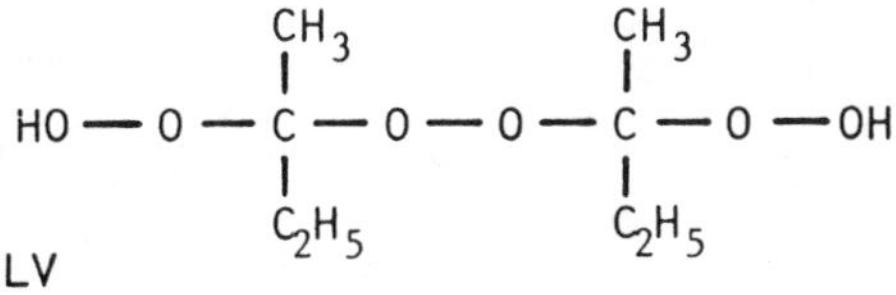

XLV

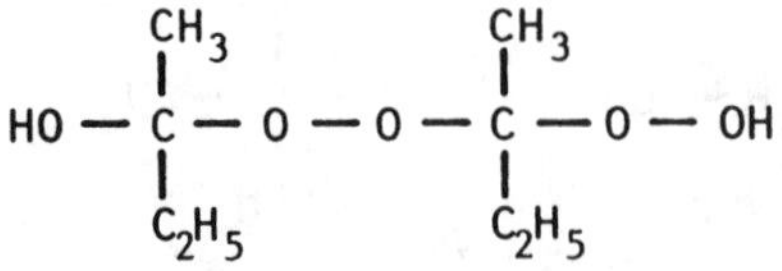

$$HO - \underset{\underset{C_2H_5}{|}}{\overset{\overset{CH_3}{|}}{C}} - O - O - \underset{\underset{C_2H_5}{|}}{\overset{\overset{CH_3}{|}}{C}} - O - OH$$

XLVI

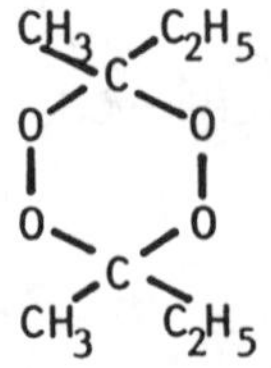

XLVII

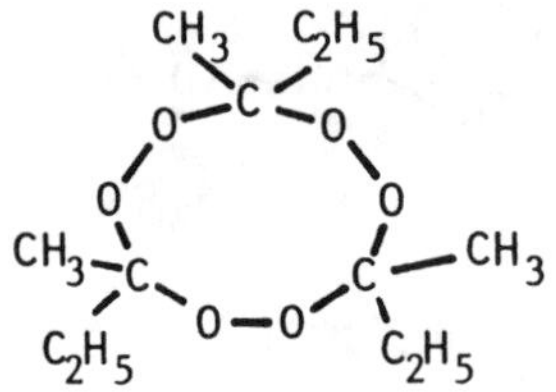

XLVIII

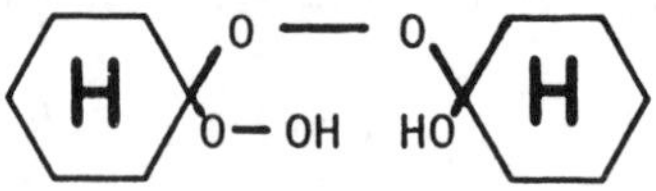

L

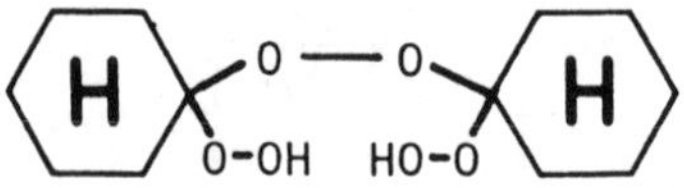

LI

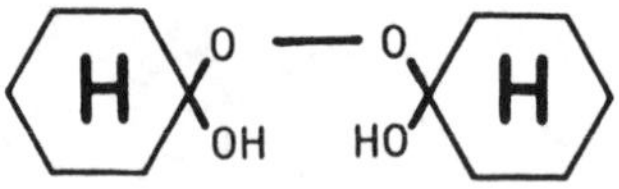

XLIX

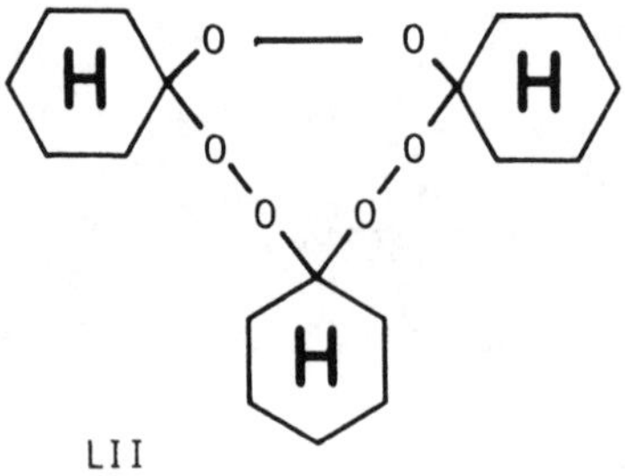

LII

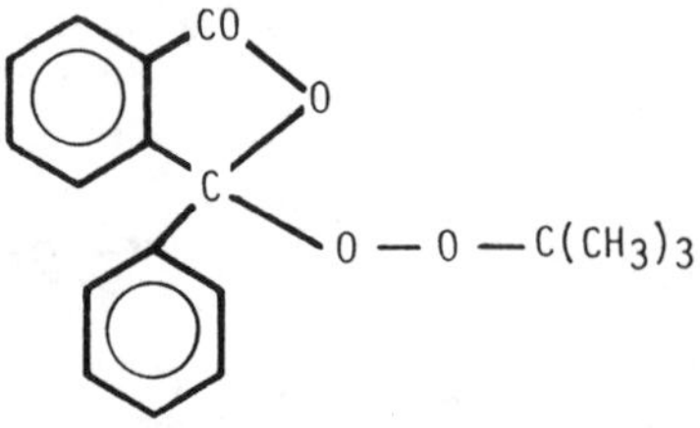

$$O - O - C(CH_3)_3$$

LIII

is the basis for the manufacture of phenol and acetone from benzene and propylene.

The 75-80% solution can be heated in small quantities in the open air and decomposes vigorously only beyond 200°C. It cannot be detonated even in very strict conditions. In experiments in which a metal drum containing 200 litres of hydroperoxide were set on fire by a wood flame, the top end was seen to give way after a few minutes and then the liquid burned with emission of black smoke. Combustion continued for half an hour without accelerating.

The 75-80% solution can be used to produce cold polymerisation of styrene and various vinyl compounds.

22.3.1.3 Tertiary butyl hydroperoxide (see 21.2.2) is generally prepared by the action of a 30% solution of hydrogen peroxide on a solution of tertiary butyl alcohol in sulphuric acid at around 20°C, followed by decantation, neutralisation, and washing. The reaction always gives tertiary butyl peroxide at the same time, and the technical grade product may contain 65 to 70% hydroperoxide and 25 to 30% peroxide, with the rest made up of tertiary butyl alcohol and a little water. This solution is not sensitive to impact, is stable to heat to at least 80°C, releases flammable vapours, and has a flash point which varies according to composition between 35 and 45°C. When ignited in the open air, it burns calmly. It is used mainly to make peroxy-esters by reaction with organic acids or their derivatives (anhydrides, acyl chlorides). It can also be used to make peroxides by reaction with ketones: for example, 2,2-di(tertiobutyl-peroxy)butane (XXIX) is manufactured industrially by the action of hydro-peroxide on methyl ethyl ketone.

22.3.2 Commercial alkyl and aryl peroxides

The industrial importance of these peroxides is rather small. Tertiary butyl peroxide is manufactured in small quantities. Of all the peroxides it is one of the thermally most stable, but that is precisely why it has limited use, because it must be raised to a fairly high temperature to obtain radicals in any useful concentration.

Mention should also be made of cumyl peroxide (XXXII), which is obtained as a by-product in the manufacture of the corresponding hydro-peroxide. It is a solid body which melts at 39°C and is stable up to at least 100°C. It can be used to vulcanise natural rubber or Perbunan. It is low-risk, even when not phlegmatised. Small quantities of cumyl and tertiobutyl peroxide (XXXIII), which melt at 15.5°C, are also produced. They are low-risk substances.

Similar to the alkyl peroxides are some cyclic peroxides such as 3,3,6,6,9,9-hexamethyl-1,2,4,5-cyclononane (XXXIV), a white powder smelling of camphor which melts at 63°C, and phthalide peroxide* (LIII), which is a colourless crystalline substance which is insoluble in water and melts at around 105°C without decomposing. Its stability is comparable to that of tertiary butyl peroxide (indeed, it may be noted that the − O − O − group in it is bonded to a tertiary and a secondary carbon atom).

22.3.3 Commercial organic per-acids

Peracetic acid is the main organic per-acid to be sold commercially. It is

delivered in the form of a solution at a concentration ranging from 35 to
40% which contains water, acetic acid, a small amount of H_2O_2, and traces
of acetyl peroxide. This solution gives off irritant and lachrimatory
vapours and is sufficiently volatile for its flash point to be between 40
and 50°C. It is highly corrosive on most metals, including aluminium. It
has poor thermal stability because it slowly releases gas at ordinary
temperature, which is why it is stored in containers fitted with vents. It
is not sensitive to impact, but it is a strong supporter of combustion and
is liable to ignite straw and cotton. There have been cases of accidents
in which 40% peracetic acid spilt on a wooden floor has reacted with a
flame and started a fire. When heated in small quantities (125 ml) in an
open container, the solution decomposes vigorously at around 120°C, but
without exploding.

Peracetic acid is also used for bleaching various textiles, both
natural and synthetic (nylon, etc.), at a temperature of around 60°C. For
this purpose it is sometimes prepared in situ, and in that case it is
important to ensure that the medium remains strongly acid, since a high pH
favours the formation of acetyl peroxide, which is more dangerous than
peroxyacetic acid.

Of the other per-acids mention should be made of monoperoxyphthalic
acid (XXXV), which is manufactured easily by oxidising phthalic anhydride
with H_2O_2. It is a white powder which is more stable than perbenzoic acid.
The latter product has practically never been used, but it should be noted
that the presence of certain substituents on the benzene nucleus improves
stability, thus allowing the industrial use of m-chloroperbenzoic acid, a
white powder with a melting point of 88°C, and p-nitroperbenzoic acid,
which melts with decomposition at 138°C.

22.3.4 Benzoyl peroxide

Benzoyl peroxide, which Brodie discovered in 1858 when treating benzoyl
chloride with hydrated barium peroxide, was first manufactured industrially
in 1900 by reacting benzoyl chloride with sodium peroxide. It is now
manufactured using the same chloride with hydrogen peroxide in an alkaline
medium. It is a solid, crystalline substance which is insoluble in water,
melts in the pure state at 105°C, and cannot be heated in the liquid state
without rapid decomposition.

Sulphuric acid in a 92% solution reacts strongly with benzoyl peroxide
and ignites it. Farmer [7] reports that a mass of 7 g of peroxide placed
in an evacuated desiccator over sulphuric acid exploded spontaneously with
a loud noise eight hours later. This might be caused by condensation in
the peroxide of traces of SO_3 vapours. It is therefore advisable to dry
wet peroxide over a neutral agent (anhydrous sodium sulphate, for example).
Other concentrated mineral acids (PO_4H_3, etc.) do not have the same effect.
Benzoyl peroxide can be treated with 90% nitric acid with moderate heating
to form m-nitrobenzoyl peroxide. Benzoyl peroxide is hardly sensitive to
the action of alkalis: caustic soda causes it to decompose at only a slow
rate when cold.

When a quantity of about 1 gramme of benzoyl peroxide is gradually
heated in the open air, at a temperature close to its melting point it
deflagrates without flame, producing a low noise and a white cloud. If a
small 1 metre trail of 10 grammes of benzoyl peroxide is ignited at one
end, decomposition occurs which propagates at a rate of 15 to 40 cm/s

depending on the granulometry of the product.

It is sensitive to friction, deflagrating readily in a ground porcelain mortar. Deflagration has been reported when benzoyl peroxide spilt on the floor was swept away with a straw brush; it should have been swept away only after copious watering. It is more sensitive to impact than P.E.T.N., and even when wetted with 10% water, it still produces weak explosions under the impact of a 5 kg weight falling from a height of 2 m, although with 20% water it is completely insensitive to impact. We know of a serious accident which once occurred in a workshop where an attempt was made to reduce benzoyl peroxide to a fine powder in a ball-mill, an operation which must never in any circumstance be carried out.

In contact with a flame it catches fire easily in air and burns strongly, giving off a large red flame and whitish smoke containing diphenyl vapours.

In tests involving the ignition of 2 kg of benzoyl peroxide housed in a wooden case, an explosion was observed with flying wood splinters. An explosion is therefore a real danger with a large quantity of this peroxide when it is dry or insufficiently wetted or phlegmatised, and, with due allowance, the explosion is comparable to that of gunpowder, although the effect in the lead block is very weak, just 10% of picric acid. It is a substance which does not detonate. Under confinement its burning velocity is of the order of 600–800 m/s.

The properties of its explosion have been calculated in 21.1.4. It is generally accompanied in the open air by a secondary explosion, but the latter is almost always incomplete, which explains the appearance of a large black cloud of unburnt carbon in which can be observed white trails due to the condensation of the vapour of diphenyl which is formed.

The thermal stability of this peroxide is quite good. It can be heated for several hours at 80°C without appreciable decomposition, but at 93°C the product turns yellow and loses oxygen quite rapidly. When subjected to the Dutch test (see 16.1.3), it deflagrates at 106°C. Earlier experiments by Farmer [7] using the method of heating in a vacuum (see 16.3.4) have shown that at 49°C benzoyl peroxide loses about 0.002 cm³ of oxygen per gramme per hour, and 0.15 cm³ at 80°C (this was with an industrial product).

Prat [8] describes an explosion which occurred in 1943 with serious effects when a mass of 400 g of peroxide was being dissolved in chloroform in a balloon flask heated in a water bath. He concluded from subsequent tests that the explosion was initiated in the chloroform vapour above the hot liquid in the proximity of the wall which had been raised to 100°C by the water in the bath.

Other cases of explosion have been reported during recrystallisation of benzoyl peroxide. Isopropyl alcohol has sometimes been recommended for this recrystallisation process, but it seems safer to purify this peroxide by dissolving it in chloroform at ordinary temperature and then using cold methanol to precipitate it.

Benzoyl peroxide has sometimes been used in the dry state, supplied by the manufacturer in 500 gramme sachets, which meant that the user did not have to weigh it out, which reduced handling but not the high risks involved in storage.

Like the peroxides of p-chlorobenzoyl and 2,4-dichlorobenzoyl, benzoyl peroxide is a high-risk substance when it is dry or contains less than 10% water. It is also often used in the form of a paste with 70% at most of peroxide and a phthalate, in which case it is a low-risk substance. Pastes

are also sold containing both benzoyl peroxide and dichlorobenzoyl peroxide
because the latter, which is more active, accelerates the setting of masses
with a base of unsaturated polyesters.

In some countries benzoyl peroxide mixed with tricalcium phosphate is
used in milling to bleach flours. It was used in Great Britain in the
1930s to make ignition caps (lighting substance).

Furoyl peroxide which, because of the aromatic nature of the furan
nucleus, is comparable to benzoyl peroxide, is a solid which melts at 86°C.
It is not manufactured industrially because it is four times more sensitive
to impact than benzoyl peroxide and has no practical advantage over it.

22.3.5 Other commercial acyl peroxides

Commercial acetyl peroxide is a medium-risk solution containing at most 27%
peroxide in a phthalate. The solution, which has a slightly corrosive
effect on the skin, gives off vapours which irritate the eyes. It must be
stored at a moderate temperature because too low a temperature causes
highly dangerous peroxide to crystallise out in the pure state.

Other commercial peroxides in the same family are:

	Thermal stability	Risk
Propionyl peroxide in a 28% solution maximum	Medium	Low
Normal octanoyl peroxide, technical	Medium	Low
Isononanoyl peroxide*, technical (XXX)	Low	Medium
Decanoyl peroxide, technical	Medium	Low
Lauroyl peroxide	High	Low

The latter is a crystalline substance which melts at 55°C, is
insensitive to impact (no explosion in the Sevran test with a 10 kg weight
falling 3 m), and ignites only with difficulty. However, if a large
quantity is heated in a confined space, it deflagrates weakly. The
commercial product, which contains 95 to 98% pure peroxide, the impurities
being lauric acid and its calcium salt, is one of the peroxides which can
be handled with least danger. It is used, amongst other things, in the hot
setting of acrylic resins.

22.3.6 Acetyl cyclohexane sulphonyl peroxide

To the acyl peroxides above may be compared the peroxide of acetyl cyclohexane sulphonyl (XXXVI). This compound, which has been known since 1952
[9], is manufactured by the direct action of oxygen and sulphur dioxide on
a solution of acetic anhydride in cyclohexane

$$2C_6H_{12} + 2SO_2 + 2O_2 + (CH_3 - CO)_2O \rightarrow H_2O + 2C_6H_{11} - SO_2O - O - CO - CH_3.$$

The raw product recrystallised in water and then clarified in iced water is generally stored in the form of a paste with about 30–35% water. It must not be allowed to dry out since the dry product is sensitive to impact. It is a solid which melts at 35–36°C and has a characteristically pungent smell.

Manufacturing this peroxide is a somewhat delicate operation since beyond a certain limiting temperature (about 10°C) the product is liable to decompose either in the reactor or in the washing and purifying apparatus. It has low thermal stability and is kept wetted in freezers maintained at around − 20°C, with the temperature not being allowed to rise above − 5°C. It is used mainly in the manufacture of polyvinyl chloride. At ordinary temperatures (15–20°C) the paste with 30% water sometimes decomposes quite vigorously in the open air into gaseous products but with no smoke. The dry product is capable of an extremely violent explosion.

22.3.7 Peroxy–esters

Commercial peroxy–esters are all tertiary butyl esters. The following are some of the most commonly used.

Tertiary butyl perbenzoate, obtained in 1946 by Milas, is a liquid with a sweet smell which is insoluble in water and crystallises at around 10°C but remains readily supercooled. At its normal boiling point (125°C) it decomposes appreciably. The commercial technical product contains, in addition to tertiary butyl alcohol, a little butyl peroxide formed during manufacture. It is not very sensitive to impact and is quite stable at ordinary temperatures. It is used between 70 and 110°C because below 65°C its half life is too long for any practical use. It is used in the vulcanisation of rubber, as a drying agent for paints and varnishes, and above all as a polymerisation catalyst in the manufacture of polystyrene and polyester resins.

It has been said that this perbenzoate is stable and can be distilled at a reduced pressure of 2 mm of mercury at 75–77°C [12], but a large European producer [13] recommends that this operation should not be attempted, since there is a danger of explosion because of the formation of hydroperoxide, and indeed Schnur [14] describes a case of just such an explosion which was highly destructive. This decomposition of tertiary butyl perbenzoate has been studied by Verhoeff and Van den Berg [15].

Tertiary butyl perpivalate (trimethylperacetate) (XXXVII) is a colourless liquid which is insoluble in water and which crystallises at around − 10°C. It decomposes slowly at ordinary temperature but no decomposition is detected at − 15°C. The commercial product is about 95% pure.

Tertiary butyl–2–ethyl perhexanoate (XXXVIII) is found under the trade name of tertiary butyl peroctoate*.

Amongst the other commercial tertiary butyl per–esters are
− the peracetate, a liquid used between 65 and 110°C because its half life is too long at ordinary temperature,
− the permaleate (monobutyl ester), a solid which melts at 118°C,
− the monoperoxyphthalate (XXXIX) and the diperoxyphthalate (XL) which are solids,
− the perisobutyrate (XLI),

- the diethylperacetate, a liquid.

22.3.8 Industrial peroxycarbonates

It was the search for polymerisation 'catalysts' which are active at
ordinary temperatures that brought peroxydicarbonates onto the market.
Manufacturing these substances consists in slowly adding the corresponding
chloroformate to a 30 or 35% solution of hydrogen peroxide mixed with soda,
well stirred, and cooled to 5°C. Since the percarbonate is usually wanted
in already phlegmatised form, the hydrogen peroxide is put in a solution
(or mixture) with a diluent or phlegmatiser. The input of chloroformate is
regulated in such a way that the reactive mixture remains steady at around
15°C, with 25°C taken as the danger temperature. After the reaction, the
equation for which is

$$H_2O_2 + 2NaOH + 2Cl - CO - O - R \rightarrow 2H_2O + 2NaCl + RO - CO - O - O - CO - OR,$$

the sodium chloride is separated by filtration from the solution and the
resulting solution is dried on anhydrous sodium sulphate.

Isopropyl peroxydicarbonate (XLII), which was prepared for the first
time in 1950, was manufactured industrially in the early 1960s under the
abbreviated name of isopropyl percarbonate*. It is a solid substance which
melts at 10°C and has a density of 1.08 in the liquid state. It must be
stored at around - 15°C because if it is allowed to heat up, it begins to
decompose at its melting point with emission of gas bubbles. The velocity
constant of this decomposition reaction is high, with the result that the
product gradually heats up and decomposes at increasing speed to the point
where it explodes with considerable violence given that it has a calorific
value (1100 to 1200 kJ/kg) greater than most commercial peroxides. Indeed,
this peroxide, which, in the test in the steel tube with nozzle plates (see
16.2.3) has a limit diameter of 8 mm, equal to that of benzoyl peroxide,
gives a value of 27 (compared with 100 for picric acid) in the explosive
pendulum mortar (see 14.3.3), which is much higher than the value found for
benzoyl peroxide.   Its explosion produces flammable gases and vapours
(ethane, acetone, acetaldehyde, and isopropyl alcohol), so that there is a
serious risk of a secondary explosion of a mixture of these gases with air.
Experiments have also shown that an overdriven detonation (see 14.4.5) can
be produced by initiating the substance with a strong explosive booster.

Alkalis accelerate the decomposition of isopropyl peroxydicarbonate,
and it is also strongly decomposed by concentrated sulphuric acid, whilst
it deflagrates vigorously in contact with a flame. Its sensitivity to
impact, however, is quite low. It is only rarely used in a 'technically
pure' state, being normally used in a phlegmatised state either in a 50%
(medium-risk) or a 25% (low-risk) solution. It is used in particular to
polymerise methacrylates, vinyl chloride, and other ethylene compounds.
When cold it gives iodine from KI, which makes it easy to titrate active
oxygen in preparations of the substance.

Cyclohexyl peroxydicarbonate (XLIII) is a crystalline substance which
melts with decomposition at 46°C. It is generally sold wetted with at
least 5% water.

Other commercial peroxydicarbonates which should be mentioned are those
of ethyl (50%, phlegmatised), 2-ethyl hexyl (52%, phlegmatised), normal or
secondary butyl (52%, phlegmatised), benzyl (87% plus water), and cetyl in

a white powder which melts at 57°C.

Isopropyl tertiobutylperoxymonocarbonate (isopropyl and peroxybutyl carbonate) (XLIV) is a liquid which is insoluble in water, crystallises at around 3°C, is relatively volatile (its flash point is about 50°C), and is decomposed by heat into carbon dioxide, acetone, and tertiary butyl alcohol. The explosion reaction has a lower calorific value of about 1250 kJ/kg and gives gases at more than 600°C. It is a very effective catalyst in the polymerisation of ethylene.

22.3.9 Methyl ethyl ketone peroxide

Commercial methyl ethyl ketone peroxide is a solution in a phlegmatiser or a solvent of the various peroxides which are formed when H_2O_2 acts on ketone. Among the latter are dihydroperoxy peroxide (XLV), hydroxy-hydroperoxy peroxide (XLVI), and the two cyclic peroxides (XLVII and XLVIII). The end product may also contain 1 to 8% non-oxidised ketone. It would not be easy to separate out these various constituents and would even be pointless given the uses to which the substance is put. Depending on the conditions of manufacture and the mode of phlegmatisation, preparations are obtained with varying percentages of active oxygen and explosive properties, as can be seen from the tests in a pressurised covered container described by Siemens [1]. The following values for two phlegmatised commercial mixtures with methyl phthalate bring out very clearly the variation in properties [16].

Percentage of active oxygen	Limit diameter in the steel tube with nozzle plates	wbm (in the pendulum mortar)
9%	1 mm	18
11%	6 mm	26

The 50% commercial product sold in France is a liquid with a density of 1.1 and a flash point of about 50°C when the phlegmatiser is a phthalate but close to 100°C when the peroxide is mixed with 8% water and an adequate hydrosoluble solvent. In the latter case, it is a low-risk substance.

The product patented in America [10] is a homogeneous, limpid, highly stable liquid with the composition

methyl ethyl ketone peroxide	26
methyl phthalate	18
polypropylene glycol	36
distilled water	20.

A product similar to methyl ethyl ketone peroxide is methyl isobutyl ketone peroxide*, the 62% solution of which in a phthalate is a low-risk substance.

22.3.10 Cyclohexanone peroxides

The action of 30% hydrogen peroxide on cyclohexanone in an acetic acid solution gives a mixture of various solid peroxides, the main ones being:

- the bisperoxide 1-hydroxycyclohexyl (XLIX),
- 1-hydroxycyclohexyl and 1-hydroperoxycyclohexyl peroxide (L),
- the bisperoxide 1-hydroperoxycyclohexyl (LI),
- a cyclic triperoxide (LII).

Of the first three substances, with respective melting points 73, 78, and 83°C, the second predominates, but the first is the most active in initiating polymerisations. The commercial peroxide, called 'cyclohexanone peroxide', is a mixture produced in the reaction with 10% water added. In this form it is not very sensitive to impact, but it decomposes slowly at around 75°C. It is used above all in the setting of varnishes or resins of unsaturated polyesters. The same mixture is sometimes sold as a 50 or 60% paste with triethyl phosphate.

In the dry state the peroxide is highly sensitive to impact and is even liable to detonate. In spite of its low active oxygen content it is the most active peroxide for initiating polymerisations. Depending on the conditions of manufacture, a mixture is obtained which is more or less rich in the compound XLIX, which means that it is possible to make industrial preparations with various activities.

22.4 ACCIDENTS AND SAFETY MEASURES WITH ORGANIC PEROXIDES

22.4.1 Accidents involving commercial organic peroxides

In the discussion in 21.3 peroxides were treated as accidental explosives, but commercial peroxides have occasionally shown themselves to be unwanted explosives. The following is a description of various accidents selected from the most informative.

22.4.1.1 Accidents during transport

1° On 6 February 1962, a lorry was transporting 1.5 tons of methyl ethyl ketone peroxide in a 60% solution in methyl phthalate, as well as a 50% solution of hydrogen peroxide. While driving through West Bromwich near Birmingham, the driver noticed that smoke was pouring from the lorry and drove it onto some waste land. In spite of the efforts of the firemen there was an explosion which caused considerable damage to nearby houses. The effects of the accident were equivalent to those of 50 kg of TNT. Following this accident, the British manufacturer lowered the concentration of methyl ethyl ketone peroxide from 60 to 50%.

2° On 3 April 1962 in Norwich, U.S.A., an articulated vehicle was being unloaded in a factory yard of methyl ethyl ketone peroxide, as well as benzoyl and lauroyl peroxide, making 18 tons in all. A fire broke out, resulting in a very short space of time in an explosion which killed four firemen and shattered windows up to 2 km away. It is likely that the fire was started by friction from a parcel during handling.

3° We also know of an explosion of 150 kg of benzoyl peroxide on board a van which was violently struck by another vehicle.

22.4.1.2 Accidents during manufacture

1° On 29 September 1953 in Tonawanda, U.S.A., at the end of manufacture of tertiary butyl peracetate, a serious explosion killed eleven people and gouged a vast hole in the earth where the workshop had been.

2° In 1963 in the east of France, an attempt was made to manufacture peracetic acid in a hastily improvised apparatus not designed for the purpose. During the operation the temperature of the reactive medium rose to the point where it exploded, killing the operative and hurling fragments of metal over a distance of more than a hundred metres.

3° In November 1964 in a factory in France, during an operation for treating some 100 kg of diammonium peroxymonophthalate with a 50% solution of sulphuric acid, the mixture underwent a fizzing decomposition, filling the workshop with hot, toxic fumes. One of the operatives, who had not been able to escape in time, died several days later from burns received.

The mistake was made in this operation of pouring the acid onto the perphthalate, instead of first pouring the acid into the apparatus and then feeding in the perphthalate in small amounts, which would have wetted it. The apparatus used on the day of the accident was not, as it had been on earlier occasions, a mixer with several centimetres clearance between the vat and the stirring mechanism, but a Werner kneader with an inner covering of stainless steel and a clearance of 1 to 1.5 mm between the vat and the blades, with resulting friction of the solid product, still not wetted with liquid, inside the apparatus.

4° In May 1966 in Spain, an operation to prepare methyl ethyl ketone peroxide left 220 kg of the product in a filtering apparatus after drying on anhydrous sodium sulphate. Instead of removing it, it was left there for six hours, where it corroded the metal gauze of the apparatus, with the result that iron and nickel salts contaminated the product and catalysed its decomposition, leading to a strong explosion with four dead and heavy damage.

3° In 1966, a mistake in a factory led to the accidental mixing of sulphuric acid and tertiary butyl hydroperoxide, resulting in an explosion.

22.4.1.3 Accidents during storage

1° Around 1969 in Ribécourt in the Oise in France, a depot containing almost a ton of benzoyl peroxide exploded, causing damage comparable to the effects of an explosion of 300 kg of gunpowder.

2° In 1972, during a very hot summer in the Netherlands, isononanoyl peroxide decomposed strongly in a depot.

Surprise has often been expressed at the damage by some accidental explosions of peroxides, since it seems considerable when compared with the effects of classic explosives, given the low calorific value of these peroxides. We believe that there are two explanations for this:

(a) Some peroxides have a *rate of decomposition* (rate of pressure rise in the decomposition in a closed vessel) much higher than that of the classic deflagrating explosives, sometimes even higher than that of gunpowder.

(b) The products of the decomposition of peroxides are *combustible* gases and vapours which mix with air to form an explosive gas mixture. It is often the secondary explosion of this mixture which causes the serious destruction observed. Indeed, in some accidents two successive noises of explosion have been heard.

It should be added that since 1965 there have been far fewer and far

less serious accidents caused by organic peroxides. There are two reasons
for this:
(a) Since we have much better knowledge of the properties of peroxides, we
know what precautions to take to prevent explosions.
(b) Fewer of the dangerous technically pure peroxides are sold than used to
be the case and there has been considerable development in the use of
preparations with a lower peroxide content which fall into the medium- and
low-risk groups, with only very few high-risk peroxides now being
manufactured.

22.4.2 Safety in the manufacture of peroxides

Safety in the manufacture of an organic peroxide is based in the first
place on the use of a tested operating mode perfected initially in the
laboratory and then in half-scale tests. Normal manufacture should not
deviate from this safe operating mode without first having conducted new
tests. It must not be forgotten that any change in the concentration of
the substances used or in their respective proportions may lead to the
formation of different products which are more sensitive than the desired
product (see 22.3.9 and 22.3.10). All production must be governed by
written instructions laying down procedures to be followed in the event of
any unexpected discrepancy. For products which are to be made at low
temperatures (peroxydicarbonates in particular), the instructions must
state an emergency temperature (usually $15°C$ above the normal reaction
temperature) at which the reactive mixture must without fail be drowned.
   With many peroxides the accident most to be feared during manufacture
is an explosion. It is therefore advisable to base the building of a
workshop for producing organic peroxides on the methods followed in
factories manufacturing sensitive explosives. The workshop should contain
cells with three sides made of strongly resistant walls and a light fourth
side (a skylight) giving onto an area from which the workforce is banned.
Operations are carried out behind a strong wall in a gallery containing the
dials of measuring instruments and valves controlling the movement of
fluids. Operatives can observe the apparatuses through inspection holes
covered with thick glass pierced in the strong wall. The apparatuses in a
cell are laid out on two or three levels since many product movements are
made by gravity. Doors giving access to the cells at the level of the
control gallery should be made of metal and, when closed, rest against
solid angle irons made in the masonry.
   Those parts of the apparatus which are in contact with the products
being treated must be free of any metal (especially copper metals) or any
other substance likely to decompose peroxides. Stainless steel is the
material most used. All equipment must be scrupulously clean, being washed
before use and finished off with a rinse in pure water (demineralised
water). When apparatuses such as reactors, filters, and washing vats do
not have an open top, they should be closed with light lids which are
easily blown to one side by a release of gas, since all confinement must be
avoided. It is advisable for the reactor to be fitted with a fast emptying
system controlled from the service gallery to evacuate decomposing liquids
through a wide pipe into a water-filled vat located outside the building,
as in the classic technique of 'drowning' in nitroglycerine factories.
   When working with dangerous peroxides, the risks are reduced by
operating with diluted solutions and producing peroxide in phlegmatised

form directly in the reactor.

Organic peroxides are usually manufactured in distinct operations (in batches), but those which are formed by a sufficiently rapid reaction lend themselves to continuous manufacture, as is the case with lauroyl peroxide obtained from the action of lauroyl chloride on hydrogen peroxide and soda. Continuous manufacture is a safer means of achieving identical daily production than batch manufacture.

22.4.3 Safety in the use of organic peroxides

As in many other industrial operations order and cleanliness in a workshop are safety factors, but in this case they are absolutely essential since any contamination of the peroxide by foreign bodies or dusts may initiate a dangerous decomposition. Peroxides have caught fire because they were poured into a poorly cleaned recipient which still contained residues of a polymerisable substance.

Apparatuses and containers used should have a shape which allows easy cleaning. Stainless steel and pure aluminium with polished surfaces are especially suitable, as are impermeable plastic materials. A container must be replaced as soon as a crack is discovered. Heavy metals (lead, copper, etc.) or steel are to be avoided as much as possible, especially at workstations where they could come into contact with peroxides, because of the risk of rust. Before use containers must be washed and passivated. They are washed first with water containing a detergent and then with a solvent, followed by treatment with a strong acid before being rinsed in pure water. They will subsequently be washed at quite frequent intervals.

Special care will be taken to ensure that peroxides do not mix with the salts of heavy metals, especially of activators. This might mean a workshop having one set of scales exclusively for weighing peroxides, as well as different dustbins for different kinds of waste, since there have been cases of explosions being caused by using one dustbin for all forms of waste. Smoking must be banned in a workshop where peroxides are used, not only because the place often contains flammable materials, but also because any contamination of peroxide by tobacco ash could be dangerous since the ash contains traces of manganese salt which has a catalytic effect.

Containers housing peroxides should be covered with a light lid, and care will be taken to prevent wet peroxides from losing water and to prevent evaporation of a volatile solvent from a solution of peroxide in the solvent.

No more than the amount needed for a half-day's work should be taken into a workshop using peroxide. If peroxide is spilt by accident on a floor or table, it must, if solid, be wetted or diluted with an inert powder, or, if liquid, be absorbed by perlite or vermiculite. Only then can it be swept away. Some sensitive solid peroxides have been seen to deflagrate under the effect of a simple, everyday straw brush. Cleaning cloths should be used only to remove small drips or stains and should then be put into airtight metal bins.

Unused peroxide should never be poured back into its original container on top of peroxide still inside.

In operations using an organic peroxide, it is the peroxide which should be added gradually to the reactive mixture, and not the other way round. In this way, the concentration of peroxide in the product to be treated always remains low. If the peroxide is highly active at the

operating temperature, it must be added *very slowly*. A case is known in
which an operative was killed by an explosion because he took too short a
time to pour a few kilogrammes of benzoyl peroxide into a polymerisation
vat.

If an accelerator has been added to a resin to be polymerised, care
must be taken to ensure that it is well dispersed throughout the entire
mass before adding the peroxide catalyst, since there would be a danger of
explosion if the latter were poured in at a point where the accelerator was
not diluted.

Not only must written safety instructions be posted up in the workshop,
but the workforce must also have been instructed in the risks specific to
peroxides, and the necessary protective clothing must be worn (goggles,
face masks, gloves, etc.) In the workshop or close by there must be
supplies of clean water to wash off any splashes on the body, as well as a
cupboard containing first aid equipment, including, in particular, an eye
solution in case the eyes are affected by peroxide dusts or drops.

Peroxides should not be placed too close to a source of heat, and the
workshop should preferably be heated by hot-water radiators (70°C at most).

Large quantities of water are normally the most effective extinguisher
for fires involving organic peroxides.

22.4.4 Safety in the storage of organic peroxides

Safety of storage will be covered by the regulations in force in a given
country, but the following additional points should be noted.

Even with peroxides which are stable at normal temperatures, it is
advisable to ensure that the temperature of a depot remains moderate in
summer. This reduces the drop in the active oxygen content which all
peroxides undergo during storage. The temperature in a depot is limited by
means of a watering system on the roof, which is also extremely useful if a
fire should break out in the vicinity of the depot.

Given the importance of avoiding anything which might contaminate
organic peroxides, they must, after manufacture, be put in packages which
will be used for both storage and transport to make transfer unnecessary.
Furthermore, safety is enhanced if the product is broken down into small
quantities. The end user should also keep peroxides in the packing used to
transport them until they are to be used.

These packages, in the case of peroxides liable to decompose strongly
(high-risk group), must consist of low-resistance containers in order to
avoid the effects of confinement. Some peroxides may be stored in metal
containers. The metals which have no harmful effects on peroxides are
firstly pure aluminium and secondly stainless steel. Tin-plated or
galvanised iron are suitable for some peroxides. However, the most
commonly used apparatuses are made of plastics, especially polyethylene.
They are often housed inside protective cardboard boxes.

It is preferable not to place packages of peroxide standing on top of
one another in a warehouse or depot, and to ensure that they are not in
contact with one another or too close to a wall, so that if the contents
heat up, the heat will not be easily passed on to neighbouring packages.
If, during a warehouse inspection, a package is seen not to be leakproof,
it must be removed at once.

The user will normally be well advised to store organic peroxides in
the same packing as was used for transport, with a unit capacity of less

than 50 kg. However, the question has been raised whether manufacturers using large quantities might not store a liquid peroxide in a large stainless steel tank after transport in a tanker. If that is so, then a calculation must be made of the maximum control temperature not to be exceeded in a mass of the size of the tank envisaged, and one must also in most cases provide for continuous refrigeration with recording of the temperature in the central area of the liquid, together with an alarm system in case the temperature rises.

22.4.5 Disposal of organic peroxides

Disposing of unused peroxides or wastes containing peroxides can be a delicate problem. There is no general solution, but the following are methods which might be used:

1˙ Acyl peroxides and per-esters can usually be destroyed by hydrolysis (or saponification) using strong bases. The safest method consists in feeding them *gradually* into a methanol solution of soda. If aqueous soda is used, it must be in very large quantities†.

2˙ Peroxydicarbonates are easily destroyed by the action of a solution of 5% aqueous soda. In the case of peroxydicarbonates which are unstable at ordinary temperature, as most of them are, the peroxide can simply be spread out in a very thin layer on the floor and left to decompose gradually by itself as it heats up. The operation must be carried out in the open air and well away from any source of ignition.

3˙ Peroxides which are not stable at ordinary temperature can quite simply be spread in a thin layer on the floor, where they will gradually decompose as they pass from the refrigerated state to the ambient temperature.

4˙ Solid peroxides can be spread in a thin layer on a bed of wood chips and sawdust which is then set alight. This is the destruction method used on a burning site in factories producing intentional explosives. It is important to avoid any local accumulation of the product to be destroyed and to start the fire with an appropriate relay.

Peroxides in liquid or solution form can be destroyed in the same way after absorbing them into vermiculite or perlite. Destruction by fire is proportionally more safe as the product contains more phlegmatiser.

5˙ Peracetic acid and other soluble peroxy-acids can, after dilution in twenty times their weight in water, be neutralised with care and then flushed into the drains.

BIBLIOGRAPHICAL REFERENCES

[1]   Siemens, A. M. (1962) *Brit. Plastic*, p. 357
[2]   Noller, D. C. *et al*. (1964) *Ind. Eng. Ch.* 56 18

---

† When destroying a peroxide with soda, the peroxide should be added in a succession of small quantities and with the liquid being stirred. Indeed, this is true whenever any kind of explosive substance is destroyed by a chemical agent (acid, ammonium sulphide, etc.). Explosions have sometimes occurred because of a failure to take these precautions.

[3]   Clancey, V. J., Owen, A. J. & Taylor, A. J. (1970) *R.A.R.D.E. Memo 21*

[4]   Guillet, J. E. & Meyer, M. F. (1962) *Ind. Eng. Ch. Prod. Research Devel.* 1 226

[5]   Le Roux, A. (1955) *Mém. Poudres* 37 49

[6]   Chester, M. *et al.* (1967) *C.A.* 66 1241

[7]   Farmer, R. C. (1921) *J. Soc. Ch. Ind.* 40 385

[8]   Prat, J. (1948) *Mém. Services Chim. Etat* 34 385

[9]   Graf, R. (1952) *Annalen* 578 50

[10] Leveskin, N. G. United States Patent 3 507 800 of 21 April 1970

[11] Yoshida, T. *et al.* (1985) *J. of Hazardous Mat.* 12 27

[12] (1964) *Angew. Chem.* International Ed. 3 269

[13] Laporte Chemicals Ltd. (1958) *Sales Leaflet No. 9*

[14] Schnur, R. C. (1981) *Chem. Eng. News* 59 No. 19, 3

[15] Verhoeff, J. & Van den Berg, P. J. (1984) *J. Therm. Anal.* 29 533

[16] Mohan, V. K., Becker, K. R. & Hay, E. (1982) *J. Hazardous Mat.* 5 197

23

Ammonium nitrate and its thermal decomposition

23.1 GENERAL PROPERTIES

23.1.1 General observations

Ammonium nitrate is a very important product in the chemical industry, and is manufactured in millions of tons a year. Most of it is used to make fertilisers (simple nitrogen fertilisers and compound fertilisers). It is also a constituent in many nitrated explosives. It is the raw material in the manufacture of nitrous oxide (see 23.4.1) and is also used as a nutritive agent for bacteria in the fermentation industry (for example, in the production of citric acid). It is found commercially in the form of crystals, grains, or spherules, the latter being obtained by a process dating from 1932 but only developed since 1945 which consists in pouring off from the top of a tower 50 m or more high (called a prilling tower) a hot concentrated solution of nitrate separated by the holes of a watering rose whilst a current of air rises up through the tower†.

23.1.2 Physical properties

Pure ammonium nitrate is a colourless salt which melts at 169.6°C and is highly soluble in water (100 g of water dissolves 66 g of nitrate at 20°C), with solubility increasing rapidly with temperature. In the solid state its polymorphism is remarkable, since, at ordinary pressure, it comes in no

---

† These spherules, which are also called 'prills' in the fertiliser industry, may be 'high density' or 'low density' (see 25.2.1).

less than five crystalline forms† which have the following ranges of
stability:

        form I   —   cubic – above 125˚C
        form II   —   quadratic – between 84 and 125˚C
        form III   —   monoclinic‡ – between 32 and 84˚C
        form IV   —   orthorhombic – between – 18 and 32˚C
        form V   —   quadratic – below – 18˚C.

   Form IV, which is stable at ordinary temperature, has a specific
gravity of 1.73 g/cm³. The transformations, also called transitions, IV →
III, III → II, and II → I, are endothermic, whilst the transformations IV →
III and II → I are accompanied by dilation (decrease in density), and the
increase in volume of about 3.6% which accompanies the transition IV → III
is particularly large.   By contrast, the transformation III → II is
accompanied by contraction (the volume diminishes by about 0.2%).
   The orthorhombic form IV is found in crystals obtained by evaporation
at ordinary temperature of an aqueous solution of ammonium nitrate.   They
are needle-shaped crystals which can easily be deformed and can be bent
between the fingers.   Form III of NH_4NO_3 is similar to form III of KNO_3
which is the stable form of saltpetre at ordinary temperature and up to
126˚C.
   Transformations II → III and IV → III are observed only if the nitrate
is slightly humid. When the substance is dry, there is a direct transition
from II → IV at around 50–55˚C, as Hendricks et al. [7] observed in 1932.
That is why, in experiments of differential thermal analysis, a recording
is obtained like that in Fig. 23.1 in which, after heating to 160˚C, the
nitrate loses its humidity, and, on cooling to around 55˚C, a direct
transition is observed from II to IV.   If, during storage, variations of
temperature take the product through the temperature of 32˚C by alternate
heating or cooling, the resulting dilations and contractions gradually
reduce the grains to smaller particles, which reduces the capacity of the
product to 'flow' and which may also damage the packing.

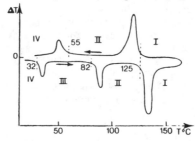

Fig. 23.1 – Differential thermal analysis of ammonium nitrate (mass 1.5
      g). Heating occurs at a rate of 1˚C per minute. From Morand [3].

---

† Bridgman made a study in 1915 of the diagram of state of these various
forms at pressures up to 3000 bars, and found a sixth form which is stable
only under very high pressure.
‡ Monoclinic form with almost orthorhombic parameters.

Potassium nitrate readily forms solid solutions with ammonium nitrate (up to around 20% KNO_3). The differential thermal analysis of these mixed crystals has been studied by Morand [2] who found that solutions containing less than 6% potassium salt give curves similar to those of pure ammonium nitrate with the three transformations IV → III, III → II, and II → I during heating, but at different temperatures. For example, transformation IV → III begins at 22°C (instead of 32°C) with the solid solution with 4% KNO_3. Solutions at more than 6% show no more transition at temperatures in the range 0 to 95°C, and an X-ray examination shows that these solid solutions consist at ordinary temperature of form III (quasi–orthorhombic monoclinic) with a stability range which has increased both at higher and lower temperatures. As early as 1946, Campbell [3] had shown that for solid solutions containing from 8 to 10% potassium nitrate, transformation IV → III takes place at around – 20°C.

The preceding observations explain why ammonium nitrate containing 10% potassium nitrate has been recommended for use as a fertiliser, because suppressing the transition IV → III prevents the grains of nitrate from disintegrating into dust, the technical term for which is 'degranulation'.

A leading British manufacturer adds to nitrate intended for use as a fertiliser a small quantity of anhydrous magnesium nitrate which, on hydrating, fixes the small quantities of water present in ammonium nitrate, thus preventing the transition IV → III.

23.1.3 Hygroscopicity and caking

Ammonium nitrate is hygroscopic. The vapour pressure of saturated aqueous solutions of the substance is considerably lower than the saturating vapour pressure of water (Table 23.1), which is why the nitrate, even when dried above calcium chloride, contains a small quantity of water (of the order of 0.1%) trapped either between the crystals or in the faults inside them. To dry ammonium nitrate completely, it must be kept for a long time in a high vacuum in the presence of phosphorus pentoxide.

Table 23.1

Vapour pressure of saturated solutions of ammonium nitrate compared with that of water (in mm Hg)

Temperatures °C	0°	10°	20°	30°	40°
Saturated aqueous solution of ammonium nitrate	4	6.7	11.2	18.3	31.5
Water	4.58	9.21	17.53	31.84	55.32

The hygroscopic nature of ammonium nitrate has important practical consequences:

1° If it is not in a place with a dry atmosphere or in an air-tight packing, ammonium nitrate gradually absorbs moisture and its crystals are covered with a film of saturated solution which may impregnate any porous

substances with which the wetted nitrate is in contact.   Thus, ordinary
wood and textile sacks may become impregnated with ammonium nitrate.

2° The film of solution between the crystals alters their facies, with
the large crystals tending to grow at the expense of the smaller.   In
addition, the daily variations of temperature in the slightly humid mass
lead to dissolution of the salt followed by recrystallisation between the
granules, which become cemented together, as it were, leading to gradual
agglomeration during storage into a hard mass.   This phenomenon, which is
observed both in large piles of nitrate in bulk and inside sacks piled on
top of one another, is called *binding* when it leads to a substance whose
crystals can easily be re-separated manually, and *caking* when it turns the
substance into a hard block.   Caking occurs easily in piles in which the
substance near the bottom is subjected to the pressure of the substance
above it, and it makes for difficulty of handling.

Various attempts have been made to remedy the caking of nitrate, but
none of them is completely satisfactory.   Whetstone and Holmes [8] have
shown that various dyes added in small quantities (0.05 to 0.5%) modify the
facies of form IV, which produces not needle-shaped crystals but tablets,
so that the product cakes less readily.   Sulphonated fuchsine (acid magenta
dye) is fairly effective, but the use of dyes for this purpose is not very
widespread.   Also used as anti-massing agents are amine acetates with a
long chain or sodium alkylnaphthalene sulphonates in a concentration of
between 0.02 and 0.05%.   A more commonly used method is the addition of
finely-powdered substances.   The mechanism of this 'fluxing' has been
studied by Frey [35].   Some of the substances used for this purpose are
kieselguhr, talc, and calcium or magnesium carbonate, added to the nitrate
in concentrations of between 1 and 4%.   Clay and zinc oxide have also been
recommended, as have many other products.

In the United States since around 1920, ammonium nitrate for use as a
fertiliser has often been mixed with a soft substance which will coat the
grains and so protect them from water vapour in the air.   Two main types of
nitrate fertiliser were manufactured in this way around 1946:
(a) nitrate containing between 0.75 and 1% of raw mineral wax with 3 to 4%
kaolin;
(b) nitrate containing between 1 and 1.5% of a mixture of vaseline,
paraffin, and resin (called a P.R.P. mixture) and 4 to 6% of kaolin or
kieselguhr.

The molten P.R.P. was either poured into the nitrate cooling vat or
sprinkled in pure liquid state through holes in a pipe onto the nitrate as
it was carried along by a conveyor belt.

It was a nitrate of type (b) which exploded in Texas City and in Brest
in 1947, and we shall discuss below the value of these organic additives.

23.1.4   Chemical properties of ammonium nitrate

Even very pure ammonium nitrate may contain, in addition to traces of
water, small quantities either of nitric acid or, more rarely, of ammonia.
The acidity of the substance is measured by the pH at 20°C of a 10% aqueous
solution.   If the pH is less than 4.5, the product must be considered as
slightly acid.

Ammonium nitrate is a *chemically stable* substance, since at ordinary
temperature and pressure, as well as over a wide range of both, it can be

stored indefinitely without decomposition. At temperatures slightly above its melting point it undergoes reactions which are studied in detail below (see 23.2). The various reactions of this nitrate under the effect of heat were reported by Berthelot in 1869. Some of them may be explosive in nature, but ammonium nitrate is only a weak and quite insensitive explosive (see Chapter 24). The decomposition reactions of ammonium nitrate are altered appreciably by various catalysts. Thus Montagne [5] used platinum black to decompose a decinormal aqueous solution slowly at ordinary temperature or in one hour at 100°C, according to the equation

$$5NH_4NO_3 \rightarrow 9H_2O + 4N_2 + 2HNO_3.$$

Ammonium nitrate has oxidising properties, but they are less pronounced than those of the alkali metal nitrates. Cellulose substances are particularly sensitive to the oxidising effect of ammonium nitrate, as is shown by the following experiment: an intimate mixture obtained by trituration in a heavy grinding machine of 85% ammonium nitrate and 15% sawdust which is then wetted with a small amount of water turns brown and then black in a few hours at 100°C; after six days in an oven at the same temperature it ignites spontaneously if the mass exceeds a few dozen grammes, and burns vigorously. Similarly, it has frequently been observed that sacks made of textiles, especially jute, which have contained ammonium nitrate and which have not been washed, may ignite when put to dry near pipes carrying steam at around 100°C because they are steeped in nitrate. This oxidising property explains why adding even very low concentrations of combustible substances to ammonium nitrate alters its explosive properties considerably. It gives rise to deflagrations when heated to a temperature of around 200°C with metal aminosulphates (formerly called sulphamates) [1], which means that there is a danger of an accidental explosion when ammonium nitrate is in contact with fabrics fire-proofed with amino-sulphates.

When it is hot (around 80–100°C), ammonium nitrate loses a little ammonia and becomes acidic, which explains certain reactions between ammonium nitrate at temperatures below 100°C and a number of substances. Thus, Findlay and Rosebourne [34] observed that at about 100°C NH_4NO_3 reacts with cellulose or starch, giving off CO_2, H_2O, and N_2. Adding just 1% of urea, which neutralises nitric acid, is enough to prevent this reaction. This idea of stabilising ammonium nitrate with urea was later taken up by Rozman [42], who showed that with between 0.1 and 0.5% urea, the nitrate does not become acid. Its pH (measured in a 10% aqueous solution) remains, after heating for one hour at 200°C, equal to 6.5, whilst in the absence of urea it falls to 3.1. But if between 2 and 3% urea is added, the stability of the nitrate is reduced, because of the instability of urea itself. Similar results were published in 1962 by Kilman [31].

Ammonium nitrate can be titrated, like the other ammoniacal salts, by the Ronchèse method, which consists in using formaldehyde to change the ammonium ion into hexamethylenetetramine and titrating the nitric acid liberated with a decinormal solution of soda. Care should be taken when heating these solutions of ammonium nitrate with added formol, since explosive compounds can be formed, as laboratory experiments have shown. When formol, which is an aqueous solution of formaldehyde containing methanol, is heated with ammonium nitrate and the solution is evaporated, a residue is left which is made up of an explosive mixture of ammonium nitrate and methylammonium nitrate. There is also the possibility that explosive cyclonite (trinitramine cyclotrimethylene) will be formed by the reaction

$$6CH_2O + 6 NH_4NO_3 \rightarrow 2(CH_2 - N - NO_2)_3 + 12H_2O,$$

but it seems highly doubtful that derivatives of fulminic acid will be formed, as Spindler [4] has claimed.

23.2 ACTION OF HEAT ON AMMONIUM NITRATE

23.2.1 General observations

The thermochemical data concerning ammonium nitrate are gathered in Table 23.2.

As soon as it melts at 169.6°C, ammonium nitrate begins to undergo vaporisation accompanied by dissociation into ammonia and nitric acid, and this vaporisation becomes considerable at around 300°C. At temperatures around 185°C, another reaction begins in which ammonium nitrate decomposes into water and nitrous oxide, and the two reactions continue simultaneously between 200 and 300°C and even beyond.

Guiochon [21] stresses the following point, which had been unknown to or forgotten by most previous authors who studied the decomposition of ammonium nitrate by heat: a clear distinction must be made between those reactions which have their seat in the molten nitrate and those which take place between the gases created by the heating of the nitrate. If these gases are rapidly cooled as they are released and then evacuated from the area in which the nitrate is being heated, they contain only the four chemical species formed by the reactions quoted above, namely N_2O, H_2O, NH_3, and HNO_3, the latter also being liable to partial dissociation if the temperature is high enough. But if these gases are maintained at the temperature at which they were formed, they may react with one another and form water, nitrogen, nitrogen dioxide, and nitric oxide. The latter oxides appear in particular when ammonium nitrate in a closed vessel is raised to a temperature higher than 260°C.

23.2.2 The vaporisation of ammonium nitrate

Heated ammonium nitrate vaporises even before its melting point of 169.6°C, giving off a vapour which is dissociated into nitric acid and ammonia:

$$NH_4NO_3(cr, IV) \rightleftarrows HNO_3(v) + NH_3(g) - 176 \text{ kJ}. \tag{I}$$

This reaction is similar to the vaporisation with dissociation of ammonium chloride, which has been known for a long time. Like the latter, it is strongly endothermic, and it is reversible, with the vapours of acid and ammonia able to recombine to form nitrate crystals on a cold surface.

Feick [9] has made a precise experimental measurement of the vapour pressure above molten ammonium nitrate over a temperature range from 190 to 250°C, as well as of the enthalpy of molten nitrate as a function of temperature up to 270°C. From these values he was able to calculate the heat of reaction (I) at various temperatures. Table 23.3 gives the values of the vapour pressure† and Table 23.5 those of the heat of reaction.

Table 23.2

Thermochemical data for ammonium nitrate

	Heats of formation at 18°C		Molar calorific capacity (at cst. pr.) (J/mol.°C)
	F_p (kJ/mol)	F_v (kJ/mol)	
NH_4NO_3 (cr IV)	366	354	142
(cr III)	364	352	117
(cr II)	363	351	142
(cr I)	358	347	188
liquid	353	342	161

Table 23.3

Vapour pressure of ammonium nitrate, after Feick [9]

Temperature (°C)	188.2	205.1	215.9	223.1	236.7	249.1
Vapour pressure (mm Hg)	3.25	7.45	11.55	15.8	27	41

Table 23.4

Velocity constant k (in 10^{-3} s^{-1}) of the decomposition reaction of ammonium nitrate

Temperature (°C)	Cook & Abegg (original)	Cook & Abegg (corrected by Smith)	Guiochon	Keenan and Dimitriades
230	0.053	0.05	0.044	0.011
250	0.23	0.22	0.17	0.067
290	3.10	2.53	2.15	1.97

---

† Using Claperyon's equation, the heat of dissociation can be derived from the pressure vapour measured experimentally (by Feick or Brandner) as a function of temperature, and the value thus obtained agrees well with the value derived independently from calculation.

Table 23.5

Heats of reaction of vaporisation with dissociation
and of decomposition of molten ammonium nitrate, after Feick and Hainer

Temperature (°C)	169.6	200	250	300
Heat of vaporisation Q_p (I) (kJ/mol)	− 164	− 163	− 160	− 175
Heat of decomposition Q_p (II) (kJ/mol)	55	57	59	61

The above values for the vapour pressure of molten ammonium nitrate
have been confirmed by measurements made by Brandner and his associates
[10] using a method based on a completely different principle from that
used in Feick's experiments.   Brandner and his colleagues also made
measurements on the solid salt between 76 and 165°C, a range over which
they found that the vapour pressure varies from 0.0024 to 1.17 mm Hg.

It is interesting to note the particularly high value of the enthalpy
of reaction (I), which is about 2000 kJ per kg of nitrate at 250°C, and
therefore of the same order of magnitude as the heat of vaporisation of
water at 100°C, which is 2260 kJ/kg.

23.2.3 The decomposition of ammonium nitrate into water and nitrous oxide

The principal reaction of thermal decomposition of ammonium nitrate has
been known since 1798 (Deiman and associates).   The equation for this
irreversible reaction is

$$NH_4NO_3 \rightarrow N_2O(g) + 2H_2O(g). \tag{II}$$

It is exothermic, and the heat of reaction at constant pressure is
  36 kJ/mol at 18°C from the solid salt,
  59 kJ/mol at 250°C from the molten salt.

At the various temperatures at which it has been studied, it follows a
first order law, as Robertson [15] was the first to recognise, which means
that the amount da which decomposes at a given temperature is proportional
to the quantity† a of nitrate present.   Thus, da = − kadt.

---

† As Barclay and his associates [22] observed, the only thing that can in
all strictness be deduced from Robertson's experiments or similar studies
is a relation between the rate of decomposition and the mass of a system of
given composition.   They have shown by experiments on molten mixtures of
alkali metal nitrates and ammonium nitrate at 240°C that reaction (III) is,
from the kinetic point of view, of the first order in relation to the
concentration of NH_4 ions.   However, with non−diluted ammonium nitrate the
constant they find is three times lower than that of their predecessors.

In 1956, Cook and Abegg [16] confirmed this law and gave numerical values of the same order of magnitude as those of Robertson. It is difficult to make precise measurements of the velocity constant k because of the vaporisation of the nitrate (reaction I) which accompanies the decomposition (reaction II). Guiochon [21] on the one hand and Keenan and Dimitriades [14] on the other have tried to take account of vaporisation to give values for k which relate well to reaction (II). Their results, obtained by different experimental methods, are given in Table 23.4. In addition, an experiment by Feick and Hainer [11] gave $k = 1.64.10^{-3}$ s^{-1} at 290°C (a value which they believe to be too low).

The value of the activation energy, which, depending on the author, ranges from 150 to 200 kJ/mol (Guiochon gives 153 kJ/mol), implies that between 250 and 325°C each 10°C increase in temperature has the effect of almost doubling the rate of reaction.

Reaction (II) above, as Shah and Oza [13] were the first to observe and as Guiochon has since confirmed, takes place in molten nitrate (in other words in the liquid phase). Up to at least 300°C it is, together with vaporisation–dissociation, practically the only reaction which the liquid undergoes when the ammonium nitrate is pure.

The role of water – In 1950, Friedman and Bigeleisen [12] made a most curious observation: ammonium nitrate which has been dried for a very long time at 150°C in a high vacuum (10^{-5} mm of mercury) can subsequently be melted and raised to 300°C for several hours without decomposing, but if, after heating, a trace of water is incorporated and heating recommences, decomposition takes place at the usual temperatures. This observation was confirmed by Keenan [17] in 1955.

The role of nitric acid – Veley showed as early as 1883 that when ammonium nitrate is heated, it loses ammonia and becomes acidic because a small quantity of nitric acid remains, at least in part, dissolved in the molten salt. He also found that the higher the acidity of the ammonium nitrate, the faster reaction (II) seems to be. He also showed that the nitrate with an alkaline reaction (presence of a small amount of free NH$_3$) decomposes only slowly, and also observed that the decomposition taking place in molten nitrate can be stopped by an injection of ammonia. It is to the formation of ammonia that is attributed the stabilising role of urea, which will be discussed below (23.3.3), and it is taken as an established fact that ammonium nitrate and its solutions are more stable when their pH (in a 10% solution) is higher than 4.5 than when it is lower.

The acceleration which occurs at the beginning of the reaction of ammonium nitrate when it contains nitric acid has been noted by a number of authors since Veley, but they have generally studied only the initial phases of the reaction and have usually not analysed the gases obtained. In particular, the heating experiments in sealed tubes conducted in 1955 by Wood and Wise [[18] have been subjected to close criticism by Guiochon, who concludes that the influence of nitric acid underlined by Wood and Wise was related to a reaction other than reaction (II). The thermogravimetric experiments of Guiochon on nitrate acidified by HNO$_3$ show a rate of weight loss very close to that of the pure salt, and he also finds that the slow bubbling of a stream of ammonia through molten nitrate has no effect on the evolution of its decomposition. He concludes that nitric acid has no effect on the decomposition reaction (II) of the nitrate in liquid phase. It may be that Veley's observations concerned insufficiently pure ammonium nitrate (see 23.2.6),

Smith [19] was able to measure the concentration of nitric acid and

water as a function of temperature (from 230 to 280°C) in the liquid
reactive medium in operation, and found the following results at 250°C:

molar ratios	mass percentages
$\dfrac{HNO_3}{NH_4NO_3} = 1.3 \ 10^{-3}$	nitric acid = 0.1%
$\dfrac{H_2O}{NH_4NO_3} = 30 \ 10^{-2}$	water = 0.68%

23.2.4 Other decomposition reactions of ammonium nitrate when heated

Researchers who, between 1920 and 1935, made the first measurements for the
decomposition of ammonium nitrate, and who more often than not did not
remove the gases formed from the vessel containing the nitrate, found that
in addition to reaction (II) there were other quite secondary reactions
giving mainly nitrogen.   These reactions take place in the gas phase above
molten ammonium nitrate, as Shah and Oza [13] were the first to point out
and as Guiochon confirmed by using improved methods.   Saunders [20] found
some 2% nitrogen in the gases formed by the decomposition of ammonium
nitrate at around 240°C and attributed it to the reaction

$$5NH_3 + 3HNO_3 \rightarrow 9H_2O + 4N_2. \tag{III}$$

It should be noted that this reaction (III), which consumes more ammonia
than nitric acid, explains why the concentration of HNO_3 in the vapour
increases and why, as a result, molten nitrate in equilibrium with this
vapour becomes acid.   However, Saunders has provided no proof that the
process whereby nitrogen is produced follows equation (III), and since, on
the other hand, both Kretzschmar [23] and Friedman and Bigeleisen [12] have
found oxygen as well as nitrogen in the gases formed, it seems more likely
that these gases result from the oxidation of ammonia by nitrogen dioxide
formed from the dissociation of nitric acid vapour:

$$4HNO_3 \rightleftarrows 4NO_2 + O_2 + 2H_2O$$
$$6NO_2 + 8NH_3 \rightarrow 7N_2 + 12H_2O,$$

giving overall

$$12HNO_3 + 16NH_3 \rightarrow 30H_2O + 3O_2 + 14N_2, \tag{IV}$$

which is a strongly exothermic reaction since it liberates 289 kJ per mol
of reacting HNO_3.   It should be noted in this respect that Davis and Abrams
[24] have indeed found that the ratio of O_2 to N_2 in the gas given off is
close to 3/14, as indicated by equation (IV).
      Other reactions which give nitric oxide NO and dioxide NO_2 may be
observed when ammonium nitrate is heated *in a closed vessel*, in other words

when the pressure may rise considerably above atmospheric pressure. These reactions take place in the gas phase and are appreciable only above 280°C. They have hardly ever been subjected to quantitative study, although we should mention research done by Delsemme [25] who used spectography to chart the decomposition of ammonium nitrate in a stainless steel cell with a quartz window capable of withstanding up to 100 bars. Bands of NO are detectable around 270–280°C. A remarkable result in these experiments is that the decomposition of insufficiently dried ammonium nitrate (still containing 0.4% water) culminates in a vigorous but not explosive end phase, unlike the dry nitrate. In Delsemme's experiment this end phase occurred at around 290°C when the pressure was between 50 and 60 bars.

Prolonged heating in a closed vessel of ammonium nitrate and the resulting products also leads to a gas mixture which contains, in addition to the combustible gas ammonia, oxidising gases of nitrogen oxides, so that the mixture is liable to explode as Kaiser [26] observed in experiments of a qualitative nature.

23.2.5 Isobaric thermolysis of ammonium nitrate

Ammonium nitrate heated beyond its melting point is the seat of an exothermic decomposition into N_2O and H_2O and an endothermic process of vaporisation with dissociation. The coexistence of these two reactions, *when they take place at constant pressure*, has the effect of bringing the reacting mass to a state in which it stabilises at a given temperature which is a function of the pressure and the rate at which heat is applied (external heating) or removed (refrigeration). Feick and Hainer [11] in a work of major importance established the relation between the following factors:

– P total pressure,
– p vapour pressure of the nitrate (dissociated into NH_3 and HNO_3),
– Q heat supplied from an external source (per mole of decomposed NH_4NO_3),

$$P = \left[1 - \frac{3}{2}\frac{F_I}{Q + F_{II}}\right]p,$$

where F_I and F_{II} are the heats at constant pressure of reactions (I) and (II), the values for which are given in Table 23.5. These heats of reaction vary comparatively little with temperature, so that they can be replaced in the above equation by average values in the range 230 to 300°C. On the other hand, p being known as a function of the temperature, it is possible, for each temperature, to calculate the pressure P of the working state of the system. In particular, in an adiabatic process ($Q = 0$), we find the values given in Table 23.6, which also contains the values found experimentally. The discrepancies are due in part to the fact that there are always secondary reactions (formation of N_2), as well as to errors in F_I, F_{II}, etc. and to the approximation involved in treating the gases formed as ideal gases.

With continuous removal of heat ($Q < 0$), it is possible, at a given pressure, to stabilise the system at a temperature lower than that of the adiabatic process, which is what is done in the manufacture of nitrous oxide.

Feick and Hainer's analysis has the following important consequence:

Table 23.6

Working temperature in the isobaric thermolysis of ammonium nitrate
(application of Feick and Hainer's equation)

Total pressure P (atm)	0.5	1.0	1.5	2.0

A. *Reaction with removal of heat*, equal to 44 kJ per mol of reacting nitrate
  - working temperature calculated
    as a first approximation ($^\circ$C)
	230	250	261	271

B. *Adiabatic process*
  - working temperature calculated
    as a first approximation ($^\circ$C)
	266	288	302	312

- working temperature calculated as a second approximation ($^\circ$C)	266	289	304	314
- temperature observed experimentally ($^\circ$C)	271	292	306	315

C. *Reaction with supply of heat*, equal to 59 kJ per mol of reacting nitrate
  - working temperature calculated
    as a first approximation ($^\circ$C)
	282	305	320	331

NB.   First-approximation calculations are made by taking the following
average values:

$$F_I = 159 \text{ kJ/mol} \qquad\qquad F_{II} = 59 \text{ kJ/mol}.$$

In the second approximation the calculation uses the values of F_I and F_{II}
deduced from Table 23.5 by an interpolation relative to the value of the
temperature obtained in the first approximation.

The vapour pressure of dissociated ammonium nitrate has been calculated
from the formula given by Feick and Hainer:

$$\log p \text{ (cm of Hg)} = 8.502 - 4190/T.$$

The value of $q = -44$ kJ/mol in case A is close to that which is
normally found in reactors producing nitrous oxide supplied with anhydrous
ammonium nitrate (see 23.4.1).

---

as long as reactions other than vaporisation with dissociation (I) and
decomposition into nitrous oxide (II) are only secondary, which in practice
means up to 300°C, *decomposing nitrate at a given pressure cannot rise
above a certain temperature*. At atmospheric pressure this equilibrium
temperature calculated by the above equation is 288°C, a fact verified
experimentally by Feick and Hainer, who found 290°C. They were even able
to decompose a 100 g load of molten nitrate at 315°C at 2 atmospheres, and
observed that the reaction was *calm and regular* without the gas produced
having the brown colour that would have signalled the presence of the
dioxide NO_2.

To this observation by Feick and Hainer may be compared an experiment conducted in 1922 by Munroe [27], who heated 4.5 kg of 99.1% nitrate (and 0.08% humidity) in an enamelled vessel. The gas produced turned yellow only above 290°C and when decomposition finished ten minutes after heating began the temperature had risen to 375°C without an explosion taking place.

Experiments conducted by Heinrich [47] also fall within the framework of Feick and Hainer's theory. He heated 25 g of pure nitrate in the covered case designed by the B.A.M. (see 16.2.3) to which were fitted devices to record temperature and pressure. As long as the diameter of the opening is not equal to or less than 1 mm, heating in the test conditions (four Teclu burners) did not result in an explosion. The nitrate steadily decomposed without the pressure going much above atmospheric. With an opening of 1 mm decomposition lasted for almost a minute without any rise in pressure. It was only several seconds after the end of decomposition that the researchers observed a very rapid rise in temperature, which reached 700°C, and in pressure, which rose to 300 bars, at which value the case was shattered. During most of the decomposition the temperature of the contents of the case stayed level at 280°C. Using Feick and Hainer's theory, we can calculate from this temperature that during decomposition the heat radiated from the case exceeds by 2900 joules per minute that which it receives from the burners.

23.2.6 Catalytic effect of chlorine on the thermal decomposition of ammonium nitrate

When ammonium nitrate contains chlorides or chlorinated compounds, its decomposition in the molten state is made more rapid, as observed by Veley and later by Saunders. Decomposition can then be seen, as Tramm and Velde [37] observed, below the melting point of the salt, in other words at temperatures at which the pure salt does not decompose. The decomposition reaction initiated by chlorides liberates mainly nitrogen and is especially violent, according to Tramm and Velde, when there is a small quantity of nitric acid (in a concentration such as 0.1 or 0.2%) as well as chlorine. But if ammonia is injected into the decomposing molten substance, its effect is to calm the reaction immediately.

This effect of chlorine is quite appreciable and can, according to Herquet [33], be seen with just 0.02% of the substance. Those authors who have studied it, including Braconier and Delsemme [25] and Keenan [17], are agreed on two points:

(a) The decomposition catalysed by chlorides takes place at a temperature some 50 to 80°C lower than that of pure nitrate.

(b) The decomposition is more rapid than that of pure nitrate.

For example, in experiments by differential thermal analysis Keenan [17] observed the peak of decomposition at 270°C with pure nitrate and at 225°C with nitrate mixed with 5 moles per hundred of NaCl. The height of the peak ($\Delta\theta$), which was only 6°C with pure nitrate, reached 50°C with nitrate containing chlorine (Fig. 23.2).

(c) The strong decomposition reaction caused by the presence of chlorine is initiated only after a certain induction period which becomes nil in the presence of a large quantity of nitric acid.

Hainer [39], in his measurements of the rate of decomposition of pure nitrate and nitrate with various substances added, found that at around 175°C the product containing 1% sodium chlorine decomposes 1000 times faster than pure nitrate.

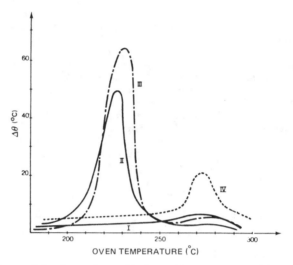

Fig. 23.2 - Differential thermal analysis - I: pure ammonium nitrate;   II: nitrate + 5% NaCl;   III: nitrate + 5% NH$_4$Cl;   IV: nitrate + 5% NaBr.   (Mass heated: 1 g;   temperature of oven rises by 2°C per minute).   After Keenan.

Guiochon [21], who used a number of methods to make a close study of this action of chloride (in the form of ammonium chloride, other chlorides, or free chlorine injected into the reactive medium), has confirmed the properties previously observed by others, such as the existence of an induction period, the influence of the simultaneous presence of a small amount of nitric acid, the different nature of the products of the reaction (nitrogen), and so on.

Bromides and iodides have a similar action to that of chlorides, but fluorides have no effect.

In the presence of a large quantity of acid (nitric or other) and chlorides, ammonium nitrate in a concentrated solution may decompose, even below 100°C [28], undergoing reaction (II) which gives N$_2$O with traces of NO, Cl$_2$, and NOCl. The equation for the reaction catalysed by chlorine† at a high temperature is

$$5NH_4NO_3 \rightarrow 2HNO_3 + 4N_2 + 9H_2O.$$

Guiochon notes that this reaction is that which ensures the greatest fall in free enthalpy.

23.2.7 The effect of various catalysts on the decomposition of ammonium nitrate

Other substances have a catalytic action, which is often as intense as that

---

† Its heat, with molten ammonium nitrate, is 139 kJ per mole of NH$_4$NO$_3$.

of chlorine, on the thermal decomposition of ammonium nitrate. Such is the case with compounds of copper, manganese, cobalt, and chromium of which Guiochon [29] has done a detailed study. Adding chromic nitrate to ammonium nitrate may initiate rapid decomposition with no induction period from 130°C.

Smith [30] has also done a quantitative study of the decomposition of molten ammonium nitrate by chromates and dichromates. When the catalyst is added to the nitrate at 210°C, there is emission of gas and an increase in temperature, and at a given moment a great quantity of foam is produced, a process which, in tests on a few hundred grammes, lasts some ten seconds. The brown-red gases are sometimes accompanied by a dark red flame, so that the phenomenon is reminiscent of the one known as 'fuming off' in the nitration of cellulose. Smith was able to establish from measurements that the temperature reached by the liquid in the final phase of decomposition is 311°C and that it results from the fixation at 765 mm of mercury (which was the pressure used in his experiments) of the competing set of reactions (I), (II), and (V). Between 30 and 40% of the nitrate decomposes according to (II) and the rest according to (V). A calculation similar to that of Feick and Hainer also leads to a temperature of 310-312°C at ordinary pressure.

When the liberated gases above the liquid ignite, they are at an initial temperature of 500°C before rising after a short delay to about 700°C, when they undergo the reactions already observed by Kaiser (see 23.2.4) which consist in a reduction of nitric acid vapour by NH_3 at first to NO_2 and then to NO, with the second reduction being more exothermic than the first.

A different reaction [5] is observed with diluted solutions (5 to 10 g of NH_4NO_3 per litre) subjected to the catalytic action of platinum black. Slowly at ordinary temperature and more rapidly at around 100°C, these solutions decompose to give off pure nitrogen, with ammonium nitrate undergoing reaction (V).

Several studies carried out since the 1960s with a view to using ammonium nitrate in solid multi-stage rocket propellants have confirmed the important catalytic effect of chromates. Thus, Fragino [41] was able to decompose in 10 minutes at 200°C nitrate with an added 5% equimolar mixture of manganese chloride and copper chromate. By adding 5% potassium chromate to ammonium nitrate, Glaskova [46] obtained a mixture which deflagrated at atmospheric pressure with a steady flame, whilst a mixture with 5% sodium chloride deflagrates only at pressures equal to at least 10 atm.

23.3   CONCENTRATED AQUEOUS SOLUTIONS OF AMMONIUM NITRATE

23.3.1   Industrial role of aqueous solutions of ammonium nitrate

Ammonium nitrate is manufactured by saturating aqueous nitric acid with ammonia whilst stirring thoroughly at a temperature which may be high (150-160°C). A hot concentrated solution is obtained in the saturator, from which is made
- either so-called crystalline nitrate by leaving it to cool in vats,
- or granulated nitrate by solidifying the product in a granulator equipped with a special stirring mechanism,
- or nitrate in spherules by allowing the substance to fall as a shower in an apparatus known as a prilling tower.

Highly concentrated solutions (around 99%) require a shorter prilling tower and give more compact spherules, but at high temperatures they lose some nitrogen, especially in the form of ammonia, and become acid.

Ammonium nitrate becomes highly soluble in water at high temperatures, whilst the temperatures at which aqueous solutions of ammonium nitrate begin to crystallise are as follows:

Water content (%)	5	7.5	10	12.5	15	17.5	20
Temperature (°C)	122	108	96	85	75	65	57

As a result, it is possible to transport at high temperatures very highly concentrated solutions of ammonium nitrate, in other words nitrate in a form which can be conveniently handled (by pump). To prevent the product from crystallising during transport, it must be loaded at a temperature sufficiently above its crystallisation temperature, for example 130°C for a 90% solution. Such transport takes place on a large scale between factories in insulated road and rail tankers.

In some factories it is also necessary to store for periods of up to several months hot concentrated solutions of between 85 and 96% ammonium nitrate, with the temperature likely to reach 140°C.

23.3.2 Properties of hot concentrated solutions of ammonium nitrate

These solutions corrode many metals, and even stainless steels will in the long run be subjected to a slight attack which releases ferric ions into the solution. They also turn gradually acid, and, if they contain chlorides, even in concentrations as low as 0.005%, they will, after a certain induction period, release nitrogen by reaction (V) quoted in 23.2.6. This reaction can be stopped immediately by introducing ammonia into the solution.

Accidental contamination of the solution by the catalysts mentioned in 23.2.6 and 23.2.7 may cause it to decompose at temperatures as low as 100°C with emission of acid gases and vapours. This decomposition may become strong enough to increase pressure in a container with inadequate openings. The reaction is similar to the nitrous reaction (homogeneous explosion) described in 23.2.6. An explosion occurred in 1969 in an ammonium nitrate factory in an intermediate storage vat for a hot solution with 94% nitrate into which calcium chloride had been introduced by accident as a result of a leak from a pipe in a tubular heat exchanger carrying brine containing 10% calcium chloride† in the ammonia evaporation system. The temperature of the vat, which was initially 140°C, gradually rose, together with the pressure, until it reached about 200°C after three hours, at which point a

---

† This accident has one thing in common with the following accident which occurred before 1939 in a nitration factory: the nitric–sulphuric mixture was cooled by a coil carrying calcium chloride brine. When a hole appeared in the coil, the saline solution entered and reacted with the acid bath, giving off a great deal of heat and forming hydrochloric acid and so causing an explosion. Following this accident, the calcium chloride brine was replaced by a concentrated solution of sodium nitrate.

deflagration began in the 4500 litres of solution present in the vat, which had inadequate vents. The workshop was severely damaged.

A similar, but less serious, accident occurred in 1968 during road transport. It was less serious because the solution, being 90%, was less contaminated by catalyst and because as soon as the driver saw vapours coming through one of the vents on the tanker, he opened the hatch, so preventing the pressure from reaching a high level.

This kind of decomposition, which leads to an explosion in a closed container, maintains a limited rate when the openings are sufficient to keep the pressure at a moderate level. In particular, the temperature of decomposition at pressures close to atmospheric stabilises at around 310°C (see 23.2.7) and there can be no explosion.

There may be more danger in reactions caused by the strongly oxidising nature of these solutions, which are liable to react very strongly with most organic materials. A fatal accident occurred in France in 1972 because a 92.5% solution had been loaded into a road tanker which had previously been used to transport an organic substance and which had not been completely cleaned. It is to be noted that the reaction between the nitrate and the residue of organic substance left on the bottom of the tanker became violent only more than an hour after loading was finished.

In order to determine whether the solutions in question can detonate, tests were conducted by I.C.I. in Great Britain and by Groothuizen [44] in the T.N.O. laboratory. It is not easy to compare the results because the operating modes were different. According to the Dutch researcher, high regime detonations (see 14.4.6) are obtained only with solutions with a concentration equal to 98% or more maintained at 210°C or above. This result is to be compared with the one found by Van Dolah [45], who was unable to detonate molten ammonium nitrate (100% solution) at 175 or 200°C, but did detonate it at 220°C. In the British tests, reported by Finch [40], a solution kept boiling at between 155 and 185°C depending on its concentration was excited by a booster of 400 g of powerful explosive. Detonation was successful when the concentration was at least equal to 93%, whilst at 150°C even a 97.5% solution does not detonate. Account should be taken of the fact that in a solution kept boiling the liquid is strongly sensitised by the presence of numerous vapour bubbles (see 15.2.11). It can be concluded from these results that there is no risk of detonation with aqueous solutions of ammonium nitrate at concentrations up to 93 or 95% and at a temperature no higher than 145°C, *provided the solutions are well free from contamination.*

It will be noted that if a solution of ammonium nitrate is caught in a strong fire, it will lose water by vaporisation, becoming more concentrated and so more dangerous.

23.3.3 Stabilising concentrated solutions with urea

In 1959, Rozman and Borodkina [42] found that adding 0.03 to 1% urea to dry ammonium nitrate or its concentrated solutions considerably reduced decomposition beyond 200°C. The pH of such solutions is about 6 to 6.5, whereas in the absence of urea it falls below 3.5 in one hour at 200°C. The experiments of Kilman [31] in 1962 may also be quoted: adding a small amount of urea to a nitrate solution prevents loss of nitrogen. For example, a 60% solution of NH_4NO_3 maintained at 180°C in a balloon flask, with the pressure above it held steady by pumping at 20 cm of mercury,

contains after 20 minutes 0.032% nitric acid and has lost 0.23% nitrogen.
If 0.1% urea has been added to the solution, it does not become acid in
these conditions, whilst with 0.3 or 0.5% urea it is slightly alkaline.

However, it is not always convenient to add even small quantities of
urea to ammonium nitrate in solution. In the case of solutions used to
manufacture nitrous oxide, for example, it would introduce impurities into
the gas produced.

23.3.4 Safety in transporting hot concentrated aqueous solutions of ammonium nitrate

Contrary to what is sometimes claimed, hot (up to 150°C) concentrated
aqueous solutions do not undergo spontaneous decomposition, at least as
long as their pH is not less than 4.5% and they contain no impurities.
Their thermal stability (kinetic stability) is good at these temperatures.
These solutions become dangerous as soon as they are contaminated by
combustible foreign bodies or by decomposition catalysts, the foremost of
which are the chlorides.

In the first place, tankers should be suited to the transport in
question. They should be insulated, except for short journeys. The type
of insulation recommended consists of an external metal envelope at least 5
cm away from the wall of the tank, since a double envelope of this kind
contains a layer of air which prevents excessive heat losses in transit.
In addition, the outer envelope may usefully be opened along the bottom to
facilitate cleaning and prevent the accumulation of substances. If the
tanker is insulated with lagging material between the inner and outer
walls, this material must be inorganic and practically free of combustible
substances†. All wooden parts and combustible materials should be avoided
in the design of the vehicle.

Since tankers are normally discharged by means of a compressed air (or
nitrogen) dip tube, they must be built to withstand a gauge pressure of at
least 2 bars. They can be fitted with a means of internal re-heating in
case the contents crystallise after too much cooling.

The tanker should be fitted with devices designed to ensure that when
the full tanker is in transit the tank cannot be subjected to too great a
pressure or too high a vacuum in relation to the atmosphere.

Only ammonium nitrate with a good degree of purity should be loaded
into the tanker, and the solution must have a pH (measured at 20°C in a 10%
concentration) higher than 4.5 and a chlorine content less than 0.01%.

When a tanker is to be used to transport nitrate in solution, it is
preferable for it not to be used for any other product. However, if a
tanker has been used to transport some other product, before it is loaded
with nitrate it must be cleaned both inside and out, and special care must
be taken to ensure that no trace of any organic substance or any other
dangerous contaminant (chlorinated compound) is left in the tank or inside
or outside the double envelope. Attention is drawn to the fact that steam

---

† Glass wool and other fibrous mineral products are often mixed with a
small amount of a combustible greasing substance, and there have been cases
of reaction with release of hot gases in this glass wool contaminated by
nitrated solutions.

cleaning may not be enough to eliminate a residue of a substance with a sufficiently high melting point.

Care should be taken during loading and unloading to ensure that no foreign body is introduced accidentally into the tanker. For unloading with compressed air, the air used must be clean and oil-free.

The workforce must wear protective clothing, especially gloves and goggles, because these solutions cause serious burns to the skin.

If it is necessary before unloading to heat the contents of a tanker, the upper hatch should be left open during heating to avoid a build-up of pressure in the tank.

If the body of the tanker or the chassis or any other part of the vehicle has been contaminated by nitrate on the outside during loading, all traces should be removed by careful cleaning before transport.

If, during transport, any abnormal heating of the contents or any vapours of whatever colour are seen, the tanker must be driven away from main roads and residential areas and, if possible, cooled by watering it with a hose pipe.

There have been cases of explosions in centrifugal pumps transferring hot solutions of ammonium nitrate when they are started up again after a period of inactivity. Such explosions are caused by lubricant penetrating along the shaft and mixing with nitrate left on the blades. They have happened mainly when the pump was working dry.

23.4 THE MANUFACTURE OF NITROUS OXIDE

23.4.1 Ways of manufacturing nitrous oxide

Using oxygen to manufacture nitrous oxide by oxidising ammonia [32] over special catalysts at temperatures between 180 and 250°C with an N_2O output of up to 70% is a safe operation only if the concentration of ammonia is held at less than 10%, in other words well below the lower flammability limit of the gas in oxygen. This manufacturing process is not used in Europe. We are beginning to recover nitrous oxide, which is sometimes found at concentrations of up to 90%, from the residual gases of certain organic manufacturing processes involving the oxidation of amines or other nitrogenous compounds. One such process is the manufacture of caprolactam, which is an intermediate product in the manufacture of Nylon 6. But in most cases the manufacture of nitrous oxide is based on the thermal decomposition of ammonium nitrate (reaction II in 23.2.3).

This manufacturing process used to be carried out in a series of discontinuous operations: molten ammonium nitrate (at about 170°C) is fed into a reactor and heated to around 250°C; the temperature must then be kept stable by cooling, and the operation is stopped when 80 to 90% of the nitrate fed into the reactor has decomposed. The process is now almost continuous, with molten nitrate or a hot concentrated aqueous solution (about 85%) of ammonium nitrate being fed into the reactor, usually at specified intervals. The use of nitrate in solution† was proposed by Vingee [43] in 1947, and it not only permits greater flexibility in running

---

† This is often called the Balcar process, after F. Balcar who took out a patent in 1952.

the reactor, but also offers greater safety and continuous decomposition of the nitrate at around 250°C in a reactor with automated controls (heating, cooling, feeding, etc.).

According to the values in Table 23.2, 37 kJ must be supplied to one mole of ammonium nitrate to raise it from 18 to 255°C, this being the normal working temperature of the reactor. However, reaction (II) has an isothermal heat of 59 kJ/mol, and at this value, even allowing for the fact that reaction (I), which involves 6 to 7% of the nitrate treated, is endo- thermic, there is still a considerable emission of excess heat. It is not practical to use this to heat and melt the solid nitrate, but if an aqueous solution of nitrate is fed into the reactor, the heat released is reduced by the amount needed to vaporise and raise to 255°C the water that comes with the solution. It is also possible to pre-heat the nitrate solution using the gases from the reactor, which are quenched to reduce parasite reactions giving higher oxides of nitrogen. The nitrate solution is circulated using a variable-delivery pump which is automatically controlled by the temperature in the reactive medium, and the system can be set up in such a way that temperature fluctuates by no more than 0.5°C during non-stop running.

The operating parameters of such an automatic apparatus can be derived from an assessment of its thermal and mass-handling properties. Thus, if an 83% solution at 170°C is fed into the top of the refrigerator unit, the gases from the reactor rising against the flow of the current are cooled from 255 to 175°C. The refrigerating capacity to be supplied to the apparatus in normal running is very small. The gauge pressure inside the reactor is a few centibars. An 83% solution does not crystallise at temperatures above 75°C and is thus easy to handle.

What comes from the reaction bath is essentially the oxide N_2O with 1 to 2% nitrogen† and superheated water vapour, as well as small quantities of ammonia and nitric acid. In order to reduce reactions in the gas phase (dissociation of nitric acid, oxidation of ammonia) to a minimum, the gas is cooled as quickly as possible, first in a vertical chimney above the reactor and then in a refrigerating unit where most of the water vapour is condensed. This quenching allows partial recombination of the ammonia and the nitric acid into NH_4NO_3.

The crude gas emerging from the refrigerator still contains a small amount of ammonia, traces of the oxides NO and NO_2, and a few fine crystals of NH_4NO_3 which did not dissolve in the water. It must be purified, therefore, and that is done by successive washing in water, soda, and water in a series of columns. Any remaining nitrogen is eliminated during subsequent liquefaction of the gas.

In theory, reaction (II) should give 0.55 kg of N_2O per kg of nitrate, and with a good apparatus and a raw material with a good degree of purity, output can be achieved of 0.51 kg/kg, compared with a maximum of 0.42 kg/kg in discontinuous production.

23.4.2 The quality of ammonium nitrate for manufacture of nitrous oxide

The ammonium nitrate used in the manufacture of nitrous oxide is a very

---

† In certain conditions, Guiochon was able, in his experiments, to obtain N_2O containing only 0.1% nitrogen.

pure crystalline product which must satisfy the following conditions:

1° It must contain less than 0.02% of organic substances, since the latter are oxidised during the reaction and so introduce impurities into the gas. In addition, the presence of organic substances increases the amount of heat released in the reactor and may cause the bath of molten nitrate to foam.

It is normally thought sufficient to check that there are no substances which can be extracted with ether in a Soxhlet or similar apparatus. The residue extracted from 50 g of nitrate is usually between 0 and 2 mg. If it reaches or exceeds 5 mg, the nitrate is not satisfactory.

2° The nitrate must contain less than 0.0002% chloride (counted as chlorine), since the presence of chloride introduces undesirable impurities (Cl_2, HCl, NOCl, etc.) into the gas produced (see 23.2.6). Even a chloride content as low as 0.01% destabilises the steady progress of the reaction.

Chlorine is titrated by nephelometry in a solution of 50 g of the product to be tested in 50 g of distilled water, to which is added 10 ml of a 10% solution of nitric acid. The results are compared with a control solution obtained by treating in the same way 50 g of pure ammonium nitrate (recognised as chloride-free) dissolved in a solution† containing 3.02 mg of ammonium chloride per litre.

The nitrate must be free of the salts of heavy metals, especially ferric salts, the presence of which in ammonium nitrate is revealed by the reddish-yellow colour of the product, which is very noticeable when the iron content (counted as Fe_2O_3) exceeds 0.02%.

According to the specifications of the Compressed Gas Association [36], the acidity of the nitrate (counted as NO_3H) must not be greater than 0.025%, which can easily be achieved by titration with decinormal soda using methyl red as indicator, but it seems that acidity, even at twice the suggested content, causes no problems in the manufacture of nitrous oxide.

23.4.3 Safety in the manufacture of nitrous oxide

In the first place, it is important to feed the reactor with very pure ammonium nitrate meeting the requirements listed above, and to avoid any contamination of the product being used during operations. In particular, when sacks of nitrate are being emptied, care must be taken to ensure that no fragment of the sack or any piece of string falls into the nitrate melting vat. If one has to dissolve nitrate in water or dilute a too concentrated solution, the water must be free of chlorine.

Formerly, when nitrate was used which was far from having the degree of purity required nowadays, explosions‡ occurred when nitrous oxide was manufactured in conditions which were frequently almost artisanal, as was the case with dentists who prepared the gas themselves for use as a pain-killer.

---

† This solution is obtained by dilution to one hundredth of a solution of 302 mg of $ClNH_4$ in a litre of distilled water. The diluted solution contains 2 mg of chloride ion per litre and the turbidity it produces with silver nitrate in the test corresponds to 0.0002% chlorine.

‡ An example of such an explosion which occurred in London in 1896 is described in a work by Daniel [6].

It has often been suggested that some 0.05 to 1% of ammonium phosphate should be added to the nitrate to stabilise the decomposition reaction, but when, as sometimes happened thirty years ago, one of the impurities in impure nitrate was ferric nitrate†, the $NH_4H_2PO_4$ precipitated iron in the state of insoluble ferric phosphate in the reactive medium.   There is now no difficulty in obtaining very pure ammonium nitrate and there is no need to add ammonium phosphate.

The heating and cooling system as well as the thermal control of the reactor must be designed with care, since it must be possible at any time during manufacture to cool the reactor without delay if the temperature begins to exceed the normal working temperature.   In this respect, the following accidents should be mentioned:

(a) A reactor working discontinuously with propane heating was loaded with ammonium nitrate.   The apparatus was fitted with an automatic device to cut the fuel supply to the burners when the molten, reacting nitrate reached a temperature of 245°C, but a fault in the mechanism left the burners on. When the temperature reached some 280 or 290°C, nitrous oxide was being produced at 15 to 20 times the normal rate, leading to a considerable increase in pressure which caused the apparatus to explode.

(b) In a pilot installation treating undissolved nitrate the heating and cooling of the reactor, which was fed on a semi-continuous basis, were achieved by using a large coil immersed in the reacting nitrate and carrying a heat-transmitting fluid (aryl silicate) passing through a special stack in which it could either be heated or cooled under the control of thermocouples, one of which was placed in the nitrate (for gradual operation) and the other in the heat-transmitting fluid (for all-or-nothing operation).   During an experiment in which the working temperature of the reacting nitrate was to be 260°C, certain disturbances occurred which caused the temperature to rise, and although the device which controlled the transition from heating to cooling functioned, the temperature continued to rise in the nitrate.   The resulting rapid emission of N_2O with pressure rise distorted the lid of the reactor, causing a leak along the flange bracket through which molten nitrate escaped into the workshop.   The inquiry found that the response time of the system switching between heating and cooling was far too long, since over a minute had elapsed between the time when the emergency temperature had been reached and the time when cooling in the reactor began to have any effect.

It should also be noted that if the coil in this installation had sprung a leak, there was a danger that the heat-transmitting fluid, which was an organic liquid, would have mixed with the hot molten nitrate and reacted very violently with it.

The accidents we have just described involved relatively progressive, quasi-homogeneous explosions (see 1.5), and the damage they caused was small because the apparatuses gave way before the whole of the product present had decomposed and thus before the pressure had reached too high a value.   It is, in fact, possible, when designing a reactor, to ensure that a given part, such as the lid or a large rupture disk on the lid, gives way at a predetermined pressure and in a direction in which it will cause the least damage.

---

† It must be remembered that ferric ions are harmful in the decomposition (23.2.6).

In an automatic installation using an 80-85% solution of nitrate, there is a better guarantee of safety. To begin with, much less heat is released in the reactor during operation than is the case in apparatuses which work discontinuously, so that with a given cooling capacity it is possible to have much more rapid control over any accidental temperature rise. All the automatic equipment for normal working can be designed in such a way that a cut in the electricity supply, an accidental fall in nitrogen pressure in the pneumatic control circuits, or a malfunction in a measuring apparatus has the effect of setting in motion an operation, such as the closing of a propane valve to stop heating, the opening of a water circuit to begin cooling, cutting the nitrate supply, and so on, which will very rapidly create conditions in the apparatus which make any acceleration of the decomposition impossible. These various regulating systems are designed in such a way that they come into operation as soon as the temperature in the reactor rises 3°C above the normal working temperature.

However, automation does not mean that the person operating the reactor can leave it. In particular, he must be there to see that the regulating mechanisms are indeed activated as soon as the excess conditions they are supposed to counter arise, and he must manually switch on the intense cooling which must be activated as soon as the temperature in the reactor rises 5°C above the normal working temperature, and which is effected by means of an external circular watering pipe fitted to the top of the reactor shroud which allows rapid cooling by a heavy shower of water.

BIBLIOGRAPHICAL REFERENCES

[1]   Heubel, J. & Canis, C. (1962) Compt. Rend. 225 708
[2]   Morand, J. J. (1955) Ann. de Chim. [12] 10 1018
[3]   Campbell, A. N. & Campbell, J. R. (1946) Canad. J. Research 24 B, 93
[4]   Spindler, H. (1948) Chem. Age (24 January), p. 132
[5]   Montagne, P. (1945) Compt. Rend. 221 663
[6]   Daniel, J. (1902) Dictionnaire des matières explosives. Paris, p. 158
[7]   Hendricks, S. B., Posnjack, E. & Kracek, F. C. (1932) J. Am. Ch. Soc. 54 2766
[8]   Whetstone, J. & Holmes, A. W. (1947) Ind. Eng. Chem. 23 717
[9]   Feick, G. (1954) J. Am. Ch. Soc. 76 5858
[10] Brandner, J. D., Junk, N. M., Lawrence, J. W. & Robins, J. (1962) J. Chem. Eng. Data 7 227
[11] Feick, G. & Hainer, R. M. (1954) J. Am. Ch. Soc. 76 5860
[12] Friedman, L. & Bigeleisen, J. (1950) J. Chem. Physics 18 1325
[13] Shah, M. S. & Oza, T. M. (1932) J. Chem. Soc., p. 725
[14] Keenan, A. G. & Dimitriades, B. (1961) Trans. Faraday Soc. 57 1019
[15] Robertson, A. J. B. (1948) J. Soc. Chem. Ind. 67 221
[16] Cook, M. A. & Abegg, M. T. (1956) Ind. Eng. Chem. 48 1090
[17] Keenan, A. G. (1955) J. Am. Ch. Soc. 77 1379
[18] Wood, B. J. & Wise, H. (1955) J. Chem. Physics 23 693
[19] Smith, R. D. (1957) Trans. Faraday Soc. 53 1341
[20] Saunders, H. L. (1922) J. Chem. Soc. 121 698
[21] Guiochon, G. & Jacqué, L. (1957) Compt. Rend. 244 771 and 1927; Guiochon, G. (1960) Ann. de Chim. 5 295
[22] Barclay, K. S., Crewe, J. M. & Smith, E. J. (1963) Nature (G.B.) 198 1054
[23] Kretzschmar, W. (1934) Z. Anorg. Chemie 219 17

[24] Davis, T. L. & Abrams, A. J. (1925) *J. Am. Ch. Soc.* 47 1043
[25] Delsemme, A. H. (1950) *Compt. Rend.* 230 1858
[26] Kaiser, R. (1935) *Angew. Chemie* 48 149
[27] Munroe, C. E. (1922) *Chem. Met. Eng.* 26 535
[28] Van R. Smit, J. (1964) *Chem. and Ind.*, p. 2018
[29] Guiochon, G. (1960) *Mém. Poudres* 42 47
[30] Smith, R. D. (1959) *Trans. Faraday Soc.* 55 516
[31] Kilman, Y. I. (1962) *Khim. Prom.*, p. 66
[32] Kobe, K. A. & Hosman, P. D. (1948) *Ind. Eng. Chem.* 40 397
[33] Herquet, M. L. (1952) *Explosifs* 5 29
[34] Findlay, A. & Rosebourne, C. (1922) *J. Soc. Ch. Ind.* 41 58 T
[35] Frey, M. (1955) *Chim. et Ind.* 73 1159
[36] Compressed Gas Association (New York) (1953) *Pamphlet P.3   Standards of ammonium nitrate (nitrous oxide grade)*
[37] Tramm, H. & Velde, H. (1934) *Angew. Chem.* 47 782
[38] Braconier, F. & Delsemme, H. (1952) *Explosifs* 5 34
[39] Hainer, R. M. (1955) *5th Symposium on Combustion*, London, p. 224
[40] Finch, A. C. (January 1968) *Note à Com. Technique de l'A.P.E.A.*
[41] Fragino, A. R. *et al.* (1967) *C.A.* 66 14336 y
[42] Rozman, B. & Borodkina, L. I. (1959) *Zhur. Prikl. Khim.* 32 280
[43] Vingee, A. U.S. patent 2.425.582 of 12 August 1947
[44] Groothuyzen, T. M. (1975) *Loss Prevention* 9 91
[45] Van Dolah, R. W. *et al.* (1966) *Bureau of Mines, Rep. env. 6773*
[46] Glaskova, A. P. (1967) *Explosifs*, p. 5
[47] Heinrich, D. J. (1964) *Explosivstoff* 12 23

24

The explosive properties of ammonium nitrate

24.1 THE EXPLOSION OF PURE AMMONIUM NITRATE

24.1.1 Ammonium nitrate, a weak explosive

It is important to *distinguish between pure and impure ammonium nitrate* because their explosive properties can be very different even at very low percentages of certain impurities. One should also beware of the incorrect terminology of a number of authors who talk of 'ammonium nitrate' when what they really mean is a mixture containing varying degrees of NH_4NO_3, or ANFO explosive, or some other mixture†.

From a theoretical point of view, and according to the definition of explosives, pure ammonium nitrate is an explosive substance since it is liable to undergo rapid exothermic reactions with emission of a large quantity of hot gases. This explosive property of ammonium nitrate was studied around 1870 by Berthelot, who believed that the full and proper explosion of the substance followed the equation

$$NH_4NO_3(cr\ IV) \ = \ N_2(g) + 2H_2O(g) + 1/2O_2(g). \tag{24.1}$$

According to this equation, the energy liberated by the explosion would be 1580 kJ/kg, whereas common explosives give between 2500 and 6000 kJ/kg. Thus, ammonium nitrate as an explosive is only moderately strong, and, as we shall see, has only low sensitivity.

---

† Thus, one work which describes the Oppau accident uses the term ammonium nitrate to refer to what was in reality 'mischsalz' (24.23).

24.1.2 The sensitivity to impact of ammonium nitrate

Munroe [1] found that ammonium nitrate is insensitive to the most violent
friction and mechanical effects, and this has been confirmed by other
researchers. Kast [2] has reported that ammonium nitrate can be exploded
by a 10 kg falling weight, but other researchers have not been able to
reduplicate this. What is certain is that if there is an explosion, it
involves only the material directly subjected to the impact and is not
transmitted in the open air to the rest of the nitrate.

Ammonium nitrate did not explode when it was subjected to the impact of
bullets with speeds of up to 1200 m/s [3]. Pascal [4] has made the same
observation.

Even when heated to 140°C, ammonium nitrate does not explode under the
impact of a large 200 kg falling weight [5], but at that temperature the
nitrate in the form of porous spherules does explode under the impact of
bullets with a speed of 1080 m/s.

24.1.3 Initiating the detonation of ammonium nitrate

Until around 1940, tests to detonate ammonium nitrate were carried out on
the crystallised salt in a form which had a bulk density higher than 0.8,
usually being close to 1. It is difficult to initiate a detonation with
such substances.

Ammonium nitrate can be exploded by a weak initiation source only when
it is placed under strong confinement. For example, Lobry de Bruyn [6],
who was probably the first to produce a detonating decomposition (or at
least an explosion approaching a detonation) in ammonium nitrate, placed
the nitrate in small thick-walled shells and initiated it with 3 g of
mercury fulminate or, better still, with 10 g of a strong explosive. The
resulting explosion reduced the shell to splinters.

Lheure [7] detonated ammonium nitrate in the form of cylindrical
cartridges with an axial hole placed in a hole of the same diameter in clay
and initiated by a detonating fuse of trinitrotoluene placed along the
axis. In 1922, Aufschläger [8] detonated ammonium nitrate in steel tubes
40 mm in diameter and several millimetres thick.

Many other similar experiments have been conducted since with nitrate
in resistant casings, in other words under *strong confinement*. The
researchers quoted above were unable to explode ammonium nitrate when it
was not under confinement. Mention should also be made of experiments,
quoted by Davis [9], which were conducted in Canada in 1942: exploding one
or two sticks of dynamite in contact with paper sacks (of various
thicknesses) containing ammonium nitrate did no more than scatter the
contents.

The first experiments in which unconfined ammonium nitrate was
detonated were performed by Munroe [1] using the elongated box method (see
15.3.2). Table 24.1 summarises the four published experiments, which were
conducted on 99.5% pure crystallised nitrate (the remaining impurities were
essentially mineral and inert). The nitrate is detonated by a sufficiently
strong initiation source, but the detonation is not stable since the hole
left in the ground does not always have the same depth. Also, when the
cross section of the mass of nitrate (test No. 4) is too small, the

Table 24.1

Munroe's tests on the detonation of ammonium nitrate
at a density of 0.95 g/cm³ in the elongated box.

No.	Substance used			Priming at one end in warm nitrate	Result	Observations
	Warm nitrate (52°C) length (m)	Cold nitrate (15°C) length (m)				
1	1	2		8 tetryl detonators	Only the detonators explode	After tests No. 2 and 3, a crater is found in the ground with a width and depth decreasing from the ignited end to the other.
2	1	2		a cartride of blasting gelatine (100 g)	The nitrate detonates	
3	3	0		two cartridges of blasting gelatine (200 g)	The nitrate detonates	In test No. 4, in the central part of the box and over a length of 0.65 mm, the nitrate was in a layer 2.5 cm thick. On either side the thickness increased to 14 cm at the ends.
4	3	0		one cartridge of blasting gelatine (100 g)	The nitrate does not detonate further than the first thick layer.	

detonation cannot propagate†.

Tests [10] using a similar operating mode but with larger initiation masses on very pure (99.9%) crystalline ammonium nitrate gave the results in Table 24.2. We can conclude from them that unconfined nitrate at a density of 0.65 g/cm³ has a critical detonating diameter close to 10 cm. According to Munroe's tests, at a density of 0.95 g/cm³ this critical diameter is higher than 14 cm. The influence of density on detonability is particularly clear if one compares tests No. 4 and 5 in Table 24.2.

In cardboard tubes 100 mm in diameter and 2 mm thick the same nitrate at densities of 0.8 g/cm³ and 0.9 g/cm³ initiated by 1 kg of picric acid undergoes only an overdriven detonation which comes to a halt after travelling between 20 and 30 cm.

When the nitrate is confined, for example in a steel tube 4 mm thick buried in clay, complete detonation is observed at a diameter of 30 mm and a density of 0.73 g/cm³, but at a density of 0.8 g/cm³ detonation ceases after travelling 0.8 m. In less resistant tubes (3 mm thick) propagation comes to a halt after 0.4 m [10].

When ammonium nitrate detonates in these experiments, the fumes produced are reddish-brown, signalling the presence of nitrogen dioxide NO_2, which suggests that, at least in part, the decomposition of ammonium nitrate follows the equation

$$NH_4NO_3(cr\ IV) \rightarrow 1/2NO_2(g) + 3/4N_2(g) + 2H_2O(g), \qquad (24.2)$$

which liberates (at constant volume) 1360 kJ/kg. The reaction

$$NH_4NO_3(cr\ IV) \rightarrow NO(g) + 1/2N_2(g) + 2H_2O(g) \qquad (24.3)$$

apparently produces too little energy (450 kJ/kg) to be able to sustain a detonation wave, and can therefore be no more than a very small part of the process.

Influence of density – With ammonium nitrate, as with all explosives, the bulk density of the substance has an appreciable effect on sensitivity, as was established as early as 1924 by Sherrick's experiments and later confirmed by many other researchers. The nitrate is easier to detonate when it is less packed, in other words when it has a lower bulk density. This variation in sensitivity is particularly marked when one compares the nitrate at 0.7 g/cm³ with nitrate at a density of 0.95 to 1 g/cm³. Belyaev and Khariton [12], working with nitrates at a low bulk density (0.7 to 0.8 g/cm³), were able to produce the regular detonation of loads of 8 to 10 cm in diameter.

The influence of the physical form of ammonium nitrate on sensitivity to priming is brought out in tests in the lead block (see 14.3.4). Thus, Aufschläger obtained the results in Table 24.3 by initiating 10 g of nitrate with an ordinary detonator.

According to a Japanese study [13], rapid cooling in a vacuum of nitrate heated to above 124°C produces a particularly sensitive form of nitrate with a bulk density between 0.4 and 0.7 g/cm³. The author states that, at a density of 0.5 g/cm³ in a thick steel tube with a diameter of

---

† The present author obtained the same result in a box 2 m long and 15 cm wide with just a 7 cm layer of nitrate (at a density of 0.65 g/cm³).

Table 24.2

Tests to detonate crystallised ammonium nitrate at a density of app. 0.65 g/cm³
(Lab. C.S.E. 1948)

No.	Cross section of the box (cm)	Booster			Nitrate			Result
		Substance	Mass (kg)	Length (cm)	Length occupied (m)	Density (g/cm³)	Mass (kg)	
1	15 x 15	Pl.C	5	15	1.85	0.65	27	Complete detonation
2	13 x 13	Pl.C	4	13	1.87	0.63	20	Complete detonation
3	11 x 11	Pl.C	2.5	11	1.85	0.64	14.6	Complete detonation
4	10 x 10	Pl.C	2	12	1.88	0.64	12	Complete detonation
5	10 x 10	Pl.C	2	12	1.88	0.66	12.5	Incomplete detonation (imprint over 1.2 m)
6	10 x 10	TNT	2	15	1.4	0.66	9.3	Incomplete detonation (imprint over 0.5 m)
7	8 x 8	Pl.C	1	8	1.92	0.67	8.3	Only the booster detonates
8	8 x 8	Pl.C	1.5	15	1.85	0.61	7.25	Incomplete detonation (imprint over 0.45 m)

NB – Pl.C designates a plastic explosive containing 88% cyclonite (RDX). It has a density of app. 1.6 g/cm³.

27 mm, this nitrate can be detonated with a No. 6 detonator at a velocity
of about 1700 m/s. Such a very low-density nitrate is manufactured only to
make so-called 'light' ammonium nitrate explosives, and it keeps its low
density only if special precautions are taken in storing it.

Table 24.3

Ammonium nitrate tests in the lead block, after Aufschläger

Nature of the substance (mass = 10 g)	Density (g/cm³)	Enlargement (cm³)
Crystals with needle-shaped facies between 1 and 1.5 cm long	0.5	215
Rhombic crystals 3 cm long and 5 mm thick	0.35	135
Nitrate crushed and passed through the 144 mesh per cm² sieve but not the 2000	0.69	200
Fine nitrate passed through the 2000 mesh per cm² sieve	0.83	189
Nitrate melted and broken into large pieces	-	15

Similarly, Winning [41] pulverised molten nitrate to obtain porous
spherules with a bulk density of 0.55 g/cm³ which he detonated at a
velocity of 1980 m/s in a paper tube with a diameter of 56 mm by initiating
it with a detonator of 0.6 g of P.E.T.N.. However, that is a special
product which differs considerably from industrial nitrates.

Influence of temperature – Jones [5] observed in 1924 in experiments
using confined nitrate (in thick steel tubes) that hot nitrate is more
sensitive to priming than nitrate at ordinary temperature. Below 120°C he
observed only incomplete explosions, whereas above 140°C he obtained
complete detonation.

Gawthrop [14] confirms this effect of temperature. Nitrate loaded at a
density of 0.71 g/cm³ into a steel tube with an internal diameter of 33 mm
detonates with a velocity of 1000 m/s when it is at 15°C and 1700 m/s when
it is at 140°C. The large difference is indicative of an incomplete
explosion reaction in experimental conditions at 15°C.

German experiments in 1928 [15] showed that in the molten state at
190-195°C ammonium nitrate is comparatively sensitive.

Finally, experiments by Deffet and his associates [16] have shown that
at around 165°C (just below its melting point) ammonium nitrate with a
density close to 0.9 becomes quite sensitive since a simple No. 8 detonator
causes it explode, especially under very strong confinement (in a thick
steel tube).

24.1.4 The detonation velocity of ammonium nitrate

Before 1945, most measurements were made on nitrate placed in tubes a few centimetres in diameter, and the loading density and the properties of the container (material, thickness) were not always indicated, which means that the published results can scarcely be compared. The following are some results given by Kast [17]:

Diameter of the steel tube (cm)	Density of the nitrate (g/cm³)	Detonation velocity (m/s)
2.5	0.84	1 460
5	0.65	1 250
8	0.68	1 490
8	0.98	2 700

Paterson and Davidson [18], working with nitrate at a density of 0.52 g/cm³, measured velocities in light tubes (negligible confinement) with different diameters from 4 to 20 cm (2230 m/s at 20 cm). Extrapolation to a diameter of infinity gives 2370 m/s. Using calculation to arrive at the velocity for reaction (24.1) gives the following values:

density g/cm³	0.5	0.6	0.7	0.8	0.9	1
velocity km/s	2.36	2.56	2.76	2.98	3.22	3.48

There was thus good agreement between the calculated and the measured value for this nitrate at a fairly low density, but with ammonium nitrate in the form of large crystals at a density of 1 g/cm³ Whetstone [40] obtained misfires in a cardboard tube with a diameter of 23 cm, and measured 1370 m/s in a 32 cm tube. Thus, the critical detonation diameter (see 14.4.4) for this substance is greater than 32 cm and the limit diameter is very much higher than 35 cm. Nitrate in the form of fine crystals detonates with a higher velocity (1510 m/s) at the same density and the same confinement at a diameter of 23 cm. Finally, Winning [41] measured a velocity of 3200 m/s with prills at a density of 0.82 g/cm³ housed in a low-resistance tube 50 cm in diameter.

However, when ammonium nitrate is detonated in the open air, the gas cloud produced is deep red because of the presence of nitrogen dioxide. However, the values relating to the chemical equilibria show that at the temperature corresponding to equation (24.1) (about 1350°C), there can scarcely be no more than 0.5% of the mixture (NO + NO$_2$) in these gases, which has led some authors [19] to believe that the explosion of ammonium nitrate is sometimes far from following equation (24.1) and that the energy liberated is appreciably less than the value (1580 kJ/kg) for that equation, since the NO and NO$_2$ oxides are strongly endothermic.

24.1.5 Explosion of ammonium nitrate by heating

As with the action of an impact caused by another explosive, conditions of confinement play a very important part in the explosion of ammonium nitrate by an increase in temperature. A study by Feick and Hainer (see 23.2.5) leads to the conclusion that pure ammonium nitrate will decompose very rapidly only in conditions in which the pressure might rise to some 50 bars.

During experiments in which he heated some 5 g of nitrate in a metal container open to the air in a high-temperature oven, Munroe [1] obtained no explosion even though the substance had been raised to 375°C† towards the end of decomposition. However, if the nitrate is placed in a steel tube closed at both ends, heating produces an explosion with shattering of the tube.

Fire experiments on varying quantities have been carried out on a number of occasions. We may quote the experiment conducted in Toulouse in 1950 by the French Professional Union representing the nitrate fertiliser industry: a ton of nitrate in paper sacks was piled in the open air on a wooden trestle under which a vigorously burning wood fire was lit. Even though white-hot firebrands came into contact with molten nitrate, the decomposition remained calm.

The experiments carried out by the British working party on ammonium nitrate were even more conclusive, because they were performed on large quantities in partly closed areas rather than in the open air. In one of them, 70 tons of nitrate in paper-lined drums were placed in an underground concreted shelter, whilst in another 45 tons in paper sacks were placed in a barge. In both tests the nitrate was subjected to an intense fire obtained by burning a mixture of wood chips and ammonium nitrate. The nitrate exploded in none of these experiments.

In all of the above experiments confinement was low or zero. Very different results are obtained in a closed vessel or under very strong confinement.

In experiments with 2.5 kg of pure ammonium nitrate heated in a steel bomb with a capacity of some 2000 cm^3, Burns and his associates [22] were able to produce a violent explosion with considerable destructive effects. However, other experiments have been performed in a bomb with an opening in one of the plugs. When this opening has a cross section of more than 1 cm^2 (or 1/40th of the cross section of the bomb), the exit thus presented to the gases makes the confinement too low for there to be an explosion. In experiments where an explosion did take place, measurements show that the temperature had risen above 300°C and that the pressure had risen to around 170 bars.

It is, in fact, possible for the gas phase in a closed vessel to explode first, since this phase contains ammonia, nitrous oxide, and nitric acid vapour. Now, reaction (III) in 23.2.4 and the reactions between ammonia and nitrogen oxides are strongly exothermic and may be explosive if the temperature at a point reaches a high enough value. The explosion of the gas phase is such that it might initiate an explosion in the liquid phase.

Clancey [23] performed experiments in which nitrate was heated either in a 140 mm shell containing 4 kg of the substance, or in a heating bomb with a nominal rupture pressure of 800 kg/cm^2. In tests with pure ammonium nitrate the containers did not burst, from which it seems possible to conclude that decomposition by heat never has the characteristics of a detonation.

---

† Herquet [20] carried out experiments in which an end temperature of 410°C was reached without the nitrate exploding.

In an attempt to explain the accident in Traskwood (see 24.2.9), a vast experiment was undertaken in the United States and led to the publication in 1966 of an important report by Van Dolah [24]. Since we do not have the space to summarise the experiments on pure nitrate (as well as on nitrate with hydrocarbons or other substances added) which are described in this report, we shall simply reproduce one of its conclusions. It was not possible in these experiments to observe a transition from deflagration to detonation in decomposing nitrate, even though experimental conditions were set up to subject it to pressures greater than 250 kg/cm².

Experiments conducted in Belgium by Deffet and his associates [16] on small quantities only and intended essentially to bring out the differences in behaviour between ammonium nitrates of varying grades or between products containing ammonium nitrate show that some degree of confinement is necessary if one wants to explode pure ammonium nitrate by heat alone. In their tests an explosion occurred at a temperature of about 350–360°C. Braconier and Delsemme [25] had already concluded in 1952 that to cause an explosion in pure nitrate by purely thermal means, one must first create a confinement which allows the gases released to produce a pressure which they estimated to be around 100 bars.

Accidental explosions resulting in injuries and death caused by heating pure ammonium nitrate or a nitrate-based product under strong confinement have occurred on *several* occasions during repair work involving a flame (welding, hot fitting, etc.) on hollow shafts in agricultural machinery, such as endless screw shafts in fertiliser spreaders, since, when these machines are being used, very fine nitrate filters into the closed space through small gaps which may then become blocked.

24.1.6 Evaluating the danger of pure ammonium nitrate exploding

Scientifically speaking, ammonium nitrate is an explosive, but from the practical point of view, as Munroe [1] stated in 1922:   'We are justified in considering that ammonium nitrate is not an explosive when it is stored in wooden containers† and kept away from explosives.' Clancey later wrote that experiment seems amply to justify the conclusion that the pure salt may rightly be considered as presenting no risk of explosion, but that the same is not true of certain mixtures.

At ordinary temperatures, at least, pure ammonium nitrate is indeed absolutely insensitive to the most violent mechanical effects to which it has been submitted. If it is detonated by another explosive, the mass of the latter must be very large or the nitrate must be in conditions of severe confinement, whilst its granulometry must be appropriate and its density not too high.

As for heat, it can never produce an explosion of pure ammonium nitrate when the latter is in the open air or in a container which does not create strong confinement. Surprise has often been voiced at the fact that the exothermic decomposition reaction of the nitrate into water and nitrous oxide (reaction II in 23.2.3) can be easily produced without explosion, but this was to forget the role played by the dissociation reaction (I). Feick

---

† To this we can now add paper and plastic, since sacks were not yet in use to store ammonium nitrate when Munroe made this judgment.

and Hainer [26] remind us that as early as 1869 Berthelot had pointed to
the potential importance of this dissociation in the evolution of reactions
of ammonium nitrate, and they show (see 23.2.5) that at pressures up to
around 3 bars the decomposition of pure heated nitrate takes place at a
moderate rate. Heating, of the kind that might result from a fire, could
lead to an explosion of pure nitrate only if the latter is in a closed
container or in one which has only small openings, so that the pressure can
reach a high value. In fact, there has never been a case (see 24.2) of a
fire affecting pure nitrate resulting in an explosion. Furthermore, pure
ammonium nitrate, even in large quantities in conditions in which the heat
released cannot dissipate, has no tendency to heat up spontaneously, as was
shown by an experiment† carried out by Burns [22] in a ship whose holds
were filled with sacks piled in 64 layers to which continuously recording
thermocouples had been attached. During a journey which included passage
through the Panama canal, the temperatures measured by the thermocouples
followed the variations in the air temperature.

Apart from cases such as the Kriewald accident (see 24.2.2), which
involved the *intentional* blasting of an explosive in ammonium nitrate to
split it up, there is, to our knowledge, not one single example of an
accidental explosion of unheated *pure* ammonium nitrate. It is therefore
quite right that ammonium nitrate, as regards both storage and transport,
should not be classified with the explosives. The precautions to be
observed when storing it are simple and are basically the same as those
which apply to the ammonitrates (see 25.2.5).

24.2 ACCIDENTAL EXPLOSIONS INVOLVING AMMONIUM NITRATE

24.2.1 Introduction

It was accidents, some of which were veritable catastrophes, which drew
attention to the dangers of ammonium nitrate and mixtures based on it. The
most important of these accidents deserve to be described in some detail,
since a study of them highlights dangerous conditions to be avoided. In
almost every case, the ammonium nitrate involved was more or less impure.

24.2.2 The Kriewald explosion (1921)

A factory in Kriewald (Silesia) belonging to a company manufacturing a
range of products, and explosives in particular, took delivery of ammonium
nitrate by rail from the Ruhr. On 26 July 1962, two carriages arrived
containing nitrate in bulk which had caked so hard that it was almost
impossible to unload it by spade. They decided to break up the hardened
mass by drilling holes in it with a miner's bar and blasting an explosive.
The contents of both carriages, some 30 tons of ammonium nitrate, exploded,
killing 19 people and blasting a cavity in the ground with a diameter of
some 20 m.

---

† This experiment is all the more conclusive since it was done not on pure
nitrate but on a nitrate similar to the one involved in the Texas City
explosion (see 24.2.5).

Experiments made by Bramkamp [27] after the accident showed that a stick of 100 g of Wetterlignosite, a nitrate explosive produced by the factory, was capable of causing at least a partial explosion of ammonium nitrate. The nitrate involved in the accident was slightly wet (about 0.3% water) and quite pure (99.5% ammonium nitrate), the impurities being mainly inorganic (ammonium chloride, sulphates, etc.).

24.2.3 The Oppau explosion (1921)

The catastrophe of 21 September 1921 in Oppau (Rhineland) is, together with that in Texas City, the most serious explosion ever caused by an unwanted explosive. It caused the death of over 500 people, injured 1900 more, destroyed most of the area around Oppau, and caused damage in the town of Ludwigshafen 1.5 km away. There is a great deal to be learnt from a study of the reports [28] on the accident, and we shall look below at some of the conclusions to be drawn from them.

To begin with, the nitrate fertiliser factory built in Oppau in 1917 by the Badische Anilin und Soda Fabrik (BASF) manufactured a 50/50 mixture of potassium chloride and ammonium nitrate, but this was replaced in 1919 in increasing quantities by a 50/50 mixture of ammonium sulphate and ammonium nitrate. This 'ammonium sulpho-nitrate' (called mischsalz in Oppau) has, like many other similar mixtures, the disadvantage of caking during bulk storage, and it was common practice to break it up by drilling holes with a miner's bar in the hardened mass and blasting explosives in it. From a set of initial systematic tests, BASF had concluded that mixtures of ammonium sulphate and ammonium nitrate are not liable to explode if they contain less than 60% nitrate salt, and the company consequently believed that there was no risk involved in subjecting the 50/50 mixture to the impact produced by detonating a cartridge of blasting explosive†, and indeed up to the day of the accident there had been more than 20 000 blastings in mischsalz without anything suspicious being observed.

The warehouse (called silo 110) which was the seat of the explosion was a half-buried building (4 m below the surrounding terrain) measuring 61 by 31 metres, which, on the morning of 21 September 1921, contained 4500 tons of mischsalz. It was estimated, both from the size of the crater blasted in the ground and from the damage caused to the surroundings, that the quantity of mixture which exploded was about one-tenth of the amount stored in silo 110, and a considerable amount of the fertiliser was actually found on the site of the explosion itself and in the immediate vicinity.

Explosions had been fired in silo 110 on the day of 20 September 1921. At 7 o'clock the following morning, the person in charge of explosions prepared blast holes, some of which were drilled in a part of the mass which had been shaken by the explosions of the day before. The accidental explosion in silo 110 occurred at 7:32 a.m. and was certainly caused by one of the planned blasts.

During an inquiry which lasted for two years, the experts appointed to determine the causes of the accident studied the explosive capacity of mischsalz and mixtures with a composition close to it. They found that the

---

† The explosive used was, in fact, a nitrate explosive of very moderate brisance.

50/50 mixture is liable to explode in conditions of high confinement and
sufficiently low density. The explosion is frequently limited to an area
close to the initiating charge, except when the latter is very large. They
also found that the physical properties of the fertiliser have considerable
influence on its liability to explode. Now, several months before the
accident changes had been made in the manufacturing process, giving a
mixture which contained less moisture than before (2% instead of 3 to 4%)
and had a slightly lower bulk density and a slightly different physical
constitution. Experiments conducted by the experts showed that these
changes made the product easier to explode.

Although analyses of samples made after the accident on the substance
which remained on the site of silo 110 found ammonium nitrate contents
slightly below 50% (between 47 and 49%), concordant evidence gave reason to
suspect that the composition was not uniform throughout the pile of 4500
tons in the silo which had been made up during the months prior to the
accident, and that there may have been pockets of several dozen tons of
product which were richer in ammonium nitrate than the 50/50 'Oppau salt'.

Now, experiments by Kast [28] show that if the ammonium nitrate content
rises from 50 to 55%, and, in particular, from 55 to 60%, the sulphonitrate
becomes considerably more liable to explode, and the explosive power of the
mixture also increases (Fig. 24.1). It is therefore conceivable that if
the area in which the blast holes were drilled prior to the deliberate
blast of 21 September was one in which the ammonium nitrate content was 55
to 60%, this product may have detonated and caused areas near to the 50/50
mixture to detonate also, but that the detonation did not spread to the
entire contents of silo 110 in areas where the composition was 50/50 and
where the caked product had a relatively high density.

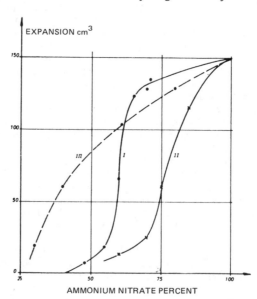

Fig. 24.1 – Expansion produced in the lead block by firing 10 g of a
mixture of ammonium nitrate with I: ammonium sulphate, II: potassium
chloride, and III: quartz sand. After Kast [28].

This catastrophe and the reports on it are highly instructive. Amongst other things, it can be seen that when the process for manufacturing the mischsalz was modified in the spring of 1921, BASF should have repeated tests comparable to those which it had carried out on the initial product in 1919-20, since an apparently minor change in the properties of the manufactured product can considerably increase sensitivity to priming.

24.2.4　The explosion in Tessenderloo (1942)

On 29 April 1942 in Tessenderloo (Belgium), 150 tons of ammonium nitrate housed in a silo exploded, killing several hundred people and causing considerable damage. The explosion was caused by blasting an explosive in the caked mass of nitrate, since it was common practice in this factory to use an explosive to break up the raw potassium chloride contained in a neighbouring silo, and on the day of the accident somebody thought it was possible to do the same with ammonium nitrate.

24.2.5　The explosions in Texas City (April 1947)

Explosions have occurred in the holds of ships laden with sacks of a product called 'ammonium nitrate, fertiliser quality' which has the following properties: it is a brown substance in the form of small, irregular grains containing 32.5% nitrogen, about 4 to 5% mineral filler, and 1% coating made of a mixture of paraffin, resin, and vaseline. Each sack, holding 45 kg of the product, had a mass of about 680 g and was made of six layers of paper, two of which were water-proofed with bitumen.

　　The freighter 'Grandcamp', a former 'Liberty Ship' with entirely metal hull and bulkheads, which was already carrying mechanical equipment†, peanut oil, and sisal twine, docked in Galveston bay, Texas City, on 15 April to take on board the fertiliser described below. They first loaded hold No. 2 with 1400 tons, and then began to fill hold No. 4, loading 800 tons on that day. The next morning, the hatch cover was opened at 8:00 a.m. and the head stevedore climbed down into the hold, where he smelt smoke. On examining the contents, he found that the smoke was coming from a point located near the side dunnage. Several buckets of water were thrown over the seat of the fire and they were beginning to unroll fire hoses when the captain gave the order not to use water in the hold to prevent the cargo from being damaged. He ordered the hatch covers to be closed and the ventilation holes to be blocked.

　　The fire on board grew, and the pressure in the holds blew open the hatches, releasing dense orange-red smoke. When the town firemen sprayed water on the ship at around 9 o'clock, the hull was hot enough to vaporise the water streaming along the bridge. At 9:12 a.m. there was an extremely violent explosion, causing considerable damage in the port and town, with huge fragments of the hull and pieces of metal thrown over a great distance. The burning bales of sisal fell back down and set fire to stores

---

† One of the holds also contained some munitions, but they played no part in the explosion because they were taken off the ship as soon as the fire was discovered.

of fuel. The explosion caused a tidal wave on nearby land.

It is most likely that the fire was caused by a lighted cigarette thrown into the hold. It may have smouldered for a long time on the night of 15–16 April and was stirred up by the draughts of air caused by opening the hatch cover in the morning.

One effect of the explosion of the Grandcamp was to blow open the hatch cover and other hatchways on nearby ships, one of which, the High Flyer 250 m away, was carrying 1050 tons of sulphur in bulk and 960 tons of ammonium nitrate from the same source as that on the Grandcamp. The sulphur had been loaded in Galveston and a large quantity of sulphur dust had been deposited on the ship's surface. A fire, probably caused by tongues of flame borne on the wind from fires on land, broke out on the High Flyer. On the evening of 16 April, attempts were made to tow this ship to a distance, and on 17 April at about 1 a.m. it was destroyed by an explosion.

More than 400 people died in the Texas City explosion. One remarkable phenomenon was that a fire broke out in a warehouse containing over 500 tons of the same nitrate fertiliser situated on the dock 50 m away from the Grandcamp but the contents did not explode.

Given the heat of combustion of the paraffin–resin–vaseline mixture added to the nitrate and that of the sacks containing the nitrate, the term Q in Feick and Hainer's formula (23.2.5) had a high enough value for decomposition at a pressure of less than 20 bars to proceed vigorously.

24.2.6 The explosion in Brest on 28 July 1947

The Norwegian ship Ocean Liberty docked in the port of Brest on 23 July. Holds 1, 3, and 5 contained a load of 3909 tons of granular nitrate similar to that involved in the Texas City disaster and contained in sacks of the same type. There were other goods as well, some of which were combustible (fuel oil, paints, lubricants, etc.). Between decks above hold No. 1 were many packages containing paraffin, polystyrene, and a large number of pelts, whilst above hold No. 3 were greasing oil, rubber tyres, and various other goods. In addition, there were drums of various flammable liquids (methyl ethyl ketone, butyl alcohol, etc.) on the deck. Hold No. 2 and the between–decks situated above it had been almost entirely unloaded when the fire broke out at around 12:30 p.m.

The first sign of fire was a white smoke, which later became yellow, coming from one of the ventilator shafts to hold No. 3. The captain gave the order to switch on the steam extinguishing system, but soon red vapours began to emerge from the other ventilator shafts to the same hold. Yellow fumes were also coming through gaps in the hold hatch cover which was vibrating intermittently, and there was a rumbling noise coming from below.

When the firemen arrived they removed the hatch cover of hold No. 3 from which were pouring large quantities of reddish–yellow fumes. The fire grew and on several occasions deflagrations threw onto the deck or into the water goods stored between–decks. At 2:0 p.m. the decision was taken to remove the ship from the port. It was towed to the east and ran aground on a sand bank.

The superstructures began to burn, and around 5:0 p.m. the fire spread to the bow. Black flames and red smoke sprang up, indicating that the oil in hold No. 2 had caught fire, and almost immediately after flames sprang from hold No. 1 which contained 739 tons of nitrate. Since the fire was becoming fierce, all ships were ordered to move away. Just after 5:25 p.m.

an explosion occurred which destroyed the fore-part of the ship and, in addition to the damage caused in the town, killed 25 people.

It is certain that the paraffin (and other materials) which had been stored between-decks above hold No. 1 melted and flowed into the hold onto the nitrate [29].

24.2.7 Observations on the Texas City and Brest disasters

1° It is wrong to speak of an explosion of ammonium nitrate in the accidents in Texas City and Brest. What exploded in Brest was *a mixture of ammonium nitrate and combustible substances* which had formed as a result of the fire. Similarly, on the freighter High Flyer it was a mixture of molten sulphur and ammonium nitrate which exploded, whilst on board the Grandcamp, in addition to the sacking material with a mass equal to 1.5% that of the nitrate fertiliser and the substance coating the grains of nitrate (1% hydrocarbons), there were many combustible materials. Thus, these shipping accidents involved nitrate with *combustible substances added*.

2° On board these ships the product was in a confined space from which the gases, even after removal of the hatch covers, could not easily escape, so that the pressure in the holds was higher than atmospheric.

3° During the fires on the Grandcamp and the Ocean Liberty (and also later the Tirrenia, described in 24.2.10), steam† was pumped into the holds after they had been closed. Far from extinguishing the fire, the steam simply made it worse by supplying heat to decomposing substances, since the latter contain within themselves the oxygen needed to burn, and there is no point in replacing the air in the holds by an inert vapour.

24.2.8 The accidents in Morgan (1918) and Miramas (1940)

In both of these accidents ammonium nitrate detonated because nearby fires threw into it shells loaded with explosives.

1° A fire broke out on 4 October 1918 in a munitions factory in Morgan (New Jersey) in a workshop for loading amatol‡ into shells. During the fire, which raged for 24 hours, shells were thrown into the air, and some hit warehouses holding 4000 tons of ammonium nitrate. Some of these shells, which probably exploded in the nitrate, caused it to detonate, blasting deep craters in the ground. After the fire it was noted that some ammonium nitrate, which had been stored in barrels in the open air in a location where they were exposed to heat radiation from the fire and to the shock waves of nearby explosions, had not exploded but had partially melted.

2° On the morning of 5 August 1940, for an unknown reason, a fire broke out in a carriage containing explosives on a track in the marshalling yard

---

† Many cargo ships are equipped with systems to drown the hold with steam. Replacing air with water vapour in this way is an effective means of fighting a fire in materials which are *simply combustible*.
‡ Amatol is an explosive composed of a mixture of ammonium nitrate and between 40 and 55% TNT.

in Miramas. Stationed on nearby tracks were trains coupled to a number of carriages loaded with munitions and artifices of war. The fire spread, causing a succession of munitions carriages to explode, and the heat of the fire shattered drums of toluene in a factory adjoining the perimeter fence of the station. The hydrocarbon ignited, forming a pool on the ground which spread down a slope towards a warehouse containing 240 tons of pure ammonium nitrate in sacks stored over an area measuring 5 m by 20 m with an average height of 1.5 m.

One hour after the fire broke out, there was a violent explosion and a large reddish-brown cloud formed over the nitrate store. When it was finally possible to enter the site and start an inquiry, a deep cavity was found in the ground measuring 3 m at its lowest point and having a roughly elliptical shape with axes measuring 39 and 26 m.

From the damage caused to nearby buildings it was estimated that the explosion had involved the equivalent of some 30 tons of picric acid and had been caused by a shell† launched from one of the munitions explosions into a part of the nitrate which had mixed with toluene, where it detonated and so caused this nitrate-toluene mixture to detonate, with the latter in turn extending the detonation to the nitrate which had not mixed with toluene [30].

Faced with these two accidents, it is interesting to note what was observed [31] on 5 June 1940 in Rouen during an air raid: an explosive bomb‡ scored a direct hit on a batch of ammonium nitrate stored in metal drums and exploded after piercing several layers of drums some 6 m thick. Some of the drums were hurled onto nearby roofs, but the nitrate did not explode and did not set fire to debris from the drums and to powder which fell onto it. This demonstrates just how insensitive and difficult to explode ammonium nitrate is when it is not under confinement.

24.2.9 The explosion at the Cherokee factory in January 1973

The factory of the Cherokee Nitrogen company near Pryor Creek in Oklahoma (U.S.A.) had been producing high-density prilled ammonium nitrate since 1968. It was loaded into carriages in the warehouse by an automatic skip mounted on wheels and driven by a propane-burning engine. At 7:20 a.m. on 17 January 1973 a fire broke out in the upper part of the workshop where the nitrate was put into sacks and which had a wooden frame and a roof with polyethylene panels. The fire was probably started by a rubber conveyor belt rubbing against and so strongly heating a blocked roller. In spite of the fire-fighting efforts of the workforce, the fire spread quite rapidly along the conveyor belts and the combustible parts of the building to the nearby nitrate warehouse, where the nitrate loader was soon engulfed in flames. At 7:45 the noise of a first explosion was heard as the propane tank shattered, followed shortly after by the noise of a more violent explosion. After the fire, a long crater was found in the ground (40 m long and 0.2 to 0.3 m deep) on the site where 3 to 6 tons of nitrate stored in sacks had been sprayed in the first explosion with propane, lubricant,

---

† Unexploded shells were found near the crater, in addition to various other kinds of debris.

‡ It is thought that this bomb was a device containing 50 kg of explosive.

and brake fluid, forming a mixture which detonated. There was considerable damage, with debris scattered over a wide range and eight people injured but no fatalities.

It is remarkable that the huge pile of nitrate in bulk form situated less than three metres from the nitrate which detonated did not explode but simply melted on the surface as a result of heat from the fire.

It can be concluded from this accident that the initial fire could probably have been controlled before reaching the skip if there had not been so much combustible material in the building. It is also obvious that a machine containing many combustible liquids and liquefied gas should not have been left in the vicinity of bagged and loose nitrate.

24.2.10 The explosion on the Tirrenia in the Red Sea

On the morning of 23 January 1954 in the Red Sea, a fire started in the hold of the Finnish freighter Tirrenia carrying 4000 tons of ammonium nitrate and 425 tons of paper to China. Between-decks, over the hold containing the nitrate, were stored 160 tons of Paris green (copper acetoarsenite). As soon as smoke was seen billowing from the ventilation shafts, all vents and hatch covers to the holds were covered and a valve was opened to let steam into the hold which was the seat of the fire. When the fire spread beyond control, the order was given to abandon ship. The vessel was rocked by a first explosion in the afternoon and then destroyed by a more violent explosion around midnight.

24.2.11 Various accidents caused by ammonium nitrate

In an article [1] written shortly after the Oppau accident, Munroe gives an account of the circumstances attending a number of fires involving ammonium nitrate in which no explosion occurred. The most remarkable is the one which broke out on 15 April 1920 in Brooklyn harbour on board the Hallfried which was carrying, amongst other goods, 1900 tons of ammonium nitrate in wooden barrels, 900 tons of which were destroyed by the fire. This and other accidents described by Munroe are quoted in the 1951 British report [21] which also contains accounts of fires which were accompanied by explosions, including the Morgan disaster (see 24.2.8), the explosions of 14 January 1917 (in Repauno), 15 September 1916 (in Oakdale), and 1 March 1924 (in Nixon), which involved ammonium nitrate produced from nitric acid derived from spent acid from the manufacture of TNT and which contained a small quantity of organic nitro-compounds. The explosion which left twenty-six people dead in Stolberg (Rhineland) in April 1920 was caused [19] by a mixture of kainite (chlorides of Na and K) and ammonium nitrate containing more than 10% of various combustible substances. This impure nitrate had been recovered from munitions processes. Similarly, the explosion which killed seventeen people in Perth Amboy (U.S.A.) in March 1924 involved ammonium nitrate recovered from amatol taken from explosive shells.

A fire followed by an explosion broke out in Repauno in 1932 in an evaporating pan treating ammonium nitrate which contained a small amount of vaseline and 0.25% ammonium chloride. Explosions have also been caused during manufacture of nitrate by the presence of oil in the compressed air used to stir the molten mass, whilst another explosion involved excessive heating of nitrate in a steel tube.

Mention should also be made of the rather serious fire which broke out on 1 September 1946 in the ONIA factory in Toulouse and which spread to a warehouse containing 200 tons of ammonium nitrate, where it destroyed the roof and a wooden gallery supporting a rubber conveyor belt, causing burning wood to rain down on the nitrate as the workers doused it with a water hose. In this incident, the nitrate did not explode.

A fire followed by explosions broke out in Traskwood (Arkansas) on 17 December 1960 after a goods train was derailed. Amongst the carriages were two containing nitrate fertiliser in prill form and others nearby carrying fuming nitric acid with a 99% HNO_3 content and paraffin. Experiments carried out by the Bureau of Mines [24] showed that a detonation is initiated immediately in the liquid phase in the mixture which is formed when a given mass of fuming nitric acid is suddenly dropped into an equal mass of burning petrol. This mixture is, in fact, a Sprengel explosive (see 17.1.1). The detonation of this liquid probably caused the ammonium nitrate in the neighbouring carriage to explode, but it is remarkable that after the accident unexploded nitrate prills were found scattered on the ground.

By a strange coincidence, another train derailment 80 km from Traskwood in February 1963 resulted in a spillage of fuel oil which caught fire and engulfed in flames a metal carriage loaded with nitrate fertiliser in sacks. During the fire, yellowish-white smoke poured from the carriage, but there was no explosion.

In January 1963 in a factory in Finland, a vat containing a 97% solution of ammonium nitrate into which was being poured nitrate recovered by sifting and a surface active agent (alkyl aryl sulphonate) exploded, killing several people. The inquiry showed that a pressure-reducing valve on a steam line had malfunctioned, allowing the temperature to rise above normal (160°C), and that there was a strong possibility that the surface active agent had been added in more-than-normal quantities (0.05%).

In November 1966, in the United States, a fire broke out one morning in a fertiliser factory in a workshop housing 25 tons of nitrate fertiliser in sacks as well as various other chemical products (herbicides, pesticides, etc.). The smoke prevented firemen from applying water where it was needed and the order was given to evacuate the factory. Two hours later there was a detonation which blasted a hole in the ground 4 m deep. It is almost certain that during the fire various combustible substances melted and mixed with the nitrate.

24.2.12   Conclusions to be drawn from the above accidents

The explosions described above fall into two groups:
(a) Five† explosions (Kriewald, Morgan, Oppau, Tessenderloo, and Traskwood) were caused either by an explosive going off in a mass of ammonium nitrate or an ammonium nitrate-based explosive mixture, or by the detonation of an explosive shell thrown into the mass, or by the detonation of an explosive mixture in contact with the nitrate.

---

† Possibly six if the Stolberg accident (1920) was, as seems likely, caused by blasting in the product.

(b) The other explosions followed a fire which spread either to impure ammonium nitrate (Texas City, Brest, Oakdale, etc.) or to nitrate which became mixed during the fire with combustible substances (Repauno, Miramas, Cherokee, etc.).

However, we know of very many other cases in which fires involving ammonium nitrate which was frequently impure did not lead to an explosion. In this respect, we may quote fires in farms where quantities of 20 to 50 tons of ammonitrate in sacks were stored immediately next to straw or hay, as well as fires in vehicles transporting 25 tons of ammonitrate in sacks where the fire started either in the engine or in deflated tyres subjected to friction to the point of bursting into flame. Even a product such as the one which caused the accidents in Texas City and Brest can burn in a large mass without exploding provided there is no confinement, as was demonstrated in 1949 in Kansas City in a fire which affected a warehouse containing 1400 tons of this nitrate.

Catastrophic accidents have always been either the result of an explosive going off in a hardened mass or the culmination of a prolonged fire in a *large* mass of *impure* nitrate containing organic substances in a ship's hold, in other words in *confined* conditions.

24.3 THE EXPLOSIVE PROPERTIES OF IMPURE AMMONIUM NITRATE

24.3.1 The sensitisation of ammonium nitrate by combustible substances

It appears from equation (24.1) that ammonium nitrate is oxygen-positive, so that the weak explosive properties it has in itself are considerably increased when it is mixed with combustible substances. By making an intimate mixture of an appropriate percentage (5 to 12%) of a combustible substance (explosive or not) with ammonium nitrate, explosives are formed with properties that make them appropriate for mining. Explosives of this type were widely used in France after they were patented by Favier in 1887, and they continue to be used not only because they are inexpensive but also because their low sensitivity to impact and flame makes them relatively safe.

It can be seen, then, that the addition of quite a low percentage (1 or 2%) of a combustible substance to ammonium nitrate, which has very low sensitivity in the pure state, transforms it into a mixture which, without having the properties required of a mining explosive, is sufficiently sensitive to be exploded (and possibly detonated) by moderate excitation.

Accidents (24.2.10) caused by ammonium nitrate recovered from military explosives such as amatol or manufactured by using nitric acid derived from spent acid left by nitration can be explained by the presence of small quantities of nitro-compounds which sensitise ammonium nitrate.

24.3.2 The effect of adding hydrocarbons

1˚ Cook [32] noted in 1924 that the sensitivity of ammonium nitrate is increased appreciably by adding 1% paraffin.

2˚ After the accident in Miramas (24.2.8), experiments [30] were carried out on mixtures of ammonium nitrate and toluene. The results, which appeared in an article published in 1948 [33], are summarised below:

A mixture of 6% toluene and 94% ammonium nitrate (the stoichiometric mixture) placed in a cartridge with a diameter of 30 mm at a density of 1 g/cm^3 detonates completely when initiated by a booster of picric acid when it is housed in a thin metal tube. The same is still true with 4 and 2% of toluene, whereas nitrate alone is insensitive in the same conditions. Even 1% of toluene makes the nitrate appreciably more sensitive. The mixture with 6% toluene gives a c.p.u. of 103 in the lead block test (see 14.3.2).

3° Cook and Talbot [34] have made a systematic study of the increase in sensitivity to priming caused by adding paraffin or various hydrocarbons to ammonium nitrate. They found that maximum sensitivity occurs when 1 to 1.5% hydrocarbon is added, although this percentage is much lower than that which gives the most powerful explosive mixture (5.6%), from which they deduced that beyond 1.5% the phlegmatising effect of paraffin is greater than its sensitising effect. Their experiments were conducted after the explosions in Texas City and Brest.

Haid and Koenen [35] also stress the fact that ammonium nitrate is at its most sensitive when 1% (or slightly more) of liquid hydrocarbon is added to it. Other authors (Brinkley, 1958) have found that maximum sensitivity is achieved when about 2% mineral oil is added to prills of ammonium nitrate.

It seems, however, that nothing was known of this sensitisation in the United States before the accident in Texas City, since a Report published in 1945 [9] contains the statement: 'Coating ammonium nitrate with approximately 1% of a mixture of pitch, resin, and paraffin does not make it significantly more liable to explode.'

Various researchers agree that 0.2% is the lowest percentage of fuel oil which, when added to porous ammonium nitrate (prills), modifies its explosive properties sufficiently for laboratory tests to detect the difference and that tests on the same product with 0.1 or 0.2% added give results which differ within an acceptable margin of error. However, other substances may have a finer sensitising effect. Bigourd [36], using the lead block method (see 14.3.4) with identical detonators to explode charges of 20 g of a porous ammonitrate (see 25.2) with a 33% nitrogen content either on its own or with lycopodium powder added, obtained extremely significant results. The cavity formed (averaged over four tests) was

$59 cm^3$ for the ammonitrate on its own,
$77 cm^3$ for the ammonitrate with 0.1% lycopodium,
$117 cm^3$ for the ammonitrate with 0.2% lycopodium.

By contrast, in the explosive pendulum mortar, mixtures with 0.1% and 0.2% lycopodium powder produced more or less the same power, equal to 62% of that produced by picric acid.

24.3.3 The explosive made of ammonium nitrate and fuel oil

The explosive made of 5 or 6% fuel oil and 95 or 94% ammonium nitrate was patented† in 1935 by Kirst and Woodbury [37], but it seems to have been the accident in Texas City which caused the Americans to consider using this type of explosive, often called a 'nitrate-fuel explosive' (ANFO). A brief study of its properties will help us to come to a better assessment of pure

---

† The patent covered mixtures of ammonium nitrate with various combustible liquids, including hydrocarbons.

or impure ammonium nitrate.

The explosives in question, which have been used for open-air blasting since 1955, are often prepared on the spot by the user, who has only to pour fuel oil onto nitrate while stirring to ensure a good distribution of the liquid. Since they are sometimes relatively insensitive, they must be initiated with a cartridge of another explosive (booster). It was quickly realised that a mixture which is made with crystallised nitrate was less satisfactory than a mixture made with nitrate in the form of spherules, especially when the latter are very porous. Ammonium nitrate is now made in the form of high-porosity, low-density prills to which fuel oil is added to give an explosive which can be initiated by a simple No. 8 detonator. It was such a product, of a quality known as 'for nitrate-fuel explosive', which caused the following accident during transport on 30 August 1972:

An articulated vehicle (tractor and trailer) transporting 18.5 tons of nitrate for explosive in polystyrene sacks was crossing an almost deserted region of Australia to deliver the product to a mine when a fault in the electric wiring started a fire in the tractor which rapidly spread to the trailer which had a wooden floor. It was not long before molten nitrate spilled out onto the road. A *closed* fuel tank situated *under* the trailer exploded in the heat of the fire, hurling its contents together with very hot metal splinters onto the pool of molten nitrate, which exploded. Three people were killed outright, a crater was blasted in the ground, and debris from the vehicle was thrown over a great distance. The lesson to be learnt from this accident is that ammonium nitrate should never be transported in a vehicle with a fuel tank located beneath it.

Melvin Cook, who began to study nitrate-fuel explosives in 1956, has published [38] measured and calculated values relating to their detonating properties (Table 24.4.). Van Dolah [39] has drawn up a set of safety regulations for worksites using these explosives on the basis of tests carried out on cartridges 1 m long and 1 m in diameter (in other words, 680 kg of explosive if one assumes a bulk density of 0.85 kg/dm^3). Table 24.5 gives distances of sympathetic detonation (with a 50% probability). It is interesting to note that ammonium nitrate at 84°C seems to be slightly more sensitive than nitrate at 15-20°C. Values for detonation velocity were also obtained in these tests: 5000 m/s for nitrate-fuel oil, and between 1700 and 3000 m/s for nitrate alone.

24.3.4 Sensitisation by various combustible substances

Every combustible substance added to ammonium nitrate gives it some degree of sensitivity. Sulphur, which readily breaks down into a very fine powder, is a good sensitiser (see the High Flyer explosion in 24.2.5). Powdered metals such as aluminium and zinc are also sensitisers. Zinc reacts particularly well with NH_4NO_3 since a mixture with equal parts zinc and nitrate is seen, when subjected to differential thermal analysis, to undergo an exothermic reaction at a temperature as low as 58°C. This same mixture in the Henkins test, as modified by Rogers, explodes after one second at 100°C (against 310°C for pure ammonium nitrate in the same test). The case is known of a fire, which was quickly extinguished, in sacks of ammonium nitrate in a railway carriage when one of the sacks was pierced by a nail and leaked nitrate onto zinc powder left on the floor from an earlier load.

Even non-explosive ammonium salts such as ammonium chloride and ammonium sulphate have a not insignificant sensitising effect when they are added to ammonium nitrate in certain concentrations because of the hydrogen they contain. This explains the Oppau disaster (24.2.3).

Finally, it has been observed that ammonium nitrate prills treated with a surface active agent become more sensitive, since the critical detonation diameter falls below that of untreated prills. A mere 0.03 to 0.05% of such an additive makes the substance as sensitive as if 1 to 1.5% fuel oil were added. The most sensitising substances are the cationic surface active agents such as sodium lauryl sulphate or sodium dodecylbenzene sulphonate.

Table 24.4

Detonation properties of ammonium nitrate–fuel oil (ANFO) explosives
at a density of 0.8 g/cm³, after Cook [38]

Nitrate/fuel oil ratio	99/1	98/2	97/3	94/6	90/10
Detonation velocity (m/s):					
measured at 127 mm diameter		2 200		2 540	2 390
ideal (calculated)		3 700		4 200	4 100
Limit diameter (m)					
(calculated)		1.55		1.4	1.6
Critical diameter (m)	0.22	0.13	0.1	0.1	0.13

Table 25.5

Sympathetic detonation of the ammonium nitrate fuel–oil explosive and
ammonium nitrate alone, the donor charge being nitrate–fuel oil,
after Van Dolah [39]

Donor charge	Acceptor charge	Distance with 50% explosion (m)
Nitrate–fuel oil 95/5 polyethylene base	Nitrate–fuel oil 95/5	5.3
Nitrate–fuel oil 95/5 1.6 mm steel base	Nitrate–fuel oil 95/5	16
Nitrate–fuel oil 95/5 polyethylene base	Ammonium nitrate	3.7
Nitrate–fuel oil 95/5 1.6 mm steel base	Ammonium nitrate	5.7 and 4.7 (a)
Nitrate–fuel oil 95/5 1.6 mm steel base	Ammonium nitrate at 83–84°C	7

(a) The 4.7 m distance was obtained in a series of tests in which the acceptor charge was protected in the front by a 1.6 mm–thick steel plate.

BIBLIOGRAPHICAL REFERENCES

[1]   Munroe, C. E. (1922) *Chem. Met. Eng.* **26** 535
[2]   Kast, H. (1926) *Z. ges. Sch. Spr.* **21** 208
[3]   Le Roux, A. (1951) *Mém. Poudres* **33** 283
[4]   Pascal, P. (1956) *Traité de Chimie Minérale.* Vol. 10, Paris, p. 217
[5]   Jones, G. W. (1924) *Army Ordn.* **5** 559
[6]   Lobry de Bruin, C. A. (1891) *Rec. Trav. Ch.* **10** 127
[7]   Lheure, L. (1907) *Ann. des Mines* [10] **12** 169
[8]   Aufschläger, R. (1923) *Z. ges. Sch. Spr.* **18** 117
[9]   Davis, R. O. E. (March 1945) *Circ. 719* of the United States Ministry of Agriculture
[10] Médard, L. (1948) *Lab. C.S.E.* Sevran
[11] Sherrick, J. L. (1924) *Army Ordn.* **4** 395
[12] Belyaev, A. F. & Khariton, Y. B. (1945) *Compt. Rend. Acad. Sc. U.S.S.R.* **48** 256
[13] Fukuyama, I. (1957) *Kogyo Kayaku Kyokai Shi* **18** 64
[14] Gawthrop, D. B. (1925) *Army Ordn.* **6** 47
[15] Jahresber. VII (1928) of the *Chemisch-Technischen Reichsanstalt*, p. 52
[16] Fossé, C. (1967) *Journées d'Etudes sur les substances instables, Brussels, 8–9 May 1967*
[17] Kast, H. (1923) *Angew. Chem.* **36** 72
[18] Paterson, S. & Davidson, J. M. (1962) *Nature* (G.B.) **195** 277
[19] Wöhler, L. (1923) *Angew. Chem.* **36** 84
[20] Herquet, M. L. (1952) *Explosifs* **5** 29
[21] Report of the Ammonium Nitrate Working Party. H.M.S.O., London, 1951
[22] Burns, J., Scott, G. S., Jones, G. W. & Lewis, E. (1953) Bureau of Mines *Rep. Inv.* 4994
[23] Clancey, V. J. (1962) *R.A.R.D.E. Interim Rep.*
[24] Van Dolah, R. W., Mason, C. M. *et al.* (1966) Bureau of Mines *Rep. Inv.* 6773
[25] Braconier, F. & Delsemme, H. (1952) *Explosifs* **5** 34
[26] Feick, G. & Hainer, R. M. (1954) *J. Am. Ch. Soc.* **76** 5858
[27] Bramkamp, W. (1922) *Z. ges. Sch. Spr.* **17** 67
[28] Kast, H. (1925) *Z. ges. Sch. Spr.* **20** and (1926) **22**
[29] Rapports de la Commission du nitrate d'ammoniun, présidée par P. Pascal, Paris, 1948
[30] Burlot, E. & Médard, L. (1940) Commission des Substances Explosives, *Rapport du 12 octobre 1940*
[31] Brisson de Laroche (1940) *Rapport à C.S.E.* (June 1940)
[32] Cook, R. M. (1924) *Chem. Met. Eng.* **31** 231
[33] Médard, L. (1948) *Compt. Rend. de la Semaine nationale de la Sécurité.* Paris, p. 82
[34] Cook, M. A. & Talbot, E. L. (1951) *Ind. Eng. Ch.* **43** 1098
[35] Haid, A. & Koenen, H. (1952) *Explosivstoffe*, p. 196
[36] Bigourd, J. (1974) *Lab. Cerchar*, note of 24 October 1974
[37] Kirst, W. & Woodbury, C. (1935) U.S. Patent 1.992.817 delivered on 26 February 1935
[38] Cook, M. A. (1958) *Bull. School of Mines of Missouri*, p. 135
[39] Van Dolah, R. W., Gibson, F. C. & Murphy, J. W. (1966) Bureau of Mines *Rep. Inv.* 6746
[40] Whetstone, J. quoted by Taylor, J (1952) in *Detonation in Condensed Explosives*, p. 143

[41]   Winning, C. H. (1965) *Fire Tech.* 1 23

25

Ammonium nitrate-based fertilisers

25.1 GENERAL OBSERVATIONS ON FERTILISERS

Of the elements necessary for plants to live the three most important are nitrogen, phosphorus, and potassium. *Simple fertilisers* are those which contain only one of these basic elements, whilst *compound fertilisers* contain two or three. Since the chemical symbols for these fertilising elements are N, P, and K, compound fertilisers are given the following abbreviated names in industry:

    N-P fertilisers
    N-K fertilisers
    P-K fertilisers
    N-P-K fertilisers.

It is customary in most European countries to express the percentage of basic elements in a compound fertiliser by a group of three numbers, of which the first is the nitrogen content (total percentage of nitrogen in the fertiliser), the second is the phosphorus content (counted as P_2O_5), and the third is the potassium content (counted as K_2O). Thus, a given NPK fertiliser composed of ammonium nitrate, ammonium phosphate, and potassium chloride would be described as NPK 16.16.8. This classification system is also applied to two-element fertilisers, or even to definite compounds which may be used as fertilisers. For example, pure diammonium phosphate† is a 21.53.0, and potassium nitrate (saltpetre) is a 14.0.46.

Of the simple fertilisers the nitrogen fertilisers may contain ammonium

---

† Certain granulated or crystallised substances sold under the name of diammonium phosphate have the formula 18.46.0 or 18.50.0 depending on the level of impurities they contain.

nitrate.   Those which do not, like anhydrous ammonia or urea, present no
risk of explosion, but the most commonly used nitrate fertilisers contain a
high percentage of ammonium nitrate.

Compound fertilisers are sometimes obtained by mixing two or three
simple fertilisers, but at present they are usually produced by reactions
on raw materials, such as the action of ammonia on superphosphates, or the
reaction of nitric or phosphoric acid on phosphate rock.   They are then
normally called *complex fertilisers*.

Sometimes, a very small amount of mineral substances useful to the
growth of plants is added to compound fertilisers.   The technical term for
the elements of these substances (boron, copper, manganese, cobalt, etc.)
in the fertiliser industry is trace elements.   Less often, small quantities
of pesticides are added to fertilisers, and these, which are organic
compounds, may, like the trace elements, have an undesirable effect on the
behaviour of fertilisers in a fire.

25.2 THE AMMONITRATES

25.2.1 Definition

The name ammonitrates† was given in France in 1946 to simple ammonium
nitrate-based fertilisers which were given a precise definition in the
regulations governing the transport by road of dangerous substances.   The
names high- and medium-content ammonitrates are given to fertilisers with
an ammonium nitrate base and no other fertilising component which fulfil
the following conditions:

(a) The chlorine content is no higher than 0.02% (in practice it is lower
than 0.01%.

(b) The percentage content of combustible substances does not exceed 0.2%
if there is more, or 0.4% if there is less, than 90% ammonium nitrate.   In
fact, all the ammonitrates produced in France contain less than 0.2% of
combustible substances, and it is by no means exceptional for there to be
0.1% or less.

(c) If any of the constituents are mineral substances, they should have no
harmful effect on the stability of the ammonium nitrate.

High-content ammonitrates contain between 93 and 98% ammonium nitrate
and have a granulometry such that 10% at most of the product passes through
a No. 31 sieve and 5% through a No. 28 sieve (as defined by the French
standards institute AFNOR).   Medium-content ammonitrates contain between 80
and 93% ammonium nitrate.

In fact, the calcareous substances which are usually added to the
ammonitrates not only do not have a harmful effect on the stability of
ammonium nitrate but actually have a noticeable desensitising effect, as
can be seen from curve IV in Fig. 25.1 compared with curve III representing
mixtures of ammonium nitrate with potassium sulphate which acts simply as
an inert substance.

---

† This is not the best term to use since the German word 'Ammonnitrat'
designates ammonium nitrate itself.   French ammonitrates have an ammonium
nitrate base but different properties from those of pure ammonium nitrate.
I.C.I's Nitram is similar to the ammonitrates under discussion here.

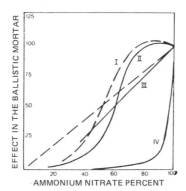

Fig. 25.1 – Results, after Clancey [12], of firing in the ballistic mortar
a mixture of ammonium nitrate with: I: ammonium sulphate (mechanical
mixture);   II: ammonium sulphate (co-crystallised);   III: potassium
sulphate;   IV: calcium carbonate.

Low-content ammonitrates are simple nitrogen fertilisers containing
less than 80% ammonium nitrate and are not considered to be dangerous in
some transport and inspection regulations.

The ammonitrates are characterised by their nitrogen content, which is
proportional to their fertilising capacity. These nitrogen contents are:
- pure ammonium nitrate (for comparison)   35%
- high-content ammonitrates   32.6 to 34.6%
- medium-content ammonitrates   28 to 32.6%.
The most commonly sold ammonitrates are those with 33-33.5% nitrogen and
those with 34.5% nitrogen. A product with more than 34.6% nitrogen is no
longer considered to be an ammonitrate, but is rather classified with pure
ammonium nitrate and is thus subjected to stricter controls than are the
ammonitrates.

Clay is sometimes added to ammonium nitrate to make ammonitrates but
the substances most frequently used are limestone, marl, or dolomite
(double carbonate of calcium and magnesium). This mineral substance is
present either as a coating around each granule or incorporated into its
mass. They are called respectively *coated* and *filled* ammonitrates.

The ammonitrates must have good spreading qualities (be free flowing)
when used in sowing machines in the fields. They should come in the form
of granules of just a few millimetres, usually between 1.5 and 4 mm, with
as uniform a size as possible. Discontinuous granulation processes, which
produced small and irregularly-shaped or roughly round agglomerates, are
increasingly being replaced by continuous processes giving regular-sized
granules. The technical term for products obtained by simultaneously
dehydrating and crystallising concentrated solutions in a tower traversed
by dry, rising gases is 'prills', which are spherical or slightly ovoid
and, depending on how they are formed, have a compact or porous structure
and lower or higher density. It is customary, in the manufacture of
prilled ammonitrates, to distinguish between high-concentration and low-
concentration processes. In the latter, the prilling tower is fed a 95-96%
solution of ammonium nitrate, the temperature in the tower being between
132 and 155°C, while in the former, high-concentration process the nitrate
is a 99% solution at least and the hot gases flowing into the tower have a

temperature between 177 and 185°C. This process gives a product with a bulk density of between 1 and 1.15 consisting of prills with low porosity, whereas the low-concentration process gives quite porous prills with a density of between 0.75 and 0.9.

It is important in the manufacture of ammonitrates to make a suitable choice of additives. Thus, although it is sometimes recommended to add from 0.5 to 3% ferrous sulphate, which would prevent changes in crystalline shape during storage, it seems preferable not to use an iron salt, which has an unfavourable effect on the decomposition of ammonium nitrate by heat.

Increasingly fewer low- and medium-content ammonitrates are produced since there is now a tendency to supply agriculture with products which have a high nitrogen content.

25.2.2 Properties of ammonitrates

Experience in storing ammonium nitrate in very large quantities, especially during the two World Wars, has shown that even in enormous piles it is not prone to spontaneous heating†. Because of the conditions they have to satisfy, ammonitrates, unlike certain other products (see 25.4), are not exposed to this risk either, since they have a relatively high pH. If they are caught in a fire, the practical absence of chlorine prevents the decomposition from being more vigorous than that of pure ammonium nitrate. In fact, the presence of calcium carbonate which may react with ammonium nitrate to give off ammonia maintains the pH at a high level, and that moderates the reaction rate of the decomposition.

When, in the manufacture of high-content ammonitrates, crushed limestone is added to the hot, concentrated solution of ammonium nitrate before passage through the prilling tower, a small quantity of ammonia is liberated by the (endothermic) reaction

$$CaCO_3 + 2NH_4NO_3 \rightarrow Ca(NO_3)_2 + 2NH_3 + CO_2 + H_2O.$$

This reaction may take place very slowly during storage of ammonitrates, but the latter contain only very small amounts of calcium nitrate in a partially hydrated form or in the form of double nitrates of ammonium and calcium, the existence of which was established by Lamberger and Pâris [13]. Ammonia from the above reaction is partly retained by adsorption on the surface of the ammonium nitrate.

---

† The apparently spontaneous heating of ammonium nitrate or ammonitrate has sometimes been observed when the product has been exposed to a high ambient temperature (35°C, for example) and then returned to a lower temperature. This can be explained by the fact that ammonium nitrate is subject to the phenomenon of 'crystalline supercooling' and that 32°C is the equilibrium temperature between the monoclinic and orthorhombic forms. Monoclinic nitrate which reverts irreversibly at a temperature below 32°C, for example 20°C, to the orthorhombic form may see its temperature at that time rise by some 13°C since (Table 23.2) the heat of transformation is about 2000 joules per mole and the specific heat is 142 joules/mol°C. This is a phenomenon similar to that which occurs with many other salts, for example hydrated sodium sulphate.

High-content ammonitrates are, like pure ammonium nitrate itself, liable to detonate, but to a much lesser degree since the mineral filler they contain acts as a diluent for ammonium nitrate. On the other hand, this same filler and the way in which ammonitrates are manufactured give them a granulometry such that the proportion of fine granules in the end product is very small, and it is the presence of fine granules which make a substance sensitive to initiation.

25.2.3 Dangers posed by the ammonitrates

The accidents which took place between 1920 and 1947 (see 24.2) led to a new attitude of caution, and after 1948 it was considered that any ammonium nitrate containing more than 0.4% combustible materials should be treated as intentional explosives from the point of view of transport and storage. Experts from East European countries wanted to know if it would be possible to define the properties of those ammonitrates which are free of the risk of explosion in conditions of storage and transport, and, with that aim in mind, conducted a series of experiments in test centres to study explosives using either the long, thick steel tube method devised by the B.A.M. (see 15.3.5), or the Belgian test (see 15.3.6). In both of these tests the ammonitrate must be loaded into the tube at its normal packing density, which can vary from 0.85 to 1.1 depending on the product. Goffart [15] has published results obtained with the Belgian method. French ammonitrates containing 33% nitrogen and most ammonitrates at 34.5% as well as similar foreign products pass these tests satisfactorily.

Hansen and Berthold [16] have objected that it is not sufficient to carry out a test of resistance to detonating initiation on the fertiliser as it is produced, saying that tests should also be made on the product as modified by thermal cycles since, during storage, it may repeatedly go beyond the temperature of 32°C and undergo decomposition (see 23.1.2). Consequently, using a method which involves repeated heating from 25 to 45°C followed by cooling back to 25°C, they subjected samples of ammonium nitrate-based fertiliser to two or five thermal cycles in the laboratory, and then subjected them to detonation tests using the B.A.M. tube method (see 15.3.5) rather than the Belgian method. They considered that the sample tested was not liable to detonation if the length of tube broken by the explosion was not more than 40% of the total length. These tests, or similar tests using the Belgian method, on high- and medium-content ammonitrates subjected to thermal cycles show that *some* (but not all) ammonitrates containing 33.5 to 34.5% nitrogen which successfully pass the detonation test in the non-modified form are able to propagate a detonation along the entire length of the tube after five, and sometimes even after two, thermal cycles, since the latter cause considerable break-down of the granular substance as well as a fall in its bulk density and the production of nitrate dusts, with the result that the product becomes more liable to propagate a detonation.

The thermal-cycle test is not realistic since, in a warehouse which contains loose or bagged ammonitrates, and even in a railway carriage housing some twenty tons of fertiliser in sacks, the thermal inertia of the substance is such that only a very small portion of the mass undergoes variations in temperature equal to those in the ambient temperature. Only a thin layer of between four and six centimetres can be altered by passing through 32°C. In the summer of 1976, which was particularly hot, French

producers of ammonitrates conducted a series of experiments in several
parts of France on ammonitrate stored in a warehouse or in a stationary
railway carriage parked on a siding unprotected from the sun. Thermometers
showed that between day and night the temperature of the ambient air varied
between around 20 and 45°C whilst the temperature in the ammonitrate varied
only between narrow limits except in certain surface layers.

The very usefulness of a detonation test on ammonium nitrate-based
fertilisers has also been criticised by King and Bauer [17], since in
practice the fertiliser is not subjected to the effect of an explosive but
is far more likely to be surrounded by fire.

The idea was also conceived of assessing the explodability of an
ammonitrate by measuring the percentage of mineral oil it can absorb and
retain, a percentage which is related to its porosity, since it is well
known that nitrate of a quality 'for nitrate-fuel explosive' (see 24.3.3)
is a porous substance capable of easily absorbing 10 to 15% of its weight
in oil, whereas the ammonitrates in prills have an oil-retention capacity
of no more than 5% and very often less than 1%. The problem of developing
a method to measure oil retention in ammonitrates giving reproducible
results is being studied by the International Standards Organisation.

25.2.4 Safety of storing, handling, and transporting ammonitrates

Although ammonitrates cannot be considered to be completely risk-free, it
is still quite easy to store, transport, handle, and use them in complete
safety provided a few simple precautions are taken. These precautions can
be expressed as three rules:

1° Ammonitrates must be kept away from explosives and care should be taken
to avoid contamination by accidental mixing with other substances, and in
particular with combustible substances.

2° Ammonitrates should be kept away from sources of heat.

3° Confinement should be avoided during storage and transport.

The same principles apply to the safety of storage of pure ammonium
nitrate (nitrate warehouses in factories producing explosives or nitrous
oxide) or of certain nitrate- and ammonium sulphate-based mixtures.

According to a Russian study [22], the pneumatic transport of ammonium
nitrate through long conduits may create static electric charges which
would be a source of danger in mines. However, we are not aware of any
accidents caused by this phenomenon in factories.

25.2.5 Ammonitrate warehouses

The building to be used as a warehouse must be a one-storey building with
no basement or cellar, and must be made of materials which do not burn
easily, although the roof, which must be light, may rest on a wooden frame
but must have an incombustible covering (slate, tiles, steel, asbestos
cement). Zinc, galvanised steel, copper, and lead must not be used. The
floor should be made of cement or some other incombustible material with as
few bitumen joints as possible. There should be no gutters, drains, or
pits inside the building where molten nitrate may collect in a fire.

One sometimes reads that fireproofed wood should be used in the
building of nitrate warehouses or vehicles to be used for transporting
nitrate, but fireproofed wood in the presence of an oxidising agent such as

ammonium nitrate burns almost as strongly as non-fireproofed wood. What is really needed is wood that is not readily impregnated by ammonium nitrate, in other words a wood with compact fibres and no cracks and which has been proofed by bakelisation, for example.

Conveyor belts and other equipment to be used in handling ammonitrates should have no parts made of flammable materials (neoprene, which is used to make conveyor belts, is considered to be not especially flammable). If the equipment has any parts made of copper, lead, or zinc (even in the form of galvanised steel), they should be protected to prevent contact with ammonitrate. Similarly, care must be taken to ensure that there are no apparatuses, such as scales, in the warehouse with chrome-surfaced parts which would rapidly form chromium salts which are dangerous in the presence of nitrate, something which does not happen with austenitic stainless (chromium-nickel) steels.

Electrical apparatuses (engines, circuit breakers, fuses, etc.) must, if possible, be located outside the warehouse, and, in any case, in a place where they cannot be covered with nitrate. Electric lighting equipment and wiring must be located far enough away from the highest point to which the product is stored to prevent it from heating. A master circuit breaker must be sited in a different building so that the electrical equipment in the warehouse can be switched off outside working hours.

The building should have windows which can be opened, from an outside catwalk for example, to ventilate the warehouse if need be and for the ammonitrate to be sprayed by fire hose in case of fire. An adequate number of fire hydrants should be sited nearby.

It is particularly important that no combustible liquid should ever be able to come into contact with the ammonitrate and, by capillary action, impregnate a large quantity of the substance, which is why an ammonitrate warehouse should be located well away from any tank of flammable liquids and measures must be taken (a low retaining wall, for example) to ensure that no pool of such a liquid can seep into the warehouse.

25.2.6 Operating an ammonitrate warehouse

A. The following should never on any account be taken into the warehouse: explosives, any substance prone to vigorous decomposition such as organic peroxides, compressed gas cylinders, flammable liquid containers.

B. Ammonitrate warehouses in factories are, as a general rule, to be used purely to store ammonitrate. The following rules should be observed in running them:

1° It is forbidden to smoke and to bring naked flames into the warehouse. The use of inspection lamps should be restricted, and, after use, the cable should not be left in contact with the ammonitrate.

2° Conveyors should be periodically cleaned and kept in good condition.

3° If the appliances used in the warehouse (scrapers, for example) cannot be lubricated outside, then care must be taken to ensure that no lubricant is dropped on the floor or the ammonitrate. There should be no excessive greasing which would create the risk of drops falling onto the nitrate when the appliance is used. Cans of lubricant should not be left inside the warehouse.

4° Vehicles or appliances driven by an internal combustion engine must not be left in the warehouse because of the danger of the ammonitrate being contaminated by a fuel leak.

5° If ammonitrate in bulk has caked and has to be broken up, then *only* mechanical means should be used. However, Cardox shells can be blasted in the caked mass without risk of explosion since rigorous experiments conducted by Koenen [23] have proved that these devices do not ignite an explosive composed of 78% ammonium nitrate with trinitrotoluene and nitroglycerine, and can, therefore, have no effect other than mechanical on ammonitrates, whatever their composition. If Cardox shells are to be used, it must be made clear in the instructions that the use of true explosive cartridges is not permitted.

C. In some commercial or maritime installations it is frequently not possible to allocate a warehouse exclusively to the storage of ammonitrate, in which case the following precautions should be taken in addition to those in A above:

1° Easily flammable solid substances such as sulphur and metallic powders should be allowed into the warehouse only if they are housed in leakproof containers and placed far enough away from the ammonitrate stock.

2° If acids and other corrosive substances, chlorates, hypochlorites, chromates, permanganates, nitrites, and the salts of heavy metals (Zn, Cu, Co, Ni, Fe, etc.) are kept in the same warehouse, they must be kept away from the ammonitrate and separated from it by a low wall or other suitable barricade, so that they can in no circumstance (especially a fire) mix with it.

3° The ammonitrate must be kept at a suitable distance from any other fertilisers (NPK fertilisers, ammonium sulphate, etc.) or products of which the composition is not properly known (such as pesticides, herbicides, disinfectants, etc.).

25.2.7 Bulk storage of ammonitrates

Factories making ammonitrates often store them in bulk and usually put them into bags just before delivery. The bulk product may be stored in piles or in concrete bays but never in wooden containers. When forming a pile, the following rule should be applied:

A pile must be no more than 8 m high and the top should be at least 1 m below the tie beams.

25.2.8 Storing ammonitrate in containers

One of the advantages of storing ammonitrates in containers is that the product is kept free from contamination by foreign bodies, so enhancing safety. If the product is stored in bags, parallelepipedal piles can be built up allowing easy circulation. It has been objected that the material used to make the containers (other than metal containers) is combustible, but there is no serious risk since this combustible material is not mixed with the nitrate, and experiments carried out in Toulouse (1950) and Heligoland (1952) have allayed fears in this respect.

The most frequently used containers are bags made of paper of several thicknesses (multi-ply paper, with one ply moisture-proof), or of a plastic material or jute lined with polyethylene. In the case of plastic bags, the ratio of the mass of the container to the mass of the contents is lower than with paper bags (for 50 kg of nitrate a polyethylene bag has a mass of 200 g and a paper bag about 550 g). Polyethylene bags (which are chlorine-free) are preferable to bags made of polyvinyl chloride since, in a fire, the latter burn more strongly than the former. The bags used must be waterproof, tightly closed, and strong enough to withstand handling in transport.

Some precautions are needed when forming regular heaps with bags. The most stable heaps are achieved by using gusseted bags since they can be stacked on pallets and experience shows that piles made of pallets are more stable and permit easier watering of the bags in case of fire.

Empty bags made of paper or any other material which have contained ammonium nitrate should not be kept in a nitrate warehouse.

When the nitrate is put in bags, it should be at a temperature below 65°C, and preferably below 50°C†.

In 1948, after the accidents in Texas City and Brest, which showed the disastrous effects of organic combustible materials added to ammonium nitrate, metal drums were thought to be a safer type of container than paper or plastic bags, but this belief is no longer held today because a metal drum subjects nitrate to conditions of confinement which, although low, are higher than when the substance is stored in bags. In addition, metal drums are good heat conductors and would cause the nitrate to heat up in a fire.

It has been suggested that only pallets made of metal or strong plastic should be used, but it has been seen from a number of fires that wooden pallets do not pose an increased risk in ammonitrate warehouses. When wooden pallets are not in use, they should be stored in a different building. They should also be inspected at regular intervals and any which are in poor condition or have become accidentally impregnated with nitrate should be discarded. 'General-purpose' pallets should be viewed with suspicion since they may have been used with other, unknown products and may have become impregnated with dangerous substances.

25.2.9 Storage on a farm or for agricultural purposes

When being used for agricultural purposes, ammonitrate must be stored only in the packed state. Suppliers should inform their customers, who normally know very little about the properties of ammonium nitrate, of elementary precautions to be taken: keep away from flammable liquids or stocks which pose a risk of fire (straw, etc.), shovel up and bury the contents of any split bags, etc.

25.3 AMMONIUM NITROSULPHATE

25.3.1 General properties

Mixtures of ammonium sulphate and ammonium nitrate, which have the trade name of ammonium nitrosulphate, are simple nitrogen fertilisers which are

---

† Pure nitrate and ammonitrates other than those which contain limestone may release acid vapours at around 70°C which cause partial nitration of the cellulosic material of the paper or the textile. The paper thus loses some of its mechanical resistance and becomes more readily flammable.

manufactured mainly in Germany and Great Britain. They are obtained either by mixing the two salts, by pouring ammonia into hot nitric acid holding ammonium sulphate in solution, or by pouring ammonia into a solution of ammonium nitrate in sulphuric acid.

After the two salts have simply been mixed, moisture may cause them to form complex salts, two of which have been identified:

$$(NH_4)_2SO_4 \cdot 2NH_4NO_3$$
$$(NH_4)_2SO_4 \cdot 3NH_4NO_3.$$

The first, which is often called Leuna salt, combines 54.8% nitrate and 45.2% sulphate and has a nitrogen content of 28.8%. The second contains 65.4% nitrate and has a nitrogen content of 30.1%. A hydrated double salt also exists:

$$(NH_4)_2SO_4 \cdot NH_4NO_3 \cdot H_2O$$

with a specific gravity equal to 1.48 g/cm^3. Double salts are always present in the products obtained by cooling hot solutions of ammonium nitrate and ammonium sulphate.

The mixture formed of equal parts nitrate and sulphate was called 'Oppau salt' in Germany in the 1920s after the name of the factory which produced it. The term 'Mischsalz' seems to apply to products containing between 48 and 58% ammonium nitrate.

The nitrate in ammonium nitrosulphate, which is always present mainly as a double salt, is only slightly subject to the polymorphic changes which cause caking, but the product does harden when stored in large piles.

25.3.2 Explosive properties of ammonium nitrosulphate

The comments made on the Oppau disaster (see 24.2.3) show that mixtures containing about 60% ammonium nitrate (and *a fortiori* those which contain more) are liable to detonate if ignition and confinement are strong enough. Ammonium sulphate cannot be considered as an inert substance added to nitrate because the ammonium ions which it contains act as a fuel. For example, the decomposition of Leuna salt according to the equation

$$(NH_4)_2SO_4 \cdot 2NH_4NO_3 \rightarrow SO_2 + 8H_2O + 3N_2$$

releases 349 kJ, whereas the decomposition of the two moles of nitrate which it contains liberates only 253 kJ. The following comparison of the heats of explosion is interesting:

ammonium nitrate	1 589 kJ/kg
Leuna salt	1 200 kJ/kg
nitrosulphate 50/50	883 kJ/kg.

Experiments by Aufschläger [11] gave results in the lead block test which confirm the explosive nature of the 50/50 mixture. The expansion produced (see 14.3.2) is 220 cm^3 for 10 g, with ammonium nitrate alone giving 244 cm^3. Tests in the resistant steel tube also demonstrate the explosive property of the 50/50 mixture.

Of the results obtained by Clancey [12] the two following deserve to be mentioned:

(a) Tests in the ballistic mortar on mixtures of nitrate and sulphate produce the variation seen in Fig. 25.1 which compares the results obtained for mixtures of calcium nitrate and calcium carbonate with those for

mixtures of potassium nitrate and potassium sulphate, which can be compared to the results obtained by Kast (Fig. 24.1).
(b) At a density of 0.8 g/cm³ the 60/40 mixture of ammonium nitrate and ammonium sulphate can detonate at a velocity of 1300 m/s and a velocity of 1500 m/s when 2% of shredded paper is added.

25.3.3 Classification of ammonium nitrosulphates

The preceding observations explain why experts at the I.M.C.O. classify ammonium nitrosulphates as follows:
1° Those which contain more than 70% ammonium nitrate are considered to be more dangerous than ammonium nitrate on its own.
2° Those which contain between 45 and 70% ammonium nitrate are classified as type A fertilisers (in other words, liable to explode but not more dangerous than ammonium nitrate itself).
3° Mixtures with less than 45% nitrate (more than 55% ammonium sulphate) are not considered to be dangerous.

25.4 COMPOUND NPK FERTILISERS

25.4.1 The potential dangers posed by NPK fertilisers

There are many different types of compound fertiliser and many ways of manufacturing them. In the final stage of production the products are given a granular shape to facilitate spreading by passing the still hot substance through a granulator which often consists of a cylinder rotating on a slightly inclined axis. In some countries compound fertilisers are sometimes passed through a prilling tower to be shaped into spherules. The aim is to produce granules which are insensitive to humidity and which can be stored without risk of caking.

With fertilisers which contain no ammonium nitrate there is no danger of explosion, but in practice nearly all solid NPK fertilisers contain nitrate and may, mainly as a result of their composition but also to some extent of their structure (granulometry, etc.), pose the following dangers:

1° The fertiliser may have weak explosive properties similar to those of certain simple nitrate fertilisers, but only those which contain a relatively high percentage of ammonium nitrate pose this risk.

2° Some NPK fertilisers may, if they are raised to a sufficiently high temperature, undergo a nitrous decomposition similar to that which takes place in hot solutions of NH_4NO_3 (23.3.2). This is an auto-catalytic reaction which, once begun, spreads to the rest of the substance. It may break out in the manufacture of fertilisers in an apparatus such as a hopper or a drying tube if, for any reason whatever, the hot substance becomes highly acidic. Chlorides assist the decomposition. In practice, there is no risk of this nitrous decomposition occurring in a neutral mixture kept below 120°C.

3° In many fertilisers containing both ammonium nitrate and a chloride a special type of deflagration may occur if a sufficient amount of heat is supplied to one point in the mass. This deflagration, which propagates very slowly from the point of ignition, has been called a 'self-sustained decomposition' or 'cigar burning', and, as we shall see later, presents considerable dangers. The expression cigar burning, coined by Parker and

Watchorn [3], is highly appropriate since it conjures up the image not only of smoke being produced but also of a high-temperature zone which gradually advances through the mass leaving a solid residue behind†. However, the analogy with a cigar must not be taken too far since a cigar burns only because of the air drawn through the tobacco, whereas in an NPK fertiliser cigar burning is a reaction of the product itself (which contains oxygen) and does not involve air. It is the catalytic action of chloride ions (see 23.2.6) present in the fertiliser which makes this decomposition easy to initiate.

4˚ Finally, fertilisers exist which are prone to spontaneous heating, sometimes by as much as 40˚C, during storage at ordinary temperature. If they reach a high enough temperature, the nitrous decomposition referred to in 2˚ above may take place.

25.4.2 Spontaneous heating of compound fertilisers

Davis and Hardesty [1] report the case of a fire caused by spontaneous heating after two weeks in a stock of some 140 tons of a mixture of 20% ammonium nitrate with 70% superphosphate and 10% powdered peanut shell. Laboratory experiments which they performed on similar mixtures showed that it is the acidity of the superphosphate which allows the ammonium nitrate to oxidise the organic substance present. More precisely, free phosphoric acid reacting on the ammonium nitrate liberates nitric acid which attacks the organic substance present. When such mixtures are heated, white fumes appear at around 90 to 100˚C, becoming more dense at around 110˚C and accompanied by nitrous fumes. If such mixtures contain ammonia in large enough quantity to raise their pH above 6, they can withstand heating to 100˚C without undergoing an exothermic reaction.

Experiments [7] have shown that slow oxidation of these mixtures at 30˚C releases gases composed mainly of CO_2 (43%), N_2 (42%), and N_2O (12%). If the organic substance present is readily oxidisable, only a small amount is needed for spontaneous heating to take place, but organic substances are quite different from one another in this respect.

Because organic substances are quite widespread in phosphate rock deposits (between 0.1 and 0.5% counted as carbon), superphosphate contains enough organic substance for mixtures with ammonium nitrate with nothing else added to be prone to spontaneous heating by 20 or 30˚C when they are stored in mass. It is an indication that the organic substance is being oxidised by the nitrate. The gases released are composed mainly of carbon dioxide and nitrogen.

Barclay and his associates [2] have studied this phenomenon, the strength of which is proportional to the acidity of the mixture. The oxidation can be prevented by calcining tricalcium phosphate at 800–1000˚C before it is turned into superphosphate, but that has the unfortunate effect of making it difficult to obtain a good superphosphate. Barclay found that adding 0.2 to 0.5% urea to a mixture of ammonium nitrate and

---

† The expression 'cigar burning' or 'cigarette burning' has been in common use in the technology of solid propellants (blocks of powder for rockets) since 1945. Of course, the deflagration velocity of these propellants is 1000 to 10 000 times higher than that of the nitrates being discussed here.

superphosphate prevents oxidation reactions from occurring under normal storage conditions. He believes that this action of urea is similar in nature to that which prevents organic substances from oxidising during some nitration processes (see 26.5.1). It is also similar to the stabilising effect which Findlay and Rosebourne [4] found when 0.5 to 1% urea is added to mixtures of 5% sawdust and 95% NH_4NO_3. If urea is not added to this mixture, the cellulose component of the wood is oxidised at 100°C with release of CO_2 and nitrogen.

This heating of fertilisers containing organic substances should not be confused with the very moderate heating by some 10°C which occurs in some compound fertilisers which contain no organic substances and which is caused by the formation of new salts resulting from the redistribution of the anions and the cations. For example, the reaction

$$NH_4NO_3 + KCl \rightarrow KNO_3 + NH_4Cl,$$

which takes place slowly in NPK fertilisers containing potassium chloride, releases 8 kJ/mol†. Levels of heating as low as this present no safety problems.

It goes without saying that manufacturers strive to produce fertilisers which give rise to negligible or only moderate spontaneous heating during storage, since any heating that raised the fertiliser to 80 or 90°C might trigger a nitrous decomposition or self-sustained decomposition.

Any spontaneous heating which may occur can easily be studied by the double Dewar vessel method (see 16.3.3.4). The test sample may be as much as one or two kilogrammes and is therefore a good representation of industrial manufacture. In some cases, when the test was extended over several days, a temperature rise which lasted for some time was followed by a slow return of the test substance to its initial temperature. For precision studies carried out in a research laboratory, one would need to use an adiabatic calorimeter such as a Calvet microcalorimeter or an apparatus like the one described in the pamphlet in reference [8].

The temperature of the substance during storage in a large pile in a warehouse can be observed by inserting temperature probes in the mass. The variation in temperature agrees with predictions based on results obtained in tests using the double Dewar vessel method.

25.4.3 The first accidents caused by the self-sustained decomposition of NPK fertilisers

The type of decomposition which will be studied in the following section was still virtually unknown in 1956‡ because compound fertilisers produced

---

† In fact, the existence of solid solutions of ammonium nitrate and potassium nitrate (see 23.1.2) means that reactions are less simple than the one represented in this equation and may involve slightly higher heat releases (see reference [10]).

‡ However, about one ton of fertiliser decomposed in a cylindrical silo in a Norwegian fertiliser factory in 1949 (12.6.15). Three people suffered slight poisoning from nitrous fumes released when the substance was being watered with a fire hose. The inquiry found that an unprotected inspection lamp left in the silo after loading had become covered with fertiliser.

before then contained much less nitrogen (particularly in the form of
ammonium nitrate) than those which have been manufactured since. It came
to light as a result of a number of sometimes quite spectacular accidents,
several of which deserve to be mentioned.

1° Eight thousand tons of 12.12.17 NPK fertiliser decomposed in a silo
in Hoechst near Frankfurt in 1961. The reaction was set off by a conveyor
belt which heated up probably as a result of accidental friction. Large
quantities of reddish-brown fumes were given off but nobody was injured.

2° On 5 November 1963 in Vlaardingen (on the banks of the river Meuse
below Rotterdam) in a warehouse containing 4500 tons of 12.12.12. NPK, a
part of the mass was found to be incandescent when workers were loading it
onto lorries. The decomposition lasted for several hours, giving off a
toxic cloud which fortunately passed through only non-residential areas.
Since an explosive had been blasted to break up the fertiliser shortly
before the fire began, it is thought that the decomposition may have been
initiated by a cartridge which failed to detonate but underwent a fizzing
deflagration.

3° On 19 February 1965, the Dutch ship Sophocles was off the Azores.
Eight days before it had taken on 5300 tons of 14.14.14 NPK in bulk in
Aruba (West Indies). This was the only merchandise on board. Some eight
hours after the watchman had made his round and found everything apparently
normal in the holds and between-decks, smoke was seen coming from the
ventilator shaft to hold No. 3. When a probe was lowered, the temperature
of the fertiliser was found to be 95°C at the top of the between-decks
above the hold, where a lighted electric lamp from the previous watch had
been left behind and become buried to some depth under the fertiliser.

The captain ordered the engines to be shut down and hold No. 3 to be
filled with CO_2 as well as 20 tons of water, but stopped the watering when
the ship began to list. Four hours later in rough seas the vessel capsized
and sank, drowning three men. The decomposition was almost certainly
caused by the localised heating of the fertiliser by the electric light.

4° On 24 December 1966, in a vast warehouse belonging to a factory in
Hoechst, decomposition started in a stock of 7200 tons of 16.11.14 NPK
(containing 0.1% copper). White smoke which soon turned brown was seen
coming from the skylight. The firemen arrived on the scene fifteen minutes
later but in spite of enormous quantities of water being hosed onto the
product, the decomposition continued for about twelve hours, releasing
toxic fumes. Nobody was affected by the gas, and it is not known what
caused the reaction.

These accidents in the years 1960-66 led to studies of the mechanism of
self-sustained decomposition and the introduction of measures to reduce the
likelihood of such reactions occurring. In spite of that, however, there
have been other accidents since 1966, some of them leading to casualties.
It has been possible in a number of cases to isolate the cause of the
deflagration as the contact between hot gases or a hot substance and the
fertiliser, although in some cases the cause has remained doubtful or
unknown. These accidents show that many NPK-type fertilisers are prone to
easily initiated 'cigar burning'.

25.4.4 Properties of 'cigar burning' in NPK fertilisers

NPK fertilisers prone to 'cigar burning' are those which contain both
ammonium chloride and ammonium nitrate (or salts containing nitrate ions

and ammonium ions, such as the combination KNO_3 – NH_4Cl). Furthermore, potassium is present in most NPK fertilisers in the form of potassium chloride, but any other potassium salt obtained from the chloride and not sufficiently purified would provide chloride ions. Just 0.5% of chloride in a fertiliser is enough for it to be able to undergo the decomposition under discussion, which is also observed in fertilisers containing no more than 2% nitric nitrogen (nitrogen from the NO_3 ions). The decomposition propagates more easily when a large solid residue can be formed (skeleton), which is why fertilisers containing bicalcium phosphate are more prone to cigar burning than those which contain ammonium phosphate.

When the fertiliser takes the form of an unconfined mass at atmospheric pressure, cigar burning shows the following properties:

1° 'Cigar burning' is ignited by localised *heating* after a certain induction period (see 3.11). The temperature which has to be reached for the reaction to be initiated depends on the type of fertiliser and may be as low as 120°C. If the source of heat has a low temperature, for example between 120 and 160°C, it must act over a long period of time of up to several hours before igniting and propagating the decomposition. The heating must generally affect an appreciable mass of fertiliser, for if the heating is limited to a very small area (for example, a very short wire at white heat), the resulting decomposition of the fertiliser is unable to propagate beyond the heated zone. Barclay [10] has published the results of a study on the induction period and the temperature at which a reaction will begin at once in a mixture of ammonium nitrate and potassium chloride as well as in a number of NPK fertilisers.

2° The fertiliser decomposes, releasing 0.35 to 0.45 m³ of gas per kg of fertiliser and leaving a solid residue of 0.3 to 0.5 kg for each kg of the initial product. This residue has a low bulk density and, although it has a porous structure, it does not readily let water through. The ambient air plays no part in the decomposition.

3° The velocity of deflagration of 'cigar burning' in NPK fertilisers can vary between 3 and 150 cm/h and remains highly constant normal to its wave front in a fertiliser with a uniform temperature, but it is much higher in the region of the fertiliser through which the gases produced escape, a region which is heated by those gases and moistened by the water which condenses in it. The velocity may be irregular because channels are formed through which the gases escape more readily.

The slowness of propagation in the zone undergoing self–sustained combustion means that it cannot be called an explosion (see 1.3), but it can legitimately be called a deflagration since the phenomenon is one of propagation of a reacting zone in a medium mainly by thermal conductivity. The phenomenon produces no violent mechanical effects but, because of the emission of hot gases which accompanies it, it presents serious dangers, as we shall see below.

4° The temperature profile in the deflagration front, which has a thickness of the order of one decimetre, shows, as Parker and Watchorn [3] found, a preheating zone several centimetres thick (often 2 or 3 cm) in which the substance is raised to around 120–135°C. It is followed by a zone of rapid temperature rise (100°C per mm or more) culminating in a peak beyond which the temperature slowly falls again (Fig. 25.2). The maximum temperature reached varies between 300 and 600°C depending on the fertiliser.

5° From the experimental study of about one hundred different mixtures Parker and Watchorn found a relation, shown by the graph in Fig. 25.3, between the maximum temperature in the deflagrating zone and the velocity†. It seems that there can be no stable propagation at a velocity below 3.5 cm/h, which corresponds to a temperature of 200°C in the deflagration front.

6˙ Certain trace elements, copper in particular, have a remarkable catalytic action. Fertilisers which are incapable of undergoing cigar burning without copper may, with just 0.01 to 0.03% of Cu (in the form of $CuSO_4$, CuO, or powdered metallic copper), propagate a deflagration at the rate of 6 to 10 cm/h. A fertiliser containing 0.3% copper may show velocities of 5 to 100 cm/h, which are considerable values. It must be asked, therefore, if it is wise to add copper to NPK fertilisers other than those which are practically free of chlorine.

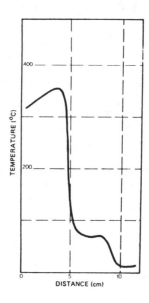

Fig. 25.2 – Temperature profile in the deflagration front of an NPK fertiliser. NB – Distances are counted positively in the direction of propagation of the deflagration.

7˙ Contamination of the fertiliser by sulphur also has the effect of facilitating cigar burning in NPK fertilisers.

8˙ If decomposition is produced, for example by external heating, in an NPK fertiliser housed in a container with strong walls, the pressure rise caused by the release of gases in a closed vessel accelerates the rate of decomposition and, although there is no detonation, gives rise to an explosion which might go so far as to shatter the container violently.

_____

† But Kjekshus and his associates found no simple relation. They were studying rather different types of fertiliser from those used in Parker's experiments.

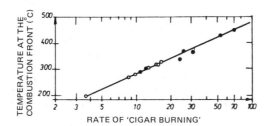

Fig. 25.3 – Relation between velocity and temperature at the deflagration front in NPK fertilisers, after Parker and Watchorn.

25.4.5 Applying the Frank–Kamenetskii criteria to NPK fertilisers

Using the formula (3.16b) given by Hainer (see 3.9), it has been possible to perform a laboratory study for various NPK fertilisers of the variation in critical diameter over a temperature range going from 125 to 200°C for small masses of fertiliser. Van Elteren [20] heated the substance in small cubes of wire gauze (stainless steel) with edges equal to 2, 4, 8, and 16 cm and measured the highest temperature to which each cube could be heated without the fertiliser decomposing completely. With the edge of the cube substituted for the radius r_{cr} in equation (3.16b), the points found by experiment and plotted on a graph of log r_{cr} to $1/T_0$ give for various NPK fertilisers almost parallel straight lines from the slope of which can be derived the activation energy, which is 155 kJ/mol (Fig. 25.4).

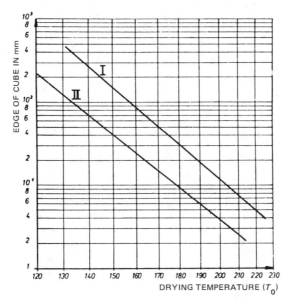

Fig. 25.4 – Decomposition by heating of NPK fertilisers in cubes (reference [20]). I = 15.8.24 fertiliser; II = 16.11.14 fertiliser.

25.4.6 Special tests for studying the dangers of NPK fertilisers

25.4.6.1 The velocity of the deflagration involved in the propagation of a decomposition is measured by a test devised by Huygen and Perbal [5] known as the *trough test*, so called because of the form of the container in which the fertiliser is placed for testing. This container, which is placed horizontally, is 50 cm long and has a cross section of 15 x 15 cm. Its walls are made of stainless steel gauze made of wire with a diameter of 1.5 mm forming meshes† 2.5 mm wide. The framework is made of bars 10 mm in diameter.

To initiate the decomposition, the substance is heated by two Teclu burners‡ with their flame directed against a steel plate 1.3 mm thick placed inside the trough at one end. The plate must be heated to dark red. To prevent the fertiliser from being heated laterally, a steel screen may be placed 5 cm from the heated end (Fig. 25.5).

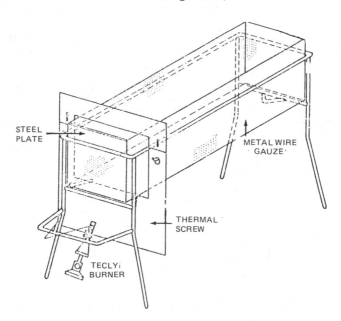

STEEL PLATE

METAL WIRE GAUZE

THERMAL SCREW

TECLY¡ BURNER

Fig. 25.5 – Trough for testing the self–sustained decomposition of NPK fertilisers.

When the trough is filled with the substance to be tested and heat is applied, the fertiliser decomposes in the vicinity of the heated end. When the decomposition affects a thickness of at least 3.5 cm of the fertiliser,

---

† For fine–grained fertiliser which would filter through this gauze a narrower mesh can be used.
‡ The substance can also be heated electrically using a heating unit (see reference [8] for the details).

the external heat source is removed and a note is made of the advance of the vertical decomposition front as a function of time. When the distances covered by the deflagration front are plotted against the time on a graph, it is possible to deduce from the rectilinear section, if there is one, the velocity of deflagration in the test.

There are three possible cases:

(a) decomposition stops shortly after external heating is stopped, in which case the fertiliser is considered to pose no danger of 'cigar burning';

(b) after the heating is stopped, decomposition continues over a certain length but stops before it reaches the opposite end to where it began;

(c) decomposition of the fertiliser advances to the end of the trough, which means that the fertiliser may undergo self-sustained decomposition.

In case (b) the fertiliser in the test conditions cannot be the seat of a stable deflagration regime because heat loss, both by lateral radiation and from the hot gases which rise vertically, means that there can be no sufficient supply of heat ahead of the deflagration front. However, a fertiliser which has given such a result in the trough test may still give rise to stable propagation in a large pile ignited at the centre, which means that the validity of the trough test, like that of other empirical tests, is only relative. If a positive result allows us to conclude that cigar burning is possible, a negative result does not prove the opposite, but indicates only that the velocity of deflagration in a large mass must be quite low. The lateral heat loss in the trough test explains why this test gives lower values for velocity than those observed in large masses of fertiliser.

Nevertheless, the trough test is useful in the search for fertiliser formulae which are not prone to self-propagating deflagration and has been officially recognised by the I.M.C.O. code for the purpose of classifying fertilisers according to their risks.

Lindeijer and his associates [14] have developed a method for measuring the deflagration speed of compound fertilisers under pressure to up to 7 atm. They found that this velocity is a linear function of the pressure, which gives at one atmosphere the same value as the test trough when the fertiliser being studied gives rise to the propagation of cigar burning in the trough. This enables us, in the case of fertilisers where the decomposition does not continue in the trough test, to measure a value relative to atmospheric pressure by extrapolating from the results obtained under pressure.

25.4.6.2 A test known as the high-temperature zonal decomposition test can be used to determine whether a fertiliser at a temperature such as 80, 100, or 110°C is liable to undergo 'cigar burning' even though at ordinary temperature it shows either zero or low-velocity propagation. This test [8], which is similar to the trough test, is conducted in a container with full metal walls.

25.4.6.3 The characteristics of nitrous decomposition are determined in tests which are different depending on whether we are dealing with a fertiliser which melts almost entirely or only in part. For a fertiliser which is liable to melt (as is the case with fertilisers rich in ammonium nitrate), the so-called beaker test consists in heating a tall beaker (diameter 70 mm, height 130 mm) containing 50 g of fertiliser over an electrically heated sand bath while stirring the mixture. Just before the substance reaches its decomposition temperature (a rough measurement of which is made in a preliminary test), the rate of heating is reduced from 15°C/min. to 3°C/min. and the following are noted:

(a) the temperature at which nitrous decomposition begins, in other words the temperature at which the liquid foams because of the large number of bubbles formed throughout its entire mass;

(b) the maximum temperature recorded by a thermometer inserted into the decomposing substance;

(c) the time (in seconds) between the beginning of the decomposition and the moment when the temperature begins to fall.

The substance is then weighed to determine the percentage weight loss of the fertiliser.

For example, a given fertiliser containing 55% ammonium nitrate, 30% superphosphate, and 15% potassium chloride began to decompose at 210°C; the maximum temperature was 310°C; decomposition lasted 55 seconds, and the weight loss was 52.6%.

Fertilisers which do not melt are subjected to the rotating oven test. The apparatus consists of a stainless steel cylinder 80 mm in diameter and 150 mm long with one full end and the other containing an opening 40 mm in diameter. It is filled with 150 g of fertiliser and heated by burners while rotating on rollers at a rate of 60 turns a minute. A thermocouple inserted into the substance records the temperature. When the fertiliser has lost its moisture, it is heated at a rate of 1 to 2°C a minute until nitrous fumes are given off. A note is then made of the temperature, the duration of gas emission, and the maximum temperature reached.

There is also a fixed-oven test in which just 12 g of fertiliser are heated in an apparatus which allows the temperature to be recorded and the gases to be collected for subsequent analysis. This test gives curves of temperature rise which vary considerably depending on whether there is nitrous decomposition, 'cigar burning', or no reaction in the fertiliser in the conditions to which it is subjected.

25.4.6.4 The test in the double Dewar vessel (see 16.3.34) is easy to apply to compound fertilisers. It is conducted on approximately 2 kg of the substance, the container being immersed in a liquid bath which is maintained at a temperature of 75°C. It can record heat releases as low as 0.4 joules per gramme per day.

25.4.7 Dangers of deflagration in NPK fertilisers and ways of fighting it

The flame speed in unconfined NPK fertilisers, where the latter are prone to the phenomenon, is always very low (100 or 1000 times less than that of common pyrotechnic substances), with the result that the phenomenon is not accompanied by destructive mechanical effects. Any damage caused by cigar burning of NPK fertilisers results mainly from the temperature reached in the substance, which is high enough to char wood. The gases produced have no appreciable oxidising properties and, as a result, cannot accelerate the development of a fire, but they sometimes have a high enough temperature to set fire to a wooden roof framework or to initiate decomposition in a nearby pile of fertiliser.

The gases which are formed contain, in addition to a great deal of water vapour, the nitrogen oxides N_2O, NO, and NO_2, nitrogen, chlorine, and chlorine compounds (HCl, $NOCl$, etc.) which make them toxic, so that anybody fighting a fire inside a building must protect his respiratory tract by wearing a mask or a self-contained breathing apparatus. The gases also make the atmosphere murky, so complicating even further the job of those who have to deal with the incident. By contrast, gases outside the buildings, being hot, rise into the air, so that gases at ground level some ten metres away from the point of emission have an NO_2 content between 0.0002 and 0.001%, which can have no serious effect on the human organism (at least during the fairly short exposure times experienced in a fire). This is why, in some accidents, there have been no serious cases of gas poisoning outside buildings containing fertilisers, even though several hundred tons of toxic gases were given off. It is possible, however, for atmospheric conditions to lead to dangerous concentrations of toxic gases at ground level.

If an NPK fertiliser decomposes in the hold of a ship, the solid substance may be turned into a fluid slurry which can unbalance the cargo and lead to the risk of the ship capsizing.

It is difficult to fight a self-propagating decomposition in a mass of NPK fertiliser because the ignited centre is often located at some depth, whilst the water hosed onto the mass flows along the surface and is unable to penetrate more than a few centimetres into the pile unless very high-pressure hoses are used. As with ammonium nitrate, water vapour and chemical extinguishing agents are ineffective because air is not involved in the decomposition. Water is useful only for the cooling effect it has when applied to the deflagration front.

25.4.8 Preventing NPK fertilisers from decomposing

It is the presence of chlorine (in the form of chloride) or catalysing elements (such as copper salt) which makes NPK fertilisers subject to self-propagating decomposition. It is therefore possible to manufacture much safer fertilisers by using potassium sulphate rather than potassium chloride, but the latter, obtained by double decomposition of sylvinite, often contains small amounts of chloride. A good solution to the problem is to use pure potassium nitrate, especially since it reduces the tendency to caking when added to ammonium nitrate. Patents exist which describe the methods used for obtaining chlorine-free saltpetre by treating potassium chloride in suspension in a 65% solution of nitric acid with liquid nitrogen dioxide.

However, since potassium chloride is still the least expensive of the potassium salts, it is likely that it will continue to be used for a long time in the manufacture of NPK fertilisers liable to decompose. Every effort must be made to produce fertilisers with a sufficiently high pH (5.5 at least), but the most important precaution is to avoid anything likely to initiate decomposition during storage. A study of accidents which have happened shows that the main causes of ignition are the following:

1° Lighted electric lamps left in contact with the fertiliser;

2° fertiliser left in contact with something hot during or after repairs involving the use of heat (blowpipe, etc.);

3° allowing fertiliser to come into contact with hot spots created by defective electric equipment (bare wires, etc.);

4° pipes carrying a hot fluid (or steam) in a warehouse or hold of a ship containing fertiliser.

It is important, therefore, to ensure that none of these sources of heat is able to act on fertiliser either during storage (in a factory or an agricultural establishment) or during transport, and any substance likely to be the seat of a fire (hay and straw on farms; empty bags, etc.) must, of course, be kept away from the fertiliser. The risk comes not so much from the quantity of combustible material present as its proximity to the fertiliser.

Care must also be taken to keep away from the fertiliser any substances prone to dangerous reaction, such as acids and some powdered metals, or of which the composition is not known (herbicides, pesticides, disinfectants, etc.). Finally, as with simple nitrogen fertilisers containing ammonium nitrate, there must be a total ban on bringing explosives into the area.

When building a warehouse for the storage of NPK fertilisers, easy access must be provided (for fire fighting), as must also windows or panels which can be opened to let gases out and water hydrants for hosing any decomposing fertiliser. Heating and electrical apparatuses, including conductors, must be located where they cannot come into contact with the fertiliser. Fluorescent lights working at low temperature are much safer than incandescent lights. None of the equipment should contain parts made of galvanised, chromium–plated, or copper metal. When operating an NPK fertiliser warehouse in a factory, the rule should be followed of never storing fertiliser which has not been sufficiently cooled, preferably to below 50°C, and certainly not when it is above 65°C.

If any repair involving the use of fire is to be carried out in a warehouse, the fertiliser should be taken out, if possible, and a wide area cleared around the point of repair. If this is not possible, all piles of fertiliser or any apparatus containing fertiliser (hoppers, etc.) should be covered with fireproof tarpaulins. The use of fire should be subjected to the procedures described in fire regulations.

25.4.9 Detecting the decomposition of NPK fertilisers

When maintenance staff do their rounds in warehouses, they can detect gases given off by the decomposition of NPK fertilisers from their characteristic odour even if the point of decomposition is invisible in a large pile of fertiliser. Detection based purely on maintenance rounds is safe only if the rounds are made every half hour since that is all the time it may need for fumes from a decomposing pile to fill the whole warehouse and impair visibility. For that reason, it is desirable to use methods of detection which can sound the alarm when the decomposition has just begun and which can also give a fairly precise indication of where the decomposition is.

Attempts have been made, therefore, to develop automatic detection equipment. It is not possible to monitor the temperature in the piles since that would involve inserting too many thermometers into the mass, which is not very conductive. Nor is it possible to use thermometers which work on infra–red radiation situated above the piles, although they may be useful as portable equipment to pick out the approximate location of the decomposition when it is still in the initial stages.

Jarcsek [9] describes an apparatus used in a factory in the north of France which is based on the variation in electric conductivity of a solution which absorbs gases (such as chlorine and hydrochloric acid) which are produced when an NPK fertiliser decomposes. It is sensitive to 0.01 cm^3 of Cl_2 per m^3 and is graded to measure 0 to 0.4 cm^3 per m^3. It has a response time of 20 seconds. The apparatus, which faces in seven directions (taking in air for analysis through seven tubes), analyses the sample taken from each direction every fifteen minutes. It allows any decomposition to be detected when at least 5 kg of fertiliser are affected.

An apparatus which has proved its effectiveness in Germany consists of

a sensor which contains two ionisation cells and is based on the following
principle: the air in the space between two electrodes can be made into a
permanent conductor of electricity by ionisation from a sealed radioactive
source†. The sensor contains two such cells, one of which is hermetically
closed and contains pure air, while the other is open to the ambient
atmosphere. As long as that atmosphere is pure air, both cells have the
same conductivity, but if heavy gases (Cl_2, NO_2, etc.) get into the one
which is open to the air, the conductivity falls and the apparatus with
both cells mounted in a Wheatstone bridge then allows a current to flow
which is amplified and routed to an indicator panel. One sensor of this
type must be fitted for approximately every 100 m² of warehouse area and
the apparatuses must be fitted at different heights since the path followed
by fumes from decomposition cannot be predicted (because of the effects of
draughts, temperature differences, etc.).

The apparatus is triggered not only by gases from the decomposition of
NPK fertilisers but also by cigarette smoke and exhaust gases from internal
combustion engines. One difficulty that had to be overcome in developing
ionisation sensors was the deposit of dust that covers them, given that
fertiliser warehouses are very dusty places. The dust is shaken off every
half hour by means of an electromagnetic device placed above each sensor
which momentarily lifts it by magnetism and then drops it.

The instrument panel which gives a reading of the electric signals from
the various sensors can be installed in the factory fire station, for
example. It is fitted with red indicator lights and an audio alarm.

25.5 NITROGENOUS SOLUTIONS USED AS FERTILISERS

25.5.1 Definitions

Two main kinds of aqueous solution are used in the manufacture of compound
fertilisers or directly as simple nitrogen fertilisers. They are
1˙ solutions of urea and ammonium nitrate,
2˙ solutions of ammonium nitrate and ammonia.

25.5.2 Solutions of urea and ammonium nitrate

Urea, $CO(NH_2)_2$, a solid substance (F_V = 325 kJ/mol) which melts at 132˙C,
and ammonium nitrate form a eutectic mixture which melts at 44.7˙C and
contains 47% urea. Clearly, it needs only a moderate amount of water added
to this binary mixture to obtain a solution which does not crystallise at
ordinary temperatures. The composition of the most commonly used solutions
is not very different from

>   urea   33
>   ammonium nitrate   43
>   water   24.

At ordinary temperatures, these solutions are practically devoid of any
explosive property, and even solutions containing only 8 to 10% water can
be exploded only with great difficulty.

---

† In the apparatus in question, this source is provided by [241]americium in
a quantity with an activity of 72 microcuries.

The stoichiometric binary mixture of urea and ammonium nitrate contains 20% urea and is not a very sensitive explosive since in the card gap test (see 15.3.7) it behaves like ammonium nitrate on its own. It can be detonated if the ignition is powerful enough but it has quite a large critical diameter. It has, however, been proposed for use as an explosive by absorbing it in moist adsorbing earth which makes it easier to explode using a mechanism similar to the one mentioned in 14.3.4 with reference to propyl nitrate. This mixture, and mixtures with a similar composition, may ignite when heated to around 190°C, giving rise to a deflagration which may be quite vigorous. An explosion of this kind may have occurred in 1966 in the United States [19] in a hot solution of 35% urea, 45% ammonium nitrate, and 20% water in a bend of a pipe with steam tracing. Fairly dehydrated solid deposits may have been heated up over a period of time.

There have been other explosions in fires involving tanks containing mixed solutions of urea and ammonium nitrate. They led to experimental research by Perbal [21], who showed that partial confinement of the product plays an important part in the development of decomposition within it when it is heated. This must be taken account of in both storage and transport.

25.5.3 Solutions of ammonia and ammonium nitrate

Ammonium nitrate can fix anhydrous ammonia to form a solution called a Divers solution. The stoichiometric mixture $3NH_4NO_3 + 2NH_3$ has the following theoretical explosive properties:

Heat of explosion (at constant volume)	3 600 kJ/kg,
Explosion temperature	2 560°K,
Gas volume at NTP	1 060 dm³/kg.

This mixture has, in fact, been suggested for use as an intentional explosive (explosive slurry).

A liquid is available in France under the name of Barrett's solution, or various other trade names, which contains three components in the proportions

ammonium nitrate	69
ammonia	24
water	7,

and which is added by manufacturers of compound fertilisers to potash or phosphate substances to make complex fertilisers. Similar solutions with more water are sold in other parts of Europe. The question of the safety of these solutions must be raised since calculation indicates that the one with the above composition has a heat of explosion (at constant volume) of over 2300 kJ/kg. We have very few experimental results in this respect, the most pertinent [18] being that a mixture containing 24% NH_3 and 16% H_2O has a critical detonation diameter very much higher than 20 cm. It can also be said that the free ammonia present in these very high pH solutions means that they must not be prone to the deflagrations described in 23.3.2 in reference to aqueous solutions of ammonium nitrate.

BIBLIOGRAPHICAL REFERENCES

[1]   Davis, R. O. E. & Hardesty, J. O. (1945) *Ind. Eng. Chem.* **37** 59
[2]   Barclay, K. S., Crewe, J. M. & Thatcher. K. F. J. (1961) *Nature* (G.B.) **191** 1189

[3]   Parker, A. B. & Watchorn, N. (1965) *J. Science Food Agric.* **16** 355
[4]   Findlay, A. & Rosebourne, C. (1922) *J. Soc. Chem. Ind.* **41** 58
[5]   Huygen, D. G. & Perbal, G. (1965) *Communication LEF/65/XIII* to the
       Réunion Technique de l'ISMA
[6]   Kjekshus, S. E., Mostad, F. & Steen, J. F. (1967) *Communication*
       PSF/67/XX to the third Réunion Technique de l'ISMA
[7]   Hardesty, J. O. & Davis, R. O. E. (1946) *Ind. Eng. Chem.* **38** 1298
[8]   ISMA & APEA (1973) *Epreuves pour la stabilité thermique des engrais*
       at the ISMA, 28 rue Marbeuf, Paris
[9]   Jarcsek, F. (1969) *L'industrie chimique*, p. 369
[10]   Barclay, K. S. (1966) *Proc. Internat. Cong. on Chemical Fertilizers.*
       Pergamon, London, p. 31
[11]   Aufschläger, R. (1924) *Z. ges. Sch. Sprengst.* **19** 25
[12]   Clancey, V. J. (1962) *R.A.R.D.E. Inter Report*
[13]   Lamberger, J. & Pâris, R. A. (1951) *Bull. Soc. Chim. France*, p. 984
[14]   Groothuizen, T. M., Lindeijer, E. E. & Pasman, H. J. (April 1970)
       Stikstof
[15]   Goffart, P. (October 1973) *Bull. tech. Sécurité et Salubrité*, No. 6
       Institut national des industries extractives, Belgium
[16]   Hansen, G. & Berthold, W. (1972) *Chemiker Ztg* **96** 449
[17]   King, A. & Bauer, A. (1977(*Rapport du 29 juin 1977*, Queen's
       University, Kingston, Ontario
[18]   Laurila, P. (1968) private communication
[19]   Anderson, J. F. (1967) *Safety in Air and Ammonia Plants* **9** 70
[20]   Van Elteren, J. F. quoted by Perbal, G. (1971) Thermal Stability of
       Fertilisers. In: *Proceedings No. 124 of the Fertiliser Society*
       Conference, London, 25 November 1971
[21]   Perbal, G. (1983) *Inst. Chem. Eng. Symp. Ser.* Cf. (1984) *CA* **101** 11
       688 k
[22]   Zhootukha, G. A. *et al.* (1985) *CA* **102** 48255 p
[23]   Koenen, H. B.A.M. Tgb. No. T 5 6130/52 and IV 1280/52

26

Nitro-compounds and nitric esters

26.1 GENERAL OBSERVATIONS

The NO_2 group is the most important explosophore. It is found in true *nitro-compounds*, where it is linked directly to carbon, in *nitroamines* where it is linked to nitrogen, and it forms the radical of *nitric esters* when it is linked to oxygen.

Aromatic nitro-compounds, which have been manufactured industrially for a very long time, include important intentional explosives such as TNT. Aliphatic nitro-compounds, the simplest and most frequently used of which is nitromethane, were a later addition to the market. Some of them are unwanted explosives.

The oldest known nitric ester is glycerol trinitrate, which is commonly called nitroglycerine, but some nitric esters are unwanted explosives. A part of this chapter is devoted to the nitric esters of cellulose (which bear the trade name of nitrocelluloses).

Many nitroso compounds, in other words substances which contain the explosophore group NO, are formed endothermically and are, for that reason, prone to quite violent explosion. Furthermore, those nitroso compounds which contain the nitroso group linked to nitrogen, such as nitrosamines and nitrosamides (the − N − NO group), are often very unstable.

26.2 NITROMETHANE CH_3NO_2

26.2.1 Brief history

Obtained for the first time by Victor Meyer in 1872 by reacting silver nitrite with methyl iodide, nitromethane has for a long time been prepared by the reaction of sodium chloroacetate with sodium nitrite in an aqueous

solution. The quantity produced by this reaction is no higher than 52%
and, in addition to nitromethane, methyl nitrite and small quantities of
unstable nitro and nitroso compounds are formed. In addition, distillation
of this raw, moist nitromethane gives rise to a small emission of nitrous
fumes [1].

This manufacturing process was replaced around the 1950s by direct
nitration of methane using nitric acid vapour, a reaction which had been
studied as early as 1936. More recently still, nitromethane, together with
other nitroalkanes, has been obtained by the reaction of nitrogen dioxide
on propane.

Although nitromethane seems no longer to be used as a monopropellant,
its use as a convenient reactive medium, as a raw material used in the
manufacture of various organic compounds, and as a solvent are becoming
widespread. As a solvent, it has very low toxicity.

26.2.2 General properties

Nitromethane is a colourless liquid which is more volatile than water. At
$20°C$ it can dissolve almost 2% of its weight in water. Table 26.1 lists
some of its properties. It gives rise with water to an azeotropic mixture
which boils at $83.5°C$ at atmospheric pressure and is composed of 77.1%
nitromethane. It is a flammable liquid with a flash point (in closed cup)
close to $35°C$.

Nitromethane dissolves many anhydrous metallic salts, aluminium
chloride in particular, which makes it possible to carry out Friedel and
Crafts reactions using nitromethane as a solvent. It also dissolves
oxidising salts such as nitrates and perchlorates, and can therefore give
rise to explosive solutions (see 17.1.4). When these solutions evaporate,
they often leave behind an explosive addition compound, as is the case with
$Cu(NO_3)_2.CH_3NO_2$.

Nitromethane has good thermal stability (kinetic stability). It hardly
decomposes when heated under pressure at $200°C$, although it does take on a
slight yellow colour. It has even been possible to arrive at a rough
measurement of its critical temperature and pressure ($315°C$ at 63 bars),
although in these conditions there is a risk of explosion. Makovky and
Grunwald [2] made a quantitative study of its thermal decomposition using
tubes containing 4 ml of CH_3NO_2 at a temperature between 312 and $340°C$ and
a pressure close to 40 bars. They found that the decomposition follows a
first order law in which the initial phase, as at low pressure, is the
splitting of CH_3NO_2 into $CH_3^·$ and $NO_2^·$, after which these radicals react in a
complex way, leading to end products containing NO, HCN, CO, HCHO, and H_2O.
The activation energy in their experiments was 205 kJ/mol. The induction
period of the explosion of the vapour varies, according to Urbanski and
Pawelec [3], from 3 minutes at $460°C$ to 3 seconds at $570°C$, and in this
temperature range the activation energy is 188 kJ/mol. Various catalysts
accelerate decomposition at low temperatures. For example, the oxide Cr_2O_3
permits decompositions between 220 and $245°C$ at 36 atm. In the substances
produced by this catalysed decomposition is found a large quantity of
ammonium hydrogen carbonate $NH_4.H.CO_3$.

26.2.3 Explosive properties of nitromethane

The explosive properties of nitromethane remained unknown for a long time.

Table 26.1

Properties of mononitroalkanes

		nitro methane	nitro ethane	1-nitro propane	2-nitro propane
Specific gravity at 20°C	g/cm³	1.138	1.050	1.001	0.988
Melting point	°C	- 28.6	- 89.5	- 104	- 91.3
Normal boiling point	°C	101.2	114	131.2	120.2
Vapour pressure at 18°C	mm Hg	24.5	14.7	6.3	11.6
Heat of vaporisation at 25°C	kJ/mol	38.3	41.6	43.4	41.3
Heats of formation at 18°C					
liquid F_p	kJ/mol	113	136	165	181
liquid F_v	kJ/mol	105.5	126.5	153	169
gas F_p	kJ/mol	75	94	119	139
gas F_v	kJ/mol	70	87	110	130
Solubility in water at 20°C					
ml of nitroalkane per 100 ml of water		9.5	4.5	1.4	1.7
Flammability limits		7.3 - 33	3.4 - 30	2.3 - 34	2.5 - 28
Flash point (closed cup)		35	30	37	32

The first published reference to the possibility of its exploding came only in 1938 [4], even though it might have been predicted from its heat of formation that it must be a fairly powerful explosive. Its calorific value (see 2.9) exceeds 4700 kJ/kg and the test in the lead block [5] gives a value of 134 for its c.p.u. (see 14.3.2). The possibility of detonating the substance has also been underestimated for far too long.

Nitromethane is hardly sensitive to impact and equally insensitive to initiation since, even in a thick metal tube, it cannot be detonated by a No. 8 detonator [5], although it can be detonated by initiating it with a booster of 10 g of P.E.T.N. However, a rise in temperature leads to an increase in its sensitivity, so that at around 70°C it can be exploded with the No. 8 detonator.

Its critical detonation diameter at 20°C is about 20 mm, and it has a detonation velocity of 6300 m/s at a diameter of 30 mm. Highly accurate research [6] has shown that this velocity falls by about 4 m/s per degree of temperature rise because of the decrease in the specific gravity of the liquid.

Bellinger and his associates [7] have studied the sensitivity of nitromethane when it is fed into and transferred along metal pipes to see how it would behave as a monopropellant. They found that the sudden application of a pressure of 140 bars causes it to explode in a dead end, although the explosion does not propagate along the pipe. Using the drop-weight test, they found that it explodes in the presence of air or oxygen. They concluded that nitromethane can be stored and transported in the conditions which apply to a volatile flammable solvent, avoiding high impact.

In the test in a steel tube with nozzle plates (see 16.2.3) with an opening measuring 1 mm, nitromethane boils and its vapour burns externally, with no explosion in the tube.

26.2.4 Subsequent studies on the danger of nitromethane exploding

Every study made before 1956 concluded that nitromethane was so insensitive that it could be stored and transported in the conditions which apply to a simple flammable liquid. Around 1954, increased production led to it being transported in tankers, but two quite unexpected explosions occurred in such tankers in the United States.

On 20 January 1958 in Niagara Falls, a rail tanker carrying 35 tons of nitromethane parked on a siding was struck violently by another carriage moving under gravity and exploded, blasting a massive five-metre deep crater in the ground and causing considerable damage. A similar tanker exploded on 1 June 1958 at Mt. Pulaski (Illinois), killing two railway workers and injuring many others.

These detonations triggered new research which did not fully explain the 1958 disasters but did bring out several points, of which the two most important are:
(a) Nitromethane may explode in a gas-filled space which is subjected to strong adiabatic pressure. Now, it is possible to have strong compression by applying only a moderate amount of energy. In tests conducted by Ide and his associates in the B.A.M.'s steel plunger apparatus (see 15.2.5.4), an impact with an energy of 1 joule (1 kg falling from 0.1 m) was able on every occasion to cause an explosion in 80 mm³ of nitromethane in the presence of 240 mm³ of air. Since the explosion left behind undecomposed

nitromethane, it must have occurred mainly in the gas mixture consisting of air and nitromethane vapour. In similar tests in which air was completely replaced by nitrogen, no explosions were observed. These tests give plausibility to the idea that liquid nitromethane is detonated by the explosion of a large bubble in the gas phase, but an impact which does not involve vapour has no effect: in tests carried out in the United States, metal drums containing 200 litres of nitromethane were dropped from an aeroplane flying at some height without exploding on impact with the ground. This can be compared with what was said in 15.2.3 concerning tests with nitroglycerine.

(b) The sensitivity to detonation of nitromethane is increased considerably when 2 to 10% of a cyclic or acyclic nitrogenous base such as aniline, morpholine, or triethylamine is added. Sensitivity to mechanical impact is probably also increased. Now, the rail tankers involved in the 1958 explosions were suspected of having also been used to transport butylamine and they may not have been properly cleaned before the nitromethane was loaded.

Nitromethane is only one example of liquids with low sensitivity which nevertheless have explosive properties and are dangerous when handled in large storage and transport tankers where things can happen which do not occur in drums or packages since large containers are fitted with devices (valves, flaps, various pipes, etc.) in which the clearance between parts can trap air in the presence of the sensitive liquid. In addition, the huge mass of the contents is such that the dynamic effects which occur during acceleration and deceleration reach values much higher than those found in small containers. The rocking of the liquid mass can certainly exert sudden and violent compression on pockets of gas within it.

26.2.5 Metal derivatives of nitromethane

Nitromethane may react in the acidic tautomeric form acinitromethane (formerly known as isonitromethane or nitrolic acid)

$$CH_2 = N \overset{O}{\underset{OH}{\diagup}}$$

in which the H atom in the OH group is readily replaced by a metal. Nitromethane, which is not very soluble in pure water, is highly soluble in an aqueous solution of sodium hydroxide. The corresponding salt, $CH_2 = NO.ONa$, is easily isolated by adding nitromethane to a methanol solution of CH_3ONa with ether or tetrahydrofuran and then evaporating the liquid. Analysing this salt by infra-red spectography shows that it contains an anion $(CH_2 = NO_2)^-$. It is the formation of the acinitromethane ion which allows titration of strong alkalis (NaOH, KOH, etc.) in an alcohol solution using nitromethane in the presence of a blue 6B indicator.

It has been possible to prepare the salts which acinitromethane forms with many metals. In the dry state they are dangerous explosives which are quite sensitive to impact and flame. When water is poured onto dry sodium salt, it reacts explosively with a flash, and it reacts far more strongly than nitromethane itself with many organic (halogenated, carbonylated) substances.

When Nef caused a hot reaction between mercury chloride and an aqueous solution of sodium salt in 1894, he obtained mercury fulminate from the dehydration of the mercury salt of acinitromethane:

$$(H_2C = N \underset{\diagdown O}{\overset{\diagup O}{}})_2Hg \rightarrow 2H_2O + (C = N - O)_2Hg,$$

which is why it is important to avoid contact between nitromethane and mercury or a mercury compound, particularly in an alkaline medium. It would seem to be wise to take the same precaution with compounds of lead or silver.

When nitromethane has been left to dry for a long time in contact with an ion-exchanging zeolite (10 A molecular sieve), a derivative containing soda has formed which then gave rise to a very strong reaction [47].

26.2.6 Precautions in the storage and use of nitromethane

Nitromethane should preferably be stored in thin-walled containers such as the 250-litre metal drums used for transport which have a thickness of about 1.5 mm. If it is to be stored in a large tank of ordinary steel, stainless steel, or aluminium, then the tank should be located in a place where it cannot be hit by metal fragments thrown off by a nearby explosion. It may be shielded by concrete screens, for example. The storage site for both drums and tanks should be located where the nitromethane cannot be heated by a fire in the vicinity or contaminated by other substances.

When nitromethane is being used, it must be kept free of contamination by bases, and must not be allowed to come into contact with soda, which would ignite it. When it is being moved by pump or gas pressure, the rise in pressure should be limited.

Devices for stopping detonations can usefully be inserted into transfer lines to protect equipment and tanks. One such device recommended by an American manufacturer contains a cluster of four small-diameter tubes with a short larger segment in the middle (Fig. 26.1), while another device studied in the Sevran laboratory in 1955 [9] consists essentially of a section of plastic pipe with precise geometrical properties (Fig. 26.2).

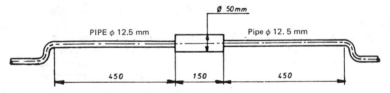

Fig. 26.1 - Expansion chamber section of an American device to stop the detonation of nitromethane.

26.3 ACYCLIC NITRO-COMPOUNDS

26.3.1 Nitroalkanes

Alkane nitro-compounds have been manufactured industrially only since 1936, following the work of Rass [10]. They are obtained in the United States by nitrating propane at around 400°C with compressed nitric acid, but they can also be obtained by nitrating propane with nitrogen dioxide, a reaction which was studied as early as 1936 by Urbanski and his associates. The conditions of the reaction, which have been under study in France since 1970, have led to industrial manufacture by the combined reaction of oxygen from the air and nitrogen dioxide on compressed propane at around 250°C, leading to cracking of the propane and the fixing of NO_2 radicals which give

    2-nitropropane
    nitromethane
    1-nitropropane
    nitroethane,

in that order of quantity. Separating them by distillation is an easy matter. Butane and pentane can be nitrated in the same way.

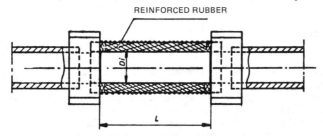

Fig. 26.2 – Device for stopping the detonation of nitromethane, created in the Sevran laboratory ($L > 5\ D_i$ and $D_i < 15$ mm).

The first terms in the series of mononitroalkanes are colourless liquids with physical properties similar to those of nitromethane (see Table 26.1). Like the latter, they are used as solvents or as raw materials for obtaining organic compounds (amines, etc.). In particular, they readily condense with aldehydes or ketones, a reaction which has been studied by Boileau [11].

Primary nitroalkanes (which contain a CH_2NO_2 group) and secondary nitroalkanes ($CHNO_2$ group) may, in a basic solution, assume the acinitro form with the groups

$$-CH = N\begin{matrix} \nearrow O \\ \searrow OH \end{matrix} \qquad \text{and} \qquad \begin{matrix} \searrow \\ / \end{matrix} C = N \begin{matrix} \nearrow O \\ \searrow OH \end{matrix}$$

which is not possible with the tertiary nitroalkanes. It is possible to isolate the salts of these nitro-compounds in the solid state, which are less sensitive than those of nitromethane but must nevertheless be treated with caution.

The first terms of the nitroalkanes have far less pronounced explosive properties than nitromethane. Nitroethane can be detonated, but only with difficulty. As for the nitropropanes, the best that can be achieved is a low-order detonation (with a low velocity, see 14.4.6). In practice, the nitropropanes can be treated as non-explosive substances except when they are raised under confinement to a very high temperature. In the accident which happened in June 1958 (see 26.2.4), a tanker carriage containing 2-nitropropane coupled to the same train as the tanker containing the nitromethane which detonated was hit by metal splinters, setting fire to the nitropropane which burned calmly in the open air without exploding.

The ignition temperatures of the first nitroalkanes are of the same order as those of nitromethane, namely 420 to 430°C. Nitroethane becomes sensitive to impact when it contains amines, for example 5% n-butylamine. When nitroalkanes (nitroparaffins) are anhydrous, they have no corrosive effect and can be stored in containers made of ordinary metals, but in the presence of moisture they react, in their tautomeric (acinitro) form, with metal. A metal derivative may have been involved in the rail tanker accidents in 1958. To prevent this corrosion of metal, it has been recommended that nitroalkanes should be stabilised in their true nitro-compound form by adding a small amount of phosphoric acid or monobutyl phosphate.

26.3.2 Polynitromethanes

Dinitromethane $CH_2(NO_2)_2$, which is difficult to obtain, has no industrial importance but it can safely be assumed that it is a sensitive explosive with a high calorific value (about 5400 kJ/kg).

Tetranitromethane $C(NO_2)_4$, the physical properties of which are given in Table 26.2, was for a long time a costly substance because it was prepared by the slow reaction from cold between highly-concentrated nitric acid and acetic anhydride. This preparation, which was normally made in 5-litre glass flasks placed in a current of cold water, was not without its dangers since, on occasion, the reactive mixture heated in the flask and decomposed very strongly with a large emission of gases. A fatal accident happened in the United States in 1960 during one such preparation because the cold-water refrigeration system had not been switched on. There has been increased interest in this tetranitro hydrocarbon since the discovery of a method of making it more cheaply and in reasonable safety by nitrating acetylene with nitric acid [12].

Statements are to be found in the chemical literature to the effect that tetranitromethane is not in itself explosive [13]. It is pointed out [14] that in the pure state it cannot detonate because it has too high an oxygen content. However, a Briska detonator explodes it in the lead block cavity (see 14.3.2), causing a far from negligible expansion, and it can be detonated practically without confinement by a booster of 15 g of P.E.T.N., its detonation velocity being 6500 m/s [15]. The smoke from the explosion is highly coloured because of the nitrogen dioxide it contains.

Tetranitromethane is a very oxygen-rich substance which mixes with all kinds of combustible liquids to give highly sensitive and very dangerous explosives which have sometimes caused fatal accidents. The best known occurred in 1920 at the University of Munster (Westphalia) in a chemistry lecture when 10 g of a mixture of tetranitromethane and toluene detonated, throwing out metal splinters which killed ten students. And yet this mixture, like many other mixtures of $C(NO_2)_4$ and hydrocarbons, burns calmly when ignited in the open air in small quantities.

Schwob [16] made a study of mixtures of tetranitromethane and light (saturated) petrol in 1934 at a time when the addition of a *small* amount of this nitro-compound was intended to improve the qualities of hydrocarbons used as fuels: adding about 1% $C(NO_2)_4$ to a fuel for use in Diesel engines

Table 26.2

Properties of acyclic polynitro-compounds

Substance		Relative density at 20°C (g/cm³)	Melting point (°C)	Normal boiling point (°C)	Heat of formation F_p (at 18°C) (kJ/mol)
Trinitromethane	$CH(NO_2)_3$	1.61 (a)	26.4	46 (c)	50 (b)
Tetranitromethane	$C(NO_2)_4$	1.63	13.9	126	– 37
Trichloronitromethane	CCl_3NO_2	1.66	– 69	112.2	
Chlorotrinitromethane	$CCl(NO_2)_3$	1.66	5.75		23.4
Fluorotrinitromethane	$CF(NO_2)_3$	1.79	– 29		218
Hexanitroethane	$C_2(NO_2)_6$	2.25	150 (d)		– 117
1,1-dinitropropane	$CH(NO_2)_2 - CH_2 - CH_3$	1.27	– 42		171
2,2-dinitropropane	$CH_3 - C(NO_2)_2 - CH_3$	1.30	53		224
1,3-dinitropropane	$CH_2NO_2 - CH_2 - CH_2NO_2$	1.36	– 20		187

(a) Value for liquid trinitromethane at 27°C
(b) Value for solid trinitromethane; for the liquid F_p = 29 kJ/mol
(c) Boiling with decomposition
(d) Melting with decomposition

increased its ketane index by 10 to 20 units.

Small quantities of tetranitromethane are formed during the nitration of various aromatic hydrocarbons, and this was once thought to be the cause of explosions in spent acids from nitration, but the 1983 study referred to in 18.4.2 claims that they were more likely to have been caused by nitrogen tetroxide.

Considerable precautions should be taken when using tetranitromethane, not only because its vapours are toxic but above all because it reacts very strongly with a large number of other substances, such as lead tetraethyl, although explosives made of 36 to 61% $C(NO_2)_4$ with $Pb(C_2H_5)_4$ are patented [13]. Mixing these two liquids can give rise to spontaneous explosions. Tetranitromethane is hypergolic† with alkylamines and arylamines (aniline, etc.) and other liquids but not with nitrobenzene or furaldehyde. Mixtures with benzene, toluene, and nitrobenzene ignite only between 500 and 520°C. However, as the accident in Munster shows, when these mixtures are under partial confinement, combustion can lead to detonation.

In tetranitromethane one of the NO_2 groups is highly unstable both in the vapour and the liquid. The vapour decomposes into radicals above 150°C according to a first order reaction

$$C(NO_2)_4 \rightarrow (NO_2)_3C^{\cdot} + NO_2^{\cdot}$$

the activation energy being 171 kJ/mol. Subsequent reactions then give a mixture of CO, CO_2, N_2, NO, and NO_2. When the liquid is treated with soda in an alcohol solution it gives a salt of trinitromethane

$$C(NO_2)_4 + NaOH + NaOC_2H_5 \rightarrow (NO_2)_2C = N\begin{smallmatrix} \nearrow O \\ \\ \searrow ONa \end{smallmatrix} + NaNO_3 + C_2H_5OH.$$

It was by separating and then decomposing this highly explosive yellow salt with diluted hydrochloric acid that *trinitromethane*, also called nitroform, used to be made, whereas this trinitro compound can now be produced at an acceptable price by nitrating acetylene in the presence of a mercury–based catalyst [17].

Trinitromethane $CH(NO_2)_3$ is a volatile liquid with highly irritant vapours which readily forms the salts of its acinitro form

$$(NO_2)_2C = N\begin{smallmatrix} \nearrow O \\ \\ \searrow ONa \end{smallmatrix}$$

which, in the dry state, are sensitive to impact and to a temperature rise. The potassium salt, which decomposes slowly at ordinary temperature, explodes at around 95–98°C. A case of an apparently spontaneous explosion of trinitromethane has been reported [18]. It may have been caused by the

---

† A mixture of an oxidising agent and a liquid fuel is called hypergolic (see 17.1.1) if both liquids react immediately when brought into contact at ordinary temperature and if the reaction results in ignition after a fairly short induction period (between a fraction of a second and one minute).

presence of impurities†.

26.3.3 Polynitro-compounds of alkanes

Quite a large number of dinitro, trinitro, etc., compounds of alkanes are
known of, although they are scarcely ever produced industrially. When
treated with bases, they give highly sensitive salts of the acinitro form.
One way of preparing dinitro hydrocarbons is to add dinitrogen tetroxide to
an alkene (olefin), but various other products are formed at the same time.
Gaseous ethylene reacts readily at ordinary pressure with liquid dinitrogen
tetroxide at 4°C and leads to a mixture of 40% 1,2-dinitroethane, unstable
nitroethyl nitrite, and nitroethyl nitrate produced by oxidation of the
nitrite. The mixture is made more stable by the addition of methanol which
separates nitroethanol from the nitrite. It has not proven possible to
exploit this process industrially.

The same process gives 1,2-dinitropropane when N_2O_4 is added to
propylene.

1,2-dinitroethane is a crystalline substance which melts at 40°C and
decomposes slowly into nitroethylene and nitrous acid (or nitrous fumes)

$$NO_2CH_2 - CH_2NO_2 \rightarrow NO_2CH = CH_2 + HNO_2.$$

Decomposition is rapid in the presence of alkalis. The substance can be
stabilised by adding acids. Its explosive properties have not been studied
but it is certainly a more powerful explosive than nitromethane.

By treating 2-nitropropane with a 70% solution of nitric acid at around
210°C at more than 60 bars, 2,2-dinitropropane is obtained

$$CH_3 - C(NO_2)_2 - CH_3.$$

This reaction must be carried out in strictly controlled conditions since
it can give rise to strong explosions [42].

Similar to tetranitromethane is *hexanitroethane* which is also a hydrocarbon nitrated to maximum. It is a high-density crystalline substance
which begins to decompose at around 80°C and which melts and decomposes at
around 150°C. Its properties have been studied [19], since it is a combustion supporter that could be used to advantage in propellants. It
undergoes a first-order thermal decomposition, has a half life of 400 hours
at 70°C, and is not very sensitive to impact.

26.3.4 Nitro-compounds related to nitroalkanes

Alkyl chlorides, such as CH_3Cl and C_2H_5Cl, can be nitrated in conditions
similar to those which apply to gaseous alkanes. Generally, the first NO_2

---

† We had occasion in 1933 to prepare a small quantity of trinitromethane
from tetranitromethane and were able to preserve this trinitro compound for
several days without decomposition. Indeed, there have been no reports of
spontaneous explosions of the purified product in the semi-industrial
preparations which have been made since 1965.

group which is substituted for hydrogen fixes on the chlorine-carrying carbon atom.

Nitrotrichloromethane, commonly called *chloropicrin*, was formerly prepared by treating picric acid with a chlorinating agent such as calcium hypochlorite (chloride of lime)) but is now obtained by the simultaneous action of chlorine and nitric acid on isopropyl alcohol or acetone, or by chlorinating nitromethane [20] with sodium hypochlorite. Chloropicrin is also formed by the action of aqua regia on many organic substances.

Nitrotrichloromethane CCl_3NO_2 is a toxic liquid with lachrymatory vapours. Amongst other things it is used to kill various crop-eating animals. At its boiling point (see Table 26.2) it decomposes slowly into $COCl_2$ and $NOCl$. When hot, it reacts extremely violently with amines such as aniline. Its chemical properties are described in a monograph [21].

Although less sensitive than nitromethane, chloropicrin may detonate according to the reaction

$$CCl_3NO_2 \rightarrow CO_2 + 0.5N_2 + 1.5Cl_2$$

when the liquid under confinement in a steel tube with a diameter of 33 mm is initiated by a booster of P.E.T.N. [15], but in a thin-walled aluminium container with a diameter of 30 mm there is an overdriven detonation which is capable of propagating only over a very short distance.

Nitroethanol $NO_2CH_2 - CH_2OH$ is a relatively stable liquid when pure and not very sensitive to impact or ignition. Its nitric ester is an explosive comparable to nitroglycerine but with very poor thermal stability.

Trinitroethanol $(NO_2)_3C - CH_2OH$ can be obtained from trinitromethane by the action of formaldehyde or its polymer (trioxymethylene) [12]. It is a crystalline substance which melts at 37°C and which is unstable and highly sensitive to impact, but its acetic ester is a colourless oily liquid which is much more stable and far less sensitive to impact.

The sodium salt of trinitromethane can be used for the easy synthesis of organic compounds containing trinitromethyl groups $(NO_2)_3C$ such as 2,2,2-trinitroethyl-4,4,4-trinitrobutyrate

$$(NO_2)_3C - CH_2 - CH_2 - CO - O - CH_2 - C(NO_2)_3$$

which has been proposed for use as an intentional explosive.

Since the 1960s, many organic compounds containing nitro groups have been made for a variety of uses. They may have explosive properties, especially if their formula shows them to be close to stoichiometric, like 2-fluoro-2,2-dinitroethyl malonate [22]

$$CH_2 \begin{cases} CO - O - CH_2 - CF(NO_2)_2 \\ CO - O - CH_2 - CF(NO_2)_2 \end{cases}$$

The ready reaction [45] of ammonia on trinitroethanol in an aqueous solution gives a yellow precipitate of bis(trinitroethyl) amine $HN(CH_2 - C(NO_2)_3)_2$, a crystalline substance which melts at 116°C and is an explosive which is sensitive to impact, unstable, and prone to spontaneous explosion a few weeks after it has been prepared. It seems that the accumulation of three NO_2 groups on the same carbon atom makes the molecule chemically unstable.

The dipotassium salt of nitroacetic acid

$$\overset{O}{\underset{KO}{\diagdown}}N = CH - COOK$$

is, like the comparable nitromethane compound, highly sensitive to water
(see 26.2.5) with which it reacts explosively [48].

26.3.5 Nitroalkenes

Nitroethylene $CH_2 = CHNO_2$ is a yellowish, strongly lachrymatory liquid
which can be distilled at a pressure of 70 mm of mercury and a temperature
of around 35°C. Boileau and Runavot [23] describe a process for obtaining
the substance by dehydrating nitroethanol. It is prone to polymerisation
(of the vinyl type), a process which is very rapid in a base medium. It
can be kept in a benzene solution with a small quantity of acetic acid
added. Nothing is known of its explosive properties.

Nitropropylenes with an NO_2 group on one of the two carbon atoms which
carry the double bond have similar properties and are also very unstable.

26.4 AROMATIC NITRO-COMPOUNDS

26.4.1 General properties of aromatic nitro-compounds

A large number of the aromatic nitro-compounds have (or had) uses outside
the realm of explosives, with the result that the following are both
unwanted as well as intentional explosives:
- trinitrobenzene, which has been used as an accelerator in vulcanisation;
- trinitrotoluene, which, by reduction to triaminotoluene followed by di-
azotisation, gives methylphloroglucinol, which is used as a developer in
photography;
- 2,4-dinitrophenol, which, in addition to its pharmacological use, is used
to make a developer, diaminophenol, and sulphur-based dyes;
- picric acid (2,4,6-trinitrophenol), formerly used to dye wool and silk,
is now used mainly to make picramic acid (2-amino-4,6-dinitrophenol), which
is an intermediate product in the dye industry.

In addition, many other aromatic nitro-compounds are either pesticides,
such as dinitro-o-cresol, or intermediate products in the organic chemical
industry used in the manufacture of pharmaceutical products, perfumes,
dyes, etc.

The commonly used aromatic mononitro- or polynitro-compounds, with NO_2
groups in the meta position in relation to one another, have good thermal
stability. Most of them can be heated for several weeks at 100°C without
decomposition, which would be shown by a change in the melting temperature
or by the emission of nitrous fumes detectable by starched zinc iodide
paper. However, if the NO_2 groups are in a different position, as in
2,3,4,6-tetranitroaniline, at least one of them is mobile and makes the
compound unstable, as can be shown by a test in which it is heated to 75°C
(see 16.3.5).

There is no real correlation between chemical stability and the
temperature of deflagration in so far as the latter can be the same (if the
operating mode is the same) for two nitro-compounds which have different
stabilities at normal temperatures, the one being able to withstand heating

at 95°C over more than eight days whilst the other at the same temperature is already giving off nitrous fumes after several hours. None the less, the deflagration temperature as measured by the Dutch test (see 16.1.3) can tell us whether a nitro-compound contains impurities which make it less stable, since such impurities lower the deflagration temperature by some dozen (or several dozen) degrees.

When considering two benzene nitro-compounds differing only in the number of NO_2 groups on the nucleus (for example, 2,4-dinitro-m-xylene and 2,4,6-trinitro-m-xylene), it used to be stated, over-simplistically, that the explosive properties of the dinitro-compound were negligible unlike those of the trinitro-compound. This is far from being true, although dinitro-compounds are less sensitive to impact and less powerful than trinitro-compounds. Indeed, even a benzene mononitro-compound may give rise to an explosion in abnormal, extreme conditions of temperature or confinement. This point was made by Berthelot in 1887 and confirmed in particular by experiments by Condit and Haynor [24]. Mononitroxylene vapour (a mixture of isomers) decomposes in a closed vessel at around 320°C with a sudden rise in temperature and pressure. With nitrobenzene a similar explosive decomposition takes place at around 350°C. It has also been noted that the addition of one or more heavy alkyl radicals reduces the explosive properties, but does not eliminate it altogether, as can be seen with 2,4,6-trinitro-3-pentadecylphenol, a solid which melts at 90°C.

Various types of numerical data for nitro-compounds will be found in Tables 14.3, 14.4, and 15.2.

26.4.2 Aromatic nitration

The nitration of aromatic compounds, in other words the reaction

$$ArH + HNO_3 \rightarrow ArNO_2 + H_2O,$$

is irreversible and strongly exothermic (about 125 kJ/mol). It is normally carried out in the presence of sulphuric acid, which used to be thought of as fixing the water produced in the reaction, and it is indeed the case that, per mole of substance to be nitrated, the heat released during the action of a mixture of sulphuric acid and nitric acid, which is called commercially a nitrosulphuric mixture, is that of the preceding reaction plus the heat of mixing of sulphuric acid with water.

It is now thought, however, that sulphuric acid facilitates nitration by the formation of nitryl ions:

$$H_2SO_4 + HNO_3 \rightarrow (HSO_4)^- + (NO_2)^+ + H_2O$$

and that it is the $(NO_2)^+$ ion which is the agent of aromatic nitration. When nitration is carried out with nitric acid alone, this nitryl ion results from the reaction

$$2HNO_3 \rightarrow (NO_2)^+ + (NO_3)^- + H_2O.$$

The presence of an alkyl group on the benzene nucleus facilitates nitration, since the added nitro group is in the ortho or para position. The presence of a nitro group makes the later addition of NO_2 groups less easy, and these groups assume the meta position, which is why dinitration (adding a second NO_2 group) and even more so trinitration require the reacting substances to be at a higher temperature and to contain a higher concentration of nitryl ions, in other words to have a lower water content in the nitrosulphuric mixture. Because of these more demanding conditions, dinitration and trinitration do not take place without there also being other reactions (called nitration parasite reactions in industry) which consist mainly of oxidations, either on the nucleus by the formation of nitro phenols or on the side chain by the formation of aromatic nitro acid, and which can go as far as oxidation to CO_2 accompanied by splits in the aromatic molecule with formation of tetranitromethane and by the formation of sulphur compounds (sulphones, etc.). These undesirable reactions not only reduce the output of the main reaction but also introduce into the dinitro- or trinitro-compound produced impurities which generally have an unfavourable effect on its sensitivity and stability.

Although good progress has been made in the study of the mechanism of aromatic nitration†, we are still heavily dependent on practical experience with these reactions gained over a hundred years when it comes to defining the conditions which allow us to work in safety.

The system composed of the substance to be nitrated, the resulting nitro-compound, and the nitrosulphuric mixture is almost always a two-phase system, at least one of which is liquid‡. For the exchange of chemical species to take place rapidly between these two phases, it is necessary to stir the whole system well, and the system must also either be heated for the nitration reaction to be initiated or completed, or cooled to evacuate the heat released by the reaction, all of which means that the reactors, called nitrators, in which the reaction takes place must be fitted with agitators and means of regulating the temperature.

Until around 1950, industrial aromatic nitration was almost entirely a series of discontinuous processes carried out in nitrators with a capacity which had become quite considerable, sometimes more than 20 000 litres. Such apparatuses have a double wall and internal cooling coils. Later, however, continuous nitration apparatuses appeared which must be connected to automatic devices which control the flow of the reacting liquids, their temperature, etc. on the basis of information supplied by a variety of monitoring devices, the most important of which are thermometers. The development of such apparatuses was no easy task, but they have the great advantage from the safety point of view of limiting the amount of dangerous substances present at any time in a given production schedule, and in particular the mass of chemical system in a dangerous stage of development. However, because the complex instrumentation connected with the apparatus is adapted specifically to a given substance, a continuous nitrator can be used only for the species for which it was designed, which is why there are still many discontinuous nitrators to be found in the industry, since they can be appropriately modified to nitrate different substances.

Many different aromatic nitro-compounds are produced, and when they are manufactured discontinuously, they can be obtained in a variety of ways.

---

† A bibliography for this research can be found in a paper by Albright and Hanson [25].
‡ There is a solid phase in processes in which a solid substance to be nitrated is introduced into the nitrating acid mixture. This is the case with the nitration of naphthalene.

Either the nitrosulphuric mixture can be poured onto the substance to be nitrated or onto that substance in solution in sulphuric acid, or the substance to be nitrated can be poured into the nitrosulphuric mixture. Pouring time, temperature, length of agitation after pouring, etc., all vary from one substance to another, and with a given apparatus there is always a procedure which must be followed to the letter, otherwise there is a risk that the reaction will evolve towards an explosion.

For some substances which are decomposed by sulphuric acid, nitration is carried out with a mixture of concentrated nitric acid and acetic anhydride. When these two constituents are in equimolar quantities (or almost), such mixtures contain acetyl nitrate (see 18.5.4). It is advisable to work with an aceto-nitric mixture containing either less than 50% or more than 85% HNO_3. A safer nitration process can be achieved by alternately pouring small quantities first of nitric acid and then of the substance to be nitrated into the acetic anhydride, so that there is always much less than 50% free nitric acid in the mixture.

26.4.3 Causes of explosions in aromatic nitration

Explosions are almost always attributable to one of the three following causes:

1. *Breakdown in the stirring system* - If the mass is not mechanically stirred during pouring, the two phases are in contact only over a small surface area and the temperature is not uniform, with the result that a reaction may occur locally with a considerable rise in temperature and, when stirring begins, the reaction in a mass hotter than it should be becomes too rapid and results in an explosion.

Fritz [26] has described a case of this kind in an operation to nitrate mononitrobenzene into dinitrobenzene. The explosion destroyed an entire building. The nitrosulphuric mixture was fed into the nitrator containing the mononitrobenzene without stirring by a first operative in a control room some distance away. The person who took over from him then switched on the agitator, whereupon alarming noises were heard and then there was a large emission of nitrous fumes followed two or three minutes later by an explosion. It is not clear why the agitator did not work, but its failure to do so should have been signalled by an audio alarm linked to a servo mechanism for closing the nitrosulphuric inlet valve in case of an agitator malfunction, but this servo mechanism was not in working order.

2. *Cooling failure* - The reaction takes place at a temperature which rises to a value at which the rate of reaction is very rapid and at which parasite reactions become particularly predominant. These reactions then lead to decomposition of the organic phase with rapid emission of gases and nitrous fumes.

The cooling system set up for a given nitration process may prove to be inadequate if the reactants are mixed too rapidly. Any change in the way in which an operation is carried out may create dangerous conditions.

Excessive local heating of the nitrating medium may be caused by the accidental introduction of a foreign body. The explosion which killed eighty people in Rheinsdorf in June 1935 was caused by a cotton glove falling into residues of dinitrotoluene contaminated by nitrosulphuric acid, so initiating an uncontrollable decomposition which caused large quantities of TNT in nearby buildings to explode.

3. *Substances present in the wrong ratio* - In this respect, a case is

quoted in which the substance to be nitrated had first to be dissolved in sulphuric acid, but the quantity of acid fed into the apparatus was only two thirds what it should have been because the zero on the acid gauge column was in the wrong place. When nitrosulphuric acid was then poured onto this solution with its excessive concentration of aromatic substance, the reaction took place too rapidly and ended in an explosion.

4˙ An explosive gas phase may be formed, even when there is no air present, by vapours of nitric acid or dinitrogen tetroxide mixed with the vapour of the substance to be nitrated when the latter is volatile. Such an explosive gas mixture ignites easily at a low temperature on a hot spot on the wall of the apparatus.

In short, the agitator, the cooling system, and the feed gauges should be checked at frequent intervals and monitored in operation.

The intensity of electric current flowing through the motor driving the agitator can be used to warn of agitator breakdown: if the current becomes weak, it is an indication that the agitator shaft is no longer meeting resistance, which means agitation has stopped.

In the manufacture of nitro-compounds an explosion sometimes occurs during purification treatment after the nitration process itself. For example, during distillation at reduced pressure a breakdown in the pumping system causes the pressure, and therefore the temperature, to rise in the apparatus. Another cause of explosion during distillation of a mononitro substance is the presence of dinitro-compounds in the raw material being treated. Since the latter are less volatile, they accumulate at the foot of the column, so it is advisable to drain them off at frequent intervals.

Interrupting a nitration process or putting off for too long the purification of a raw nitro-compound can often be dangerous. A case has been reported of a naphthalene nitrator exploding after the nitration process when raw dinitronaphthalene left at rest in contact with the spent acid from the nitration for twelve hours at 60˙C began to decompose. At such a relatively low temperature dinitronaphthalene alone would probably have been stable in contact with a nitrosulphuric mixture, so the reaction must have been initiated by the presence of impurities (possibly nitroso compounds).

26.4.4 Nitro-compounds of benzene

Nitrobenzene (mononitrobenzene) $C_6H_5NO_2$ is a flammable liquid which boils at 211˙C. Explosions have sometimes been reported during distillation of this substance, for which there would seem to be two causes:
(a) the distilled liquid was a raw product of nitration containing certain impurities such as dinitrobenzene or nitrophenols;
(b) at the end of distillation the liquid and the vapour in the column overheat considerably, especially if they are heated with a naked flame. But if the correct procedures are followed, distillation can be carried out without decomposition. In fact, instead of distilling the product alone it can be steam distilled and then dried.

Anhydrous aluminium chloride is soluble in nitrobenzene, which makes it easy to carry out Friedel and Crafts reactions using this substance. The temperature must be strictly controlled since there is some considerable danger above 160˙C. It was probably such a reaction which caused the serious explosion near Basel in 1973. An explosion had already been reported twenty years earlier [46] when anhydrous aluminium chloride was added to nitrobenzene containing 5% phenol.

Dinitrobenzene $C_6H_4(NO_2)_2$ (*m*-dinitrobenzene), which melts at 90°C, is the substance which is used in the R.I.D. and other regulations as a point of comparison for deciding whether or not to classify a substance as an explosive, dinitrobenzene itself not being classified as such. It explodes in the Sevran drop-weight test at an impact energy of more than 200 joules, but does not explode in the test in a steel tube with nozzle plates with an orifice of 1 mm.

Trinitrobenzene (1,3,5-trinitrobenzene) melts at 120°C and is a more powerful explosive than TNT.

26.4.5 Nitro-compounds of toluene

The nitration of toluene gives mainly liquid *o*-nitrotoluene (b.p. 222°C) and solid *p*-nitrotoluene (m.p. 52°C), but they are always accompanied by liquid *m*-nitrotoluene (b.p. 230°C) as well. These mononitro-compounds have weak explosive properties similar to those of nitrobenzene, but they are liable to undergo explosive decomposition at a relatively low temperature when they are in a strongly acid medium, as is shown by the following accident [27]: when *p*-nitrotoluene was being dissolved in a 93% solution of sulphuric acid which was normally heated to 80°C, a fault in the mechanism controlling the heating vapour allowed the temperature to rise to 135°C, causing a strong explosion.

Dinitrotoluenes are particularly interesting examples of unwanted explosives, on the one hand because their use on a large scale has given rise to explosions, and on the other hand because most regulations (in particular those covering transport) do not classify them as explosives.

Six dinitrotoluenes can be derived from the three mononitrotoluene isomers. The most important are the 2,4-dinitro (m.p. 70°C) and the 2,6-dinitro (m.p. 60.5°C) isomers. Fractional crystallisation can be used to separate the pure, or technically pure, 2,4 isomer which constitutes the substance known commercially as *crystallised dinitrotoluene*, as opposed to *raw dinitrotoluene*, a substance which melts at around 56 to 60°C (with no clear melting point). Finally, a substance known as *liquid dinitrotoluene* can be manufactured by nitrating a special blend of mononitrotoluene. It contains numerous isomers and sometimes also a small percentage (about 2%) of 2,4,6-trinitrotoluene. When cooled, it deposits crystals at around 1°C.

Liquid dinitrotoluene in a thick steel tube with an internal diameter of 33 mm cannot be detonated no matter what primer is used. In the same conditions raw dinitrotoluene undergoes an overdriven detonation which stops after travelling a distance which is shorter as the loading density is greater. Crystallised dinitrotoluene in the same conditions undergoes stable detonation for all values of loading density, but if it is not under confinement it produces no more than an overdriven detonation which stops after only a short distance [28a].

Cook and Partridge [29] have measured the detonation velocities of 2,4-dinitrotoluene at a density of 0.95 g/cm³ without confinement at various diameters. They obtained values which increase from 2500 to 3400 and 3950 m/s when the diameter is raised from 4 cm (which, at this density of 0.95, is more or less the critical diameter) to 10 cm and then 25 cm. Other experiments by Médard on a substance with a similar granulometry gave velocities which increase at a diameter of 10 cm from 3400 m/s (for Δ =

0.95) to 5810 m/s (for Δ = 1.48). At a diameter of 6 cm the velocity is lower than the above at low densities but rises to the same value of 5810 m/s for Δ = 1.48. At this point the velocities measured are certainly close to the velocity of ideal detonation, which must be of the order of 6000 m/s for 1.5 g/cm^3. The same experiments also show that a substance with a larger granulometry detonates at each diameter with a velocity lower than that of the fine-grained substance. Price and his associates [30] have published similar results. Clearly then, physical structure is no less important than chemical composition in determining liability to explode.

Raw (and very probably also liquid and crystallised) dinitrotoluene may explode when it is kept for a long time in the molten state at a high temperature. Bateman [31] describes a most instructive case from 1972: a halt in production left molten dinitrotoluene in a pipe 5 cm in diameter and some 100 m long linking two workshops in a factory. The pipe was placed inside a casing through which flowed expanded steam at a temperature which should normally not have exceeded 130°C, but which, during the pause in production, rose to almost 210°C. After ten days in these conditions the molten dinitrotoluene exploded in several places in the pipe, causing some damage in the vicinity. Each explosion was a deflagration affecting only a few decimetres of pipe with no general propagation.

Experiments conducted after this accident in small-diameter metal containers showed that isothermal heating for 240 hours at 167°C triggers an exothermic decomposition which leads to a rise in pressure. The same thing happens at higher temperatures after a heating period which varies inversely with temperature. At the moment of explosion, the temperature inside the dinitrotoluene is around 250°C. It may be that in a very large mass of the substance a temperature of 130-150°C on the surface is enough to trigger self-sustained decomposition after a very long time.

This accident underlines the risk of heating to too high a temperature when using heating steam. With saturated steam one only has to measure the pressure to find the temperature, but if, as was the case in the accident described above, the steam comes from the expansion of superheated steam, the expanded steam may become even more superheated and a pressure gauge reading does not tell us what the temperature is, so it is necessary to have a thermometer in the superheated steam. In fact, the best solution is to cool the steam using a water-injection apparatus to obtain saturating steam. Using an insufficiently cooled superheated steam has also caused explosions in treatments other than those involving nitro-compounds.

2,4,6-trinitrotoluene is that well-known intentional explosive TNT. Like trinitro-m-xylene, it is a little more sensitive to impact than trinitrobenzene, even though the latter is more 'powerful'. The same kind of differences are also found between the dinitro-compounds of benzene, toluene, and xylene but in practical terms they are insignificant.

26.4.6 Nitronaphthalenes

Industrial *trinitronaphthalene* is a mixture of several isomers with a (not sharply defined) melting point close to 150°C. Its explosive capacity, which had already been pointed out in 1929 [33], was defined with precision in 1940 [34]. At densities of 0.6 to 0.8 g/cm^3 the critical detonation diameter is higher than 30 mm, but falls when the substance is compressed to a density of 1.5 g/cm^3, when its detonation velocity is 5800 m/s.

Calvet [35] successfully studied the detonation of the substance in the molten state at 180°C. Using the Dautriche method, he found that, in this state, in which decomposition begins with the formation of bubbles giving a density of 0.9 g/cm³, an explosion propagates at more than 8000 m/s. This is probably not a regular detonation so much as a regime halfway between a detonation and an homogeneous explosion.

Dinitronaphthalenes were thought for a long time to be non-explosive compounds. They do not detonate in the test in an elongated box (see 15.3.2) but the industrial product (which is a mixture of 1,5 and 1,8 isomers) can be detonated in large-diameter cartridges. The velocity of detonation is 4600 m/s at a density of 1.3 g/cm³, the critical diameter then being about 50 mm [36b].

26.4.7 Nitrophenols

The presence of the NO_2 group on the nucleus of a phenol increases its acidic property. Thus, picric acid (2,4,6-trinitrophenol) is a strong acid which replaces the nitric acid in nitrates.

2,4-dinitrophenol (I), a solid which melts at 115°C and is insensitive to impact but gives 35% explosions with a 10 kg weight falling from 3 m, detonates well in the elongated box test (see 15.3.2) at a density of 0.6 g/cm³. In a cartridge 30 mm in diameter without confinement (paper casing) at a density of 0.85, a Briska detonator produces only an incomplete over-driven detonation, with yellow traces on the floor indicating that some of the substance has escaped the explosion. In the same conditions, a booster of 30 g of picric acid produces a stable detonation at a velocity of 2300 m/s.

4,6-dinitro-o-cresol (II), a solid which melts at 86°C, has a critical detonation diameter higher than 35 mm at a density of 1, but can, under strong confinement, be detonated completely by a strong primer. Under a 10 kg weight falling from 3 cm, 50% explosion is observed [36a].

2,6-dinitro-p-cresol (III) and *2,4-dinitro-m-cresol* (IV) have similar explosive properties.

2-amino-4,6-dinitrophenol (V), also called *picramic acid*, consists of red crystals which melt at 169°C and has explosive properties similar to the preceding substances but is more sensitive to impact [37].

The behaviour of nitrophenols in a fire is quite remarkable. Munroe [38] describes an accident which happened on 28 September 1921 in Sparta when some 100 tons of picric acid in wooden barrels were destroyed by an extremely violent fire but did not detonate. Several other cases of this kind are known of, including the burning down in June 1940 of warehouses holding 110 tons of picric acid. This is all the more remarkable since TNT fires generally end in the substance detonating when the mass exceeds a few tons.

It is not known what would happen, however, in a fire involving a very large mass of picric acid not divided into separate lots (250 kg barrels) but kept in one mass. It should also be noted that fires involving picric acid or other nitrophenols have the property just described only when they are free of saline compounds (see 30.4).

However, like all the other nitro-compounds, nitrophenols cannot be kept for a long time at a relatively high temperature without danger of decomposing. Dartnell and Ventrone [39] describe the explosion in October 1969 of a storage tank containing some six tons of 4-nitro-m-cresol (VI), an intermediate product in the manufacture of a phosphorus ester used as a pesticide. When it has been heated for a long time, this nitrocresol may polymerise, giving a less stable polymer than the monomer, and undergo a very strong decomposition into gaseous products and fumes. This strong decomposition takes place after 16 hours when the substance is stored at 185°C, and after 45 hours at 165°C. In a closed vessel the very rapid explosive decomposition creates high pressures.

26.4.8 Other aromatic nitro explosives

It can be taken that all aromatic nitro-compounds have more or less marked explosive properties. Many others than the ones quoted above are produced industrially.

The artificial perfumes known as 'musk Baur' are dinitro- or trinitro-compounds of tertiobutylbenzenes. 'Musk xylene' (VII) in particular is easily detonated in a steel tube and, in the drop-weight test, has a sensitivity similar to that of picric acid. 'Musk ambrette' (VIII) and 'musk ketone' (IX) are difficult to detonate at their packing density, which is close to 0.9.

The nitro-compounds of chlorobenzene and dichlorobenzene are also explosive.

2,4-dinitromethylaniline (X) (m.p. 178°C), which is an intermediate substance in the manufacture of tetryl from dinitrochlorobenzene and methylamine, can be detonated only with a strong primer. Its critical detonation diameters are given on Fig. 14.5

2,4,6,2',4',6'-hexanitrodiphenylamine (XI) or dipicrylamine, called hexyl in the explosives industry, has, like *2,4,6-trinitroaniline* (XII) or picramide, a marked acidic property because of the action of accumulated NO_2 substituents on the amino group. It is because of this that it has uses in analytical chemistry for detection and titration of potassium, since at 30°C 100 g of water dissolves 11.6 g of sodium salt and only 0.146 g of potassium salt, thus allowing quantitative precipitation of potassium in an aqueous solution by a solution of sodium dipicrylaminate.

26.5 NITRIC ESTERS

26.5.1 Nitric esterification

Nitric esterification (known industrially as nitration) is the reaction of an alcohol with nitric acid

$$ROH + HNO_3 \rightarrow R - O - NO_2 + H_2O.$$

It liberates approximately 25 kJ/mol and is less exothermic than aromatic nitration, but the oxidation of alcohols by nitric acid may produce up to fifty times more heat than the above nitration. These oxidations are initiated when nitrous acid or nitrogen dioxide is present in the nitrating medium, which is why, when ethanol is nitrated, either by nitric acid alone or with a nitrosulphuric mixture, a small amount of urea is added to destroy the nitrous acid.

In a strongly acid medium, and especially when a nitrosulphuric mixture is being used, nitric esterification is a reversible reaction, but water

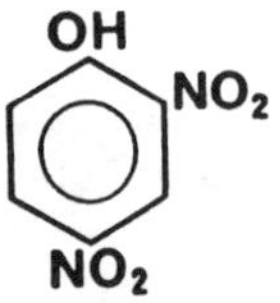

I 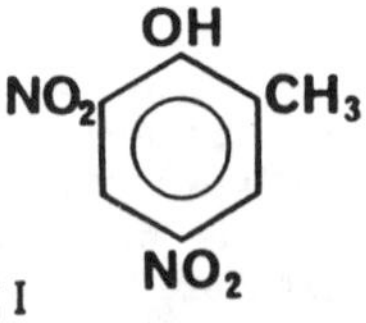   II 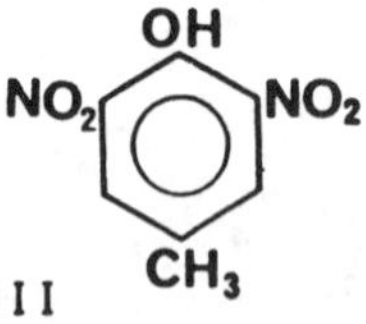   III

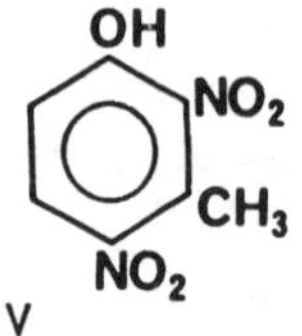

IV 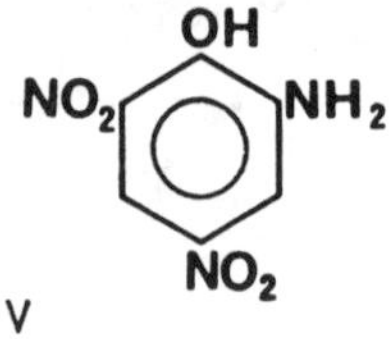   V 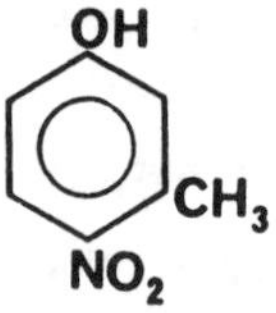   VI

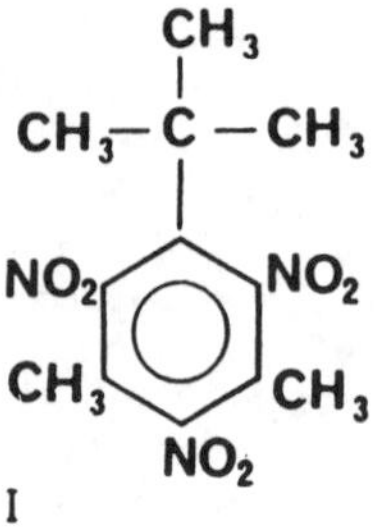

VII 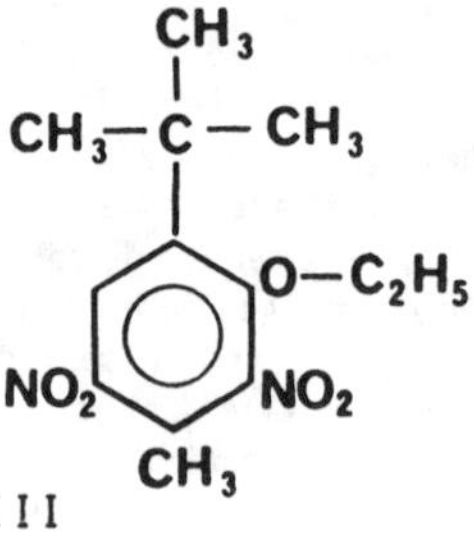   VIII

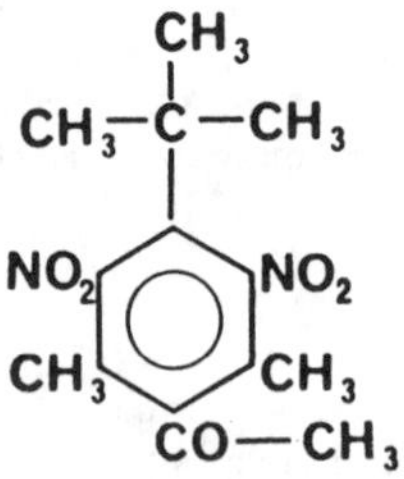

IX 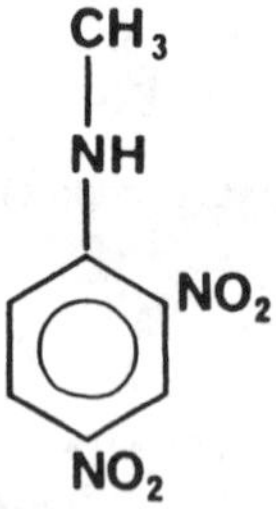   X

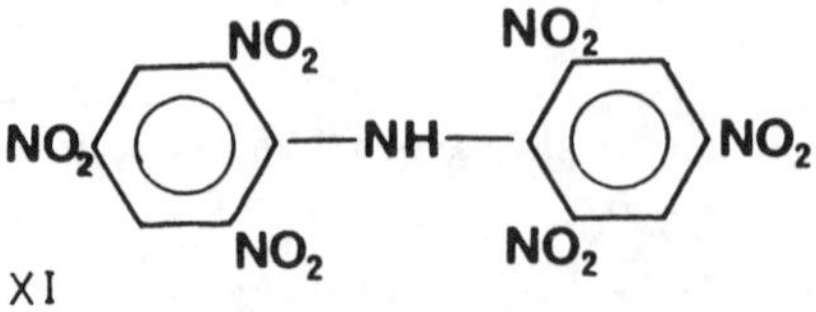

XI 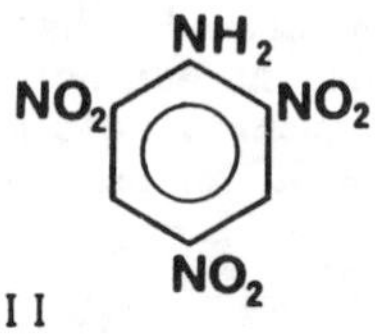   XII

alone does not act on nitric esters, which have remarkable resistance to hydrolysis, even at around 100°C.

Spent acids from nitration (by NHO_3 or a nitrosulphuric mixture) are often unstable, so that they must be separated from the nitric ester as soon as nitration is over. They contain dissolved organic compounds which gradually oxidise, leading to the possibility of a violent decomposition. It is advisable, therefore, not to look for nitration conditions giving the best output of nitric ester but rather for conditions in which the spent acid can be stored without becoming the seat of a dangerous exothermic reaction.

26.5.2 Methyl nitrate

Methyl nitrate CH_3NO_3 is the simplest of the nitric esters. It is not difficult to manufacture but the process is not without its risks. Roig [40] describes a safer manufacturing process in which methyl nitrate is obtained in the form of a 60% solution in methanol. It is an explosive liquid, sensitive to impact and initiation, with a detonation velocity close to 7000 m/s, although in tubes just a few millimetres in diameter it only undergoes a low-regime detonation. It is highly flammable. In moderate quantities in a container wide open to the air, it burns with formation of nitrous fumes, but in sizeable quantities or under some confinement combustion leads to detonation.

Formerly used as a methylating agent at a time when dimethyl sulphate was not a common substance as it is now, it caused a serious explosion in a factory in Saint-Denis in November 1874. Attempts were also made to use it for 'doping' various fuels. As such, it was transported in an 8-10% solution in diesel oil and then added to the fuel. But at around 0°C this solution, known as 'methylated oil', separates out, forming a liquid layer on the bottom of the drum which is very rich in methyl nitrate, and this was the cause of a serious explosion in a factory in the Paris area in 1963 which led to these 'methylated oils' being abandoned. Methyl nitrate is also thought to have been the cause of a highly fatal explosion in a car race.

Around 1945, methyl nitrate-methanol mixtures were studied for use as propellants, but unfortunately even when they contain an appreciable amount of methanol, such mixtures are still liable to detonate. Hasty tests using a No. 8 detonator in glass tubes 2 cm in diameter had led a researcher to believe that the 40% methanol mixture was incapable of detonating, but a serious explosion showed this not to be the case. Quite clearly, the preliminary tests of sensitivity had used a primer that was too weak and a tube with too small a diameter (see 15.3.1).

26.5.2b Alkyl nitrates

The higher homologues of methyl nitrate can also be used for doping the performance of fuels and are less dangerous. They are quite volatile liquids (see Table 26.3) which freeze only at a very low temperature but which are flammable none the less.

Ethyl nitrate $C_2H_5NO_3$ is much less sensitive to impact or initiation than methyl nitrate. However, if it is mixed with 30% absorbing earth, it can be easily exploded, even without confinement, with a No. 8 detonator.

Its detonation velocity in a tube with a diameter of 60 mm has been found
to be equal to 6020 m/s [41]. Its critical detonation diameter is about 45
mm, but in a thick-walled steel tube a strong primer will still detonate it
at a diameter of 25 mm. When heated at a rate of 10°C per minute in a
steel bomb, it explodes when the temperature reaches 180°C.

Normal propyl nitrate $CH_3 - CH_2 - CH_2NO_3$, and certainly also isopropyl
nitrate $(CH_3)_2CH - NO_3$, housed in a steel tube with a diameter of 80 mm,
detonates regularly when primed with 400 g of a P.E.T.N. explosive. In the
same conditions butyl nitrate and pentyl nitrate do not detonate.

Normal propyl nitrate is a monopropellant with a flame temperature of
around 1100°C but which does not decompose readily at pressures below 50
bars.

26.5.3 Nitrocelluloses and their classification

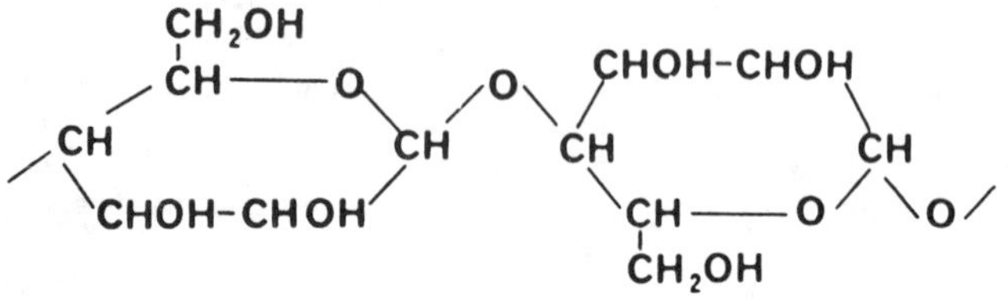

Fig. 26.3 – Unit of cellulose, $(C_6H_{10}O_5)_2$.

Cellulose is a natural macromolecular compound found widely in the
vegetable kingdom and having a basic structural unit which contains a
heterocyclic ring of glucopyranose (Fig. 26.3). These groups join to form
very long chains of up to 10 000 units. Their length, in other words the
degree of polymerisation of the substance, depends on the origin of the
cellulose. Parallel chains cluster together to form the cellulose fibre.
The nitrocellulose industry uses two types of cellulosic substance:
(a) cottons (for nitro-cottons) made up of short fibres called linters;
(b) wood pulps obtained by treating chopped-up wood with agents such as
bisulphite detergent which remove the non-cellulosic constituents in wood.

Cottons are subjected to a degreasing and bleaching treatment and come
in the form of floss. Wood pulps are also bleached, either with a chlorine
agent or, more commonly nowadays, by the action of compressed oxygen. They
come in the form of flocks. The chemical treatment which is needed to make
cellulose suitable for nitration always causes some hydrolysis at the level
of the oxygen bridges linking the glucopyranose groups and so reduces the
degree of polymerisation in direct proportion with the energy of the
treatment. The degree of polymerisation is measured by the viscosity of
solutions in acetone or some other solvent of the nitrocellulose derived
from the raw material.

The formula for cellulose can be written in an oversimplified form as
$C_6H_7O_2(OH)_3$ in order to highlight the alcohol hydroxyls. It is then a
triol which may give various esters, and in particular nitric esters, which
are called nitrocelluloses in the industry even though the term cellulose
nitrates, which is becoming more widespread, is preferable.

The nitration of cellulose by immersing it in a nitrosulphuric mixture

Table 26.3

Properties of alkyl nitrates

Substance	Density at 20°C	Normal boiling point (°C)	Heats of formation at 18°C			
			of the liquid (kJ/mol)		of the vapour (kJ/mol)	
			F_p	F_v	F_p	F_v
Methyl nitrate	1.21	66	151	142	121	115
Ethyl nitrate	1.11	88	190	180	154	146
Normal propyl nitrate	1.04	110.5	215	202	174	164
Isopropyl nitrate	1.03	102	230	216	191	180

is a topochemical reaction, in other words the random fixation of NO_2 groups along each chain in the hydroxyls. The degree of nitration of a cellulose can be assessed from its nitrogen content, which is generally measured by the Devarda method. Complete esterification would give a cellulose trinitrate $C_6H_7O_2(NO_3)_3$ with a nitrogen content of 14.14%, but in reality it is very difficult to obtain a nitrocellulose which contains more than 14% nitrogen. A dinitrate, which is represented stoichiometrically by $C_6H_7(OH)(NO_3)_2$, contains 11.11% nitrogen, but there is no such thing as a definite dinitrate since the nitrocelluloses form a continuous series, from the lowest nitrate content achievable, which is 7%, to the most highly nitrated substances, with no discernible dinitrate.

Nitration hardly modifies the appearance of cellulose. A cotton floss for nitration gives a nitro-cotton floss that only an experienced operative can distinguish by touch from non-nitrated floss. Similarly, nitrated wood pulp bears a very strong resemblance to the initial flock substance. The chemical properties of nitrocelluloses are almost identical whether they come from cotton or wood pulp.

The nitrocelluloses fall into two groups according to their nitrogen content:

(a) Nitrocelluloses with a nitrogen content higher than 12.6%, which include the highly nitrated cottons, or *gun-cotton*, containing 13.2 to 13.5% nitrogen, used in the production of smokeless powders. All these nitrocelluloses are soluble in acetone but insoluble in a mixture of ether and alcohol, and they have mainly military uses.

(b) Nitrocelluloses with a maximum nitrogen content of 12.6%, soluble in the ether-alcohol mixture as well as in acetone. To this group belong *soluble gun-cotton*, containing between 11.9 and 12.4% nitrogen, and the various *nitro-cottons* which are nitrocelluloses with non-military uses. They are also called *collodion cottons* because they can be used to make collodion, in other words a nitrocellulose solution in the ether-alcohol mixture, although the term collodion has since been extended to solutions in solvents other than this one.

The nitro-cotton used in the manufacture of celluloid has a fairly low nitrogen content (about 11%), whilst the one used in the making of dynamite contains about 11.8% nitrogen and must be obtained from a cotton which has undergone very little degradation so that it can retain without exudation the nitroglycerine that it must fix in a large quantity of up to twelve times its own mass. Nitro-cottons used in the manufacture of varnishes, lacquers, and paints contain 12 to 12.5% nitrogen nowadays.

Nitrocelluloses in floss or flock form are substances with a fibrous structure, a low bulk density, and a certain degree of crystallinity, like cellulose itself, as can be seen from an X-ray analysis. This structure is preserved when the fibrous and quite hydrophilic substances are soaked in water or alcohol, but it is destroyed by the action of solvents of the acetone type. If the solvent in which a nitrocellulose is held in solution is evaporated, the nitrocellulose is left in a solid, amorphous, compact, horn-like form with a density close to 1.5. It is said to be *gelatinised*. Gelatinisation can also be produced by hot kneading of a nitrocellulose with a substance, called a *gelatiniser*, which acts as a non-volatile solvent and which remains in the end product. Gelatinisers which are used to obtain a flexible substance are called *plasticisers*. Thus, industry manufactures, under the name of nitrocellulose *flakes* or *chips*, substances containing 16 to 20% gelatiniser, sometimes with pigments added, for use in the manufacture of nitrocellulose paints (or lacquers).

26.5.4 Chemical stability of nitrocelluloses

Industrial production of nitrocelluloses began in 1846, but the substance
had only poor stability and underwent rapid decomposition with self-heating
culminating in an explosion.   In 1847, the pyroxylin factory in Faversham
exploded, leaving twenty one people dead, and an accident at the Poudrerie
du Bouchet killed several workers.   Other disasters led to the abandoning
of the manufacture of nitrocelluloses until Sir Frederick Abel discovered
the means of making a stable product around 1865.   The instability of
nitrocelluloses after nitration and neutralisation by prolonged rinsing in
cold water is caused by the presence of unstable substances, similar in
nature to sugar nitrates, and sulphuric acid which is either sequestered in
the solid lattice or occurs in part in the form of HSO_4 residues fixed on
the hydroxyls.   All these undesirable substances can be eliminated from
nitrocellulose if it is subjected to prolonged treatment in boiling water
for about twenty hours either at atmospheric pressure at 100°C or in an
autoclave at a temperature such as 120°C. Contrary to earlier belief, this
washing in hot water is not made more effective by adding carbonate to
neutralise the acid which gradually forms in the water during treatment.
Washing in a very weak sulphuric solution stabilises nitrocellulose just as
well.
    Abel also gave us the test named after him which consists in heating
nitrocellulose at 65°C in a test tube in the presence of potassium iodide
paper to detect the release of nitrous fumes.   If a nitrocellulose is well
stabilised, the paper does not react for twenty minutes.
    Whereas a suitably stabilised nitrocellulose has a deflagration
temperature which remains steady at around 180°C in the Dutch test (see
16.1.3), with a poorly stabilised substance this temperature may fall to
120°C or even less.   Such a substance cannot be put to dry in an oven at
90°C without exploding in less than an hour.   It would probably explode
after several months storage in its packing at ordinary temperature.
    Even when properly stabilised, a nitrocellulose will slowly decompose
at ordinary temperatures.   The reaction is accompanied by the release of
gas products which are predominantly nitrogen oxides, so leading to a slow
fall in the nitrogen content of the nitrocellulose.   In technical terms it
is said to denitrate.   To give an idea of the variation with temperature of
the stability of a well-stabilised nitrocellulose, we may quote the 'law of
correlation' stated by Vieille which claims to give no more than an order
of magnitude: heating for one hour at 110°C is the equivalent of one day
at 75°C, or five days at 60°C, or one month at 40°C.   From this a simple
calculation gives the thermal coefficient (see 3.5) of the decomposition
reaction of nitrocellulose as about 2.4 over the range 40 to 110°C.

26.5.5 Explosive properties of nitrocelluloses

The thermochemical properties of nitrocellulose depend essentially on its
nitrogen content n (per 100).   For nitro-cottons†, the following formulae

---

† These formulae are also valid for nitrated wood pulps or any other
nitrocelluloses which have not undergone strong decomposition.

give to less than 1% the heat of formation at constant volume and the upper calorific value:

$$F_V = 5\ 774 - 255\ n \quad (J/g)$$
$$Q_V = 582\ n - 3\ 380 \quad (J/g).$$

In the dry state fibrous nitrocelluloses, in other words nitro-cotton in the form of floss and nitrated wood pulps in flock form, are highly sensitive explosives, both to impact and initiation. They catch fire on contact with flame. When they form a thin layer several centimetres thick in the open air combustion takes the form of a fairly rapid deflagration. In a large mass, very rapid deflagration takes the form of an explosion creating high pressure or even a detonation. Under confinement there is always a detonation.

When they are soaked in large quantities of water or a non-explosive liquid (hydrocarbon, alcohol, etc.), the sensitivity of these fibrous substances is reduced and may become very weak if the liquid content is high enough.

Gelatinised nitrocelluloses, even when they are dry and have completely lost all traces of solvent, are less sensitive to impact or initiation than are fibrous nitrocelluloses but they can still be easily initiated. If a large enough primer is used, they can even be detonated in the absence of confinement, as was shown by the case of B powders† in the shape of flat cartridges [43]. Gelatinised nitrocelluloses which contain a sufficient quantity of non-volatile gelatiniser may become very weakly sensitive or even totally insensitive if, in addition to the gelatiniser, they contain a fair quantity of inert substances such as pigments.

In summary, the explosive properties of nitrocelluloses depend in a highly complex way on the following factors:
1˙ the structure, whether fibrous or gelatinised, of the nitrocellulose;
2˙ the quantity of soaking liquid in the case of fibrous products or the amount of non-volatile gelatiniser in the case of gelatinised substances;
3˙ the nitrogen content of the nitrocellulose: the higher this content, the more marked the explosive property.

Consequently, it is not easy to give simple rules for assessing risk, but the following points may be made:
(a) For a given quantity of soaking liquid, a fibrous nitrocellulose wetted with water is less sensitive than the same substance when wetted with an alcohol, with methanol or ethanol, making the product less sensitive than propyl or butyl alcohol.
(b) Substances may be gelatinised to various degrees depending on the treatment given to them. For a given quantity of gelatiniser incorporated into the substance, one may have either a highly compact product or a more or less porous one, with the latter being more sensitive.

26.5.6 Classification of nitrocelluloses in transport regulations

United Nations experts, working mainly from tests on the behaviour of

---

† B powders are French powders with a gelatinised nitrocellulose base and stabilised with 1.5% diphenylamine.

packages containing nitrocelluloses in a fire, have drawn up the following classification:

Nitrocelluloses containing less than 25% water or alcohol or less than 18% plasticiser on the one hand, and those with a nitrogen content higher than 12.6% and more than 25% alcohol or more than 18% plasticiser on the other are classified as explosives.

In class 4.1 (flammable solid substances) are found nitrocelluloses with a maximum nitrogen content of 12.6% and at least 25% alcohol or 18% plasticiser, as well as nitrocelluloses containing at least 25% water no matter what the nitrogen content.

The water-tightness of containers holding nitrocelluloses wetted with water or alcohol is clearly an essential condition for safety of transport. Substances in floss or flock form wetted with water are much safer since, if they are engulfed in flames, they burn only gradually as they lose water through heating.

26.5.7 Safety in the manufacture and use of nitrocelluloses

The manufacture of nitrocellulose is comparatively safe if, as is almost always the case now, it is not produced in dry form. During stabilisation it is immersed in a large quantity of water. During nitration it stands in a large quantity of acid, and a decomposition may occur, known technically as 'fuming off', although there are usually no flames, which releases large quantities of nitrous vapours and throws off acid. This reaction is initiated by impurities present in the substance to be nitrated, such as a spot of lubricant.

However, if, after nitration, the raw nitrocellulose is thoroughly spun dry, explosive decompositions are still possible. There may even be a detonation if the ratio of the mass of acid absorbed to the mass of solid substance soaked with it falls below 1.2 for nitrocelluloses with a 13.8% nitrogen content or below 1 for nitrocelluloses with a 12.5% nitrogen content, as is shown by tests [44] in steel tubes with diameters of 36 or 52 mm†. It should be noted that the liquid soaking the nitrocellulose at the end of the drying process does not have the same composition as the spent acid from nitration but is much richer in HNO_3 (30 to 35% as opposed to 20% in the spent acid). There is selective adsorption by the nitro-cellulose of HNO_3 in preference to H_2SO_4. A mixture of 100 g of a nitro-cellulose with a 12.6% nitrogen content and 90 g of an acid mixture with 35% HNO_3 may be thought of as the association of 131.5 g of a binary mixture of nitrocellulose and HNO_3 with a relatively low oxygen balance (an almost stoichiometric mixture) and 58.5 g of an inert mixture of H_2O–H_2SO_4.

During the tests referred to above it was noted that sensitivity to primers increases with density and that the percentage of liquid soaking the substance is a more important factor than its nitrogen content. The tests also showed that under moderate confinement priming the substance has the effect of producing a deflagration which frequently develops into a detonation.

---

† This suggests that in a large nitrator detonation is still possible with percentages of soaking acid higher than those in the tests.

In industrial manufacture such explosions causing considerable damage never occurred as long as the nitrocellulose still contained a high level of acid liquid after drying. Care must therefore be taken when increasing the centrifugal force of the dryers being used.

When using nitrocelluloses, in floss or flock form, the main precaution is to ensure that the substance always contains the same percentage of water or alcohol as when it left the manufacturer. Consequently, the lids on the containers used for transport must always be put back in place after each use. Most accidents, consisting of flash fires sometimes accompanied by an explosion, happened, like the one in Saint-Denis in September 1931, because nitrocellulose was left for several hours in the open air in the weighing shed.

Nitrocellulose in the form of flocks readily gives off dusts which are deposited throughout the workshop. It is advisable to keep the ground wet by watering it and to carry out frequent cleaning with wet sponges. Where dust occurs, the workforce should wear a headpiece completely covering the hair.

Soiled or unused substances should be put in a water-filled airtight bin until they can be destroyed either by spreading the substance in a thin layer on a bed of wood chips and burning it or by chemical means since nitrocelluloses are easily denitrated when put to soak in a lukewarm solution of ammonium sulphide.

Gelatinised products are less dangerous than fibrous nitrocelluloses *provided gelatinisation was complete*. They present hardly any hazard other than the risk of fire, although if one does break out it is very strong and frequently accompanied by a release of nitrous fumes. A fire under confinement turns into an explosion. If the product is incompletely gelatinised and has retained some degree of porosity, there is a risk of detonation even in the absence of confinement.

NB – Quinchon's book [49] gives an account of more recent discoveries in the area of nitrocelluloses.

BIBLIOGRAPHICAL REFERENCES

[1]   Desseigne, G. & Giral, H. (1952) *Mém. Poudres* 34 13
[2]   Makovky, L. & Grunwald, T. B. (1959) *Trans. Faraday Soc.* 55 952
[3]   Urbanski, T. & Pawelec, M. (1959) *BiulWojskowcj Akad. Tech. im J. Dabrosk* 8 120 and (1960) *C.A.* 54 18959
[4]   MacKittrick, D. S. & Bergsteinsson, I. (1938) *Ind. Eng. Chem. Analyt. Ed.* 10 630
[5]   Médard, L. (1951) *Mém. Poudres* 33 125
[6]   Campbell, A. W., Malin, M. E. & Holland, T. E. (1956) *J. Appl. Physics* 27 963
[7]   Bellinger, F., Friedman, H. B. *et al.* (1948) *Ind. Eng. Ch.* 40 1320
[8]   Ide, K. H., Haeuseler, E. & Swart, K. H. (1961) *Explosivstoffe* 9 195
[9]   Médard, L. (1957) *Mém. Poudres* 39 47
[10] Hass, H. B., Hodge, E. B. & Vanderbilt, B. M. (1936) *Ind. Eng. Chem.* 28 339
[11] Boileau, J. (1953) *Mém. Poudres* 35 supplementary volume (Thesis 1953)
[12] Ficheroulle, H. & Gay-Lussac, A. (1952) *Mém. Poudres* 34 55 & 121
[13] U.S. patent 2.486.773 granted to J. A. Wyler (1 November 1949)
[14] *Jahresbericht V* (Berlin 1925) *Chem. Tech. Reichsanstalt,* p. 101
[15] Médard, L. (1949) *Lab. C.S.E.*

[16] Schwob, R. (1950) *Mém. Poudres* **32** 153
[17] Wetterholm, A. (1963) *Tetrahedron* **19** supp. 1, p. 155
[18] Milone, M. (1933) *Gazz. Chimica ital.* **63** 453
[19] Noble, P. *et al.* (1963) *A.I.A.A. Journal* **1** 395
[20] Cheylan, E. (1950) *Mém. Poudres* **32** 417
[21] Jackson, K. E. (1934) *Chem. Rev.* **14** 251
[22] Hill, M. E. & Ross, D. L. (1969) *J. Chem. Eng. Data* **14** 410
[23] Boileau, J. & Runavot, Y. (1953) *Mém. Poudres* **35** 39
[24] Condit, P. C. & Haynor, R. L. (1949) *Ind. Eng. Chem.* **41** 1700
[25] Albright, L. F. & Hanson, C. (1969) *Loss Prev.* **3** 26
[26] Fritz, E. J. *ibid* p. 41
[27] Hunt, J. K. (1949) *Chem. Eng. News* **27** 2.504
[28] Médard, L. (a) (1952) *Mém. Poudres* **34** 99; (b) (1955) *Compt. Rend.* **241** 1036
[29] Cook, M. A. & Partridge, W. S. (1955) *J. phys. Chem.* **59** 673
[30] Price, D. *et al.* (1970) *Comb. and Flame* **14** 145
[31] Bateman, T. L., Small, F. H. & Snyder, G. E. (1974) *Loss Prev.* **8** 117
[32] Wöhler, L. & Wenzelberg, O. (1933) *Angew. Chemie* **46** 173
[33] *Jahresbericht VIII* (1929) of the C.T.R.
[34] Médard, L. (1952) *Mém. Poudres* **34** 397
[35] Calvet, E. (1941) *Ann. Fac. Sciences Marseille* [2] **15** 1
[36] Médard, L. (a) (1947) *Lab. C.S.E.*; (b) (1955) *Lab. C.S.E.*
[37] Sartorius, R. (1948) *Lab. C.S.E.*
[38] Munroe, C. (1922) *Ind. Eng. Chem.* **14** 552
[39] Dartnell, R. C. & Ventrone, T. A. (1971) *Loss Prev.* **5** 53
[40] Roig, F. (1951) *Mém. Poudres* **33** 159
[41] Médard, L. (1954) *Mém. Poudres* **36** 74
[42] Denton, W. I. *et al.* (1948) *Ind. Eng. Chem.* **40** 381
[43] Médard, L. (1939) *Mém. Art. franç.* **18** 277
[44] Médard, L. & Vidart, A. (1956) *Poudrerie de Bergerac*
[45] Ville, J. (1960) *Mém. Poudres* **52** 21
[46] Anon. (1953) *Chem. Eng. News* **31** 4915
[47] Bretherick, L. (1979) *Chem. in Britain* **15** 431
[48] Lyttle, D. A. (1949) *Chem. Eng. News* **27** 1473
[49] Quinchon, J. (1984) *Les Nitrocelluloses* (Vol II: *des Poudres, Propergols et explosifs*). Librairie Lavoisier, Paris

27

Ethylene compounds

27.1 GENERAL OBSERVATIONS

27.1.1 Overall view

Ethylene hydrocarbons (alkenes) have a heat of formation some 125 kJ/mol lower than that of the corresponding saturated acyclic hydrocarbons (alkanes). With alkadienes (diolefins) the difference depends on the position of the two double bonds in the molecule. It is lower than twice 125 kJ/mol for hydrocarbons with conjugated double bonds, such as 1,3-butadiene $CH_2 = CH - CH = CH_2$, and has a value of about 230 kJ. It rises to more than 250 kJ with the allene hydrocarbons, in which the two double bonds are carried by the same carbon atom (about 293 kJ), and it is close to 250 kJ in the case of the other alkadienes (Table 27.1).

The result is that, whereas alkanes are very stable substances up to temperatures of at least 600°C, ethylene hydrocarbons are liable to decompose more or less readily and sometimes even to explode.

On the other hand, because of their unsaturated nature they readily polymerise, either alone or with the participation of other substances (oxygen, nitrogen oxide, etc.), often forming explosive substances.

This chapter will study ethylene, propene, some of their compounds, and ethylene oxide. The latter compound is closely related to ethylene and has given rise to explosions. Propadiene is treated in 28.4.2.

27.1.2 Explosive ethylene gums of nitric oxide

It has been known for some fifty years that in ducts carrying coal gas or

other gases containing hydrocarbons formed by pyrolysis, deposits form
which have a consistency ranging from that of very viscous liquids to that
of fairly hard solid masses.   Their technical name is 'gum', although the
word resin would be more appropriate.   They are undesirable not only
because they form dusts or may hinder the working of parts such as meters
or valves, but also because some of them are explosive.   It has been found
that the latter always contain nitrogen (4 to 12%) and that they come from
complex reactions between nitrogen oxides (monoxide, sesquioxide, dioxide)
and ethylene compounds, both of which are present in the gases in question.

Table 27.1

Heat of formation of compounds with a double ethylene bond

Compound	Physical state	F_p (kJ/mol)
Ethylene	gas	− 52.5
Propene (propylene)	gas	− 20.5
1−butene	gas	− 0.8
2−*cis*−butene	gas	7
2−*cis*−butene	liq.	31
1,2−butadiene	gas	− 162
1,3−butadiene	gas	− 109
1,3−butadiene	liq.	− 88
Isoprene	liq.	49
Propadiene	gas	− 192
Vinylidene fluoride	gas	334
Trifluoroethylene	gas	496
Tetrafluoroethylene	gas	640
Octafluorocyclobutane	gas	1 473
1,3−cyclopentadiene	gas	− 136
1,3−cyclohexadiene	gas	− 109
Ethylene oxide	gas	52
Ethylene oxide	liq.	77
Propylene oxide	gas	93
Propylene oxide	liq.	121
Vinyl oxide	gas	13

The gases in coke ovens contain these nitrogen oxides, but they are also to be found in the mixture called 'conversion gas'† which, like the coke oven gases, generally provides hydrogen used to synthesise ammonia. The hydrogen is cleaned of any remaining carbon monoxide in an apparatus called a 'liquid nitrogen wash unit' which works at a very low temperature (about - 190°C). Explosive gums of nitrogen oxides are deposited in the apparatus in the tube stacks of heat exchangers at very low temperatures (between + 15°C and - 185°C). They sometimes explode, causing considerable damage and killing people in the vicinity.

In spite of a large body of research, we still know very little about the mechanism governing the formation of these gums of nitrogen oxide, but it seems that a small amount of oxygen must be present in the gases. Compounds with double conjugated bonds, such as cyclopentadiene and buta-diene which are present in the gases in question, seem to be especially prone to react with nitrogen oxides. Even as little as 0.01 mg/m³ of these oxides gives rise to the formation of gums. In ammonia plants various measures can be used to reduce considerably the nitrogen oxide content of the gases before they are fed into the nitrogen washer, but the low amounts of oxides which get into the apparatus still form gums, so the gases must be continually analysed to see how much oxide (counted as NO) there is in the system. As soon as the oxide level reaches some 2 or 3 kg, the apparatus is switched off, and after deriming the gums are destroyed by circulating a 10% solution of sodium methanol through the exchangers.

It is also possible to reduce the quantity of explosive gums which are deposited in the exchangers by placing filters with a packing of activated carbon ahead of the gas inlet to the various exchangers at places in the circuits where the temperature lies in the range - 80 to - 120°C. Such filters, which stop almost 90% of ethylene hydrocarbons and nitrogen monoxide, must be fitted in pairs containing a working filter with the gases to be purified travelling through it in an upward direction and a filter being regenerated by a downward-travelling current of warm nitrogen, after which a portion of the activated carbon containing gums which cannot be eliminated is removed from the bottom of the filter and replaced by an equal amount of new activated carbon in the top. After each process of regeneration the extracted carbon is analysed to see how much nitrogen it has retained in the form of gum so that it can be included in the oxide balance.

It is clearly no easy matter to measure concentrations of nitrogen oxide of the order of 10^{-8}. The method used always involves changing all the oxides into NO_2 which can then be measured colorimetrically by a Griess reagent. Pierrain [9] describes an apparatus which makes use of nascent oxygen to perform the oxidation. It is not necessary to use a method which gives an absolutely correct value; it is sufficient simply for the value given to be in a constant ratio (such as 0.8) to the true content, as long as it is always the same method which is used to establish the nitrogen oxide balance. A method for measuring these oxides has now been developed which uses the chemiluminescence in the reaction of nitrogen monoxide with

---

† Conversion gas is what results from the equilibrium reaction (conversion) $CO + H_2O \rightleftarrows CO_2 + H_2$ by which is removed most of the CO present in the gas mixture which comes from cracking heavy hydrocarbons (fuel oil) in the presence of oxygen and water vapour.

ozone.

27.2 ETHYLENE

27.2.1 General properties of ethylene

Ethylene, the first term in the alkene series, is a gas which liquefies
readily. Its critical temperature and pressure are 9.2°C and 50.3 bars.
The orthobaric density of the liquid at 0°C is 0.345 kg/dm³. It has a
faint ethereal odour and although it is not very toxic, it does have a
slight anaesthetising effect. The main danger is that it ignites easily,
having a flammability range which is more than twice that of its saturated
isologue, ethane.

27.2.2 The decomposition of ethylene by heat

When heated, ethylene decomposes at relatively low temperatures to give
mainly carbon, methane, and hydrogen. At high temperatures aromatic
hydrocarbons are also formed, probably with acetylene as an intermediate
stage. In a study of the pyrolysis of diluted ethylene by argon at 1000 to
1100°C in a shock tube, Skinner and Sokolowski [2] did indeed find that the
first phase in the decomposition of C_2H_4 is into $C_2H_2 + H_2$.

In a study of the thermal decomposition of ethylene at 625°C Burk and
his associates [1] found butenes and butadiene among the initial products
(after decomposition of just 2.5% of the substance)

$$2C_2H_4 \rightarrow C_4H_8$$
$$2C_2H_4 \rightarrow H_2 + C_4H_6,$$

and then other products (propene, liquid hydrocarbons, etc.) resulting from
the action of C_4H_8 or C_4H_6 on C_2H_4, but very few gaseous alkanes. Other
authors have confirmed these results: at a pressure of 10 bars ethylene
diluted in argon gives acetylene, hydrogen, and free carbon at high
temperatures.

The thermal decomposition of compressed ethylene may give rise to the
propagation of a deflagration flame in steel tubes when decomposition is
initiated at one end. Lawrence and Cook [3], using a very strong primer (5
g of thermite), observed propagation in ethylene at 50 bars and 120°C, but
at 160 bars the gas has only to be at 30°C. When it is primed with 1 g of
gun-cotton, the decomposition propagates in ethylene at 70 bars at ordinary
temperature [4]. The energy needed to initiate deflagration decreases as
the temperature rises or if the ethylene contains a gas such as oxygen or
acetylene.

Adding a diluent gas in sufficient quantity makes propagation by
deflagration impossible. According to Lawrence and Scott 10% of nitrogen
prevents propagation even at 160 bars.

The two weakly exothermic reactions

$$C_2H_4 \rightarrow 2C + 2H_2 \tag{I}$$
$$C_2H_4 \rightarrow C + CH_4 \tag{II}$$

have theoretical explosion temperatures at constant volume of 1010 and

1800°K respectively. The pressure rise factors are 6.2 and 6.9. They do not seem to be capable of detonating; propagation has been observed only in the form of a deflagration.

27.2.3 Polymerisation of ethylene

At pressures of several thousand bars and a temperature of around 100°C ethylene polymerises into polyethylene. It can also be polymerised by the action of various catalysts. Some substances, such as anhydrous aluminium chloride, are so active that they trigger explosive polymerisation with simultaneous decomposition into gas products (hydrogen, etc.). Solvents can be used to control this reaction.

27.2.4 Flammability limits of ethylene in air and oxygen

A. *At ordinary pressure* – The flammability limits of ethylene in air are 2.7 and 35% and in oxygen 2.9 and 80% at ordinary temperature (about 20°C). At 100°C the lower limits fall to 2.3 and 2.4% respectively, the upper limits being about 37 and 82. In air close to the upper limit of between 30 and 35% ethylene, the flame is not very luminous.

The effects of adding nitrogen or carbon dioxide to ethylene have been studied by Jones and Kennedy [5]. Their results for carbon dioxide are shown on the diagram† in Fig. 27.1. From their results for nitrogen it can be deduced that the limiting safe mixture of ethylene and nitrogen contains 6.2% ethylene.

B. *At a pressure higher than ordinary pressure* – A rise of a few bars leads to a considerable change in the upper limit. Concordant measurements by Hashiguchi *et al.* [7] and Lamprecht [6] establish this limit at

Pressure in bars		1	5	10	20
	in air	35	47	56	64
Upper limit					
	in oxygen	80	87	90	92

These considerable changes in the upper limit are due in part to the fact that pressure favours reaction (II) given above at the expense of reaction (I). Similarly, in mixtures of carbon dioxide, air, and ethylene, Scott *et al.* [4] have found that the curve for the upper limit shifts towards higher ethylene contents when the pressure rises. The lower limit is practically unaffected (Fig. 27.1).

An important experimental study enabled Hashiguchi *et al.* to determine the flammability diagram of ethylene–oxygen–nitrogen mixtures up to an initial pressure of 50 bars and up to 100°C (Fig. 27.2). At the same time,

---

† On this diagram the upper limit in air is 28.6 because the ethylene used by Jones and Kennedy was an industrial gas which contained 2.7% saturated hydrocarbons and only 96.6% ethylene.

they measured the pressure in the explosion of mixtures close to the limits. In particular in mixtures containing 85 to 91% ethylene with 15 to 9% oxygen at an initial pressure of 5 to 30 bars, the pressure rise factor ranges from 5.4 to 8.5 since, as the initial pressure rises, more methane is formed (exothermically), so raising the explosion temperature. At low initial pressures (2 to 4 bars) mixtures close to the upper limit still contain, after explosion, a fair percentage (3 to 7%) of undecomposed ethylene as well as a small amount of oxygen.

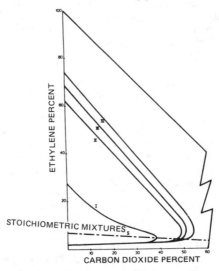

Fig. 27.1 - Flammability diagram of air-carbon dioxide-ethylene mixtures at atmospheric pressure (curve I) (after Kennedy and Jones [5]) and at 18 bars (curve II), 35.5 bars (curve III), and 70 bars (curve IV) with ignition by 0.01 g of gun-cotton (after Scott *et al.* [4]).

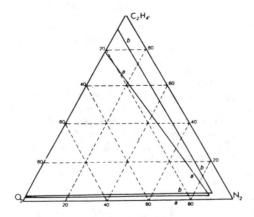

Fig. 27.2 - Flammability diagram of ethylene-oxygen-nitrogen mixtures at ordinary temperature for a pressure of 1 bar (curve a) and 50 bars (curve b), after Hashiguchi.

27.2.5 Consequences for safety

1° It can be seen that ethylene, particularly when compressed, must be classified with the unwanted explosives. When manufacturing polyethylene at high pressure, care must be taken to exclude even the smallest traces of every substance, such as oxygen, which is liable to cause it to explode.

2° In reactions in which ethylene is the raw material it is vital to know the limits at high temperatures and at pressures of a few bars, as can be seen from the following example: in the manufacture of ethylene oxide by direct oxidation of ethylene by oxygen in the air over a catalyst at 12 to 25 bars and around 325°C, the gases, after separating out the ethylene oxide which has formed, are recycled with fresh air and ethylene, taking care to ensure that there is less than 6% oxygen and maintaining the C_2H_4 content between 4 and 6%. These gases contain surplus nitrogen as well as carbon dioxide from the fraction of ethylene which has burnt.

3° Using ethylene to ripen fruit. Ethylene[†] is the most widely used gas for artificially ripening bananas and other fruit. Using the substance in ripening warehouses was formerly the cause of explosions when the ethylene content in air was allowed to exceed the lower flammability limit in the presence of a source of ignition (often a cigarette). This kind of accident becomes impossible when the ethylene is fed to the air as an ethylene-nitrogen mixture containing 5.5% ethylene since that degree of concentration is lower than the safety limit (see 9.2.4).

27.3 ETHYLENE OXIDE

27.3.1 General properties of ethylene oxide

Ethylene oxide, or oxirane, which is the simplest of the oxygen-containing heterocyclic compounds has the formula

$$H_2C \longrightarrow CH_2$$
$$\diagdown \diagup$$
$$O$$

Its boiling point is 10.7°C and it is therefore stored in the liquid state at relatively low pressure (2 bars at around 25°C) in metal containers, but it is easily used in the gas state. Table 27.2 lists some of its physical properties. It mixes completely with water as well as with many organic solvents, but at ordinary temperatures carbon dioxide and ethylene oxide are only partly miscible.

Ethylene oxide is highly reactive and its use has caused a number of explosions. Meigs [15] mentions explosions with mercaptans and with an alcohol. In 1959, a serious explosion was caused by ethylene oxide flowing rapidly back into aqueous hydrazine. In April 1962, a similar large explosion was caused by ammonia accidentally flowing back into a storage tank holding ethylene oxide. Other cases have also been reported. It is

---

† Acetylene and other gases have the same effect but ethylene is virtually the only gas used now. It takes only 0.002% of the gas in air to produce the desired effect on fruit.

known to react very violently with chlorine, and it reacts readily with
compounds containing labile hydrogen (alcohols, amines, organic and
inorganic acids, etc.).

Table 27.2

Properties of ethylene oxide

Normal boiling point	10.5°C
Critical temperature	196°C
Critical pressure	72 bars
Vapour pressure at 20°C	1.47 bars
Vapour pressure at 50°C	3.9 bars
Specific gravity of the liquid at 20°C	0.875 kg/dm³
Specific gravity of the liquid at 50°C	0.843 kg/dm³
Heat of vaporisation at 10.5°C	25.5 kJ/mol
Specific heat of the vapour at 25°C	48.2 J/mol.°C

Its highly toxic effect on insects, discovered in 1928, has led to its
use as a gaseous insecticide to protect fruit trees and cereals. It was
then found to be a powerful bactericide and is now used in hospitals as a
general disinfectant and to make viruses inactive. Finally, it is also an
important intermediate product in the basic organic chemistry industry (in
the manufacture of glycol and many compounds).
     It is only moderately toxic on people: its vapours have an irritant
effect on the eyes and the respiratory tract.

27.3.2   The isomerisation and polymerisation of ethylene oxide

When maintained at a temperature between 300 and 400°C, ethylene oxide
vapour gradually isomerises into acetaldehyde. This reaction, which is
exothermic (releasing 113 kJ/mol), is catalysed by alumina, in which case
it takes place at around 200°C. The effect of this isomerisation is to
reduce considerably the ignition temperature of the vapour, which is 455 to
460°C for ethylene oxide alone but only 300 to 350°C for ethylene oxide
containing 10 to 20% acetaldehyde and 204°C for the latter on its own [30].
     At around 100°C and above liquid ethylene oxide polymerises, releasing
between 2100 and 2500 kJ/kg depending on the degree of polymerisation
reached. The products formed are mainly polyethylene glycols in whitish
plastic masses. Polymerisation may occur at ordinary temperature and even
at around − 50°C under the effect of anhydrous aluminium chloride or
stannic chloride, in which case the reaction is very rapid and violent
enough for it to be explosive in a closed vessel. Ferric chloride also
causes polymerisation but the effect is less violent. This polymerisation
is a non-homogeneous reaction in which the walls of the container or any

solid bodies in suspension play an important part. Adsorbent earths act in
the same way and in some cases the action leads to ignition of the ethylene
oxide vapour.

After a number of accidental explosions of cylinders containing 100 kg
of ethylene oxide, Gupta [18] carried out experiments which showed that the
walls must be completely free of bases and chlorides in order to prevent
dangerous polymerisations.

It is rare for polymerisation to shatter steel cylinders containing 10
to 25 kg of ethylene oxide because the heat can easily dissipate, but the
contents are totally transformed into a solid mass containing no monomer.

Lead, zinc, and probably other metals can initiate the polymerisation
of ethylene oxide. The liquid polymerises somewhat less rapidly in a
nitrogen atmosphere than in air, whilst polymerisation occurs more rapidly
in contact with carbon dioxide than with air and ethylene carbonate $CO_3C_2H_4$
is formed at the same time [22].

27.3.3 Flammability limits of ethylene oxide in air

The limits of mixtures of ethylene oxide with air have been the subject of
various experimental studies. In 1930, Jones [28] found the values of 3
and 80 for the limits at atmospheric pressure in an *open* tube with upward
propagation. Subsequently, a more complete study by Burgoyne and Burden
[10] revealed the full complexity of the phenomena, which are represented
by the curves in Fig. 27.3.

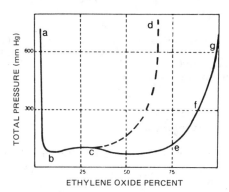

Fig. 27.3 – Flammability limits of air–ethylene oxide mixtures as a
function of pressure, after Burgoyne and Burden.

In a *closed* vertical tube with a diameter of 5 cm curve abcd for
downward propagation gives the limits as 3.6 and 68%, whilst for upward
propagation curve abefg gives the limits of 3.6 and 100% at atmospheric
pressure. In the area inside abcd the flames have the usual properties of
flames of mixtures of combustible vapours with air: they have little
luminosity with weak mixtures but are more luminous with rich mixtures;
between curves cd and cef the flame is pale blue; along fg the flame is
that of ethylene oxide without oxygen (see 27.3.4). At pressures below

0.093 bars, flames no longer propagate†.

It is also possible to observe cool flames at atmospheric pressure in the vapour of ethylene oxide raised to around 300°C.

There are thus two types of flame for mixtures with air: the first are similar to the flames of an ordinary combustible gas up to about 70 or 80% of ethylene oxide, whilst the second type, which occur at higher levels of richness and are observed only in upward propagation, are those in which self-decomposition reactions play a part alongside the reaction with oxygen. Of course, in all matters relating to safety, it should be assumed that the flammability range of ethylene oxide goes from 3 to 100%.

It is easy to ignite ethylene oxide mixed with air: the minimum ignition energy is about 0.1 millijoule for the stoichiometric mixture at atmospheric pressure and around 25°C.

According to the general rule, the addition of an inert gas reduces the flammability range. At atmospheric pressure mixtures with carbon dioxide containing less than 11.5 % C_2H_4O‡ are non-flammable in air [29]. At lower pressures mixtures with a higher ethylene content are non-flammable (for example, 25% if the pressure is 0.2 bars). Peters and Ganter [16] have plotted families of curves for pressures between 0.08 and 1.013 bars. Mixtures of ethylene oxide with chlorofluorohydrocarbons have also been proposed [17], such as the one which has the composition

	in mass	in gas volume
Ethylene oxide	12%	27.3%
Dichlorodifluoromethane	88%	72.7%

The analogous 16% (in mass) mixture, which does not propagate an upward flame in a tube with a diameter of 5 cm, gives rise to propagation in larger-sized containers. The limit is reached for 12.5% (in mass) of C_2H_4O at around 60°C. These mixtures are often used at temperatures between 40 and 60°C.

27.3.4 The explosion of ethylene oxide vapour

According to a study [26] on the effect of heat on the vapour of ethylene

---

† According to Peters and Ganter [16] ignition is still observed at 0.04 bars, but they were igniting the mixtures with an electric spark in a 50 cm³ pipette and it is therefore probable that they were not observing flames capable of long propagation. The same authors observed that the lower limit in a closed vessel falls from 3.7 (at 1.013 bars) to 2.8% at 0.7 bars and then rises when the pressure falls below 0.7 bars.

‡ Since CO_2 and C_2H_4O have very similar molar masses, the percentage volumes of gas mixtures are practically equal to the mass percentages. The gas from a cylinder containing a mixture of CO_2 and C_2H_4O does not have a constant composition during emptying. The 10% ethylene oxide mixture is used in the United States under the name of 'carboxide' and in Germany under the name of 'Cartox'.

oxide, the vapour (without air) ignites at around 570°C.   When the vapour
is heated to around 400°C it decomposes, giving gas products composed of 7%
H_2, 50% CO, 36% CH_4, and 7% C_2H_6.

If a source of thermal energy (an incandescent wire) is introduced into
ethylene oxide vapour, decomposition is initiated locally and propagates
with a deflagrating flame at pressures above a threshold of slightly less
than one bar.   The pale blue flame at this pressure was first observed by
Burden and Burgoyne (see 27.3.2).   Friedman and Burke [24], using a special
burner, were able to stabilise this flame and measure† its fundamental
speed:

at 25°C	2.7 m/s	(at 1.013 bars)
70°C	3.5 m/s	(at 1.013 bars)
70°C	4 cm/s	(at 0.8 bars)
70°C	4.8 cm/s	(at 0.2 bars).

The products of decomposition at 70°C have been analysed: 54% of ethylene
oxide decomposes according to reaction (I) and 46% according to reaction
(II)

$$C_2H_4O \rightarrow CH_4 + CO \tag{I}$$
$$C_2H_4O \rightarrow 1/2C_2H_4 + H_2 + CO. \tag{II}$$

The flame temperature is not very high (about 1190°K at a constant pressure
of 1.013 bars).

Burgoyne *et al.* [12] studied this deflagrating decomposition at 125°C
in experiments in a stainless steel bomb with a capacity of 2440 cm³.
Central ignition was achieved by incandescent heating to melting point
(1400°C) of a nichrome wire 18 mm long.   The study was carried out on pure
ethylene oxide vapour and on mixtures with nitrogen.

Recordings of pressure as a function of time (Fig. 27.4) have the usual
form.   The ratio p_1/p_2 of maximum pressure to initial pressure is about 2.2
when p_1 = 1.013 and reaches 6.4 for p_1 = 11 bars.   Beyond that it increases
only very slowly.   These explosions are relatively slow.   The low value of
p_2/p_1 when p_1 lies between 1 and 3 bars is due in part to the fact that the
decomposition of C_2H_4O is partial.   At p_1 = 3 bars among the products is 8%
of undecomposed ethylene oxide.   At high values of p_1 the pressure factor
intervenes, favouring reaction (I), which is strongly exothermic (135
kJ/mol at constant volume) at the expense of the weakly exothermic reaction
(II) (35.7 kJ/mol).

The percentage of nitrogen to be added to ethylene oxide to prevent it
from deflagrating rises from 35% when the ethylene oxide is at a partial
pressure of 1.013 bars to 67% at 8.6 bars.   Temperature has little effect
on the nitrogen content needed to prevent explosion: it remains the same
to within 2% from 89°C to 184°C.   These results are in good agreement with
later experiments by Grosze-Wortmann [31].   The result is that to make the
gas phase in an ethylene oxide container non-explosive at 50°C the partial
pressure of the nitrogen used as a diluent in this phase must be greater
than 3.5 bars (absolute pressure).

---

† Gerstein [25] found higher values for the speed and calculated as 1 J the
minimum ignition energy for the vapour not mixed with air.

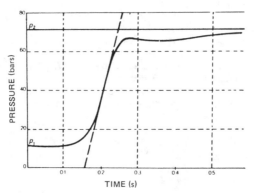

TIME (s)

Fig. 27.4 – Recording of pressure during an explosion of ethylene oxide at
125°C. p_1 = 10.7 bars; p_2 = 70.6 bars; $(dp/dt)_{max}$ = 665 bars/s.

The nature of the decomposition of ethylene oxide has led to the substance being considered for use as a monopropellant. Gordon and Greene
[11] experimented with it in a reaction chamber at 50 bars and analysed the
gases produced from a sample taken before expansion at the entry to the
nozzle. The composition of the gases is not very different from that found
by Heckert and Mach and the temperature is about 1070°C.
    At high pressures reaction (I) predominates. Taking it as the typical
reaction involved in the explosion of ethylene *vapour*, calculation gives
the following characteristics:

calorific value	3 050 kJ/kg
explosion temperature at constant volume	1 850°K
pressure rise factor	π = 12.5.

The minimum ignition energy is 1.5 J at 25°C at a pressure of 1 bar.
    Courtney and his associates [14] have studied the explosion of ethylene
oxide by an electric spark. The values they have published (Table 27.3)
clearly show the effect of temperature and pressure on flammability with a
spark. It will be noted in particular that at ordinary temperature (25°C)
and atmospheric pressure the minimum energy needed to produce an explosion
is some 10 000 times greater than the minimum ignition energy for mixtures
of the substance in air (see 10.3.7).

27.3.5 Decomposition of liquid ethylene oxide

In the pure state the liquid is stable at ordinary temperature. A charge
of 100 g of dynamite can be exploded in contact with a container filled
with liquid ethylene oxide without producing any other effect than a highly
localised decomposition [27]. In other tests [19] a pressure of 1400 bars
applied in 0.15 seconds to the liquid caused no decomposition.

27.3.6 Safety in the storage and use of ethylene oxide

Ethylene oxide should be stored in containers with extremely clean walls.

Before filling, new containers must be cleaned thoroughly, removing all traces of rust or saline deposits, and then dried out completely. All cylinders returned by customers must be emptied of any liquid residues they might still contain and their walls thoroughly cleaned. They should then be rinsed with pure ethylene oxide before refilling.

Table 27.3

Minimum ignition energy of ethylene oxide vapour,
after Courtney and his associates [14].

Pressure atm	Energy liberated by the condensers in joules		
	at 25°C	at 100°C	at 175°C
0.125	225	225	225
0.3	–	–	8
0.5	11	6	0.5
0.75	2	1.3	0.2
1	1.5	0.6	0..08
1.5	–	–	0.015
2.5	–	–	0.012
2.75	–	–	0.007
4	–	–	0.004

It is sometimes recommended to run water over tanks in summer to prevent their temperature from rising above 30°C. During transfer care should be taken to avoid sudden pressure shocks which would heat the vapour by adiabatic compression. It is best, in fact, to keep ethylene oxide under nitrogen pressure at all times, taking care to use pure, perfectly dry nitrogen for the purpose.

The question of whether copper alloys should be banned from equipment is a controversial one. It seems that these alloys were formerly avoided because ethylene oxide was thought to contain a small amount of acetylene and it was deemed necessary to avoid the possibility of copper acetylide being formed. However, the substance manufactured nowadays is free of acetylene. There are those who believe that copper and its alloys favour polymerisation, but the experience of some manufacturers shows that pure ethylene oxide can without inconvenience be stored in steel cylinders with brass valves.

Tanks, conduits, and metal equipment should be earthed to discharge static electricity.

Because ethylene oxide vapours ignite readily in air, all equipment and pumps for transferring the liquid should be located in well-ventilated workshops (preferably open on three sides). Electric equipment should be Class III.

In case of fire powdered sodium bicarbonate seems to be the most effective extinguishing agent. Water is also useful as a diluent in case of spillages: when the substance is diluted with 22 times its mass in water, it can no longer burn.

When ethylene oxide is made to react in a closed container, care should be taken to eliminate substances which catalyse polymerisation. Non-return valves and non-return traps should be placed along lines carrying any fluids which react strongly with ethylene oxide to allow strict control over mixing.

Finally, the toxicity of the vapours must be allowed for. Fortunately, concentrations in the atmosphere well below those which cause death in some thirty to sixty minutes have an irritant effect on the eyes which gives ample warning of danger.

27.4 OTHER ETHYLENE COMPOUNDS

27.4.1 Propene

Propene (or propylene), $CH_2 = CH - CH_3$, like ethylene, is liable to undergo explosive decomposition, but only when subjected to a very high pressure [8] of the order of several kilobars, in which case it will decompose into carbon, methane, and hydrogen. At lower pressures and at temperatures above 150°C it undergoes relatively slow polymerisation, but when aluminium chloride is present the polymerisation process may be explosive.

It has been noted that the upper flammability limit in air varies quite rapidly with pressure: from 11% at 1 bar it rises to 20% at 10 bars. The same phenomenon occurs in oxygen where the limit rises from 59% to 75% for the same variation in pressure. As with ethylene, mixtures which have a composition close to the upper limit engender high explosion pressures, because the fraction of gas which does not burn undergoes decomposition into hydrogen and methane.

27.4.2 1,3-butadiene

In its normal form 1,3-butadiene is composed almost entirely of the *trans* isomer. In industry it is called simply butadiene because 1,2-butadiene has no industrial use.

Butadiene is a gas with a critical temperature of 152°C. When heated at high pressure it could decompose explosively like ethylene, but it has never been seen to explode at atmospheric pressure in the complete absence of oxygen. The main danger with butadiene lies in the great facility with which it forms polymerised peroxides in the presence of oxygen (21.3.6). In the United States this reaction is called 'pop corn' because the polymer granules resemble lightly-roasted grains of corn. These peroxides are insoluble in non-polymerised hydrocarbon and are deposited on the bottom of containers as explosive solid masses which are extremely sensitive to impact or heat. Hendry and his associates [32] have made a detailed study of their stability. These peroxides can be destroyed by a concentrated solution of soda.

On various occasions, in particular in 1951 in Sarnia [23], explosions causing considerable damage have been caused by these polymerised peroxides in the manufacture of butadiene. There have been numerous studies of the conditions in which they are formed, of which the latest, by Hendry [21], has been used by manufacturers as a basis for establishing procedures which are safer than those previously followed but which cannot be guaranteed to remove all risk of accident. Amongst other measures, they include the adding of an inhibitor, usually p-t-butylcatechol, and constant supervision during storage of the percentage of this inhibitor still present in the butadiene.

When starting up production and during storage in tanks or cylinders, one essential safety measure is the complete elimination of oxygen present as air or iron oxide on the walls by flushing the apparatus with nitrogen, treating it with a diluted (5%) solution of sodium nitrite at 90°C, and finally rinsing it carefully with pure water.

There is a description in the literature [33] of an explosion caused by explosive gums (see 27.1.2) in June 1958 in Sarnia. The gums had formed because an inert gas that was not free of nitric oxide was used to compress a mixture containing 50% butadiene stored in a large tank during transfer to another workshop. An explosion in the gums triggered an explosion in the butadiene peroxide present in the tank.

27.4.3 Propylene oxide

$CH_2 - CH - CH_3$ Propylene oxide†, a liquid with a boiling point of 34.5°C,
  \ /   has flammability limits in air of 2 and 22%. Decomposition
   O   of its vapour into CO, CH_4, C_2H_6, free C, etc. releases,
depending on the equation used, between 27 and 31 kcal/mol, or 450 to 500 kcal/kg, which suggests that it is prone to deflagrate like ethylene oxide. However, Burgoyne and his associates [12] did not observe any decomposition when it was subjected at 125°C and 11.4 bars to the effect of the white-hot wire which ignites ethylene oxide. Explosive decomposition seems likely at higher temperatures which are conducive to the formation of methane.

27.4.4 Other ethylene compounds

Isoprene (2-methyl-1,3-butadiene), a liquid with a boiling point of 34.1°C, forms peroxides in air when it is not stabilised (by t-butylcatechol, for example). The polymer peroxide (which is not very highly polymerised) is soluble in isoprene. When the solution evaporates it leaves a residue of an explosive plastic substance which explodes under impact or above 100°C.

Cyclopentadiene (I) and *cyclohexadiene* (II) can be detonated by a fairly weak primer.

Vinylidene chloride $CH_2 = CCl_2$ (1,1-dichloroethylene) forms an explosive

---

† It has also been called 1,2-epoxy propane.

polymer peroxide in air when it is not stabilised.

Given its low heat of formation, *vinyl oxide* $O(CH = CH_2)_2$, a liquid with a boiling point of 28.3°C, is probably liable to undergo explosive decompositions when suitably primed. These decompositions have not been reported in the chemical literature.

BIBLIOGRAPHICAL REFERENCES

[1]   Burk, R. E., Baldwin, B. G. & Whitacre, C. H. (1937) *Ind. Eng. Chem.* 29 326

[2]   Skinner, G. & Sokolovski, E. M. (1960) *J. phys. Chem.* 64 1028

[3]   Lawrence, W. W. & Cook, S. E. (1967) *Loss Prevention Sympos. Houston,* p. 10

[4]   Scott, G., Kennedy, R. E., Spolan, I. & Zabetakis, M. (1965) *Bureau of Mines,* R.I. 6659

[5]   Jones, G. W. & Kennedy, R. E. (1930) *Anesthesia and Analgesia,* p. 6

[6]   Grewer, T. & Lamprecht, J. (1970) *Chemie-Ing. Techn.* 42 1234

[7]   Hashiguchi, Y. *et al.* (1966) *Kogyo Kagaku Zasshi,* p. 593

[8]   Russell, F. R. & Mueller, R. H. (1952) *Chem. Eng. News* 30 1239

[9]   Pierrain, J. (1953) *Chimie et Ind.* 70 189

[10] Burgoyne, J. H. & Burden, F. A. (1948) *Nature* (G.B.) 162 181

[11] Greene, S. A. & Gordon, L. J. (1957) *J. Am. Rocket Soc.* 27 798

[12] Burgoyne, J. H., Bett, K. E. & Muir, R. (1960) *Symp. Chem. Process Hazards* 1 30

[13] Burgoyne, J. H., Bett, K. E. & Lee, R. (1967) *Symp. Chem. Process Hazards* 3 1

[14] Courtney, W. G., Clark, W. J. & Slouch, C. M. (1962) *J. Am. Rocket Soc.* 32 1530

[15] Meigs, D. P. (1942) *Chem. Eng. News* 20 1318

[16] Peters, G. & Ganter, W. (1938) *Angew. Chem.* 51 29

[17] Haenni, E. O. & associates (1959) *Ind. Eng. Chem.* 51 685

[18] Gupta, A. K. (1949) *J. Soc. Ch. Ind.* 68 179

[19] Wilson, E. M. (1953) *J. Am. Rocket Soc.* 23 368

[20] Heckert, W. H. & Mack, E. M. (1929) *J. Am. Ch. Soc.* 51 2706

[21] Hendry, D. G. *et al.* (1968) *I.E.Ch. Prod. Res. and Devel.* 7 136

[22] Baize, T. H. (1961) *Ind. Eng. Chem.* 53 903

[23] Alexander, D. S. (1959) *Ind. Eng. Ch.* 51 733

[24] Friedman, R. & Burke, E. (1953) *J. Chem. Phys.* 21 165; (1955) *5th Sympos. Combust.,* p. 596

[25] Gerstein, M., McDonald, G. E. & Schalla, R. (1952) *4th Sympos. Combust.,* p. 375

[26] Peytral, E. (1926) *Bull. Soc. Chim.* 39 206

[27] Hess, L. G. & Tilton, V. V. (1950) *Ind. Eng. Chem.* 42 1251

[28] Jones, G. W. & Kennedy, R. E. (1930) *Ind. Eng. Chem.* 22 146

[29] Perraudin, R. (1970) personal communication

[30] Hilado, C. J. & Small, H. (1975) *J. Fire and Flammability* 6 44

[31] Grosze-Wortmann, H. (1970) *Chem. Ing. Technik* 42 85

[32] Hendry, D. G. *et al.* (1968) *I.E.Ch. Prod. Res. and Devel.* 7 145

[33] Alexander, D. S. & Finigan, C. M. (1959) *Petroleum Refiner* 38 285

[34] Robey, R. F. *et al.* (1944) *Ind. Eng. Chem.* 36 3

28

Acetylene

28.1 PROPERTIES OF ACETYLENE

28.1.1 History and importance of acetylene

The name for acetylene was suggested in 1860 by Berthelot who was the first to study the properties of this gas which had been discovered in 1836. But it was only after work by Moissan in 1890 had led to the manufacture of calcium carbide that acetylene assumed an industrial importance which has continued to grow. Since 1930 methods based on the pyrolyis of various hydrocarbons have been competing with the use of calcium carbide as a means of obtaining acetylene.

Acetylene was first used around 1892 for lighting (especially for car headlamps). This use is now restricted to certain lighthouses and buoys. It was the invention by Charles Picard in 1901 of the oxyacetylene blowpipe which led to the rapid development of the acetylene industry as a result of the many uses of the oxyacetylene flame in steel welding, scarfing, hard facing, surface cementation, and oxygen cutting. Finally, since the 1930s acetylene has become increasingly important as a starting point for synthesising many organic substances including, amongst others, butyne diol, vinyl chloride, and other vinyl compounds (acrylonitrile, etc.).

28.1.2 Physical and physiological properties of acetylene

In ordinary conditions acetylene is a colourless gas slightly less dense than air (d = 0.906 approximately). One litre of this gas has a mass of 1.17 g at 0°C and 760 mm Hg and 1.109 at 15°C and 760 mm Hg, which are the standard conditions of temperature and pressure in industry. Its critical temperature and pressure are 35.18°C and 61.9 bars. At pressures below 100 bars and temperatures below 250°C it is more compressible than an ideal gas. The molar specific heat at constant pressure, equal to 43.5 J/˙mol at 15°C and ordinary pressure, increases quite rapidly with temperature. The ratio of the two specific heats is 1.23 at 15°C but rises steadily to 1.32 and 1.45 at 10 and 20 atm respectively.

Acetylene is soluble in many liquids (see 28.3.2). Numerical values for its thermodynamic and various physical properties can be found in the work of Miller [1] which is a veritable 'bible' of acetylene and its industrial uses.

Like methane, ethylene, and many other gases, acetylene can form with ice a compound which has been called acetylene hydrate but which is really a clathrate. Villard [2], who discovered it, assigned to it the formula $C_2H_2.6H_2O$, but in reality it has a composition close to $C_2H_2.5.75H_2O$. It has the following dissociation pressures:

− 15.4°C	0°C	+ 7°C	+ 15°C
1 atm	5.75 atm	12 atm	33 atm,

which is why, at a pressure of a few bars below 0°C, moist acetylene may form plugs of solid hydrate which block conduits.

Pure acetylene in the diluted form has a fine and pleasant odour which can be detected at a concentration of 20 parts per million [3] and becomes very strong and unbearable at concentrations of 0.3 to 0.5%.

Acetylene is not very toxic and has anaesthetising properties which were once put to use. It stimulates rather than depresses the respiratory tract and inhaling an oxygen–acetylene mixture rapidly leads to anaesthesia with muscular relaxation. However, non–flammable anaesthetics have now taken its place.

The human organism can survive for at least thirty minutes in an atmosphere containing 100 mg/m³ of acetylene.

28.1.3 Chemical properties of acetylene

Since acetylene is an unsaturated hydrocarbon, it reacts readily with many substances, as described in the chemical literature. We shall mention here only those which may be explosive.

Chlorine gives 1,2–dichloroethylene and 1,1,2,2–tetrachloroethane when added to acetylene in the presence of a catalyst in strictly controlled conditions, but it may also decompose explosively, especially if a small amount of oxygen is present or if the gas is exposed to bright light:

$$C_2H_2 + Cl_2 \rightarrow 2C + 2HCl.$$

An accidental reaction of this kind occurred in Marl in 1948 in a plant manufacturing tetrachloroethane, causing the acetylene to burn in the pipes distributing it to the workshop.

Since the formation of acetylene is very strongly endothermic (Table 28.1), the compound is thermodynamically unstable at all but very high temperatures. It can undergo decompositions which give substances which are less exothermic or endothermic, and carbon, hydrogen, and saturated hydrocarbons. Very many products are formed from the effect of heat on acetylene, their nature varying with temperature and pressure, and the

Table 28.1

Heats of formation of acetylene compounds and propadiene
(in the gaseous state unless otherwise indicated)

Name (in the 1965 organic nomenclature)	Formula	Synonym (or former name)	Heat of formation (at cst. pr.) (kJ/mol)
Acetylene	$HC \equiv CH$		-227
Propyne	$HC \equiv C - CH_3$	Methyl acetylene; allylene	-185
Propadiene	$CH_2 = C = CH_2$	Allene	-192
1-butyne	$HC \equiv C - CH_2 - CH_3$	Ethyl acetylene	-165
2-butyne	$CH_3 - C \equiv C - CH_3$	Dimethyl acetylene; crotonylene	-146
Butene-yne	$HC \equiv C - CH = CH_2$	Vinyl acetylene	-289 (a)
Butadiyne	$HC \equiv C - C \equiv CH$	Diacetylene	-452 (a)
1,5-hexadiyne	$HC \equiv C - CH_2 - CH_2 - C \equiv CH$	Bipropargyl	-416
1,5-hexadiene-3-yne	$CH_2 = CH - C \equiv C - CH = CH_2$	Divinyl acetylene	-355
3-chloropropyne (liq.)	$HC \equiv C - CH_2Cl$	Propargyl chloride	-132 (a)
3-bromopropyne (liq.)	$HC \equiv C - CH_2Br$	Propargyl bromide	-178 (a)

(a) Calculated values

presence of substances acting as catalysts.   There are two main types of decomposition: *polymerisation* and *dissociation* into the elements carbon and hydrogen.   The latter, which is easily initiated by an electric spark in compressed acetylene, is almost always explosive, whereas polymerisation may not be explosive because it is a reaction – or rather a complex set of reactions – which, per mole of initial acetylene, releases less heat and much less gas than dissociation, since some of the products created by the polymerisation of acetylene are solids with a very high molar mass.

The effect of heat alone (without electric excitation) has been the subject of many studies.   At temperatures below 500°C polymerisation is virtually the only reaction which takes place.   Beyond that temperature, polymerisation is accompanied by dissociation into simple products (carbon, hydrogen, and methane), and as the temperature rises this reaction becomes increasingly more frequent than polymerisation.

The kinetic stability of acetylene is quite remarkable.   Briner [4] heated acetylene to 220°C without observing decomposition at atmospheric pressure.   After three days of heating at 340°C only some 3% of the gas has been polymerised.   However, at very high pressure (300 bars) decomposition is more rapid and may be observed even at 100°C.   The reaction in question is a polymerisation into various hydrocarbons, amongst which, as Berthelot reported, are to be found benzene, styrene, and solid substances with a high molar mass.   Schläpfer and Brunner [5] have measured the percentage of acetylene which polymerises at 420°C as a function of time: it rises from 15% after 30 minutes to 71% after 300 minutes.

Experiments carried out by Bone and Coward in 1908 showed that, at 1000°C, polymerisation has become very weak and that the products of dissociation are simply carbon, hydrogen, and methane.   They found that acetylene can be placed in a container heated to 800°C without immediate deflagration.

In the presence of certain solids with a catalytic effect acetylene can decompose at much lower temperatures than those given above.   Thus, Moissan and Moureu [49] observed that when cold acetylene is passed over pyrophoric iron, nickel, or cobalt, the divided metals are raised to incandescence and the acetylene decomposes.   Minkoff and his associates [6] observed that when acetylene is heated in the presence of a kaolin substance or charcoal, polymerisation may take place at ordinary pressures at a temperature as low as 185°C.   Such catalytic activity may well be involved in some cases of internal heating in cylinders of dissolved acetylene (see 28.3.8.2).

Since polymerisation reactions are quite exothermic, if they occur in conditions such that the heat cannot be dissipated, they lead to a rise in temperature, so making it possible for C_2H_2 to decompose into its elements by explosive dissociation.

Acetylene can be polymerised by light into a yellowish solid, cuprene, of unknown composition.   Schläpfer and Stadler [27] obtained this polymer in 1926, together with a number of tar products, by polymerising acetylene in the presence of copper at around 220°C.   The substance has a very high molar mass and the stoichiometric ratio of C to H is higher than unity.

Various values, ranging from 300 to 600°C, are given in the literature for the temperature at which acetylene dissociates explosively.   Using the evacuated vessel method, which was a steel tube in this case,   Miller and Penny found that at pressures of between 3 and 25 atm the explosion takes place at 400–425°C.   However, in the presence of powdered substances of all kinds, rust, alumina, silica gel, kieselguhr, charcoal, etc. explosion takes place at 280–300°C.

28.1.4 Conditions for the propagation of an explosion in gaseous acetylene

The dissociation of acetylene is a strongly exothermic reaction. It even releases, per mole of gas, more heat than is released per mole of mixture by the combustion of the stoichiometric mixture of acetylene and air. The products of dissociation are raised to a high temperature and so form a flame which has a temperature not lower than that of the combustion of the mixture with air. This flame is highly luminous because of the presence of particles of solid carbon. It is capable of self-propagation either as a deflagration or a detonation.

The deflagration of acetylene is easily initiated by an electric spark or an incandescent metal filament. Both sensitivity to ignition and the fundamental flame speed depend to a very large degree on pressure. Early researchers (Maquenne in 1895 and Berthelot and Vieille in 1896) observed that at atmospheric pressure decomposition initiated at a point in the container does not spread, but that propagation does occur at pressures higher than 2 bars†. In reality, this critical value of ignition pressure, in other words the limit pressure considered in 4.7, depends to a large extent on the dimensions of the container, and Le Chatelier observed quite correctly in 1920: 'It is believed that at atmospheric pressure explosive decomposition cannot be transmitted in a mass of acetylene which is free of air, but that is certainly not true since in gasometers with a capacity of several cubic metres acetylene stored at atmospheric pressure may undergo a regime of spontaneous decomposition if that decomposition is initiated by a sufficiently voluminous flame.' This view was confirmed by the explosion in a German factory in 1943 of a very large-capacity gasometer containing acetylene at a gauge pressure of 0.02 bars when a bomb was dropped on it from an aeroplane. The damage extended over a very large area.

Indeed, Berthelot and Vieille [9] had already found in their 1896-7 research that the limit pressure depends on the container as well as the nature of the ignition source, since a primer of 0.1 g of mercury fulminate is more effective, in other words causes ignition at a lower pressure, than a platinum wire raised to white heat.

In 1925, German researchers found the following values for the pressure threshold above which they were able to explode acetylene:
- in a tubular container with a diameter of 4 cm   2.2 bars
- in 0.67 litre cylinder   1.8 bars
- in a 20 litre container   1.52 bars.

Dietz [10] later found that when acetylene is subjected to the effects of an incandescent platinum wire, explosion takes place in a 0.55 litre container between 1.4 and 1.68 bars, but it becomes possible at much lower pressures if the ignition source is very strong, as was demonstrated by the accident in Marl referred to above in which a deflagration was transmitted along pipes 50 cm in diameter containing acetylene at a pressure which was no higher than 1.04 bars. Following this accident, Ebert [11] showed, by experiments in a pipe 30 cm in diameter, that at a pressure of 1.4 bars an explosion cannot be triggered by melting a metal wire or even by a charge

---

† Until 1925 some authors believed that this was a gauge pressure, but Berthelot and Vieille only ever made measurements in absolute pressure. This explains certain discrepancies in the literature published between 1900 and 1930.

of 20 g of an explosive such as TNT, but that an explosion can be triggered
by a shock wave caused by the breaking of a plate of sheet metal under
pressure according to the shock tube mechanism (see 12.13).

Duff and his associates [12] were even able to explode acetylene at 0.8
bars, but such low-pressure explosions always need a large-size container
and ignition must involve the whole cross section.

The above applies to containers with one dimension not much greater
than the other two, but in *very long* tubes decomposition initiated locally
in the acetylene by a hot spot at one end does not produce a general rise
in pressure as it does in a compact container. Experiment shows that a
deflagration propagates only if the diameter of the tube exceeds a given
value which is higher as the gas pressure is lower. The same is true of
detonation. On this subject, Table 28.3, which is based on Fig. 3 in a
paper by Sargent [13], gives a number of values for acetylene at ordinary
temperature, although it is the order of magnitude rather than the precise
value that should be considered.

Table 28.2

Minimum pressures necessary for the propagation of a deflagration
in acetylene in very long tubes

Diameter (mm)	5	10	15	25	50
Minimum pressure (bars)	5.8	3.9	3.0	2.3	1.7

In the case of *dry* acetylene, the pressure threshold falls when the
initial temperature of the gas rises, and in a container with a capacity of
about one litre it falls to 1.33 bars at 100°C and 1.1 bar at 140°C. By
contrast, if the acetylene is saturated with water vapour, the values are
higher than with the dry gas:

1.7 bars at 50°C with 7.1% water vapour
1.4 bars at 80°C with 19.4% water vapour.

Explosions in moist acetylene are more powerful than in dry gas.

Table 28.3

Minimum pressures at which the decomposition of
acetylene-based mixtures can be initiated [14]

Minimum total pressure (bars)	Percentage of gas diluting the acetylene					
	CO_2	N_2	He	H_2	C_4H_{10}	C_3H_8
2	15	23	19	19	8	10
2.7	23	32	31	31	11	13
4.5	33	47	48	49	17	20
6.2	38	53	55	58	19	24
7.9	41	55	58	61	21	26

When acetylene is added to a gas with which it does not react, the critical decomposition pressure rises. Experiments conducted by Berthelot [9] gave approximately 4-7 and 10 bars for mixtures containing 50-67 and 75% hydrogen. Another work on this effect which deserves mention is that of Jones and his associates [14] who obtained the values in Table 28.3 in a container with a capacity of 638 cm³. Butane, a hydrocarbon with a high specific heat, is very effective in reducing the liability of acetylene to explode, a result which agrees with the statement made in 8.3.6 regarding inert gases.

28.1.5 Deflagration pressure and burning velocity of acetylene

In their experiments in a 50 cm³ metal bomb Berthelot and Vieille measured the following pressures (in bars):

initial pressure	2.18	3.5	5.86	11	20.7
final pressure	9.4	19	42	92	213

showing that the pressure ratio (π) increases from 4.3 to 10.3 when the initial pressure rises. Even when the latter is 11 bars, the ratio of 8.4 which then obtains shows that the explosion is only partial, with some of the acetylene remaining in the final mixture. The researchers found that after cooling the pressure in the container is very close to the initial pressure, from which they deduced that the chemical equation for the explosion is

$$C_2H_2 \rightarrow 2C + H_2, \qquad\qquad (28.2)$$

and for this reaction they calculated, on the basis of the numerical data available at the time,

$$T_2 = 2750°C \qquad\qquad \pi = 11.$$

Our present knowledge of chemical equilibria at a high temperature leads to a less simple decomposition equation than this, since the products of the explosion include monatomic hydrogen H alongside molecules of H_2 and a small quantity (about 5%) of acetylene. The percentage of these gases varies slightly with the initial pressure. Consequently, the explosion temperature must be between 2800 and 2900°C and the π factor between 10.6 and 11. The calculation is not entirely reliable because of the little known effect of free carbon. Sixteen explosion experiments by Miller and Penny [15] with an initial (absolute) pressure of 9 atm gave a mean value for the final pressure of 100.2 atm, the π factor thus being 11.1. Of course, during the cooling which follows the explosion shifts in equilibria cause dissociation of the C_2H_2 present at a high temperature. In addition, methane and a small quantity of ethylene are formed.

The value of 11 for the pressure rise factor π is the one used when calculating the maximum pressure likely to be created in practice in an apparatus in which acetylene is deflagrating.

As for the fundamental flame speed, the values published range from 0.1

m/s to several hundred metres per second, depending on the value of the initial pressure and even more so on the dimensions of the apparatus. From this point of view the deflagrating flame of acetylene alone behaves like that of mixtures of air with combustible gases (see 6.1.5).

At (gauge) pressures of 0.5 to 1 bar an acetylene deflagration can no longer propagate in tubes with a diameter of less than about 1 cm, whereas in the same conditions the flame of air–acetylene mixtures propagates in tubes ten times narrower. There is no reliable value for the minimum ignition energy of acetylene on its own, but it is of an order of magnitude some 1000 times greater than that of the balanced air–acetylene mixture.

28.1.6 The detonation of gaseous acetylene

Gaseous acetylene may detonate if suitably primed. The first measurements of detonation velocity made in 1898 by Berthelot and Le Chatelier [16] gave values of up to 1000 to 1600 m/s when the initial pressure rises from 5 to 30 bars, but since the gases were in a tube with a diameter of 6 mm, the phenomenon produced was not an ideal detonation (see 13.3.1), and, in addition, at initial pressures of less than 10 bars a deflagration probably preceded the detonation. However, the values thus obtained do confirm the considerable influence of the initial pressure on the evolution of the decomposition of acetylene initiated at a point. Somewhat more accurate measurements by Penny [17] in long metal tubes measuring 12.5 and 25 mm gave a detonation velocity of 1817 and 1870 m/s respectively, from which it can be deduced that the ideal detonation velocity is 1923 m/s. An *a priori* calculation of the latter is difficult given the nature of the carbon formed, which is not graphite, and that of several chemical species (CH molecules, etc.) found with hydrogen at the high temperature of the detonation. Manson [18], following the simple equation (28.2), calculated velocities increasing from 2070 to 2110 m/s when the initial pressure rises from 1 to 5 atm. The pressure in the Chapman–Jouguet plane would then be between 23.3 and 23.6 times the initial pressure. Similar values (2050 m/s and a factor of 21.6) were calculated by Penny, who took account of the dissociation of H_2 into $2H$ at high temperatures.

In 1936, Bone and his associates measured a detonation velocity of 2150 m/s in acetylene at atmospheric pressure, but since the primer was very strong, it was probably an overdriven detonation. Mention should also be made of Duff and his associates [12] who used a solid explosive to detonate acetylene at an (absolute) pressure of 0.8 bars in a tube 76 mm in diameter and 16 mm long, and measured a velocity of 1870 m/s.

The propagation of an acetylene explosion in tubes obeys laws similar to those which govern the explosion of mixtures of air and combustible gases. Thus, when a deflagration wave in acetylene advances along a tube, it may at a given moment turn into a detonation after travelling a certain predetonation distance (see 13.3.5). Sargent [13] has brought together everything that is known on the subject and turned the results into a graph showing the range in which predetonation distance is to be found as a function of initial pressure. For example, at 2 bars a detonation, which could occur only if the diameter of the tube is equal to at least 50 mm, begins after a predetonation distance of between 5 and 20 m, depending on the conditions (temperature, dimensions, etc.). The graph gives no more than an order of magnitude for predetonation distances. Only by methodical experimentation would it be possible to establish a cluster of curves for different diameters.

Values for predetonation distances which agree with those of Sargent (Table 28.4) were measured experimentally by Miller and Penny [15] in a tube 25 mm in diameter and 30 m long.

Table 28.4

Predetonation distance for acetylene [15] in tubes with a diameter of 25 mm

Initial pressure (abs. atm.)	3.5	3.8	5.0	20
Predetonation distance (m)	9	6.7	3.7	0.9 app.

Sargent's work has the merit of explaining by means of the cascading explosion mechanism (see 13.4.4) why, when a detonation in acetylene is reflected from the end of long tubes, very high pressures are created which may be more than 150 times the initial pressure, a fact which surprised researchers around 1930 but which can be readily understood from the curve in Fig. 28.1.

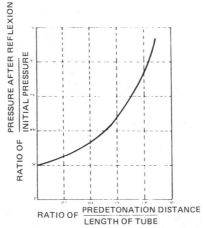

RATIO OF PRESSURE AFTER REFLEXION / INITIAL PRESSURE

RATIO OF PREDETONATION DISTANCE / LENGTH OF TUBE

Fig. 28.1 – Combined effects of a cascading explosion and the reflexion from the end of a closed tube in the explosion of acetylene. (The curve is for acetylene initially at ordinary temperature and 2.66 bars. It is not very different when the initial pressure rises to 6 bars).

The critical detonation diameter of acetylene alone, which varies with pressure, is not known with accuracy, but it is considerably greater than that of a balanced air–acetylene mixture at the same pressure.

28.1.7 Air–acetylene mixtures

The first measurements of the flammability limits of acetylene in air were made by Le Chatelier [19], who found values of 2.8 and 65 in large–diameter tubes. He also pointed out that no flame in an air-acetylene mixture can propagate in a 0.5 mm tube at ordinary pressure.

Subsequently, published values for the lower limit varied between 2.5 and 3.1. Experiments in eudiometers (2 cm in diameter) with standard spark ignition show that in 2.5 or 3% mixtures of C_2H_2 with air only a small amount of the combustible gas burns. Working with a 5 litre container and central ignition, Hölemann and Hasselmann [20] were able to establish the lower limit at 2.2%.

Since pure acetylene itself propagates a flame at a pressure slightly higher than atmospheric, the upper limit varies considerably with pressure. For practical purposes we can assume a value of 80% at ordinary pressure† and 100% at gauge pressures of 0.5 bars or more. However, as Pannetier and Laffitte [21] have shown, in experiments in tubes the upper limit varies considerably according to the state of the wall surface.

It is a fairly simple matter to calculate the detonation velocity in air-acetylene mixtures. For example, for the mixture $C_2H_2 + O_2 + 3.76N_2$ Manson [18] calculated a value of 2020 m/s, which agrees well with Breton's measured value of 2015 m/s [22]. The pressure in the Chapman-Jouguet plane is 22 bars.

According to Bresquer et al. [23], the pressure below which mixtures of air and acetylene can no longer be detonated is about 0.4 bars, whilst at atmospheric pressure the limits of detonability are 6.5 and 15%.

Using the Manson-Ferrié technique, Freiwald and Ude [24] photographed a centrally-ignited detonation in a sphere with a diameter of 1.7 m. A 12.5% acetylene mixture detonates at a velocity of 1920 m/s. The photographs also show the centripetal wave caused by reflexion against the wall of the balloon when the explosive centrifugal wave hits it.

Air-acetylene mixtures are very easy to ignite. For the stoichiometric mixture the minimum ignition energy with a spark is 0.02 millijoules at ordinary pressure and temperature. The ignition temperature found in the operating mode used by the Bureau of Mines is 305 to 310°C.

28.1.8 Oxygen-acetylene mixtures

The flammability limits of acetylene in a mixture with oxygen are about 2.5 and 95%, but if, as with air-acetylene mixtures, we accept the possibility of strong ignition, then the upper limit must be taken as 100%.

Whereas the properties of detonation temperature and pressure in an air-acetylene mixture are quite similar to those of acetylene alone‡, the equivalent values for oxygen-acetylene mixtures are much higher. T_2 exceeds 4000°K, the pressure in the Chapman-Jouguet plane is some 50 times higher than the initial pressure, and the velocity is of the order of 3000 m/s. Indeed, accidental explosions of oxyacetylene mixtures in pipes supplying welding equipment are extremely violent.

Measurements by Litchfield [25] suggest that the detonability limits (see 13.3.10) of oxyacetylene mixtures at atmospheric pressure are 9 and

---

† Given strong ignition and a large surface area (see 28.1.4), the upper limit is 100% at ordinary pressure.
‡ It must not be forgotten, however, that it is much easier to initiate a detonation in these mixtures than in pure acetylene.

68% for spherical detonation with a high-energy ignition spark of 490 joules, whereas Breton gives a lower limit of 3.5% for propagation in a tube. The discrepancy between this value and Litchfield's is surprising even though the propagation mode was different, being spherical in the first case and linear in the second.

28.1.9 The liquid and solid states of acetylene

Acetylene can be liquefied as easily as carbon dioxide. The saturation vapour pressure at 0°C is 26.7 bars, the liquid having a specific gravity of 0.46 g/cm³. The triple point occurs at − 80.6°C and 961 mm of mercury (1.28 bars). Thus, solid acetylene, which is a low-density substance resembling paraffin wax, sublimes without melting at atmospheric pressure. Conversely, the expansion of liquid acetylene at atmospheric pressure gives a solid. When ignited in the open air, it burns quite slowly with a smoky flame.

When acetylene was used for lighting, it seemed quite natural not to prepare it at the point of use but rather to store it in the liquid state in pressurised containers, as was already the practice in 1895 with other gases (SO_2, NH_3, etc.). The first manufacturers thought they were dealing with a liquid no more dangerous than other commonly-used liquefied gases. Thus, Claude [26] was able to raise a platinum wire to white heat in liquid acetylene at about − 80°C without an explosion occurring. Consequently, in 1896 it was authorised to store liquid acetylene under pressure in metal containers which had first been subjected to a hydraulic test at 250 bars. However, the industrial liquefaction of acetylene did not become widespread because serious accidents were reported from the outset, whilst experiments by Berthelot and Vieille [9] showed that liquid acetylene can be easily exploded in a closed vessel at ordinary temperature, creating a pressure of more than 5 kilobars in a container charged at a rate of 360 g per litre.

An experimental study of the explosive properties of liquid acetylene has been published by Mayes and Yallop [27]. When fired in the ballistic mortar, it has a power of 118 (picric acid being 100). In the British friction test (see 15.2.2) its sensitivity is found to be comparable to that of picric acid, whilst in the drop-weight test its insensitivity coefficient (see 15.2.5.3) is 500 (picric acid being 100). The detonation velocity has been measured at 1480 m/s at 32°C and 2290 m/s at − 79°C, varying with the density of the liquid, as might be expected. Particularly interesting results have been obtained for the transmission of the gas-phase explosion in the liquid phase in a vertical metal tube 25 mm in diameter: when the pressure is at least 3.5 bars, a detonation initiated in the gas is transmitted to the liquid, whereas at lower pressures, in other words at temperatures below − 63°C, the form of ignition used caused only a fairly slow deflagration in the gas which ignited a deflagration in the liquid which propagated at a velocity of about 0.4 cm/s.

Experiments by Breck [28] found that the minimum ignition energy for liquid acetylene at − 30°C was several times that for the gas at the same pressure, from which it can be concluded that decomposition must begin in the vapour bubble produced by the spark before being transmitted to the liquid.

Liquid acetylene is no longer used in the pure state, but a liquid acetylene-ethylene mixture is manufactured with a molar concentration of 25% acetylene (23.6% by weight) which is transported and stored at low temperature. At - 75°C its vapour pressure is less than 3 bars, the partial pressure of acetylene being no higher than 1 bar. This liquid does not propagate decomposition when a 100 joule spark is ignited in it, and it is therefore sufficiently insensitive for practical handling. When it is vaporised in a vacuum-insulated evaporator, it gives a gas mixture which can be used in various welding operations.

The explosive properties of solid acetylene were the subject of an experimental study by Rimarski and Metz [29]. It proved to be fairly insensitive to impact and friction and, when ignited in the standard way in the lead block, it gives an expansion of 410 cm³ per decagramme, a value which agrees well with its calorific value (about 1900 kcal/kg) and its gas volume at N.T.P. (860 dm³/kg). Its detonation velocity has been found to be 2400 m/s in a cylinder in which the substance is housed at a density of 0.5 g/cm³.

Solid acetylene can thus be manipulated quite safely, which explains why patents were taken out for the transport of acetylene in the form of compressed blocks similar to blocks of dry ice. However, the idea was never followed up in practice because of the dangers posed by an atmosphere containing gaseous acetylene in proximity to the permanently sublimating solid substance.

28.2   ACETYLENE MADE FROM CALCIUM CARBIDE

28.2.1   Calcium carbide

The process of reacting calcium carbide with water is still widely used in industry to manufacture acetylene. This carbide, as X-ray studies of its structure have shown, is a true acetylide, so the decomposition with water follows the equation

$$CaC_2 + 2H_2O \rightarrow C_2H_2 + Ca(OH)_2. \tag{28.3}$$

One kilogramme of pure carbide would give 373 litres of dry C_2H_2 (measured at 20°C and 760 mm of mercury) or 395 litres of gas saturated with water vapour in the same conditions of temperature and pressure. However, the industrial carbide rarely gives more than 330 litres per kg because its purity is rarely more than 80 to 82%.

Calcium carbide for use in the manufacture of acetylene must normally satisfy certain conditions defining the different types of carbide by their granulometry, the amount of acetylene produced, and the purity of the gas. In addition to the crushed carbide (which passes through the 80 mm sieve but not the 125 mm), there are three other grades of quality (50/80, 25/50, 15/25), and their output (at 20°C and 760 mm Hg) of gas saturated with water vapour must be at least 320 l/kg. The phosphine content, which is the most undesirable impurity present in acetylene, must be no higher than 0.05% by volume. Quality control conditions will also describe procedures for sampling and testing. (Translator's note: BS 642 governing carbide grade is now suspended. DIN standard 15-80 mm is applied.)

Calcium carbide is transported in 50 or 100 kg containers or drums which always contain a small amount of acetylene produced by the reaction of moisture present in the air with carbide. The level of C_2H_2 in this air-acetylene mixture may sometimes exceed the lower flammability limit (2.2%), which explains certain fortunately quite rare accidents which have happened during the handling of drums of carbide. There have been cases of internal explosions when a drum was being rolled along the ground. The mixture can be ignited by pieces of the carbide itself or of foreign bodies in the carbide rubbing against the walls. These explosions tear open the lid and can even go so far as to rip the shell apart, throwing out the contents, with the risk, if not of injuring, then at least of burning the handler.

In factories making calcium carbide the product is stored still hot in drums which are closed immediately. It has been known for quite some time that in a climate in which the humidity in the air is lower than 20 g per m^3 an atmosphere cannot be created in the drum containing more than 2% acetylene. It would seem, therefore, that a barrel which explodes cannot have been waterproof and that during transport water or very humid air entered the barrel through a crack or through the drum 'breathing' during cooling. In any case, barrels should not be dropped or subjected to impact during handling, and the lid should be removed with care, using tools which are not likely to produce a spark (bronze chisels, in particular).

Calcium carbide is sometimes dispatched to users in large containers which, after emptying, should be purged with nitrogen to cleanse them of any air–acetylene atmosphere which is liable to explode during operations prior to refilling. It is also advisable to purge them again, if only with dry air, before actually refilling them.

28.2.2 Impurities in acetylene made from calcium carbide

Industrial calcium carbide rarely contains more than 82% pure carbide CaC_2. The impurities it contains come either from the raw materials used in its manufacture or from the material making up the electric furnace in which it was made. Lime, which is present in the carbide at levels of between 8 and 12%, is in the eutectic form with CaC_2 and as the molecular combination $CaC_2.CaO$. The industrial carbide contains, in addition to silica, alumina and small inclusions of coke, various impurities which are harmful because water causes them to release gases which contaminate the acetylene which is produced. These impurities not only have an unpleasant odour, but some of them also make the acetylene less stable. In addition, they cause a number of problems in some of the uses to which acetylene is put. These harmful impurities in calcium carbide are:

(a) Calcium sulphide CaS and aluminium sulphide Al_2S_3 which come from the sulphur present in coal (although some of the sulphur is eliminated during manufacture in the form of volatile compounds). These compounds are decomposed by water and may liberate a small amount of H_2S. However, in the limewater found in generators of the carbide-to-water type, H_2S is not released at ordinary temperatures and up to 70°C because the equilibrium

$$H_2S + OH^- \rightleftarrows H_2O + SH^- \tag{28.4}$$

is completely displaced to the right. Furthermore, Moissan has found that in the decomposition of carbide containing sulphur small quantities of organic compounds and vinyl sulphide and disulphide are formed.

(b) Calcium phosphide Ca_3P_2 and smaller quantities of calcium arsenide Ca_3As_2, which derive from the reduction by carbon of the phosphates and arsenates found in the limestone used to make the lime. Calcium phosphide Ca_3P_2 reacts with water by releasing phosphine PH_3, the impurity which gives raw acetylene its well-known smell of garlic. Similarly, calcium arsenide gives arsine. These two gases are not very soluble in limewater, and thus are given off as gases in the manufacture of acetylene.

(c) Calcium silicides which come from the reduction of silica by coal. The two main ones are calcium monosilicide CaSi, which is slowly hydrolysed in limewater and releases hydrogen and silanes (SiH_4, Si_2H_6), and calcium disilicide, which gives off only hydrogen when hydrolysed in a non-acid medium. When calcium carbide is attacked by water, these silicides do not decompose to any large extent and are found almost intact in the residual lime, which, if it is treated with a concentrated acid, will thus release silanes. Silicon is also present in calcium carbide in the form of silicon carbide SiC which is found completely intact in the residual lime.

(d) Calcium nitride Ca_3N_2, calcium cyanide $Ca(CN)_2$, and calcium cyanamide $CaCN_2$, which are derived from the nitrogen present in coal. The quantity of these impurities varies according to the process used. Moissan has found that the total quantity of nitrogen present in various industrial carbides varies between 0.02 and 0.31%.

It is the nitride Ca_3N_2 which gives ammonia when water acts on the industrial carbide. Calcium cyanamide is decomposed by cold or lukewarm water into dicyanodiamide and urea, but gives very little ammonia in the conditions of temperature and pressure found in acetylene generators.

Calcium cyanide is not decomposed by water and is found transformed into thiocyanate (sulphocyanide) in the residual lime in the manufacture of acetylene.

(e) In carbide furnaces ferrosilicon forms a dense molten mass which sinks to the bottom, which is why industrial calcium carbide frequently contains ferrosilicon in quite large lumps which have escaped magnetic sorting.

Vinyl sulphides are liable to polymerise exothermically and so initiate polymerisation and decomposition of the acetylene itself.

Impurities in the air-acetylene flame burn to give acid products (PO_4H_3, etc.) which used to encrust the cockscomb burner used for lighting. When an oxyacetylene flame is being used, the impurities present may raise the phosphine and sulphur content in the solder lines, thus lowering the quality of certain types of solder, in particular those made of aluminium alloys. The presence of silane may lead to a deposit of silica which, although very thin, lowers the quality of hard facing.

If cylinders of dissolved acetylene contain impurities, some of the phosphine remains in the solvent and some remains in the porous substance but it reduces the solubility of the gas and the porosity of the filling.

In organic synthesising processes most of the gaseous impurities in acetylene are poisons to the catalysts used and damage the quality of the synthesised substance.

The result of all this is that, since the early days of the industry, acetylene has had to be purified before use.

28.2.3 Acetylene generators

There are a number of quite different types of apparatus, or generator, for manufacturing acetylene from calcium carbide. Depending on the maximum pressure reached in the apparatus, they can be one of two types:
- generators which have a hydraulic seal to limit the gauge pressure to 0.1 bar,

– pressure generators, ranging from 0.1 to 1.5 bars.
These apparatuses will normally be required by regulation to conform to an
authorised type, and the regulations will also cover conditions of use,
maintenance, and installation in a workplace.
From the point of view of the working of these apparatuses, one can
distinguish between:
– *dry lime generators* which use barely one litre of water per kilogramme of
carbide, so that the lime is formed as a powder. Such generators generally
work at a temperature close to 100°C.
– *wet generators* which use 6 to 10 litres of water per kilogramme of
calcium carbide, in other words a large surplus of water in relation to the
amount which is involved in the reaction, which allows a limit to be set on
the heating caused by the considerable heat generated by the hydrolysis of
the carbide, which is about 189 kJ per kg of industrial carbide giving 300
litres of acetylene. Consequently, these apparatuses work at a temperature
which is generally between 60 and 85°C. The residual limewater retains
some of the gaseous impurities which are produced at the same time as the
acetylene. Wet generators themselves fall into different categories. Some
can be classified as *contact generators*, in which the production of gas is
regulated by the relative displacement of the mass of water and the mass of
carbide placed in a metal basket. From the administrative point of view,
these are pressure generators. By contrast, the so-called *carbide-to-water*
generators, in which the carbide is dropped into water, are almost always of
the type in which the pressure is less than 0.1 bars. In these apparatuses
the carbide is gradually fed into a large supply of water, and the process
can be automated with the carbide arriving along an Archimedes screw which
can be stopped or started depending on the volume of gas present at any
given time in the gasometer following on from it.
The water evacuated from these carbide-to-water generators holds lime
slurry in suspension and is channelled through drains to lime pits for
decantation. There have been cases of ignition and even small explosions
in these drains because the effluent pouring into them releases some of the
acetylene which it holds in solution, and this may, in spite of the
presence of large quantities of water vapour, produce an explosive mixture
of air and acetylene. There seem to be two main reasons why this mixture
ignites. On the one hand it may contain small pieces of hot carbide coated
in lime which lose this coating in the drain and come into contact with
gas, and on the other hand, although less frequently, there is a release of
spontaneously ignitible gases, phosphine and silane, which give the flames
a livid greenish colour. This happens when fairly impure calcium carbide
is used. The fact that only partially decomposed pieces of carbide are
evacuated can be explained by defective agitation in the generator.
Such explosions in evacuation drains carrying waste lime from the
generators can be avoided by not covering the drains with full slabs or
plates, in spite of the problems which are then caused by water vapour.
Any covering should be made of expanded metal or grills. Lime pits should
not be covered over for the same reason.
A generator of the carbide-to-water type should be fed with carbide
with the correct granulation for which the apparatus has been designed,
since the total time taken for a piece of carbide to decompose is roughly
proportional to its average size, being approximately 20 minutes for 5 cm
pieces and less than one minute for granules measuring between 2 and 4 mm,
whilst the rate of decomposition for carbide 'fines' can be very fast
indeed. One can readily imagine that the accidental introduction of

massive amounts of powdered carbide into a generator designed to treat 50/80 mm granules will produce such a rapid release of acetylene that a veritable internal explosion will occur, blowing off any parts attached to the casing, expelling all the water from the hydraulic seal and violently throwing very hot gases and carbide out of the apparatus. When these gases mix with the air in the workshop, they sometimes explode. It is therefore extremely important to feed a generator with carbide of the granule size indicated on the service plate fixed to the apparatus.

One type of accident which used to happen frequently in acetylene generator rooms was ignition in the hopper feeding the generator when calcium carbide was poured into it. This ignition sometimes caused an explosion in the carbide skip positioned above the hopper. In many cases these accidents were caused by the presence in the carbide of pieces of ferrosilicon or some foreign body made of steel. It should be noted that any acetylene in the hopper is not only hot but also very dry since it is in the presence of excess carbide. When pieces of ferrosilicon fall from a certain height onto a metal wall, sparks are created which are visible in the dark, although experiment has shown that in most cases these sparks do not have enough energy to ignite acetylene, which is fortunate since it is almost impossible to avoid the presence of ferrosilicon in calcium carbide.

The question has also been raised whether the impurities found in raw acetylene as it is produced in the generator do not make it spontaneously ignitible. Rimarski and Konchak [30] on the one hand and Schläpfer and Brunner [31] on the other have carried out experiments in a variety of different conditions which led them to the conclusion that for spontaneous ignition to be possible much higher percentages of impurities need to be present than are normally found in raw acetylene. However, it is by no means certain that these experiments faithfully reproduced the conditions prevailing during the formation of raw acetylene in a generator.

Whatever the cause of accidental ignition, it can be prevented by creating an inert atmosphere in both hopper and skip. The generator can be fitted with a device which ensures that whenever the cover is moved, it not only uncovers the entrance to the hopper but also lets in nitrogen (at a pressure of around 0.5 bars). The nitrogen must obviously be introduced at several points at suitable levels in order to drench the atmosphere in the hopper and skip very rapidly.

There have been cases of abnormal heating in a carbide-to-water generator, apparently as a result of a malfunction in the water supply or the stirring mechanism. Care must be taken not to open the apparatus too soon since it may contain pieces of white-hot calcium carbide coated in lime which have been calculated to have a temperature of 750°C and which will without fail explode an air-acetylene mixture on contact. Nitrogen must be fed into the apparatus and water circulated through it.

An acetylene generator must be operated, then, according to a whole set of rules which vary in detail from one apparatus to another.

When acetylene from a generator is used for welding without first being dissolved under pressure (see 28.3), it should not be possible for either the supporter of combustion (oxygen or air) with which it is mixed in the blowpipe or other apparatus, or for a flame (flashback), to return to the gas holder or generation chamber. For this purpose various safety devices are fitted between the generator and the point of use: a hydraulic valve, a submerged-valve interceptor, a dry interceptor, etc. A detailed description of these devices together with diagrams can be found in a brochure [52] published by the International Permanent Commission on Acetylene.

28.2.4 Purifying acetylene

Very many patents have been taken out for the purification of acetylene
obtained from calcium carbide.   They are almost all based on selective
oxidation of the impurities. Many of them have no practical value, either
because the procedure used gives totally insufficient purification, or
because it is difficult to apply if accidents are to be avoided. Thus, it
has been proposed to pass acetylene mixed with a small quantity of oxygen
over activated carbon, but the oxidation of PH_3 and other impurities over
charcoal readily causes the acetylene itself to react, sometimes to the
point of exploding. Active charcoal should only be used without oxygen and
only to complete the purification of acetylene after it has been treated
with one of the classic purifying agents when very pure acetylene is
needed.

It has been proposed to scrub raw acetylene with diluted sulphuric acid
(20–25%), but although this completely removes NH_3, it only very partially
removes PH_3, AsH_3, and sulphur compounds.

One method which was once in use and which is highly effective consists
in passing raw acetylene through bleaching powder, diluted if need be with
slaked lime, but the process sometimes gave rise to explosions which were
attributed either to the formation of explosive nitrogen chloride from the
ammonia present in the impure acetylene, or to the formation of explosive
dichloroacetylene.   Another similar purifying substance is a solution of
sodium hypochlorite.   To avoid the formation of explosive chlorinated
compounds of acetylene its pH level must be kept high, for example by
adding $NaHCO_3$ or Na_2CO_3.

The most commonly used methods nowadays fall into one of three types:
Treatment with a mixture of chromic and sulphuric acid.   Purification is
achieved by passing raw acetylene through a substance made of diatomite
(kieselguhr) which has absorbed an acid solution of sodium dichromate. The
substance comes in a variety of formulae, its quality depending to a large
degree on that of the diatomite used, which must have a low bulk density
(0.15 to 0.25) and contain only traces of carbonate and organic substances.
The end product has a fine orange–yellow colour and a bulk density of about
0.5. It should be used only with fairly dry acetylene, otherwise the heat
of fixation of the water by sulphuric acid raises the temperature enough to
initiate decomposition of the acetylene. When it is used up, the substance
has a green colour (salt of Cr^{3+}) and cannot be regenerated by oxygen from
the air, unlike Catalysol, which is discussed in the next paragraph.

Treatment with activated ferric chloride.   Work by Granjon [32] in
1910–12 led him to manufacture a substance with good purifying properties
and capable of being regenerated several times after use, thus making it
very economical. It is sold under the name of Catalysol. It is a solution
with a ferric chloride and ferric hydroxide base to which is added copper
sulphate, manganese salt, and mercury, and which is then absorbed by
kieselguhr. Phosphine is oxidised into phosphoric acid by the ferric ions,
which are reduced to the ferrous state. When acetylene which has been
passed over a bed of this purifying agent is found to contain 30 volumes of
PH_3 per million, the purifier must be replaced or regenerated by the action
of air which oxidises the ferrous ions. Prolonged use of this agent is
dangerous because it liberates mercury from mercury chloride (see 30.6.5).

Treatment with concentrated sulphuric acid.   Purification on beds of a
powdered purifying agent is convenient in smaller factories, but where
large quantities of acetylene are to be purified, it is now almost always

done with concentrated sulphuric acid (over 90%), which acts as follows:
(a) Phosphine is dissolved as phosphonium hydrogen sulphate PH_4SO_4H, which is then gradually oxidised into phosphoric acid together with water and sulphur dioxide. Arsine is similarly oxidised into arsenic acid.
(b) Hydrogen sulphide, vinyl acetylene, and divinyl acetylene are oxidised with the formation of sulphur dioxide.
(c) Ammonia is obviously retained in the sulphate state.

This action of sulphuric acid is capable of reducing impurities present in acetylene to minute quantities, but it loads it with sulphur dioxide (15 to 20 volumes per million). An apparatus for purifying acetylene with sulphuric acid contains a refrigerator, in which much of the moisture in the raw acetylene condenses and the gas is reduced to around $0°C$ or even less, followed by one (or two) towers in which the acetylene rises through Raschig rings or comparable elements (Pall rings, Berl saddles) over which concentrated sulphuric acid flows from jets in the top of the tower. This is followed by a tower in which the acetylene is washed with soda (in concentrations of between 5 and 10%) which is circulated by a pump in order to hold back sulphur dioxide and droplets of sulphuric acid carried along by the current.

Sulphuric acid used for purification must be acid made from sulphur, since acid made from pyrites or blende contains various impurities (arsenic or mercury compounds, etc.) which catalyse the decomposition of acetylene, producing a black tarry mass in the tower. The more concentrated the acid, the more complete is purification. Generally, in an apparatus working continuously, some of the used acid is eliminated at the foot of the tower and replaced by fresh acid to maintain concentration constant at the point of injection.

Care must be taken to ensure that as much as possible of the sulphur dioxide in the acetylene is eliminated in the soda tower, otherwise it would pass into the dryer filled with calcium chloride and react with it to form calcium sulphite as a fine dust and hydrogen chloride

$$CaCl_2 + SO_2 + H_2O \rightarrow 2HCl + CaSO_3. \qquad (28.5)$$

This hydrogen chloride may react with acetylene to form vinyl chloride, which is an undesirable impurity, and it may also cause the acetylene to decompose in the dryer.

Used sulphuric acid is sent either to lime pits or the factory sewer. If it contains enough phosphonium sulphate, heating the acid with water liberates phosphine, which normally ignites in air and burns rather like will-o'-the-wisps on the surface of the water.

28.2.5 Safety in the manufacture of dissolved acetylene from calcium carbide

There are two parts to a factory producing dissolved acetylene. The first contains all the equipment which comes before the compressors, where the acetylene is at a pressure only 5 to 25 millibars above atmospheric. In the second the acetylene is compressed and sent to cylinders in which it is dissolved in solvent. So the 'low-pressure' part contains the generators, a gasometer which acts as a regulating store, equipment to purify the raw acetylene, and finally the dryers, whilst the 'high-pressure' section contains the compressors, vessels in which the gas gives off any water and lubricants it may have carried along, and pipes taking the acetylene to the *charging racks* in other words horizontal pipes fitted with connectors to which the containers to be charged are attached by flexible pipes.

It is clear that if all these apparatuses are to be operated safely it is necessary to follow to the letter an important set of rules which cannot be given in detail here since they vary from one apparatus to the next, but the essential features can be summarised as follows:

1˙ *Rules for preventing the formation of an air-acetylene mixture* or for limiting the effects of an explosion of such a mixture should one form. The procedure for starting up the generators must include prior purging with nitrogen followed by acetylene. When it is shut down, the generator must either have a nitrogen atmosphere or be filled with water.

When starting up a factory again after a prolonged shutdown, the same purging with nitrogen and then acetylene must be followed, and the same applies also to an apparatus, such as a dryer or a purifier, which has had to be opened for maintenance or reloading.

Apart from manual generators with a very small production time, carbide is poured into the generator feed hopper with a current of nitrogen, and if the carbide is positioned over the generator in a skip or container, the latter must also have a nitrogen atmosphere.

The pressure on the acetylene in the circuit leading to the compressor must always be somewhat higher than atmospheric so that, if the apparatus is not air-tight, air is not sucked in together with acetylene. For this reason manostats (such as devices with membranes of an alloy of copper, zink, and nickel) are mounted on the compressor intake pipes to give off an audio alarm and shut down the compressor engine if the pressure falls below a value such as 5 millibars. The device is not mounted under the engine cover but in the open air so that any acetylene leak (and such leaks do occur) does not lead to the formation of an explosive gas mixture around an electric engine producing sparks.

The flexible pipes used to connect the cylinders to be filled to the racks are fitted at the free end (the cylinder end) with a non-return valve which prevents air from getting into the pipes when they are not hooked up to a cylinder.

2˙ *Rules for preventing acetylene from decomposing at high pressure* or for protecting the workforce in case of an explosion. The compression ratio (at each level of a compressor) is limited by release valves. When there are three stages, the (gauge) pressures are usually 2.5 bars at the first stage, 10 bars at the second, and a maximum of no more than 25 bars at the third. Efficient refrigerators are placed between each stage with alarms which sound if there is not enough cooling water. The compressor cylinders are well lubricated either with a classic lubricant or by segments made of graphite or teflon.

Dryers or equipment for separating out any oil left in the acetylene are installed behind strong concrete screens which allow the operatives to open and close the drain valves in safety, since experience has shown that acetylene can decompose during such operations. Operatives are not allowed to go behind these protective screens when the apparatus is under pressure, and before they are opened the gas circuit must first be purged with nitrogen.

The number of valves fitted to the high-pressure circuits are kept to a minimum since it is often when such valves are operated that acetylene begins to decompose. All valves must be operated slowly, and a valve should not be opened between a high- and a low-pressure section. When a batch of cylinders is full, the compressor must be turned off, the cylinder valves should be closed, any compressed gas left in the circuit between the compressor and the rack should be allowed to flow back to the gasometer, and finally the control valve to the rack should be closed.

Devices to halt an explosion are inserted on the one hand between the compressors and the dryers and oil separators and on the other along the pipes leading to the charging rack.

Many charging areas are fitted with a system which allows all the gas in the high-pressure circuit to be emptied very rapidly in case of fire and the compressor to be switched off at the same time. The most suitable device for this purpose contains pneumatic valves which are kept closed by the pressure (of several bars) of nitrogen in a circuit from which the nitrogen can be released into the air by operating pull handles placed at various points in the workshop. This kind of system is a 'fail-safe' apparatus since the acetylene in the circuit cannot be compressed if the nitrogen pressure falls.

3° *Rule for preventing acetylene from liquefying in cold weather.* The pressure at the exhaust in the final stage of the compressor must not exceed the following values as a function of ambient temperature:

$^\circ$C	− 20	− 10	0	+ 10 and above
bars (in gauge pressure)	10	15	20	25

A manostat on maximum switches off the compressor engine when the pressure reaches 24.5 bars.

28.2.6 Devices for halting acetylene explosions

In 1897, Claude and Picard designed a device for stopping the propagation of an explosion in a pipe carrying acetylene at pressures of up to 20 bars. It consisted of a tube filled with a calibrated granular substance, usually granite, which divides the gas into a multitude of small-bore channels with a tortuous path. These devices do not act in quite the same way as a flame arrester (see 6.5.4), since they contain small blocking components, the working of which is explained in a paper by Lagarde [33]. Such apparatuses work very well in standard installations, but they cannot be used on pipes in which the pressure is subjected to considerable and sudden variations since they may then lose particles of granite which are carried downstream.

In 1968, Air Liquide developed a device for halting explosions in which the active element is a cylindrical buffer made of compressed aluminium wool and having a diameter equal to that of the body of the apparatus. The diameter of the aluminium fibres, the way in which they are prepared, and the compactness of the cylindrical buffer have all been designed to ensure that, while working effectively to stop a detonation wave, they cause only a small pressure drop, about 0.8 bars, in the gas during normal working. They function in the following way: the pressure of the explosive wave on the buffer pushes it towards the opposite mounting and compresses it at the same time; the gas circulates with more difficulty and much more slowly in this compacted mass, whilst at the same time the side of the buffer hit by the detonation front heats up considerably and the aluminium fibres are

sintered to a thickness of several millimetres.   Experiments have shown
that the decomposition wave from the acetylene does not travel beyond the
centre of the buffer, the downstream half of which at least is found to be
free of acetylene black.   This device, like the first, is symmetrical, so
both sides work when struck by a decomposition wave, and it works just as
well in static mode (zero flow in the pipe) as with the gas in motion.

A high-pressure explosion-stopping device used in Germany consists of a
cluster of twenty odd flexible steel tubes with thick walls and an internal
diameter less than 1 mm.   This type of device is used mainly on charging
racks where one is fitted between each cylinder and the rack.

In chemical plants acetylene sometimes has to be transported between
workshops at a pressure of a few bars or, even more frequently, at low
pressure (between 0.03 and 0.06 working bars) but in high volume, and the
pipes, which are sometimes very long, may have a diameter of over 0.6 m.
In such cases, there are two types of device for halting explosions:
(a) When the diameter is no greater than 0.2 m, it is easy to install a
flame arrester made, as Echard [34] reports, of a cluster of tubes with an
internal diameter of some 10 mm, which is less than the flame quenching
diameter for pure acetylene at about atmospheric pressure.
(b) On large-diameter pipes it is possible to fit towers filled with
Raschig rings which may be either dry or wetted with water or a suitable
organic liquid.   The inlet and outlet gas pipes must be perpendicular to
the axis of the tower and have a dead end covered with rupture disks (Fig.
28.2), as described by Schmidt [35].

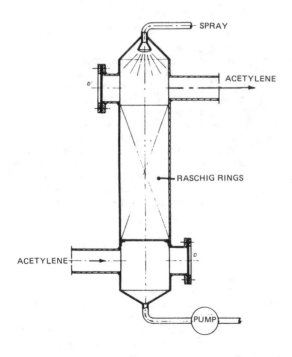

Fig. 28.2 - Tower for stopping an explosion in acetylene.

Ivanov and Kogarko [35] have published the results of tests carried out on such towers. For a given ring size the pressure of the acetylene must not exceed a certain value which rises as the rings become smaller, but in practice it is possible to use small rings without too much pressure loss. The two Russian authors add the following information: with metal rings of 15 mm and 26 mm the pressure of the acetylene must not exceed 2.5 and 2 atm respectively, the height of the tower being between 1.5 and 2 m. At higher pressures with these rings the dry tower does not stop an explosion even if the height is increased, but it will be stopped if water is run over the filling. Other details on Raschig ring towers for acetylene will be found in the paper by Miller and Penny [15]. The effectiveness of these towers, wet or dry, has been proven both by prior experimentation and accidental decompositions.

There are also explosion-stopping devices for high-volume, low-pressure (0 to 1 bars of gauge pressure) delivery, with no filling and in the form of long tubes with water or another liquid in the bottom. The design of one such device can be found in a paper by Sutherland [37].

In equipment used in the chemical industry it is necessary to fit an explosion-stopping device both before and after each apparatus carrying gaseous acetylene to protect it from decomposition waves coming from both upstream and downstream.

28.3 DISSOLVED ACETYLENE

28.3.1 The history of dissolved acetylene

Claude and Hess [38] had the idea in 1896 of using acetylene dissolved in acetone at a pressure of about 10 bars. In the following year Le Chatelier had the idea of storing this solution in containers filled with a porous mass, which had the advantage of making the gas come out in a steady stream. A small factory was opened in Malakoff near Paris in 1898 making 15 m^3 a day which were stored in cylinders containing acetone and a porous mass and which were intended for use in lighting trams.

It was soon realised that the porous mass had the added advantage of increasing safety, and it is now the high quality of this mass which guarantees the safety of transport and use of cylinders of acetylene.

After 1900, the new applications for acetylene brought about the rapid development of the industry of dissolved acetylene, which offers users acetylene in a convenient form without the need to run their own generator. The number of cylinders of dissolved acetylene in use in the U.K. currently falls not far short of one million.

28.3.2 Acetylene solvents

Acetylene is only moderately soluble in water (about 1 dm^3 of gas to 1 litre of water at ordinary pressure and temperature), but it is much more soluble in many organic liquids, acetone being the most notable since it is almost the only solvent used in the acetylene industry and has been tested for solubility many times since Berthelot. Earlier measurements made at pressures no higher than 12 bars had led to the conclusion that Henry's law is satisfied, in other words that the volume of gas dissolved per unit volume of solvent is proportional to pressure. Roughly speaking, at a

pressure of P atmospheres acetone at around 15°C dissolves $24P$ dm³ of gas
(measured at 15°C and 1 atm) per litre of solvent.

The results of precise measurements of solubility can be expressed
either in grammes of acetylene per kilogramme of solvent or by the Bunsen
coefficient, which is the ratio of the gas volume dissolved per unit of
volume of the solvent to the pressure, a ratio which has a constant value
only when Henry's law is obeyed: $S = v/P$, where v is the volume of gas at
0°C and 1 atm.

Table 28.5 gives results obtained by Lagarde and Cambon [39] expressed
as what the acetylene industry calls the 'coefficient of solubility by
volume': $S_V = 1.021S$, which is a kind of Bunsen coefficient in which the
volume of gas v is measured at 15°C and 1 atm (rather than 0°C and 1 atm.).
The same table also gives a certain coefficient of expansion d. This term
designates the quite large increase in volume which occurs when acetylene
is dissolved in a solvent; it is the ratio of the mass (in grammes) of
dissolved gas to the increase in volume (in cm³) of the solvent, and it
depends on the pressure. The higher this coefficient d, the better the
solvent. Expansion plays an important part in the filling of cylinders of
dissolved acetylene.

Table 28.5

Solubility of acetylene in acetone and dimethyl formamide at 15°C,
after Lagarde and Cambon [39]

Pressure (bars)	Acetone		Dimethyl formamide	
	Solubility coefficient S_V	Expansion coefficient d	Solubility coefficient S_V	Expansion coefficient d
1	28		40	
10	23.8	0.54	25.5	0.585
15	25.1	0.53	24.8	0.58
20	28.7	0.51	27	0.567
25	35	0.50	29.8	0.555

In the case of acetone Henry's law applies quite well at temperatures
above 50°C but quite badly at temperatures below 0°C. The coefficient S_V
at 15°C stills varies quite considerably with pressure: it reaches a
minimum at around 7 bars and is about 27 at a pressure of 18 bars, which
tends to be the pressure currently used when filling cylinders of dissolved
acetylene. The dissolution of acetylene in acetone is accompanied by a
considerable release of heat, some 160 calories per gramme of dissolved
acetylene.

Of the other solvents which have been studied, only dimethyl formamide
$H.CO.N(CH_3)_2$ is of any industrial interest. At between 15 and 20 bars its
coefficient S_V is close to that of acetone, but compared with the latter it
has the disadvantage of having a very high coefficient at low pressures (S_V
= 37 at 2 bars), which means that when all the dissolved gas in a cylinder
is drawn off, more of it is left behind in this solvent than in acetone.

28.3.3 Porous masses for use in cylinders of dissolved acetylene

Containers were initially filled with porous material to facilitate the
dissolution of compressed acetylene. Liquid is distributed throughout this
entire mass, where it then presents a very large surface in contact with
the gas phase, so allowing the gas to dissolve more readily. Conversely,
when the gas is removed from the cylinder, the porous mass allows the gas
to be released at a steadier rate and prevents the otherwise inevitable
drawing off of liquid droplets in the gas.

The porosity of a porous mass is the ratio of the volume of empty
spaces it contains to its total volume, and it is this empty space which is
available for absorbing the acetylene solution into the substance. The
first porous mass, made in 1897, consisted of porous ceramic bricks made by
a special technique and having a porosity of 75 to 80%. Fine channels were
bored into the mass to facilitate gas extraction. Because of their poor
mechanical resistance these porous bricks crumbled and were soon replaced
by other substances. The porous mass known in France as A.D.A.A., which is
still used in a large number of cylinders, was developed in 1901. It
consists of a special concrete made of pieces of charcoal and a cement made
from kieselguhr, asbestos, and zinc oxychloride. This concrete with water
added was put in the empty cylinder in the form of a paste and then heated
to eliminate the water, so forming *in situ* a mass which stuck to the wall
and which had a porosity of between 75 and 77%. Subsequently, a porosity
of 80% was achieved by using a more suitable charcoal. Its bulk density is
between 0.42 and 0.46 kg/l.

Of the porous masses for use with acetylene, this was the first
belonging to the type called coherent or monolithic, since subsequently
non-coherent porous masses were to be proposed which were either powdered
substances containing granules of charcoal, granulated substances (with a
pumice base, for example), or fibrous materials such as kapok, goat's hair,
or peat. Filling cylinders with these non-coherent substances is an easy
matter, but most of them suffer from the disadvantage that during use they
gradually settle and so no longer fill the cylinder completely, with the
result that they have gradually been abandoned in favour of the coherent
substances.

Around 1948, a coherent porous substance appeared which was described
as a 'sand-lime mass'. Chemically, it is a calcium silicate with a
composition comparable to that of wollastonite, $CaSiO_3$, mixed with asbestos
fibres, and it is formed *in situ* in the container by heating at around
200°C an aqueous slurry containing lime and siliceous sand. With suitable
raw materials and a suitable 'cooking' technique, the mass which is formed
in the cylinder has a low bulk density of 0.25 to 0.27 kg/dm³, a porosity
of 90 to 92%, and good mechanical resistance. During heating, the mass
shrinks slightly and does not adhere to the wall.

It is very important for safety reasons that all manufactured porous
masses should conform to the prototype which was subjected to tests in
order to be licensed (see 28.3.6). It is also important when the cylinders
are being filled to ensure that there are no cavities in the porous mass,
since any local small area in a gas cylinder filled with acetylene solution
not absorbed by the porous mass constitutes a zone in which decomposition
can begin more readily. Experiments with cylinders in which an empty space
of some 30 cm³ was deliberately created in the porous material have shown
that in the internal ignition test such cylinders explode after filling at
pressures below those at which a normal cylinder explodes.

28.3.4 The explosion of acetone solutions of acetylene

Berthelot and Vieille [9] found in 1897 that when the gas phase above an acetone solution of acetylene is ignited by melting a platinum wire at a pressure of up to 10 bars, the gas explosion is not transmitted to the liquid, whereas at 20 bars transmission does occur. The saturated solution at 10 bars was not exploded by any of the types of ignition tested.

In 1898, Vieille [40] and his associate Claude carried out experiments on the effect of the porous mass which was in use at that time, namely ceramic bricks pierced by fine channels. They placed small crushing manometers (blocks with piston and crushers†) in a highly resistant test vessel with a capacity of 3.5 litres with the following results:
(a) in the vessel with no absorbent material and filled with acetylene at a gauge pressure of 16 to 18 bars, the explosion ignited by a white–hot wire creates a gauge pressure of between 150 and 180 bars;
(b) in the vessel filled with dry porous bricks the explosion spreads to the edge of the bricks and into the distributing channels but penetrates only a few millimetres into the pores of the brick next to the ignition point; the pressure recorded is less than twice the initial pressure;
(c) in the vessel filled with bricks steeped in acetone and then saturated with acetylene at 16 bars, the pressure rise on ignition is very small, being a few bars at most;
(d) in a vessel filled as in (c) and then raised to 55°C, which increases the gauge pressure to 29 bars, the explosion propagates through every channel but hardly penetrates the pores of the bricks except for those next to the ignition point; the pressure recorded is 60 bars.

These experiments show the extent to which an explosion in a container is limited by using porous material to absorb an acetylene solution. Later researchers have confirmed this major effect of such materials.

Subsequently, in 1922, Picard and Lagarde [33] conducted experiments in a test bomb containing acetone saturated with pressurised acetylene, with the gas phase taking up some 15% of the total capacity. The gas was ignited by melting a tungsten wire with a diameter of 0.2 mm. The result was measured by the ratio of the total mass of carbon left by the explosion to the (calculated) mass of that from the gas phase. This ratio, which does not exceed 3.35 as long as the gauge pressure of saturation is no higher than 11 bars, rises to 11.6 at 12 bars and then rises rapidly to 37 at 15 bars. This shows that the explosion is not transmitted from the gas to the solution at pressures of up to 11 bars, but is transmitted to quite a large extent at higher pressures.

28.3.5 Regulations governing cylinders of dissolved acetylene

Where regulations exist, they will typically cover such things as the design of the cylinder and the material from which it is made, the porous mass, the percentage of acetone to acetylene, the free space allowed inside the cylinder, and the charging pressure.

---

† This small apparatus with crushers was once used to measure the pressure reached in firearms and is therefore well–suited for measuring the pressure created by an acetylene explosion.

Two different types of porous mass used in geometrically identical cylinders or one porous mass used in cylinders of different shape and dimensions will not have the same capacity to halt an explosion since the conditions for evacuating heat depend on these geometrical properties. As a result, the regulations in some countries refer to an approved cylinder with a shell made to the same design in the same factory using the same metal and built to the same diameter, and the filling should also be made in the same factory from the same porous mass. Such cylinders should also hold the same quantities of solvent and acetylene at the same pressure and contain the same amount of free space.

A cylinder will be licensed if it satisfies approved tests such as:
– a test to ensure that in a complete cylinder charged with acetylene with a given excess of gas, the gas phase does not disappear completely when the cylinder is heated to a given temperature;
– a test in which the cylinder is dropped in a vertical position from a given height before the next test is carried out;
– an internal ignition test to establish that the porous mass does, in fact, stop an explosion.

28.3.6 Internal ignition or backfire test

The internal ignition test is essential to ensure that the porous material really is capable of preventing an explosion in a cylinder charged to the permitted maximum with acetylene. Such tests were carried out as early as 1898, but only in special test containers with a capacity of 3.7 litres, which are quite different from commercial cylinders, and at a pressure of 12 bars, whereas the maximum permitted pressure was 10 bars. In 1925, the test was performed at 25 bars with an acetylene overload of 20%.

Nowadays the internal ignition test is performed on a cylinder which has the same dimensions, design, and filling as a commercial cylinder, with a special part attached in place of the valve. The explosion chamber, which has a capacity of 175 cm^3, is connected by a 4 mm channel to the inside of the cylinder, and ignition is obtained, as in the 1925 tests, by melting a tungsten wire 0.2 mm thick and 15 mm long at 110 volts. This high-energy mode of ignition ensures that the gas in the explosion chamber is detonated and that the detonation is transmitted to the upper section of the porous material. The temperature of the cylinder must be 35°C.

A cylinder passes the test if, in the twenty four hours following the explosion, the cylindrical section has not split or swollen.

28.3.7 The presence of oxygen in acetylene in a cylinder

The presence in acetylene of a small quantity of oxygen, even at a level such that the mixture is outside the flammability limits, may cause an explosion, or at the very least decomposition, in a cylinder of dissolved acetylene, which is why, in charging factories, care is taken to avoid anything which might introduce air into the gas circuit and to remove air from new cylinders before they are used. To this end, cylinders fitted with their porous material are charged with solvent and nitrogen at a pressure of some 500 p.s.i., left at rest for several hours, and then slowly emptied with the gas being bubbled through water, after which they can be filled with acetylene.

However, the main cause of oxygen getting into acetylene is either the incorrect use of a blowpipe or the fact of leaving the cylinder valve open after use for several days or even weeks. Consequently, in factories which manufacture dissolved acetylene a special treatment is applied to cylinders returned by the customer which are suspected of containing air, in other words:
- to cylinders returned with the valve open;
- to cylinders in which the residual pressure is lower than 0.3 bars and which have an acetone deficit which is set at 1.5 kg in the case of a 6 m³ gas cylinder.
This treatment consists in charging the cylinder on the rack at a pressure of 6 bars and then, after fitting it with a pressure-reducing valve, emptying it *slowly* through a steel tube leading to a bucket of water. This operation removes any air present. It is then possible to replace the missing amount of solvent and fill it in the normal way.
When the condition of the porous mass in the cylinder has to be tested, an operation which requires the cylinder valves to be removed, the work must be organised in such a way that no more than one hour elapses between removing and replacing the valve, which should be unscrewed for no longer than it takes to inspect the filling. If, when the valve has been un-screwed, the cylinder is found to be at reduced pressure, which may happen if it has been left in the cold, it must, after inspection, be suspected of containing air and treated as described above.

28.3.8 Accidents caused by cylinders of dissolved acetylene

28.3.8.1 Explosions caused by external heating

In addition to the possibility of a cylinder of dissolved acetylene being caught in a fire, it still happens all too frequently that a cylinder explodes or begins to leak, as a result of negligence that could have been easily avoided, and causes an explosion in the ambient atmosphere. The following accidents may be quoted in this respect:
- The case of a cylinder left in very cold weather next to a brazier. The valve began to leak and the resulting air-acetylene mixture exploded.
- The case of cylinders on a worksite struck by hot particles from work with a blowpipe carried out in the vicinity or on an upper level. It is usually the rubber outlet pipe on the cylinder which catches fire and leads to a gas leak.
- The bad habit acquired by some welders when their work is interrupted of hanging the feed pipes to the blowpipe over the top of the cylinder leaving the blowpipe dangling down with the flame licking against the side of the cylinder. The strong local heating thus produced burns a hole in the side leading to a leak of gas products from the decomposition of that part of the contents heated in this way. These gases ignite at once in the air. In such cases the cylinder does not usually explode, but it might do if the porous mass were defective.
Such accidents can be avoided by educating the workforce, which must be taught to keep acetylene cylinders well away from heat sources, not to coil rubber pipes around the bottom of the cylinder, and to make sure that any lighted blowpipe which is temporarily out of use is placed sufficiently far away from the cylinder. Cylinders not being used should be stored in a warehouse located well away from combustible materials.

28.3.8.2 Explosions caused by internal heating

It sometimes happens in acetylene-charging workshops that the gas in a cylinder which has just been filled decomposes, heating the cylinder and causing it to explode. This may happen when the full cylinder is lifted from the rack or only several hours later when the stored cylinder is not being handled in any way. Such accidents happen when, in an earlier use, a small amount of oxygen gets into a cylinder fitted with a defective porous mass, since a filling in good condition should 'stop an explosion'.

It also happens, although quite rarely, that spontaneous heating of the contents of a cylinder of acetylene is noticed only several weeks (or even two months) after filling, and without the cylinder having been used in the meantime. When the gas in a cylinder decomposes as slowly as this, the reaction consists mainly of polymerisation of the acetylene, and it produces only a moderate pressure rise, so the cylinder withstands the decomposition and the exothermic process inside it ultimately slows down. The pressure and temperature fall again without further incident.

If, during use and as a result of the wrong pressure being set in the gases supplying a blowlamp, a small amount of oxygen feeds back into a cylinder of acetylene, the decomposition described above may be initiated and develop more or less rapidly. Cases have been reported of cylinders containing no more than half their initial load exploding in a workshop without being touched twenty four hours after use.

The harmful effects of oxygen, already referred to in 28.1.3, are made even worse in cylinders of dissolved acetylene because of the pressure in the cylinder on the one hand, and adsorption phenomena on the other which lead to oxygen trapped in the pores being more condensed than the oxygen in the gas phase. Furthermore, it is known that in porous masses which contain charcoal the oxygen adsorbed by the latter gradually oxidises the carbon into CO_2. This strongly exothermic reaction heats the acetylene solution in the vicinity and, if a high enough temperature is reached, it initiates decompositions which may lead to the cylinder exploding. In this respect, sand-lime porous masses, which contain nothing which can be oxidised, seem to be the safest.

These cases of spontaneous internal heating have become extremely rare since careful attention has been paid to the high quality of the porous materials used and to the correct filling of cylinders. Nonetheless, it is useful to know what to do if it should occur: if a closed cylinder of dissolved acetylene is found to be spontaneously heating, absolutely no attempt should be made to reduce the pressure inside it by opening the valve, since to do so would be to set up a motion in the gas inside the cylinder which would have the effect of fuelling the decomposition and accelerating the reaction. If the alarming phenomenon of internal heating is detected in a cylinder in use with the valve open, or in a cylinder being filled on the charging rack, the valve must be closed if, and only if, it can be done quickly, and then the workforce must be evacuated from the area. A water hose can then be turned on the cylinder to cool it from a distance and from behind a wall. In no case should the cylinder be moved to another place since explosion might be imminent.

The case of a cylinder which, because of a leaking valve, produces a flame in the air is different. The valve can be closed as long as the person doing it protects himself with a powder fire extinguisher, but he must remain ready to act again, since the leaking gas frequently re-ignites on contact with the hot metal.

Explosions caused by spontaneous heating or flashback of the blowpipe flame into a cylinder of dissolved acetylene, which were not unusual up to around 1950, have since become very rare, both because of the high quality of the sand—lime porous mass and the care taken to keep oxygen out of containers before they are filled with acetylene.

28.3.8.3 The valve breaking

If clumsy or rough handling leads to a cylinder valve being subjected to a strong knock, it may break and release a heavy flow of acetylene. In almost all such cases the gas jet ignites in the air because of the strong static electric charge on the droplets of solvent carried along in the gas (see 10.3.5).

A cylinder of dissolved acetylene, more than any other cylinder of compressed gas, should not be subjected to an impact. If an acetylene cylinder with a defective porous mass is dropped on its end from a height of one metre or more during unloading from a vehicle, a reaction may be initiated inside it which will cause it to explode in a matter of a few seconds or minutes. This reaction would not have happened, even with a defective mass, if there had been no impact. Finally, it is perfectly obvious that violent shocks may create fissures or cracks in the monolithic porous material which may subsequently grow worse and create a small but dangerous empty space.

28.3.9 Safety devices on cylinders of dissolved acetylene

In some countries the regulations stipulate that cylinders of dissolved acetylene be fitted with fusible plugs. Thus, cylinders in North America must have four plugs, two on top and two on the bottom. However, such devices do not always give the expected degree of increased safety and have even been the cause of frequent accidents.

The temperature at which the alloy of a fusible plug melts (90°C, for example) is quite regular in a batch of such plugs, but unfortunately the mounting of such devices is subject to deterioration due to handling, and quite frequently such plugs give rise to a small leak of gas. If this gas is ignited, for example by a spark from a mill or a blowpipe, the initial flame is extremely small and may go unnoticed, especially if it is at the bottom of the cylinder, but it will gradually heat the neighbouring plug until it melts and releases a large amount of acetylene forming a large flame.

Another defect with these fusible plugs is that they do not always properly release gas from a cylinder which is the seat of an internal decomposition. The poor thermal conductivity of the porous material means that a decomposition initiated far from one end of the cylinder does not raise the temperature of the end to the point at which the plug melts, even though locally in the cylinder there is a very high temperature zone in which the acetylene is actively decomposing and creating a dangerous rise in pressure.

Uncertainty over the correct working of these fusible plugs and the accidents they cause by leaking have led to them being considered in Europe as having more disadvantages than advantages. They are statutory in the United States only because of the frequent fires which occur in countries where there are more wooden buildings than buildings made of stone, brick, or concrete.

28.3.10   Contamination of oxygen cylinders by acetylene

Incorrect use of an oxyacetylene blowpipe may result in acetylene getting into the oxygen pipe and from there into the oxygen cylinder itself. This was what happened in Ahlen (Westphalia) in July 1948 when the explosion of an oxygen cylinder containing an oxyacetylene mixture killed seven people and caused heavy damage. The experiments carried out after this accident are described by Bönig and Seiler [41] and commented upon by Sauerbrei and Engel [42]. The accident resulted from the simultaneous creation of the following abnormal conditions:
(a) At the welding site the pressure in the oxygen cylinder fell below the pressure set on the pressure-reducing valve fitted to it. This may have happened during a prolonged work stoppage if the cylinder had been leaking.
(b) The pressure of the acetylene being fed into the blowpipe was higher than the pressure in the oxygen cylinder, which may have happened if the acetylene reducing-valve had been set for too high a pressure or if there was some internal defect in gas-tightness.
(c) After the welder put out the blowlamp, he left open the taps on its gas intakes.

The correct use of a blowpipe as described in the manuals written by the various competent professional bodies (see reference [43] for example) should ensure that these conditions do not arise.

Unfortunately, however, oxygen cylinders returned to the factory by the customer are sometimes found to contain a small quantity of acetylene which can be detected from its smell by opening the valve. This is why no oxygen cylinder should be loaded onto the rack for re-filling until the internal pressure has been first reduced to atmospheric pressure and, if there is a suspicious odour, the cylinder has been put to one side for rinsing with a gas containing no impurity and removal of acetylene.

28.4   COMPOUNDS WITH AN ACETYLENE BOND

28.4.1   Acetylene hydrocarbons

Acetylene hydrocarbons have a C ≡ C group in the formula. Those with less than twelve carbon atoms are endothermic (Table 28.1), and of these the hydrocarbons with C_3, C_4, or C_5 may explode when they are under high enough pressure. The classic chemistry books distinguish between hydrocarbons which are commonly called 'true acetylene hydrocarbons', such as propyne and 1-butyne, which contain an end group − C ≡ CH, from those which, like 2-butyne, do not contain such a group and are usually called 'disubstituted acetylene hydrocarbons'. The first react readily with aqueous solutions of salts of copper, silver, or mercury to form precipitates comparable to the acetylides described in 30.6. Depending on the concentration or the pH, these precipitates are either simple substitution compounds of hydrocarbon or molar combinations of such a compound with the salt. These substances, like the acetylides, have explosive properties, but it should be noted that the simple silver compound of propyne, AgC ≡ C − CH_3, is a true explosive because it contains hydrogen, whereas the Ag_2C_2 acetylide is only a pseudo-explosive (see 30.6.2). Disubstituted acetylene hydrocarbons cannot form metal compounds.

Hydrocarbons which contain two or three triple bonds and those which contain one (or more) double bonds beside the triple bond are highly explosive.

Propyne (methyl acetylene) is a highly flammable gas (Table 8.5) with a critical temperature and pressure of 129°C and 56 bars. Its properties are similar to those of acetylene, and as with the latter, it can easily be made to decompose explosively, by igniting it with a hot spot such as a white-hot metal wire or a melting wire, into carbon, hydrogen, and methane with small quantities of other more complex hydrocarbons, provided it is compressed beyond a certain point. Fitzgerald [44], experimenting in a vertical tube 5 cm in diameter, found the following values for this lower limit pressure of explosion:

4.5 bars at 20°C
3.15 bars at 120°C.

However, the general observations on these limit pressures made in 8.1.4 and the more specific comments regarding acetylene in 28.1.4 should be kept in mind, as should Kuchta's finding [50] that these limit pressures vary somewhat with the dimensions of the test container when the diameter is raised from 2 to 10 cm. As with acetylene, adding an inert gas raises the limit pressure. For example, with a mixture containing 30% nitrogen and 70% propyne it rises to around 8 bars. Saturated hydrocarbons and even alkenes also increase the limit pressure. The flame quenching diameter of propyne alone would be 3 mm at 120°C.

Calculation by the method described in 5.5.5 gives a decomposition equation with the following properties:

$$C_3H_4 \rightarrow 0.05CH_4 + 1.9H_2 + 2.95C$$
$$T_V = 2080°K$$
$$\pi = 13.7.$$

Butadiyne ('diacetylene') is a gas (b.p. 9.5°C) which explodes under the action of a weak spark, even at a pressure of less than half a bar:

$$C_4H_2 \rightarrow 4C + H_2.$$

The explosion temperature and the pressure rise factor are close to those of acetylene, namely 2900°K and 11, but the flame quenching diameter of butadiyne alone, which is close to 1 mm at atmospheric pressure, is lower than that of acetylene.

According to a German patent [51], butadiyne heated in a closed vessel, in other words under pressure, explodes at around 60°C (the pressure then being about 6.5 bars), but a mixture of 70 moles % of butane and 30 moles % of C_4H_2 may be heated without danger to 220°C (the pressure rising to 160 bars).

1,3,5-hexatriyne is a highly explosive liquid (b.p. about 75°C) which is quite unstable since, even in a 20% solution in an inert solvent, it polymerises so exothermically that some of the hydrocarbon is decomposed into hydrogen and carbon.

Vinyl acetylene (see Table 28.1) is an explosive gas. Alone it behaves more or less like acetylene at pressures from 1 to 5 bars, which means that it becomes easier to explode as the pressure rises. Its copper compound, $CH_2 = CH - CH \equiv C - Cu$, which has a bright yellow colour, is extremely explosive. In a 5% mixture with air, the lower limit pressure of explosion is about 0.2 bars.

Divinyl acetylene is an explosive liquid, an isomer of benzene, but highly unstable since it readily polymerises to form solid products which are themselves explosive and highly sensitive to friction.

28.4.2 Propadiene

Propadiene $CH_2 = C = CH_2$ is not an acetylene hydrocarbon. However, it has properties similar to those of propyne, of which it is an isomer. It is the simplest of the allene compounds, which are hydrocarbons with a carbon atom carrying two double bonds. It is flammable (Table 8.5), and has a critical temperature and pressure of 120°C and 54 bars.

Like propyne, it decomposes explosively into carbon, hydrogen, and methane together with some other hydrocarbons when a hot spot (molten metal wire, etc.) is created inside it. It reacts even more readily than propyne since on the one hand when it explodes in a closed vessel, the rate of pressure rise for the same initial conditions is considerably greater than with propyne, and on the other hand it has a lower limit pressure which has been found to be 2.2 bars at ordinary temperature [45]. When 12% propene is added, this limit pressure rises to 4.2 bars. With prolonged heating propadiene begins to polymerise at 110°C, the main product formed being a solid substance.

According to tests by Forshey and his associates [45], in the liquid state at 10°C below its normal boiling point (- 36°C) in a steel tube with a diameter of 52 mm, strong initiation (160 g of tetryl) causes it to deflagrate but not detonate. The critical detonation diameter in these conditions must therefore be more than 5 cm.

28.4.3 Propyne- and propadiene-based mixtures

The steam cracking treatments to which the heavy hydrocarbons are subjected in oil refineries gives, amongst other fractions, a C_3 fraction which is rich in propane but also contains propene, propyne, and propadiene. The mixture of these last two isomer hydrocarbons, C_3H_4, could be used, like acetylene itself, to fuel blowpipes at least for some jobs such as brazing, hardening, and oxygen cutting. However, for practical reasons they are not distributed as a solution with acetone but as complex mixtures stored in the liquid state in gas cylinders. The components which are added to these propyne-propadiene mixtures are other hydrocarbons which play the same role as acetone with acetylene, namely that of a stabiliser. Tests to verify the stability of these mixtures consist, as with cylinders of dissolved acetylene, in causing an explosion in the gas phase and noting whether or not it causes an explosion in the liquid phase. At the B.A.M. the ignition source in this test is a platinum wire, whilst in France a 60 joule spark from a discharging capacitor is struck in the gas which has been raised to 70°C and 26 bars. That the explosion is not transmitted from the gas to the liquid is proven by the very low or nil value of the pressure rise in the test vessel, which does not need to have the dimensions of a commercial cylinder since no porous mass is used and the two phases are separated by a large, uninterrupted free surface.

The hydrocarbons added to propyne and propadiene to make mixtures which cannot be decomposed by a strong ignition source are C_3 and C_4 alkanes and alkenes. Clearly, a large number of mixtures can be created by varying the percentage of C_3H_4, alkane, and alkene, and some of them have acceptable levels of stability. Since the hydrogen content of the hydrocarbons in question varies quite considerably:

propane	18.18%
butane, isobutane	17.24%
propene, butene	14.28%
butadiene	11.11%
propyne, propadiene	10.00%,

the French regulations governing the transport of dangerous substances define the mixture in question as: 'Mixtures of propyne and propadiene with saturated or ethylene hydrocarbons whose elementary composition over all includes 12.5% hydrogen'. This definition covers mixtures which satisfy the internal ignition test.

As with any mixture of liquefied gases, the gas phase and the liquid phase, which are in equilibrium at a given temperature, do not have the same composition. Consequently, if, when the contents are drawn off, it is the gas phase which is removed first, the remaining liquid phase gradually becomes richer in the less volatile components, which means that, between the beginning and the end of drawing off, the composition of the gas taken out is not constant. Action can be taken to restrict the variation to a very large extent by an appropriate choice of the percentages of saturated hydrocarbons, propane, butane, and isobutane which make up the mixture. The mixture which is sold commercially is such that the substance which remains in the cylinder after prolonged and heavy drawing off still has the stability deemed necessary. It withstands ignition by the 60 joule spark described above.

Yoshimine and his associates [46], working with a 10 litre spherical bomb at 68°C and an ignition energy of 100 joules, were able to measure the flammability limits of such mixtures. They transferred their results to a triangular diagram, taking as their coordinates the following three sums:
(a) propyne + propadiene (C_3H_4)
(b) saturated C_3 and C_4 hydrocarbons $(C_3H_8 + C_4H_{10})$
(c) ethylene hydrocarbons (propylene, isobutene, butadiene).
Point T on Fig. 28.3, which reproduces their limit curve, corresponds to the most common composition of such mixtures sold in France.

28.4.4 Halogenated compounds of acetylene hydrocarbons

Monohalogenated compounds of acetylene are substances which explode readily in both the gaseous and liquefied state.

Chloroacetylene HC ≡ CCl is produced when either dichloroethylene or trichloroethylene is heated in the presence of a base:

$$C_2H_2Cl_2 + NaOH \rightarrow HC \equiv CCl + NaCl + H_2O.$$

It is also formed from the action of chlorinating agents on acetylene. It
is a gas (b.p. - 32°C) which ignites spontaneously in air.

The dihalogenated compounds of acetylene are also explosive.

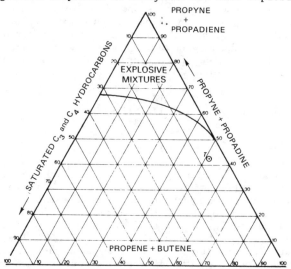

Fig. 28.3 - Yoshimine's diagram for propyne- and propadiene-based mixtures.

Dichloroacetylene ClC ≡ CCl is sensitive to impact and to heat, whilst
diiodoacetylene C_2I_2 explodes under the effect of friction or when it is
heated, with deflagration taking place depending on the purity of the
substance, between 85 and 125°C.

3-bromopropyne HC ≡ C - CH_2Br (propargyl bromide) is a liquid (b.p.
89°C) which often gave rise to violent decomposition during distillation at
atmospheric pressure. In 1964, it caused an accident [47] when heated to
185°C at 11 bars, and in 1966 the same substance exploded in a tanker pump
which had been switched on without the downstream valve being opened; the
entire contents of the tanker exploded, killing and injuring people.

These accidents led the American Bureau of Mines to make a study of the
dangers posed by the substance [45]. In the JANAF drop-weight test (see
15.2.5.5) it has a property H_{50} = 3.2 cm, which indicates high sensitivity.
It can be made to deflagrate by initiating it with a common explosive
charge (such as tetryl). In a bomb under the pressure of inert gas it has
a flame speed of more than 7 cm/s at a pressure of 60 bars. Most remarkable of all is its lower limit pressure of explosion in the vapour state:
it is 1.5 mm of mercury at 25°C. Of all other substances which have been
studied, only chlorine azide N_3Cl, which was measured by Paillard *et al.*
[48], gave a comparable value of 2 mm.

3-chloropropyne (propargyl chloride), an inflammable liquid (b.p.
57°C), has similar properties but is less sensitive to impact: more than
10 joules in the JANAF drop-weight test. Its lower limit pressure of
deflagration is 30 mm of mercury.

The two halogenated compounds above may be made less sensitive by
addition of a diluent. A mixture of 20% toluene and 80% propargyl bromide
withstands ignition even at a pressure of 40 bars.

28.4.5 Various acetylene compounds

3-propynol (propargyl alcohol) is a colourless flammable liquid (b.p. 115°C) which is liable to explode.

Butynediol $CH_2OH - C \equiv C - CH_2OH$ is a solid (m.p. 57.5°C) which may explode when heated. Cases of explosion of C_5 acetylene alcohol have also been reported. It seems wise to consider as more or less explosive any compound which has an acetylene bond.

Monovinyl acetylene $CH_2 = CH - C \equiv CH_3$ and divinyl acetylene $CH_2 = CH - C \equiv C - CH = CH_2$ very readily form explosive peroxides which have caused accidents.

BIBLIOGRAPHICAL REFERENCES

[1]   Miller, S. A. (1965) *Acetylene, its properties, manufacture and uses.* 2 vols., London
[2]   Villard, P. (1885) *Compt. Rend.* **120** 1262
[3]   Perraudin, R. (1962) Personal communication
[4]   Briner, E. & Wroczynski, A. (1911) *J. de Chimie Phys.* **9** 105
[5]   Schläpfer, P. & Brunner, M. (1930) *Helv. Ch. Acta* **13** 1125
[6]   Minkoff, G. J., Newitt, D. M. & Rutledge, P. (1957) *J. Appl. Chem.* **7** 406
[7]   Schläpfer, P. & Stadler, O. (1926) *Helv. Chim. Acta* **9** 185
[8]   Le Chatelier, H. (1920) *Le chauffage industriel.* 2nd ed. Paris, p. 251
[9]   Berthelot, M. & Vieille, P. (1896) *Compt. Rend.* **123** 523; (1897) **124** 988, 996, 1000
[10] Dietz, C. M. (1976) *Comb. and Flame* **26** 45
[11] Ebert, A. (1956) *Explosivstoffe* **11** 245
[12] Duff, R. E., Knight, H. T. & Wright, H. R. (1954) *J. Chem. Phys.* **22** 1618
[13] Sargent, H. B. (1957) *Chem. Eng.* **64** 250
[14] Jones, G. W., Kennedy, R. E. & Spolan, I. (1948) *Report 4196* of the Bureau of Mines
[15] Miller, S. A. & Penny, E. (1960) *Symp. Chem. Process Hazards, Manchester*, p. 87
[16] Berthelot, M. & Le Chatelier, H. (1899) *Compt. Rend.* **129** 427
[17] Penny, E. (1956) *Disc. Faraday Soc.*, p. 157
[18] Manson, N. (1947) *Propagation des détonations et des déflagrations dans les mélanges gazeux.* Edit. Institut Fr. du Pétrole, Paris, p. 103
[19] Le Chatelier, H. (1895) *Compt. Rend.* **121** 1144
[20] Hölemann, P. & Hasselmann, R. (1967) *Schweissen und Schneiden* **19** 325
[21] Pannetier, G. & Laffitte, P. (1945) *Compt. Rend.* **221** 469
[22] Breton, J. (1936) *Ann. Office Nat. Comb. Liq.* **11** 487
[23] Bresquer, R., Rivin, M. & Sokolil, A. (1937) *Acta Physicochim. U.S.S.R.* **7** 749
[24] Freiwald, H. & Ude, H. (1953) *Compt. Rend.* **236** 1741
[25] Litchfield, E. L., Hay, M. H. & Cohen, D. J. (1967) *Report 7061* of the Bureau of Mines
[26] Claude, G. (1899) *Compt. Rend.* **128** 303
[27] Mayes, H. A. & Yallop, H. J. (1965) *The Chemical Engineer*, p. 25
[28] Breck, D. W., Gallisdorfen, H. R. & Hamlen, R. P. (1962) *J. Chem.*

Eng. Data 7 281
[29]   Rimarski, W. & Metz, L. (1934) Autogene Metallbearb. 26 341
[30]   Rimarski, W. & Konschak, M. (1931) Autogene Metallbearb. 24 271
[31]   Schläpfer, P. & Brunner, M. (1938) Schweizer Arch. Angew. Wiss. und
        Technik, p. 42
[32]   Granjon, J. P. (1911 and 1912) French patents 434137 (12 September
        1911) and 440207 (15 February 1912)
[33]   Lagarde, H. (1952) Chimie et Ind. 67 303
[34]   Echard, J. (1949) Annales des Mines 138 15
[35]   Schmidt, H. (1971) I. Chem. E. Sympos., Manchester, p. 165
[36]   Ivanov, B. A. & Kogarko, S. M. (1964) Intern. Chem. Engin. 4 670
[37]   Sutherland, M. E. & Wegert, H. W. (1973) Chem. Eng. Prog. 69 48
[38]   Claude, G. & Hess (1896) French patent 257679 (30 June 1896)
[39]   Lagarde, H. & Cambon, J. (1955) Soudage et techniques connexes 9 7
[40]   Vieille, P. (1898) Rapport au Conseil d'Hygiène de la Seine, 11
        November 1898
[41]   Bönig & Seiler (1950) Werkstatt und Betrieb 83 145
[42]   Sauerbrei, E. & Engel, G. (1950) Schweissen und Schneiden 2 145
[43]   Institut de Soudure (Paris, 1975) Sécurité dans l'emploi des
        chalumeaux soudeurs et coupeurs
[44]   Fitzgerald, F. (1960) Nature (G.B.) 186 386
[45]   Forshey, D. R., Cooper, J. C., Martindill, G. H. & Kuchta, J. M.
        (1969) Fire Technol. 5 100
[46]   Yoshimine, M., Kern, W. G. & Belfit, R. W. (1967) J. Chem. Eng. Data
        12 399
[47]   Coffee, R. D. & Wheeler, J. J. (1967) Loss Prevention 1 6
[48]   Paillard, C., Moreau, R., Combourieu, J. & Laffitte, P. (1967) Compt.
        Rend. 264C 382
[49]   Moissan, H. & Moureu, C. (1896) Compt. Rend. 122 1240
[50]   Kuchta, J. M., Spolan, I. & Zabetakis, M. G. (1964) J. Chem. Eng.
        Data 9 467
[51]   German patent 860.212 (18 December 1952) granted to B.A.S.F.
[52]   Design and Operation of Acetylene Generators, pamphlet of the British
        Acetylene Association, London

29

Explosive nitrogen compounds

29.1 GENERAL OBSERVATIONS

Nitrogen is found, in forms other than that of the explosophores NO and NO_2 (Chapters 18 and 26), in many organic and inorganic explosive compounds. We shall examine them in the following order:
(a) Metal compounds of ammonia. The latter is not by itself explosive, but it forms metal substitution compounds which, for a monovalent metal M, have the formulae:

MNH_2 amides
M_2NH imides
M_3N nitrides,

some of which are explosive.
(b) Compounds containing the N − N bond are derived from hydrazine

$H_2N - NH_2$.

Compounds with the N = N bond include the azo and diazo compounds.
(d) The simplest of the compounds with a chain of three nitrogen atoms is hydrazoic acid N_3H. The N_3 group, substituted for hydrogen in organic compounds, gives azido compounds which are generally explosive. The metal salts of N_3H called azides are dealt with in Chapter 30. Nitrogen chains of four, five, or more nitrogen atoms almost always belong to explosive compounds.
(d) Compounds containing a halogen or sulphur bonded to nitrogen.
(e) Cyano compounds, in other words compounds containing a N ≡ C group.

Table 29.1
Heats of formation at constant pressure of various nitrogen compounds

Compound	Formula	Physical state	Heat of formation kJ/mol
Ammonia	NH_3	gas	45.8
Ammonia		diss.	81
Calcium nitride	Ca_3N_2	cr.	431
Barium nitride	Ba_3N_2	cr.	376
Silver nitride	Ag_3N	cr.	− 255
Sodium amide	$NaNH_2$	cr.	134
Hydrazine	$H_2N - NH_2$	liq.	− 51
Hydrazine		gas	− 95
Hydrazine		diss.	− 33
Hydrazine hydrate	$N_2H_4.H_2O$	liq.	243
Methylhydrazine	$CH_3 - NH - NH_2$	liq.	− 53
Methylhydrazine		gas	− 93
Symdimethylhydrazine	$CH_3 - NH - NH - CH_3$	liq.	− 52
Symdimethylhydrazine		gas	− 90
Unsymdimethylhydrazine	$(CH_3)_2N - NH_2$	liq.	− 48
Unsymdimethylhydrazine		gas	− 85
Azoethane	$CH_3 - CH_2 - N = N - CH_2 - CH_3$	liq.	− 62.5
Azoethane		gas	− 93
Hydrazoic acid	N_3H	gas	− 297
Hydrazoic acid		diss.	− 255
Tetramethyltetrazene	$(CH_3)_2N - N = N - N(CH_3)_2$	liq.	− 231
Tetramethyltetrazene		gas	− 276
Nitrogen fluoride	NF_3	gas	+ 126
Nitrogen trichloride	NCl_3	liq.	− 230
Nitrogen trichloride		gas	− 263
Tetrafluorohydrazine	$F_2N - NF_2$	gas	+ 8
cis-difluorodiazine	$F - N = N - F$	gas	− 69
trans-difluorodiazine		gas	− 81
Nitrogen sulphide	N_4S_4	sol.	− 460

NB   Diss. = dissolved in water.

29.2 EXPLOSIVE COMPOUNDS OF AMMONIA

29.2.1 Explosive nitrides

Many nitrides are highly stable compounds, some of them being unaffected by water (silicon nitride Si_2N_4, boron nitride BN, and vanadium nitride VN which is remarkably stable to heat), whilst others hydrolyse (magnesium nitride Mg_3N_2, aluminium nitride AlN). The stability of the alkali metal nitrides decreases from Li to Cs. Thus, Li_3N is the only one of these nitrides which can be prepared by the direct union of nitrogen with the heated metal. The Na and K nitrides are formed as transitional substances by the action of active nitrogen on metal, but are rapidly changed into azides. The alkaline–earth metal nitrides are more stable.

A nitride known as 'fulminating silver' was obtained by Berthollet in 1788. It is a black powder which is deposited after a few days or weeks when a solution in ammonia of the oxide Ag_2O obtained by precipitating a solution of silver nitrate in soda is left to stand. Research by Raschig and also by Olmer [1] has shown that this substance is the Ag_3N nitride, sometimes mixed with a small amount of amide $AgNH_2$. This nitride, with a high density equal to 9, explodes even in water on the slightest contact with a rod. In the dry state it is highly sensitive although it is not a high explosive† [2].

Comparable to silver nitride is a gold compound known as fulminating gold as early as the 15th century and obtained by the action of ammonia on a solution of gold chloride. Very little is known about its composition but there is every reason to believe that it contains Au–N bonds (as in a nitride or an amide). In the 17th century fulminating gold caused a famous explosion in a chemist's dispensary. This substance and other similar chemical substances have given rise to explosions [3] in the preparation of catalysts using gold salts and ammonia. As late as 1978, an explosion caused by a nitrogen compound of gold occurred in a laboratory in the Paris area. All these substances are dangerous because even in the moist state they are extremely sensitive to friction.

Cadmium nitride Cd_3N_2 is explosive, but not copper nitride Cu_3N, which decomposes calmly when heated to around $300°C$.

29.2.2 Explosive amides

Sodium and potassium amides are solid substances which are hydrolysed by water and oxidise very readily in air (to form nitrite). Some explosions which have occurred during handling of sodium amide have been attributed to the fact that the impure substance contained particles of free sodium which reacted in moist air, but such explosions can be explained quite simply by the reaction of the nitrite $NaNO_2$ with the amide NH_2Na.

Sodium amide (m.p. $208°C$) is obtained by passing ammonia over heated sodium. If the gas passed over the sodium contains oxygen, there is a risk of explosion. The amide must be stored away from air.

Silver amide is precipitated as a voluminous white substance when an

---

† Calculation shows that the gas volume produced by an explosion of Ag_3N is hardly more than 50 1 of gas per kg of nitride.

alkaline metal amide is reacted with silver nitrate, both being dissolved
in anhydrous ammonia. It is also formed in large quantities when a
solution of silver oxide or silver hydroxide in ammonia is left to
evaporate in a dry atmosphere [1]. This extremely sensitive amide may
sometimes explode spontaneously, and this compound may well have been in
the solid explosive deposit which gradually formed on a silver rupture disk
fitted to a tank of anhydrous ammonia [4].

Explosive compounds with a composition similar to that of an amide also
form gradually on the surface of mercury exposed to an atmosphere which
contains ammonia, as is demonstrated by the two following examples:
1° In 1927, a carboy fitted with an iron U tube containing mercury and used
as an acid–egg exploded after ten years' service.
2° A mercury pressure gauge had been fitted for a long time to an apparatus
containing ammonia. When it was taken down in 1932, blowing compressed air
on one of the fixtures on the pressure gauge caused an explosion.

Sampey, who describes a third incident [5], believes that the explosive
substance which had formed was produced by the dehydration of Millon's base
(ammonium mercury oxide). Certainly, it was a substance related to this
base, as was demonstrated by a study made by Michels, Dumoulin, and Gerver
[54], who show that oxygen must be present for the formation of the
explosive red–brown substance which is an insertion compound of ammonia
molecules in the lattice of mercury amino–oxide $(Hg_2N)_2O$. In moist air
this compound loses NH_3, which is replaced by H_2O, to give an equally
explosive brown substance with the formula $(Hg_2N)_2O.H_2O$. Sampey recommends
that before parts on which these dangerous deposits have formed are taken
apart or scraped, the deposits should first be dissolved with an aqueous
solution of sodium thiosulphate, which forms with mercury a soluble anion
similar to that of silver $[Ag(S_2O_3)_2]^{3-}$, well known to photographers.

Other cases have been reported by various authors, including Vasbinder
[6], which shows that explosions of silver nitride or amide happen quite
frequently in laboratories or in industry.

The conclusion to be drawn from all this is that silver and mercury
must be banned from apparatuses containing ammonia.

29.2.3 Glass silver-plating

For a hundred and fifty years, silver-plating on glass and mirrors has been
obtained by treating an ammonium solution of silver oxide with a reducer
($SnCl_2$, glucose, formaldehyde, etc.) and lightly heating it. The use of
these solutions has caused many explosions, even when they have formed no
precipitate and a fortiori when they have deposited a solid substance. One
of these explosions was reported in 1908 by Matignon [47] who declared that
he had seen 'ammoniacal silver oxide handled hundreds of times without an
explosion occurring', which proves that it takes very little with this kind
of substance to go from safe to dangerous handling conditions. It seems
that in the accident in question it was a slight solid deposit on the wall
level with the surface of the liquid which triggered the explosion. In
1924, Olmer [1] studied the conditions which guard against an explosion.
Basically, they involve diluting the ammonia solution containing silver
diammine hydroxide $Ag(NH_2)_2(OH)$. This is also recommended by Meyer [7],
who gives precise directions. In particular, the ammonia must be mixed
with a solution of silver nitrate before the soda is added. The opposite
process of redissolving Ag_2O precipitated by soda in ammonia is dangerous.

Lohmann [8] recommends using Rochelle salt, which prevents precipitation by soda.

In any case, it is advisable to use the silver–plating solution without delay, and above all it must not be allowed to evaporate. To make such a solution harmless, it simply has to be neutralised with diluted sulphuric acid.

29.3 COMPOUNDS WITH N – N AND N – N BONDS

29.3.1 Hydrazine

Hydrazine NH_2 – NH_2 in the anhydrous state is a colourless liquid with a density close to that of water, a melting point of 1.8°C and a boiling point of 113.5°C. It is miscible with water, and in its aqueous solutions it occurs as the hydrate $N_2H_4.H_2O$ (containing 64% N_2H_4) which crystallises at – 51.7°C when this 64% solution is cooled. The hydrate is stable over a wide range of temperatures and boils at 118.5°C. Aqueous solutions have a maximum boiling point of 120°C for the mixture containing 58.5% N_2H_4 (which contains 91% hydrate $N_2H_4.H_2O$). One common commercial quality is the 85% solution of hydrazine hydrate.

Anhydrous hydrazine burns in air with a blue flame. At temperatures between 100 and 400°C its vapour decomposes and, depending on temperature, pressure, and the solid walls with which it is in contact, the equation for the decomposition varies between

$$N_2H_4 \rightarrow N_2 + 2H_2 \tag{I}$$
$$\text{and} \quad N_2H_4 \rightarrow 1/3N_2 + 4/3NH_3. \tag{II}$$

This last reaction is the one hydrazine undergoes when it is heated to around 300°C.

By igniting a spark in hydrazine vapour maintained at 100°C, Bamford [9] was able to observe an explosion with a yellow flame, the overall reaction being represented more or less by the equation

$$N_2H_4 \rightarrow 0.8NH_3 + 0.8H_2 + 0.6N_2. \tag{III}$$

Jost [10] later found that it is a detonation whose velocity of 2450 m/s agrees with the value calculated by the Chapman–Jouguet theory.

The liability of anhydrous hydrazine to explode has been studied experimentally by Scott and his associates [11] and by Médard [12]. Liquid anhydrous hydrazine is quite insensitive to impact and friction, but it can be exploded under confinement by a strong ignition source, so that it is possible to measure the power of the explosion using the explosive pendulum mortar (see 14.3.3). The value obtained ranges from 1.1 to 1.25 times that of picric acid, whereas in the lead-block test (see 14.3.2) it gives an expansion only 0.6 or 0.8 times that of picric acid.

According to equation (III) above, the calorific value of anhydrous hydrazine is 2720 kJ/kg, but decomposition by equation (II) would release most energy, equal to 3498 kJ/kg. It is worth pointing out that the gas volume at N.T.P. reaches the very high value of 1540 dm^3/kg, which explains the quite high value of power in the pendulum mortar test.

It has not proven possible to detonate liquid anhydrous hydrazine, at

least at the low charge diameters tested (less than 30 mm). The same
applies even more so to hydrazine hydrate which, in fact, does not explode
in the explosive pendulum mortar chamber.

The ignition temperatures as measured by the Bureau of Mines using a
borosilicate (Pyrex) container are the following:

	in air ($^{\bullet}$C)	in oxygen ($^{\bullet}$C)
Hydrazine	270	204
Hydrazine hydrate	292	218

but in the presence of solid metallic or oxidised surfaces ignition can be
achieved at much lower temperatures.

The flammability limits of anhydrous hydrazine at atmospheric pressure
are 4.7 and 100% in air, but when no air is present, ignition, in other
words the production of a flame which propagates, can still be achieved by
using sparks to ignite hydrazine vapour mixed with argon, nitrogen, or
water vapour. In this case, the lower limit is between 30 and 40%. It is
still possible to produce a flame in hydrazine at very low pressures, such
as 12 mm of mercury, when the diameter of the tube is 27 mm.

Because hydrazine ignites or explodes so easily in a closed vessel, it
must be stored and handled as much as possible in a nitrogen atmosphere.
The danger posed by distillation can be reduced by distilling an azeotropic
mixture, for example with aniline.

Although less dangerous than the anhydrous substance, hydrazine hydrate
should be used with caution, not only because of the effect of hydrazine
vapours on the eyes, but also because it is highly reactive with a large
number of substances such as halogens and various oxidising agents, and it
reacts explosively with powerful combustion supporters such as chromium
trioxide. The chemical properties of hydrazine are the subject of a
monograph by Audrieth [13].

As with ammonia, hydrazine must not be placed in contact with mercury
and its compounds, since it readily forms extremely sensitive explosive
substances such as mercury hydrazine chloride (II), a yellow solid with the
formula

$$Cl - Hg - NH - NH - Hg - Cl.$$

29.3.2 Methyl compounds of hydrazine

Two hydrazine compounds are technically important mainly as propellants.
They are:

methylhydrazine	$CH_3.NH - NH_2$
unsymetrical dimethylhydrazine	$(CH_3)_2N - NH_2$,

liquids which are completely soluble in water and which have normal boiling
points of 87 and 63$^{\bullet}$C respectively. They are not in themselves explosive,
but their high reactivity is such that they readily give rise to explosions
with many substances, especially with powerful oxidising agents. Their

ignition temperature in air is 200°C for the first and 250°C for the
second. Their very wide flammability range goes from 2.5 to 95–98%. Like
hydrazine they are liable to form explosive compounds with mercury, and
they must only be handled in a nitrogen atmosphere.

29.3.3 Azo and diazo compounds

Azomethane $CH_3 - N = N - CH_3$ and diazomethane $CH_2 = N \rightleftharpoons N$ are explosive
gases. The second of these two compounds, which is used as a methylating
agent in organic chemistry, is used only in the dissolved state in ether or
dioxane. Aliphatic compounds containing the diazo group, for example ethyl
diazoacetate $N \rightleftharpoons N = CH - CO.O.C_2H_5$ and diazoacetonitrile $N \rightleftharpoons N = CH - CN$,
explode when heated.

Most salts of aryl diazonium explode readily in the dry state. Benzene
diazonium nitrate was studied from this point of view as early as 1881 by
Berthelot and Vieille. Those which contain nitro groups on the aromatic
nucleus and whose anion is an oxidising agent, such as m–nitrobenzene
diazonium perchlorate, which is easily prepared from m–nitroaniline, are
among the most explosive, but even aryl diazonium fluoroborates can be
exploded by impact or friction. Some of these salts are sensitive to light
and should preferably be stored in darkness. Some are so unstable that
they decompose vigorously even in solution.

An explosion occurred [14] in a factory making dye stuffs when a valve
containing crystals of aryl diazonium chloride was closed. The explosion
caused a large quantity of a solution of the same chloride to deflagrate,
causing heavy damage. The risk of a deposit of diazonium salt is reduced
if the sulphate is made more soluble than the chloride.

Salts of aryl diazonium are often used in the form of double salts with
zinc, which are less sensitive. However, a case has been reported [15] of
a spontaneous explosion of dry double zinc chloride and benzene diazonium.
A dozen such commercial double chlorides have been tested by the B.A.M.,
where it was found that the limit diameter in the test in the steel tube
and nozzle plates is less than 1 mm. However, some of them, when subjected
to the heating test in a Dewar vessel (see 16.3.3.2), are liable to heat
spontaneously at 50°C.

On the other hand, two diazonaphtholsulphonyl chlorides with a limit
diameter of 2.5 mm in the test in the steel tube with nozzle plates are
sensitive to impact and produce a small, but not negligible, expansion in
the lead–block test (see 14.3.2) of 33 cm³/dag. Thus, the aromatic diazo
compounds and their salts present a great diversity of explosive hazards.
Indeed, we are far from knowing of all the accidental explosions which they
have caused. A compound from this family should be considered to be really
risk-free only after an ad hoc experimental safety study. There have been
many cases of a new diazonium salt being prepared and handled without
explosion in one laboratory, only to explode later in another laboratory
even though the researcher had followed exactly the method of preparation
laid down by his predecessor. All too often an author declares that it is
quite safe to handle a given diazo compound, simply because he himself was
lucky enough to handle it without explosion, but does not carry out the
verification procedures which would justify his statement. A case has even
been quoted in the United States of an educational manual for preparing
organic compounds which contained a method of preparing a diazo compound
which caused accidents when it was applied by the students.

29.3.4 Nitrogen-containing blowing agents

Sodium or ammonium hydrogen carbonate, which decompose when heated to around 80–90°C and give off carbon dioxide, have been used for a very long time to form bubbles in pastry or rubber.

In 1940, 2,2–azobutyronitrile, or azoisobutyric dinitrile (formula I) as it is called commercially, was used to form bubbles in an elastomer to give a 'foam' or in a thermosetting polymerisable substance to give an 'expanded' polymer. It is a white solid which melts at 106°C, decomposing to give off nitrogen and form tetramethylsuccinic dinitrile. Decomposition takes place slowly at ordinary temperature, with the substance losing 2 to 4% of its nitrogen in a year. It is an exothermic decomposition which liberates a considerable quantity of gas (136 dm^3/kg) and which accelerates when the substance is molten at around 120°C. It is therefore an explosive substance according to the definition given in Chapter 1, although the explosion, which is never a detonation, has only minor mechanical effects. When the product is subjected, in its usual container, to the self-heating test described in 22.1.6 in relation to organic peroxides, it is found to have an 'S.A.D.T.' of 50°C, which means that the substance must never be subjected to a temperature of more than 40°C during transport or storage. The solution of this substance in acetone, when heated to around 60°C, becomes the seat of a very strong reaction with considerable release of gas.

Blowing agents with a composition similar to that of azoisobutyric dinitrile are also manufactured. Generally speaking, when a blowing agent is heated, it decomposes to a greater or lesser extent before melting and does not have a clear melting point. Those given below are approximations.

Blowing agents belong to various chemical families, but they always contain nitrogen atoms linked directly to one another. Indeed, nitrogen is the main constituent in the gases which are released when they decompose. Examples of such agents are benzene sulphonhydrazide (formula II) with a melting point of 104°C, m–benzene disulphonhydrazide (formula III; m.p. 133°C), which gives off more gas and is also more sensitive, and similar compounds derived on the one hand (formula IV; m.p. 155°C) from phenyl oxide, and on the other (formula V; m.p. 164°C) from diphenylsulphone.

Some blowing agents are nitrosamides or nitrosamines and have more pronounced explosive properties than the preceding. They include such substances as p–toluene methylnitrosamide (formula VI) used under the trade name of diactin, a yellow substance with a melting point of 61°C which deflagrates on sudden heating at around 125°C; 3,7–dinitroso–1,3,5,7–tetraaza–[3,3,1]–bicyclononane (formula VII), a yellow impact-sensitive solid with a melting point of 210°C which is more commonly called pentamethylene dinitrosotetramine.

Azocarbonamide (formula VIII), like morpholyl–1,2,3,4–thiatriazole (formula IX), is unlikely to produce serious mechanical effects unless it is heated in a closed vessel.

With the blowing agents, then, we are dealing with a wide variety of products ranging from substances which are insensitive to impact or to ignition, being sensitive only to heat, like the last two, to substances which are liable to detonate with quite high 'explosive power', like those with formulae III and VII. Manufacturers sometimes add to these undeniably explosive substances other substances (wrongly called stabilisers) which have a diluent or phlegmatising effect.

Nitrosoguanidine

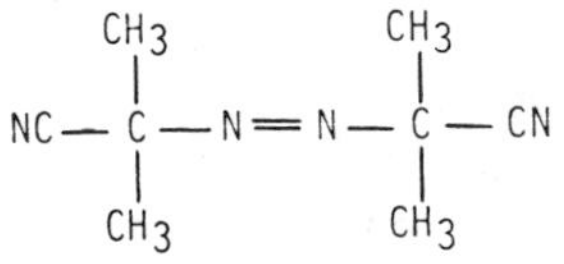

NC—C(CH₃)₂—N=N—C(CH₃)₂—CN

(I)

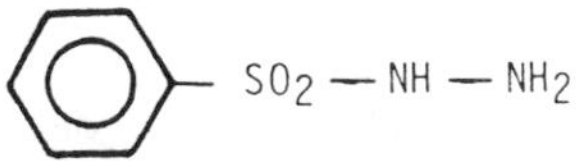

C_6H_5—SO₂—NH—NH₂

(II)

NH₂—NH—SO₂—(C₆H₄)—SO₂—NH—NH₂

(III)

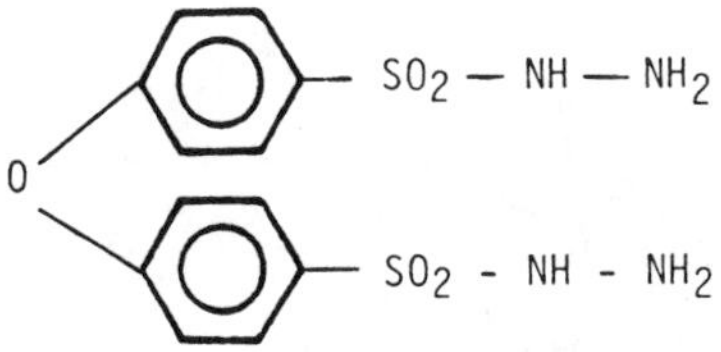

(IV)

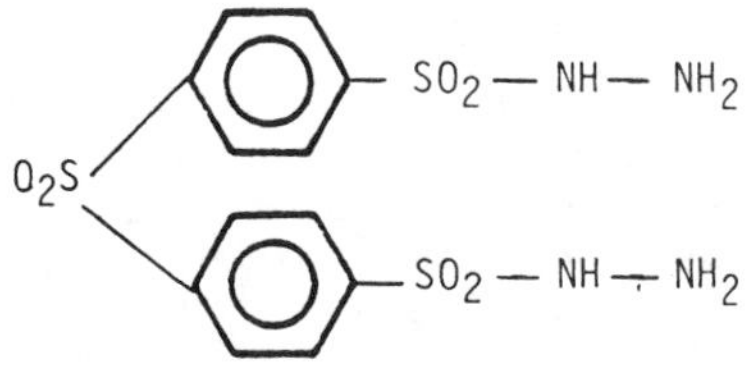

(V)

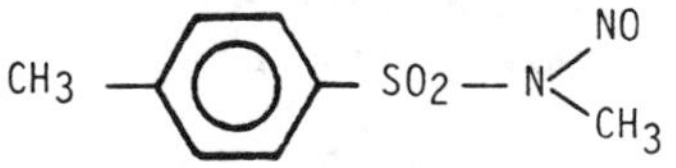

CH₃—(C₆H₄)—SO₂—N(NO)(CH₃)

(VI)

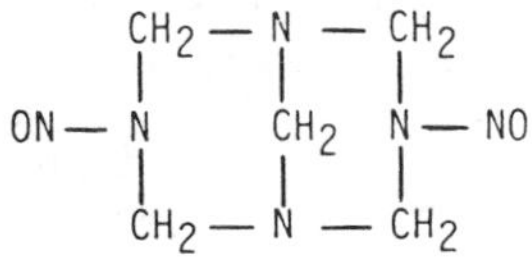

(VII)

H₂N—CO—N=N—CO—NH₂

(VIII)

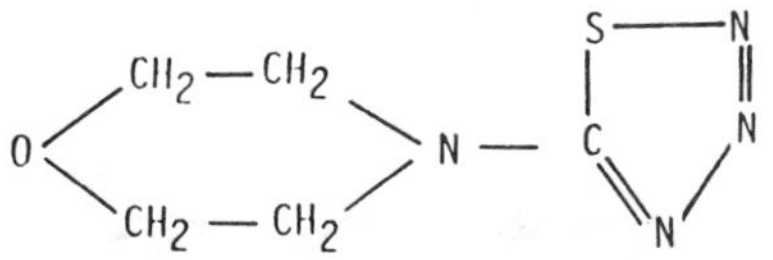

(IX)

$$NH_2 - \underset{\underset{NH}{\|}}{C} - NH - NO$$

is a pale-yellow powder which decomposes vigorously when heated to around 160°C, giving off quite cool gases. It has not been proposed for use as a blowing agent probably because of its considerable sensitivity to impact.

29.4 NITROOGEN COMPOUNDS WITH CHAINS OF THREE OR MORE NITROGEN ATOMS

29.4.1 Hydrazoic acid

The most likely structure of hydrazoic acid (or hydrogen azide) N_3H is

$$H - N = N \overset{+}{\underset{}{\rightleftharpoons}} \overset{-}{N}.$$

In the pure state it is an extremely dangerous liquid (b.p. 37°C) because it explodes with considerable brisance under the effect of the smallest mechanical actions. Great care should be taken when preparing or handling this substance other than in a highly diluted solution. A fair number of researchers have been killed or injured when handling hydrazoic acid. This was the case in the laboratory of Curtius, who discovered the substance in 1890, and then on many subsequent occasions: in 1926 in Ardeer;   in 1936 in Davies' laboratory [18];   in 1947 in the C.S.E. laboratory in Sevran, where three people received injuries which happily proved to be slight. Audrieth [19] must, therefore, be taken to the letter when he writes: 'It is not possible to be too cautious of the treacherous nature of hydrazoic acid.' Even its aqueous solutions explode readily. Work by Joyner [17] shows that solutions of more than 65% detonate with a velocity greater than 7000 m/s. Even at concentrations of 30 to 40% deflagration propagates at a rate of several metres per second.

The vapour of hydrazoic acid detonates readily even at pressures as low as 10 mm of mercury. In tubes with a diameter of 1.7 mm, the detonation velocity of the vapour exceeds 2300 m/s [20b]. According to a Russian author [60], the critical detonation diameter of liquid hydrazoic acid has the astonishingly low value of 0.08 mm. It lends itself to the methodical study of the detonation of gases at reduced pressure. In addition, it is highly toxic, its vapour having similar effects to that of hydrocyanic acid.

29.4.2 Organic compounds with a nitrogen chain

Organic compounds containing the N_3 grouping similar to that of hydrazoic acid are called azides†. Some of them are volatile, such as

---

† The salts of hydrazoic acid are called azides (see 30.4) and contain an N_3 ion whose structure (N = N = N) is completely different from that of the azido group.

methylazide $CH_3.N_3$ gas
vinyl azide $CH_2 = CH - N_3$ liquid (b.p. 30°C).

An explosion which occurred during the handling of methylazide in the presence of mercury has been attributed by the authors who describe it [51] to the formation of minuscule crystals of mercury azide (see 30.5.1), but it may actually have been a case of static electricity similar to the one discussed at the end of 10.3.4.

Grieco [52], who prepared a series of benzene compounds with N_3 azido groups and chlorine or NO_2 nitro groups on the nucleus together, warns that considerable care must be taken with these substances, which are highly unstable in light and which decompose slowly. The chlorinated or nitrated compounds of benzene sulphonylazide $X - C_6H_4 - SO_2 - N_3$ ($X = Cl$, NO_2, etc.) are as sensitive to impact as P.E.T.N. or tetryl.

All these azido compounds are more or less liable to explode, sometimes spontaneously [20]. This instability has been an obstacle to the use of cyanuric triazide (m.p. 14.5°C) as an intentional explosive.

Marsh and Hermes [48] say that the greatest precautions should be taken when working with cyanazide $NC - N_3$. An operative was badly injured [50] while handling a small quantity (0.2 moles) of this compound in a solution in acetonitrile.

There is a chain of three nitrogen atoms in benzotriazole (14.2.9.2), which have exploded, causing considerable damage [21], during distillation. Similar chains are to be found in a large number of other compounds, many of which are explosive. This is the case with diazoaminobenzene $C_6H_5 - N = N - NH - C_6H_5$, a yellow crystalline solid, m.p. 98°C, which, according to Griess, deflagrates when strongly heated.

Chains of four nitrogen atoms make a substance explosive, as is the case with tetramethyltetrazene $(CH_3)_2N - N = N - N(CH_3)_2$. One important compound is tetrazole, which occurs in two forms:

$$\begin{array}{ccc} HC\overset{\displaystyle /\!/\,N - N}{\underset{\displaystyle \backslash\,NH - N}{\|}} & \text{and} & HC\overset{\displaystyle /\,N = N}{\underset{\displaystyle \backslash\backslash\,N - NH}{|}} \end{array}$$

It is a solid which explodes if heated to above its melting point of 155°C. The hydrogen in its NH group can be replaced by metals. The salts of heavy metals are particularly explosive. Hundreds of substituted tetrazoles are known to science and many of them are explosive, especially those in which the substituent is a nitro or azido group N_3. Although some of them have been patented as intentional explosives, there has been no development in this direction, and tetrazole and its compounds are used principally in the pharmaceutical industry. It is important to take precautions against their potential explosive properties. Benson [22] has published an overview of the compounds of tetrazole. An explosion has been reported [49] during an operation involving tetrazolacetic acid.

Most of the simple heterocyclic compounds with at least two nitrogen atoms in the ring, such as pyrazine, pyridazine, pyrazole, and imidazole, have a negative heat of formation from their constituent elements which is quite high in absolute terms. It cannot be predicted from calculation whether or not they are explosive, and they have not been experimented upon from this point of view, but it is known that some of their simple compounds have given rise to explosions when heated to above 150°C.

29.5 HALOGENATED AND SULPHUR-CONTAINING COMPOUNDS OF NITROGEN

29.5.1 Nitrogen trichloride

Nitrogen trichloride NCl_3 is well known for its explosive properties, which were quick to appear in the laboratory of Dulong who discovered it in 1811. Several explosions cost him an eye and two fingers. It is a yellow, dense (d = 1.63) liquid which is quite volatile since it has a vapour pressure of about 0.2 atm at 20°C and a boiling point of 71°C. It is slightly soluble in water, in which it hydrolyses very slowly. In the liquid state it is highly sensitive to impact. It can also be detonated by simple contact with organic substances, particularly fatty ones, because the reaction is strongly exothermic and produces local heating of the liquid chloride.

Nitrogen trichloride is readily prepared by the action of chlorine on NH_4^+ ions in an acid medium: $4H_2O + NH_4^+ + 3Cl_2 \rightarrow NCl_3 + 3Cl^- + 4H_3O^+$. In a weak acid medium (pH between 3 and 5) dichloroamine $NHCl_2$ is formed, and in an alkaline medium monochloroamine NH_2Cl is formed. The latter can be isolated in the pure state only at a low temperature (around - 50°C).

When a solution of hypochlorite acts on NH_4^+ ions, the NCl_3 chloride is liberated. Dokter [53] has made a detailed study of the reactions of a solution of sodium hypochlorite on ammonium salts at temperatures of 70 to 80°C, in other words in conditions in which NCl_3 goes into the vapour state with the nitrogen and chlorine formed, and he has established that at pH levels higher than 7 or 8 only traces of NCl_3 are formed, whereas in an acidic medium hydrogen chloride vapours are formed in quantities which are in inverse proportion to the pH. In some of these experiments more than 20% by volume of NCl_3 vapour was formed in the gas phase, a concentration at which the phase may detonate in the presence of even a moderate hot spot (100°C, for example). Dokter also observed the emission of a considerable quantity of nitrous oxide, which would seem to come from the reaction with nitrosyl chloride $NCl_3 + NOCl = N_2O + 2Cl_2$.

The readiness with which nitrogen trichloride is formed by the action of chlorine, hypochlorite, or some other chlorinating agent on NH_4^+ ions as well as on amines explains the quite large number of explosions which have occurred in factory drains into which chlorinated and ammonium effluents are poured. As a rule, ammonia or ammonium salts should be banned from workshops in which chlorine is manufactured or used.

According to a Russian study [59], if the aqueous solution of sodium chloride which is used in the manufacture of chlorine by electrolysis is contaminated by ammonium salts, nitrogen trichloride is formed when the pH is less than 4.4. It may also be formed if hot chlorine gas is cooled by water containing NH_4 ions. It is important, then, in this manufacturing process to keep a check on the purity of the water and solutions used.

Nitrogen trichloride is also readily formed, as Guinchant discovered [66], by the action of hypochlorites on urea or other amides. This danger should never be forgotten when chlorine or a chlorinating agent is reacted with an organic compound containing an NH_2 group.

Nitrogen trichloride is still dangerous in a weak solution in organic solvents. A spontaneous explosion of a cold 18% solution in butyl oxide has been reported [23]. If nitrogen trichloride is to be used in solution, a 10% concentration in carbon tetrachloride (b.p. 70.7°C) is recommended, since it does not react with NCl_3 and slow evaporation will not increase the NCl_3 content and make it more dangerous.

The predominant influence of the pH level in the formation of nitrogen

trichloride leads to the following rule: if chlorine is to be reacted with
a solution containing ammonium ions, either the pH level should be kept
under constant supervision and kept below 8 during the reaction, or an
excess of soda should be added at the beginning of the operation at a rate
of 2 moles per atom of nitrogen present in the liquid.

29.5.2 Organic compounds with chlorine bound to nitrogen

Quite a large number of organic groups of amines, amides, sulphonamides,
etc. containing NHCl or NCl_2 groupings are manufactured industrially for
use as bleaches, disinfectants, or organic synthesisers. Some of them have
more or less marked explosive properties.

Chlorinating agents such as calcium hypochlorite react strongly to form
chlorinated compounds with alkylamines or their salts, and many of these
chlorinated amines are explosive. In 1914, an explosion of methyl
dichloroamine, a liquid which boils at 59°C and which may explode during
distillation, killed the chemist Sackur in the laboratory of Haber.

Urethanes with chlorine bound to nitrogen, such as $CH_3 - O - CO - NCl_2$,
decompose with considerable violence [24] when heated beyond their boiling
point. Monochlorinated urethanes give metal salts such as

$$CH_3 - O - CO - N \begin{array}{l} \diagup Na \\ \diagdown Cl \end{array}$$

which may deflagrate at quite a low temperature.

The sodium salt of N-chloro-p-toluene sulphonamide

$$CH_3 - \bigcirc - SO_2 - N \begin{array}{l} \diagup Na \\ \diagdown Cl \end{array}$$

which is sold as 'chloroamine T', explodes when heated to around 180°C.
Also explosive is the comparable dichlorinated compound

$$CH_3 - \bigcirc - SO_2 - NCl_2$$

which is sold as dichloroamine T, has a melting point of 83°C, and is used
to disinfect pipes in the food industry.

Graefe [[25] says that 1-chloroaziridine (ethylene imine chlorinated
over nitrogen) explodes very violently. A spontaneous explosion of the
cold substance occurred in France in 1962.

Some chlorinated compounds with nitrogen, such as trichloromelamine
(formula X), are relatively stable, but others have a level of sensitivity
to mechanical actions which makes them dangerous to handle, as is the case
with 1-chlorobenzotriazole (formula XI), which may ignite and deflagrate
strongly simply when it is poured into a container [62].

NHCl   Cl
 | |
 C   N ─ N
N   N   ‖
‖   N
ClHN─C   C─NHCl   N
      N

(X)   (XI)

The instability of some aromatic amines with a substituted chlorine
atom on the nucleus may be caused by the formation in some circumstances of
NHCl or NCl_2 groups. Frankenberg [63] reports an explosion which occurred
when four litres of 2-chloro-p-phenylene diamine were distilled at reduced
pressure in a large glass flask. When the temperature reached 165°C, the
pressure began to rise and an explosion followed soon after. The thermal
instability of this substance is well highlighted by a differential thermal
analysis test (see 16.2.5).

All compounds containing an N ─ Cl bond, like all compounds which have
a chlorinating action, may, on contact with ammonia or ammonium salts, form
nitrogen trichloride, so special precautions must be taken when they are
used and stored.

29.5.3 Other halogenated compounds of nitrogen

In addition to nitrogen trichloride, chlorine and nitrogen combine to form
chlorine azide N_3Cl, a highly reactive explosive gas which contains two
explosophore groups, N_3 and N ─ Cl. It is liable to explode spontaneously
even at around − 100°C in the solid state. Nevertheless, Browne and his
associates were able, with very special precautions, to prepare it in small
quantities and study its reactions (see 15.4).

Nitrogen bromide NBr_3 and especially nitrogen iodide are well known for
the considerable ease with which they explode, whereas nitrogen fluoride
NF_3, a gas which forms exothermically, is stable and non-explosive, but is
an oxidising agent which forms explosive mixtures with combustible gases.
It may also explode by rapid adsorption onto activated carbon, according to
the reaction

$$4NF_3 + 3C \rightarrow 3CF_4 + 2N_2.$$

Tetrafluorohydrazine N_2F_4 is a more stable gas than hydrazine, but it
reacts strongly with many substances, sometimes igniting and deflagrating.

The fluoroamines NHF_2 and NH_2F are explosive gases, as is fluorine
azide N_3F

29.5.4 Sulphur-containing compounds of nitrogen

There are several nitrogen sulphides, the best-known of which has the
formula N_4S_4. It is a yellow solid which sublimes when heated carefully −
which is one way of purifying it − but explodes above 200°C when it is
heated rapidly. Its explosive properties were studied in 1881 by Berthelot
and Vieille [55]. It is sensitive to impact but quite safe to handle since
two American researchers claim to have handled it without incident for

eight years, until one of them was injured by an explosion when reducing an impure sample of the substance to a powder with the intention of purifying it. The presence of impurities may have increased the sensitivity of the substance.

Nitrogen selenide N_4Se_4 is much more sensitive to impact and friction than the sulphide [56].

Some types of N – S bond in organic compounds, such as that in nitrogen sulphide, should probably be classified as explosophores, since cases have been reported of sulphur diethylaminotrifluoride exploding [58], as well as various sulphur-containing and nitrogen heterocyclic compounds, including aminothiatriazole (I) and 5-chloro-1,2,3-thiadiazole (II)

Phenyldiazonium sulphide

is an extremely sensitive solid red substance [65]. In addition to two N – S bonds, its molecule contains two explosophore diazo groups.

Given that, as Moissan has demonstrated, nitrogen sulphide forms very readily when sulphur comes into contact with liquefied ammonia, measures must be taken to keep the latter free from contamination by sulphur.

29.6 CYANO COMPOUNDS

29.6.1 General observations on cyano compounds

Of the compounds containing the C ≡ N group, hydrocyanic acid is liable to cause explosions by polymerising, even though it is not strictly speaking an explosive. Indeed, it is a seemingly paradoxical property of compounds in this family that some of them which are in theory powerful explosives are so insensitive that in practice they cannot be classified as such, but the possibility that they might explode in extreme conditions should never be lost sight of. According to Table 29.2, most of these compounds are strongly endothermic. The observation made in 2.5 concerning the effect on the heat of formation of the accumulation of electronegative groups in a molecule is particularly well illustrated by the cases of cyanogen and tetracyanomethane.

One reason why these substances are so insensitive to excitation is their very high dissociation energies:

D(NC – CN) = 127 kcal   D(H – CN) = 119 kcal
D(N ≡ C) = 165 kcal   C(Cl – CN) = 92 kcal.

The elementary reactions which may be involved in the explosion of cyano compounds must thus have especially high activation energies.

Another reason why these compounds are resistant to explosion probably

Table 29.2

Heats of formation at constant pressure of cyanated compounds

Compound	Formula	Physical state	Heat of formation F_p (kJ/mol)
Hydrocyanic acid	HCN	gas	− 135
Hydrocyanic acid	HCN	liq.	− 107
Cyanogen	C_2N_2	gas	− 309
Cyanogen	C_2N_2	liq.	− 293
Cyanogen fluoride	NC.F	gas	− 23
Cyanogen chloride	NC.Cl	gas	− 138
Cyanogen chloride	NC.Cl	liq.	− 104
Cyanogen bromide	NC.Br	gas	− 184
Cyanogen bromide	NC.Br	sol.	− 134
Cyanogen iodide	NC.I	gas	− 226
Cyanogen iodide	NC.I	sol.	− 159
Tetracyanoethylene	$(NC)_2C = C(NC)_2$	cr.	− 630
Tetracyanomethane	$(NC)_4C$	cr.	− 610
Tetracyanomethane	$(NC)_4C$	gas	− 674
Acetonitrile	$CH_3 - CN$	gas	− 74
Acetonitrile	$CH_3 - CN$	liq.	− 40.6
Propionitrile	$CH_3 - CH_2 - CN$	gas	− 51.8
Propionitrile	$CH_3 - CH_2 - CN$	liq.	− 15.5
Malononitrile	$NC - CH_2 - CN$	cr.	− 186
Acrylonitrile	$CH_2 = CH - CN$	liq.	− 151
Fumaronitrile	$trans-NC - CH = CH - CN$	cr.	− 268
Benzonitrile	$C_6H_5 - CN$	liq.	− 163
Methyl isocyanide	$CH_3.NC$	liq.	− 117 (a)
Ethyl isocyanide	$CH_3 - CH_2 - NC$	liq.	− 105 (a)
Allyl isocyanide	$CH_2 = CH - CH_2 - NC$	liq.	− 247 (a)
Mercury cyanide	$Hg(CN)_2$	cr.	− 263 (a)
Cyanamide	$NC - NH_2$	cr.	− 59
Silver cyanamide	$NC - NAg_2$	cr.	− 210 (a)

(a) Old value, rather inaccurate.

lies in their capacity to change easily either into trimers (with cyanuric nuclei) or higher polymers, which are in both cases made thermodynamically more stable by resonance.

29.6.2 Hydrocyanic acid

29.6.2.1 General properties

Hydrocyanic acid, of which over three million tons a year are manufactured in the world , is an important intermediate chemical product because it can easily be added to aldehydes, ketones, and ethylene oxide to give compounds (cyanohydrins) which can then, through dehydration or dehydrogenation, give substances such as acrylonitrile or methyl methacrylate.

It is a colourless liquid which is soluble in water in all proportions. Its main physical properties are given in Table 29.3. It is highly toxic, and also flammable. The flammability limits of the vapour in air are 6 and 41%. The limit pressure below which a mixture cannot propagate a flame is 0.066 bars [26].

Table 29.3

Physical properties of hydrocyanic acid

Melting point	− 13.2°C
Normal boiling point	25.7°C
Relative density at 18°C	0.690 g/cm³
Relative density at 50°C	0.64 g/cm³ app.
Absolute vapour pressure at 40°C	1.68 bars
Absolute vapour pressure at 50°C	2.35 bars

29.6.2.2 Explosion of hydrocyanic acid

Because of its endothermic nature, hydrocyanic acid may have explosive properties. *In theory*, explosive decomposition of the vapour according to the equation

$$HCN \text{ gas} = C + 1/2H_2 + 1/2N_2$$

would raise the products of the decomposition to around 2500°C, with the pressure rise factor being 9.6. This vapour has a calorific value (of 4800 kJ/kg), which is greater than that of hydrogen and air in the stoichiometric mixture.

The explosion above, if it could be observed, would be obtained only with a very strong initiating source. It is significant that in ignition tests of mixtures of air and hydrocyanic acid, the upper limit (41%) found at atmospheric pressure falls well short of 100%. In these mixtures the main cause of explosion is combustion with oxygen, and for mixtures at the upper limit the temperature of the products lies between 1750 and 2000°C, depending on the decomposition equation being used, which is another very high value.

It is not known what would happen if a spark were discharged in the vapour of hydrocyanic acid at high pressure (for example, at 100°C when the vapour pressure is close to 9 bars). There might be an explosion.

In experimental studies of the equilibrium

$$H_2 + (CN)_2 \rightleftarrows 2HCN$$

at 625°C and pressures no higher than 1 bar, Robertson and Pease [27] invariably observed a calm reaction.

The vapour of hydrocyanic acid is clearly a highly resistant compound, and the liquid even more so as is shown by the following experiments.

In 1924, researchers at the German Chemo-technical Institute† [28] carried out ignition tests using 15 g of picric acid on hydrocyanic acid packed in the firmly plugged shells of 7.5 cm grenades and found absolutely no evidence that the explosion was transmitted to the hydrocyanic acid. The classic test in the lead block gave a zero result. Steel cylinders with a capacity of 0.4 litres three-thirds filled with liquid hydrocyanic acid and placed on a wood fire burst in 'button-hole' fashion after some ten to fifteen minutes because of the pressure of HCN raised to a high temperature, but identical cylinders which had not burst after ten minutes heating were cooled and opened and found to contain the liquid practically undecomposed and limpid.

In experiments performed in 1954 [29], liquid hydrocyanic acid in steel tubes 4.5 m thick and with an internal diameter of 33 mm was excited by 50 g of compressed P.E.T.N. The acid was not exploded.

It cannot definitely be stated that in containers several decimetres in diameter and with an ignition source made of a booster of several kilo-grammes of powerful explosive a detonation would not be seen to propagate in liquid hydrocyanic acid. However, it is possible to state that *for all practical purposes hydrocyanic acid is not in itself an explosive*. This conclusion, which was reached by the C.T.R. researchers in 1925, has been disputed by Wöhler and Roth [30], who were able, with a strong ignition source‡, to obtain the decomposition of hydrocyanic acid with liberation of carbon, and who consider that the substance should be classified as an explosive. Their experiments are not very conclusive and would rather lead to the conclusion that hydrocyanic acid is not liable to propagate an explosion by itself.

29.6.2.3 The polymerisation of hydrocyanic acid

It has long been known that hydrocyanic acid gradually polymerises at ordinary temperature, and that a blackish-brown solid known as 'azulmic compound' is formed, the structure of which has been established by Volker.

---

† The Chemisch-Technisch Reichsanstalt (C.T.R) became the Bundesanstalt für Material-Prüfung (B.A.M.) in 1945.
‡ Wöhler and Roth subjected 3 g of hydrocyanic acid to the action of a detonator containing 1.25 g of P.E.T.N. and 0.4 g of lead azide in the cavity of a lead block 10 cm high and 10 cm in diameter. The primer thus made up one third of the load. In the standardised lead block (25 cm) with 10 g of hydrocyanic acid, they obtained no decomposition, even with a primer of 2 g of P.E.T.N.

In addition to this substance, which is a polymer with a very high molar mass, a tetramer in small quantities and, if water is present, salts of ammonium are also formed. This polymerisation, which is catalysed by OH⁻ ions, is exothermic and releases 42 kJ per mole of monomer [31].   It may cause high pressure rises in containers holding HCN, and such containers have been reported as exploding on various occasions.

The first practical research into the conditions in which this process of polymerisation takes place was done independently in 1924 by Walker and Eldred [32] in the United States and by the C.T.R. in Berlin [28].   The concordant results of these two sets of research can be summarised as follows:

Hydrocyanic acid containing a little water, especially if the latter is alkaline, turns yellow and then brown, and then the black azulmic compound separates out.   Adding a small amount of sulphuric acid (0.05 to 0.2%) stabilises the substance and polymerisation stops.

The C.T.R. tests were done in the open air at the ambient temperature (15 to 45°C).   In bulbs of non-alkaline Jena glass the pure substance does not decompose (even though it is exposed to sunlight), but if the acid contains 5 to 10% water, it changes colour and then turns into a solid polymer which shatters the bulb.   Adding 1% potash or ammonia to the acid containing 10% water causes the bulb to shatter after two days, while hydrocyanic acid containing 10% water and no alkali breaks the container only after three weeks.   When 0.1% sulphuric acid was added, it proved possible to keep the substance for several months without its changing colour.   In steel cylinders at a test pressure of 230 bars, even rapid polymerisation (with 0.1% KOH and 10% water) did not shatter the vessel (except in one case where the wall was defective).

The tests performed by Walker and Eldred consisted in gradually heating steel cylinders with a capacity of 810 cm³ containing 250 cm³ of a 99.9% solution of hydrocyanic acid, pure or with catalysts or stabilisers added, and making a note of the point at which the pressure, which climbed slowly at first, began to rise rapidly at the same time as the temperature of the cylinder rose above that of the heating oven.   The pressure rise might be as much as 70 bars.   These experiments established the stabilising effect of sulphuric acid.   It was later found that other acids (oxalic and phosphoric), as well as sulphur dioxide and cobalt oxalate, also stabilise hydrocyanic acid.   The less water the substance contains, the more stable it is.

In subsequent experiments Gause and Montgomery [31] heated 50 cm³ of HCN to a given temperature (100, 137.5, or 175°C) in a cylindrical steel bomb and noted the length of what they call the incubation period, but which we would call the induction period, in other words the time which elapses between the moment at which the system reaches the temperature of the experiment and the moment when a violent reaction is initiated.   At 175°C this period is only a few minutes long.   The main factors influencing this induction period are the temperature, the quantity of polymer added before the test, and the concentration of the soda added (0.01 to 0.02 millimoles per gramme of HCN).   The percentage of water present played a less important part in these tests.   The catalytic action of the polymer shows that we are dealing with an auto-catalytic reaction, which explains why, even when the conditions are such that there is no noticeable heating of the substance, polymerisation accelerates over time.   The effect of the percentage filling of the container tends to suggest that the contact surface between the liquid and the metal wall may play a part.   By means of

an extrapolation (which is dubious, as are all extrapolations of this kind)
the authors conclude that at 25°C the induction period of the pure product
might be 15 months.

29.6.2.4 *Safety in the storage and transport of hydrocyanic acid*

Hydrocyanic acid can be safely stored in clean tanks if the acid is pure
(less than 0.5% water) and has been stabilised. For the substance to store
well it should be made as anhydrous as possible. The most widely used and
reliable stabiliser is sulphuric acid, usually in a 0.1% concentration,
although 0.05% may be adequate. Phosphoric acid is also a good stabiliser.
When hydrocyanic acid has to be transferred to a container, the latter
should first have been well cleaned and washed with weak sulphuric acid.

    If hydrocyanic acid is found to have decomposed, which will be apparent
if it is no longer colourless, and if it is not to be used immediately, it
must be redistilled after first slightly acidifying it, if need be.

    The transport of hydrocyanic acid† is subject to the following R.I.D.
regulations: the substance must contain no more than 3% water and must
have been stabilised;   it is housed in carbon steel cylinders hydraulically
tested to a pressure of 100 bars, with the test being repeated every two
years;   the containers must be stamped with the date (month, year) on which
they were filled;   the rate of loading must be no more than 0.55 kg per
litre of water capacity.   In the U.S.A. stainless steel cylinders are
preferred, and manufacturers recommend that the product not be stored in
metal containers for more than three months.   It should also be remembered
that precautions must be taken during handling because of the toxicity of
hydrocyanic acid.

    Hydrocyanic acid absorbed in a porous material, usually cellulosic, is
sold under various trade names (Cyanox, etc.).   It is important for this
porous material not to be alkaline.   This substance, which is used as an
insecticide, is stored in strong (6 bars) metal containers reminiscent of
cylinders for liquefied gases.

29.6.3 Cyanogen

29.6.3.1 *General properties*

Cyanogen has no industrial applications at the moment, but it is of some
interest because high temperatures could be achieved if it were used to
fuel blowpipes, since it is a strongly endothermic substance whose flame
with oxygen at atmospheric pressure has a temperature of 4640°K.   It is a
readily liquefiable, toxic gas with a normal boiling point of − 21.15°C and
a vapour pressure of 4.1 bars at 15°C and about 12 bars at 50°C.

    If kept at temperatures of between 300 and 600°C, it polymerises quite
rapidly into a dark-brown solid with a macromolecular structure.   This
substance, called paracyanogen, depolymerises when heated to around 800°C
at ordinary pressure to give cyanogen.   In glass polymerisation is still
slow at 450°C, but various catalysts (K_2CO_3. KCN, etc.) are active from

---

† Aqueous solutions of 20% HCN at most can also be transported.

around 120°C [33]. At 65°C and its vapour pressure (17 bars) cyanogen is very stable, even in the presence of copper, water, or substances which, at over 100°C, catalyse the chemical change into paracyanogen. This process of polymerisation is exothermic (about 170 kJ per mol of C_2N_2). Cyanogen decomposes only above 1000°C and the process has never been reported to be explosive. Cyanogen-oxygen mixtures must be raised to beyond 800°C to be exploded by heat.

The flammability limits of cyanogen in air were found by Pannetier [34] to be 6 and 32% for wet mixtures. Perfectly dry mixtures have distinct properties reminiscent of those of air-carbon monoxide mixtures. In such dry mixtures an electric spark ignites a flame which propagates only in tubes with a small diameter (20 mm or less), and the limits are closer together (18 - 26%) than is the case with wet gases. Mixtures of cyanogen and air are prone not only to deflagrations but also to very powerful detonations, which Pannetier obtained by raising a tungsten wire to extreme red heat in a mixture with more than 19% cyanogen.

29.6.3.2 Explosions of cyanogen

Berthelot [35] exploded gaseous cyanogen using a primer consisting of a capsule of mercury fulminate. The products of the explosion are carbon and nitrogen. The properties of the explosive reaction are easily calculated as

$$C_2N_2 \text{ gas} = 2C + N_2 + 309 \text{ kJ}$$
$$T_V = 4370 \qquad \pi = 14.8.$$

The calorific value of gaseous cyanogen is 5940 kJ/kg (one and a half times that of picric acid).

Welcher and his associates [36] conducted the 8 kg drop-weight test (falling from 1.7 m) on glass bulbs containing solid or liquid cyanogen. In no case was even the slightest explosion observed. Other tests which involved the firing of perforating bullets at steel tubes containing liquid cyanogen also gave negative results. Finally, the same researchers set off several (five or eight) No. 6 detonators placed *outside* tubes containing liquid cyanogen without obtaining an explosion. We can conclude from these tests that liquid cyanogen is hardly sensitive to impact or ignition and that it is safe enough to be housed and handled in the liquid state in gas cylinders. However, it would be desirable to conduct initiation tests using a large explosive booster in order to dispel all doubts about its degree of safety.

29.6.4 Cyanogen halides

Cyanogen chloride and bromide, which are manufactured industrially, are, like the iodide, endothermic compounds. Cyanogen chloride† NC.Cl is a colourless gas which is easily liquefied (normal boiling point: 13°C) and

---

† Cyanogen chloride has an isomer with the structure of an isocyanide, C ≦ N − Cl, a gas which liquefies at − 15°C and is of no practical interest.

has a vapour pressure of 1.11 bars at 15°C and 3.65 bars at 50°C. In the pure state it can be stored without decomposing at normal temperatures (up to 30°C at least). When raw cyanogen chloride containing a small amount of water is housed in a container, the pressure of the gas phase rises because gas is released by the reaction

$$ClCN + 2H_2O = NH_4Cl + CO_2.$$

A simple calculation shows that 0.1% of water can increase the pressure in this way by 6 or 7 bars in a container with a 10% filling ullage. The pressure stops rising when all the water has reacted, unless polymerisation is initiated, since various impurities such as water, HCl, or certain salts change monomer cyanogen chloride into a solid trimer, cyanuryl trichloride, which melts at 140°C. This polymerisation process is exothermic (about 120 kJ per mole of monomer), which explains why stored cylinders containing wet cyanogen chloride have sometimes exploded. There are stabilisers, such as anhydrous sodium pyrophosphate [37], which, in low doses, prevent cyanogen chloride from polymerising, but storing cyanogen chloride containing more than 0.2% moisture is not recommended. Cyanogen bromide, a solid which melts at 51°C, is also readily polymerised by the action of hydracids.

Because these three cyanogen halides are formed endothermically, they can probably be exploded by a sufficiently powerful initiation source, but there are absolutely no experimental results on the subject.

29.6.5 Cyanocarbons

An interesting group of cyano compounds which have been the focus of attention for some time is that of hydrocarbons entirely substituted by cyano groups. The first of these compounds was obtained in 1909 by Moureu and Bongrand [38]. It is dicyanoacetylene ('carbon subnitride') NC − C ≡ C = CN, a solid which melts at 21°C. Tetracyanoethylene was prepared in 1957

$$
\begin{array}{ccc}
NC_{\diagdown} & & _{\diagup}CN \\
 & C = C & \\
_{\diagup}NC & & ^{\diagdown}CN
\end{array}
$$

and a number of others are now also known. These compounds are strongly endothermic and have been proposed for use as high-energy propellants. The flame of dicyanoacetylene burning in pure oxygen is reported [39] to have a temperature of 5260°C†. The dissociation of the compound into its elements should raise the products of the reaction to over 4000°K. However, these cyanated hydrocarbons are not exploded by impact and can withstand without decomposing the high temperatures‡ which common explosives are unable to withstand. Tetracyanoethylene can be sublimated by heating to 600°C.

Hydrocarbons which are incompletely substituted by cyano groups have acidic properties. Tricyanomethane $HC(CN)_3$ gives stable salts. Its heavy metal salts (especially Pb, Hg, and Ag) are probably sensitive explosives,

---

† This high temperature is due in part to the fact that nitrogen at high temperatures dissociates only to a very small extent.

‡ Armstrong and Marantz [40] obtained a calm flame when they directed a blowpipe flame onto dicyanoacetylene.

as are those of trinitromethane.

These cyanohydrocarbons can be compared with carbonyl cyanide $CO(CN)_2$, a liquid which reacts very violently with water and which must be a strong explosive. Its explosion into $CO + 2C + N_2$ has an explosion temperature calculated at $3450°K$.

29.6.6 Metal cyanides

The cyanides of some metals (Zn, Cd, Ag, Hg) are formed endothermically and explosions† have sometimes been reported when AgCN or $Hg(CN)_2$ were heated to prepare cyanogen. However, mercury cyanide heated gently to around $300°C$ at ordinary pressure decomposes calmly into mercury and cyanogen with the concomitant formation of paracyanogen. It is likely that during the thermal decomposition of mercury cyanide the simultaneous effect of two reactions, one endothermic (the formation of cyanogen) and the other exothermic (the formation of paracyanogen), tends to stabilise the temperature of the system at a given pressure, as happens in the thermolysis of ammonium nitrate (see 23.3.5), and that only a considerable input of heat from outside can cause an explosion.

Wöhler and Roth [30] classify mercury cyanide with the explosives, but in tests in which the substance was housed in steel tubes 21 mm in diameter and 3 mm thick at a density of 2.13 g/cm³, excitation by 10 g of P.E.T.N. did not detonate the cyanide [41]. The reaction of mercury oxide with an aqueous solution of hydrocyanic acid is so exothermic that, if it were not carried out in well-controlled cooling conditions, it would, according to Biltz [64], lead to an explosion.

Explosions of mercury oxycyanide have been reported on a number of occasions. The most serious, in Magdeburg in 1921, caused casualties when the substance was being pulverised in a ball mill. Tests by Kast and Haid [42] show that under the falling weight it has a sensitivity between that of picric acid and that of tetryl. It is also exploded by friction, and it seems to be particularly sensitive in this respect since even rubbing it with a wooden spatula has sometimes caused it to deflagrate. The reaction does seem to be simple deflagration rather than detonation, since the expansion obtained in the lead-block test is no greater than that obtained by detonating the fulminate cap on its own. The deflagration temperature, $170°C$, is comparatively low. The main decomposition reaction is

$$Hg_2O(CN)_2 = 2Hg + N_2 + C + CO + 162 \text{ kJ},$$

but a small amount of cyanogen is also released. It is important, then, not to subject this substance, which has applications in pharmacy, to any violent mechanical action.

Mercury cyanate $(NCO)_2Hg$ is not explosive in spite of what one may read in some works. The mistake arises because mercury fulminate $(CNO)_2Hg$ has sometimes wrongly been called mercury cyanate. As for the complex cyanides (ferricyanides, cupricyanides, etc.), which contain the CN group in the ligand state, they are highly stable, non-explosive compounds.

---

† It has been suggested that these explosions involved impure cyanides containing fulminates, but this has not been proved.

29.6.7 Nitriles and isocyanides

The nitriles of the first three fatty monoacids have heats of formation which are negative but too weak for them to have explosive properties, but their isomers, the isocyanides (or isonitriles)†, are more endothermic. As Lemoult [43] wrote in 1906, the terms with low molecular weight are liable to explode when they are distilled. Stein [67] describes an incident of an explosion of methyl isocyanide $CH_3 - N \gtrless C$ in 1968. The same compound gave rise to an explosion at ordinary temperature in 1985, when 0.2 ml were injected into a chromatography column. The researcher involved [68] thinks that the explosion was caused by the sudden application of pressure on the liquid.

Although quite endothermic, benzonitrile $C_6H_5 - CN$, a liquid which boils at 192°C, is chemically highly stable, even at 500°C. It decomposes at higher temperatures, releasing a large volume of gas, but the reaction is not explosive.

Dinitriles, like malononitrile, could probably be exploded by a strong enough ignition source, and the same is true of some ethylene nitriles, such as acrylonitrile, a liquid which is manufactured in large quantities by industry.

Some nitriles are liable to polymerise in a way similar to cyanogen chloride, with formation of a cyanuric nucleus.

Cyanamide $NC - NH_2$, which may be thought of as the nitrile of carbamic acid, $NH_2.COOH$, is a compound formed endothermically. Amongst its metal compounds, the best known of which is calcium cyanamide $CaCN_2$, at least one, silver cyanamide, is explosive. It was Lemoult [44] who subjected ammoniacal silver nitrate to the action of an aqueous solution of cyanamide to precipitate silver cyanamide $NC - NAg_2$, a substance which explodes at around 470°C when it is heated abruptly, but which decomposes completely and calmly according to the equation

$$2CN_2Ag_2 \rightarrow C_2H_2 + N_2 + 4Ag$$

when it is heated slowly [45]. Deb and Yoffe [46], observing that the ion $(N = C = N)^{2-}$ is isoelectronic with $(N_3)^-$, deduce that the salts formed by cyanamide with metals with a high ionisation potential must be unstable. This is the case with the cyanamides of thallium, mercury (I), and copper (II). It is advisable, therefore, to prevent calcium cyanamide from coming into contact with these metals or their salts.

It has been proposed to use the silver compound of nitrocyanamide $NC - N(NO_2) - Ag$ as a primer.

BIBLIOGRAPHICAL REFERENCES

[1]   Olmer, L. J. (1924) Bull. Soc. Chim. Fr. 35 847
[2]   Hahn, H. & Gilbert, E. (1949) Z. anorg. Ch. 258 77
[3]   Cusumano, J. A. (1974) Nature (G.B.) 247 456
[4]   Warren, (1964) Safety in Air and Ammonia Plants 6 53

---

† The term isonitrile, like the old name carbylamine, should be abandoned in favour of the term isocyanide.

[5]   Sampey, J. J. (1947) *Chem. Eng. News* **25** 2138
[6]   Vasbinder, H. (1952) *Pharm. Weekblad* **87** 861
[7]   Meyer, W. (1927) *Chem. Ztg.* **51** 804
[8]   Lohman, E. (1929) *Diamant* **51** 526;   (1931) *C.A.* **25** 3171
[9]   Bamford, C. H. (1939) *Trans. Faraday Soc.* **35** 1239
[10] Jost, A. *et al.* NASA Doc. N.63.22437;   (1964) *C.A.* **61** 1698–9
[11] Scott, F. E., Burns, J. J. & Lewis, B. (May 1949) *Report 4460* of the Bureau of Mines
[12] Médard, L. (1952) *Mém. Poudres* **34** 299
[13] Audrieth, L. F. & Ogg, B. A. (1951) *The Chemistry of Hydrazine.* New York
[14] Doyle, W. H. (1969) *Loss Prev.* **3** 14
[15] Muir, G. D. (1955) *Chem. Age*, p. 1373
[16] Carlisle, P. J. (1949) *Chem. Eng. News* **27** 150
[17] Taylor, J. (1952) *Detonation in Condensed Explosives.* London
[18] Davies, M. N. (1939) *Trans. Faraday Soc.* **35** 1184
[19] Audrieth, L. F. (1934) *Chem. Rev.* **15** 169
[20] (1970) *Nachr. Chem. Tech.* **18**
[20b] Hajal, I. & Combourieu, J. (1961) *Compt. Rend.* **253** 2346 and (1962) **255** 509
[21] Anon. (1956) *Chem. Eng. News* **34** 2450
[22] Benson, F. R. (1947) *Chem. Rev.* **41** 1
[23] Schlessinger, G. G. (1966) *Chem. Eng. News* **44** 46
[24] Chabrier de la Saulnière, P. (1942) *Ann. de Chimie* **17** 353
[25] Graefe, A. F. (1956) *Chem. Eng. News* **36** 52
[26] Peters, G. & Ganter, W. (1938) *Angew. Chem.* **51** 29
[27] Robertson, N. C. & Pease, R. N. (1942) *J. Am. Ch. Soc.* **64** 1880
[28] Anon. (1924–5) Jahresbericht IV der *Chem. Tech. Reichsanstalt*, p. 30
[29] Médard, L. (1954) Unpublished experiments conducted at Pierre Bénite with the collaboration of the Société d'Ugine
[30] Wöhler, L. & Roth, J. F. (1926) *Chem. Zeit.* **50** 761 and 781
[31] Gause, E. H. & Montgomery, P. D. (1960) *J. Chem. Eng. Data* **5** 351
[32] Walker, M. & Eldred, D. N. (1925) *Ind. Eng. Chem.* **17** 1074
[33] Perret, A. & Krawczynski, A. (1932) *Bull. Soc. Chim. Fr.* [4] **51** 622
[34] Pannetier, G. & Laffitte, P. (1948) *Compt. Rend.* **226** 341
[35] Berthelot, M. (1883) *Bull. Soc. Chim. Fr.* [2] **39** 149
[36] Welcher, R. P., Berets, D. J. & Sentz, L. E. (1957) *Ind. Eng. Chem.* **49** 1755
[37] Kharasch, M. S. *et al.* (1949) *Ind. Eng. Chem.* **41** 2840
[38] Moureu, C. & Bongrand, J. (1909) *Bull. Soc. Chim. Fr.* [4] **5** 846
[39] Kischenbaum, A. D. & Grosse, A. V. (1953) *J. Am. Ch. Soc.* **75** 499
[40] Armstrong, G. T. & Marantz, S. (1960) *J. phys. Chem.* **64** 1776
[41] Médard, L. (1949) *Lab. C.S.E.*
[42] Kast, H. & Haid, A. (1922) *Zft. ges. Sch. u. Spr.* **17** 116
[43] Lemoult, P. (1906) *Compt. Rend.* **143** 902;   Stein, A. R. (1968) *Chem. Eng. News* **46** 7
[44] Lemoult, P. (1897) *Compt. Rend.* **125** 782
[45] Chrétien, A. & Woringer, B. (1951) *Compt. Rend.* **232** 1114
[46] Deb, S. K. & Yoffe, A. D. (1959) *Trans. Faraday Soc.* **55** 106
[47] Matignon, C. (1908) *Bull. Soc. Chim.* [4] **3** 618
[48] Marsh, F. D. & Hermes, M. E. (1964) *J. Am. Ch. Soc.* **86** 4506
[49] Anon. (1976) *Inform. Chim.* No. 158, 109
[50] Coppolino, A. P. (1974) *Chem. Eng. News* **52** No. 25, 3
[51] Currie, C. L. & Darwent, B. de B. (1963) *Canad. J. Chem.* **41** 1048

[52] Grieco, P. A. & Mason, J. P. (1967) *J. Chem. Eng. Data* 12 623
[53] Dokter, T. (1985) *J. Hazardous Mat.* 12 207
[54] Michels, A. M. J. F., Dumoulin, E. M. L. & Gerver, J. H. (1956) *Rec. trav. Chim.* 75 5
[55] Berthelot, M. & Vieille, P. (1881) *Compt. Rend.* 92 1307
[56] Barker, C. K. & Cordes, A. W. (1965) *J. Physical Chem.* 69 334
[57] Mark, H. B. & Mulligan (1984) *Chem. Eng. News* 62 No. 5, 4
[58] Cochran, J. (1979) *Chem. Eng. News* 57 No. 12, 4
[59] Mulin *et al.* (1984) *C.A.* 100 141529 z
[60] Yakovleva, G. S. *et al.* (1977) *C.A.* 86 57636 s
[61] Dupré, G., Paillard, C. & Combourieu, J. (1971) *Compt. Rend.* C.273 445
[62] Hopps, H. B. (1970) *Chem. Eng. News* 49 No. 30, 3
[63] Frankenberg, P. E. (1982) *Chem. Eng. News* 60 No. 3, 97
[64] Biltz, W. (1928) *Z. anorg. Chem.* 170 161
[65] Anon. (1951) *Chem. Eng. News* 29 5473
[66] Guinchant, J. (1905) *Compt. Rend.* 140 1170
[67] Stein, A. R. (1968) *Chem. Eng. News* 46 No. 45, 7
[68] Clothier, P. Q. E. *et al.* (1985) *J. Physic. Chem.* 89 2992

30

Explosive salts

30.1 GENERAL OBSERVATIONS ON EXPLOSIVE SALTS

There are many explosive salts with highly varied chemical properties. This chapter examines

1° Salts with an oxidising anion and a combustible cation. The latter is usually a cation derived from a nitrogen base which may be either inorganic (ammonia, hydrazine, hydroxylamine) or organic (for example, amine or substituted hydrazine). To this can be added cations containing one or more combustible ligands, such as CO, NH_3, N_2H_4, pyridine, ethylene diamine, etc.

One rarely finds salts with a combustible anion (acetate, for example) and an oxidising cation (NO, NO_2 cation), but such salts are likely to be explosive.

2° Salts with an anion which contains two explosophore groups, in particular acid salts of nitro-compounds such as picrates, the salts of hydrazoic acid, and the acetylides.

3° Salts whose formation from the elements is quite weakly exothermic, for example various oxalates which are weak but sensitive explosives.

30.2 SALTS OF NITROGEN BASES

30.2.1 The explosive salts of ammonium

As well as ammonium nitrate (see Chapter 24) and ammonium perchlorate (see Chapter 19), there are other explosive ammonium salts, the heats of formation of which are given in Table 30.1.

The *chlorate* NH_4ClO_3, which can be prepared by a metathetical reaction between ammonium sulphate and barium chlorate, is unstable both in the dry

crystalline state and as an aqueous solution. It decomposes spontaneously
in three days at 20°C or in a few hours at 60°C, turning greenish–yellow
and releasing a complex mixture of gases (Cl_2, ClO_2, N_2O, O_2, etc.).

Table 30.1

Heats of formation of various salts

Compound	Formula	Heat of formation at cst. pr. (kJ/mol)
AMMONIUM SALTS		
Ammonium chlorate	NH_4ClO_3	272
Ammonium perchlorate	NH_4ClO_4	295
Ammonium bromate	NH_4BrO_3	213
Ammonium iodate	NH_4IO_3	392
Ammonium periodate	NH_4IO_4	339
Ammonium nitrite	NH_4NO_2	264
Ammonium permanganate	NH_4MnO_4	694
Ammonium chromate	$(NH_4)_2CrO_4$	1 150
Ammonium dichromate	$(NH_4)_2Cr_2O_7$	1 780
SALTS OF NITROGEN BASES		
Hydrazinium mononitrate	$N_2H_5NO_3$	250
Hydrazinium monoperchlorate	$N_2H_5ClO_4$	180
Hydrazinium diperchlorate	$N_2H_6(ClO_4)_2$	293
Methylammonium nitrate	$CH_3NH_3NO_3$	353
VARIOUS EXPLOSIVE SALTS		
Tetrammine copper (II) nitrate	$[Cu(NH_3)_4](NO_3)_2$	686
Sodium azide	NaN_3	− 21
Potassium azide	KN_3	− 1
Lithium azide	LiN_3	− 11
Calcium azide	CaN_6	− 46
Strontium azide	SrN_6	− 7
Barium azide	BaN_6	22
Cuprous azide	CuN_3	− 280
Cupric azide	CuN_6	− 586
Silver azide	AgN_3	− 310
Mercury azide	Hg_2N_6	− 592
Lead azide	PbN_6	− 483
Silver oxalate	$Ag_2C_2O_4$	669
Mercury oxalate	HgC_2O_4	678

In the crystalline state it is as sensitive to impact and ignition as
P.E.T.N. In the lead block test Aufschläger [1] obtained an expansion of
240 cm³ for 10 g against 193 cm for ammonium perchlorate, the difference

being explained by the fact that NH_4ClO_3 has a lower heat of formation than NH_4ClO_4. When heated, it decomposes and explodes at a temperature (80 to 100°C) which depends on the conditions of heating. In contact with a combustible substance (paper, etc.) its oxidising property is strong enough to produce spontaneous ignition. It is therefore a dangerous substance.

It is formed whenever a chlorate is mixed with an ammonium salt in the presence of traces of moisture. Such mixtures gradually turn yellow and in a few days give off a smell of chlorine (or chlorine oxide). In large quantities these mixtures gradually heat until they explode. A case has been reported of a drum which had been used to hold ammonium chloride and which was not properly cleaned before potassium chlorate was put in it. It exploded several days later. It is therefore very important for safety not to expose chlorates to contamination by ammonium salts and to keep them away from stocks of ammonium nitrate and fertilisers containing ammonium nitrate. The same segregation rules must be followed when loading transport vehicles.

Similarly, ammonium nitrate or any other ammonium salt should not be mixed with a chlorite. At ordinary temperature a reaction takes place which releases gases with an odour of chlorine.

The *bromate* NH_4BrO_3 is even less stable than the chlorate and is more sensitive to impact than the latter. When heated, it deflagrates in a matter of minutes at 55°C. By contrast, the *iodate* NH_4IO_3 is more stable. When heated to 150°C in moderate quantities, it melts and decomposes according to the chemical equation

$$2NH_4IO_3 \rightarrow N_2 + I_2 + O_2 + 4H_2O.$$

The *periodate* NH_4IO_4 is also exploded by heating and is much more sensitive to mechanical actions than the perchlorate, since an explosion [2] occurred when the periodate was being shovelled from one container into another.

Ammonium nitrite NH_4NO_2 forms crystals with a specific gravity of about 1.48 g/cm³. It is an unstable compound which decomposes slowly at about 30°C, releasing nitrogen and water vapour. In an atmosphere containing ammonia it is slightly more stable and can be stored at up to 60°C. Beyond that temperature decomposition is more rapid and becomes explosive at around 100°C.

A diluted (around 12%) aqueous solution of ammonium nitrite, which is used in the manufacture of nylon 6, is obtained by absorbing nitrous fumes diluted in inert gases in a solution of NH_4CO_3H in excess in order to maintain the pH above 7. This solution must be maintained at below 50°C. However, as Millon [37] pointed out, a solution of ammonium nitrite with enough ammonia added to give it a high pH decomposes only slowly at 100°C.

In the crystalline state ammonium nitrite is quite sensitive to impact and initiation. This explosive has a stoichiometric composition, and, according to the equation for the explosive reaction,

$$NH_4NO_2 \rightarrow N_2 + 2H_2O(v),$$

its heat of explosion at constant volume (lower calorific value) is 3525 kJ/kg. Its detonation velocity, when it is loaded at a density of 1.45, reaches 7730 m/s [3]. Given these properties, it is comparable to the classic nitro explosives such as TNT. Its critical detonation diameter, when it is at a low density close to 1, is of the order of 3 mm.

It may happen in the manufacture of nitric acid that when the ovens used for the catalytic oxidation of ammonia are switched on, oxidation is poor or non-existent in some sections of the catalyst. Unoxidised ammonia thus passes through these zones and mixes further on with nitrogen oxides from those areas of the catalyst which were at the correct temperature. In the condensers which follow, instead of an acid condensate like the one obtained in normal working, there is an alkaline condensate which is a solution of ammonium nitrate and nitrite with ammonia. On dry walls, in zones where the temperature is lower than 110°C, crystals of ammonium nitrite may also be deposited. These crystals, like the solution, are liable to decompose explosively if they come into contact with acid vapours. These nitrite deposits can be avoided, especially in tube stacks, by circulating a large quantity of water through the condensers and pouring these nitrite-nitrate solutions into the drain via an extraction chamber located at the base of the condensers.

The accidental formation of ammonium nitrite also played a major part in an accident which occurred in 1979 in the south of France. Waste gases from an oven in which a complex chemical reaction was taking place were expelled through a ventilator leading into a steel tube on the factory roof. At one point, when the equipment was not working properly, these gases contained nitrous vapours and ammonium nitrate dust, and they left deposits on the internal wall of the pipe of a mixture of ammonium nitrate and ammonium nitrite sufficiently rich in nitrite to cause a very powerful explosion.

NH_4NO_2 may be formed accidentally when a slightly wet inorganic nitrite mixes with an ammonium salt. This explains how a fire began in June 1972 in Great Britain on a lorry which had been loaded with sacks of ammonium nitrate without the floor having first been swept clean of sodium nitrite which had leaked from a burst sack in a previous load.

It is important, then, both in transport and storage, to keep all kinds of nitrites and ammonium salts well apart.

The formation of nitrite must be avoided in the manufacture of ammonium nitrate when aqueous nitric acid is saturated with ammonia, which means that the acid must contain no dissolved nitrous fumes. Neither must the piped gaseous ammonia contain droplets of oil from the compressors, since the reduction of nitric acid by oil produces nitrous acid.

Ammonium permanganate NH_4MnO_4 forms purple crystals which are readily obtained by the reaction of potassium permanganate with ammonium chloride. It decomposes slowly at about 70°C, and rapidly beyond 90°C. When heated abruptly to above 100°C, it explodes with a yellow flame, leaving a residue of MnO and MnO_2, and the gases produced contain O_2, NO_2, and H_2O. From a study of the induction period prior to the explosion Bircumshaw and Taylor [4] found that the activation energy of its explosion is between 109 and 113 kJ/mol. Ammonium permanganate may be formed in a mixture containing both ammonium nitrate and potassium permanganate. If the mixture also contains a readily combustible substance such as sawdust, the whole may gradually heat up until it becomes explosive, as was seen in an accident in Witten (Germany) in 1906.

The *dichromate* $(NH_4)_2Cr_2O_7$ decomposes exothermically when it is raised to around 190°C. This decomposition, which is represented by the equation

$$(NH_4)_2Cr_2O_7 \rightarrow Cr_2O_3.H_2O + N_2 + 3H_2O(v),$$

presents a number of peculiarities (role of the specific surface) which have been studied by Taylor [5]. In a fairly small mass in the open air the reaction is quite calm, but under confinement it turns into a violent explosion, since in the test in a steel tube with nozzle plates (16.2.3) the limit diameter is 3.5 mm.

30.2.2 The salts of hydrazinium

With oxidising anions hydrazine gives explosive salts similar to ammonium salts, but, unlike ammonia, hydrazine is endothermic, so that its salts have a lower heat of formation than the corresponding ammonium salts and therefore have more pronounced explosive properties. A given acid AcH can form two salts

$$N_2H_4.AcH \qquad \text{or} \qquad N_2H_5Ac$$
$$N_2H_4.2AcH \qquad \text{or} \qquad N_2H_6Ac_2,$$

with the first being the more common.

Hydrazinium mononitrate (commonly called *hydrazine nitrate*) $N_2H_5NO_3$ forms somewhat hygroscopic crystals with a specific gravity close to 1.66 which melt at 70.5°C, although there is an unstable form with a m.p. of 62°C. It is a highly sensitive explosive since it can be detonated by 0.25 g of fulminate without confinement at a density of 1.1. When melted and resolidified, it can still be detonated by a Briska detonator. The velocity in a cartridge 30 mm in diameter reaches a maximum of 5600 m/s at a density of 1.3. Its sensitivity to impact is close to that of cyclonite [6]. Clearly, hydrazine nitrate is a sensitive explosive, whereas ammonium nitrate can, for all practical purposes, be excluded from the category of explosives.

When heated without confinement it decomposes at around 200°C more or less according to the equation

$$4N_2H_5NO_3 \rightarrow 5N_2 + 2NO + 10H_2O,$$

giving only very small quantities of nitrogen oxides other than nitrogen monoxide.

When heated in a closed vessel, the decomposition culminates in an explosion, and from this point of view hydrazine nitrate behaves in the same way as ammonium nitrate.

Hydrazinium dinitrate $N_2H_6(NO_3)_2$ can be obtained by precipitating an aqueous solution containing $N_2H_4 + 2HNO_3$ with alcohol. It is unstable and decomposes when heated to beyond 80°C.

Hydrazinium perchlorate $N_2H_5ClO_4$, when heated, first dissociates slowly into hydrazine and perchloric acid, a reaction in every way similar to that of ammonium perchlorate. But abrupt heating causes it to explode at around 260°C. This salt is highly sensitive to impact.

Hydrazinium diperchlorate $N_2H_6(ClO_4)_2$ is a salt with a density of 2.2 which melts at over 210°C and has been considered for use as a propellant. Drying it is a delicate operation which has caused explosions.

30.2.3 Methylammonium nitrate

Methylammonium nitrate $CH_3NH_3NO_3$, known commercially as monomethylamine nitrate, is the simplest of the amine nitrates. It has been manufactured industrially in large quantities for quite a long time, since it is one component of some blasting explosives of the slurry type. It is a substance which forms hygroscopic crystals with a specific gravity of 1.45 g/cm³. When it is pure, it melts at 111°C and has good thermal stability up to around 150°C. Using the method explained in 14.2.4, the following explosive properties can be easily calculated:

$$T_V = 2105°K \qquad Q_V = 3560 \text{ kJ/kg} \qquad V_0 = 1190 \text{ dm}^3/\text{kg}.$$

Its properties have been studied by Le Roux [7]. In the Sevran drop-weight test (see 15.2.5.2) it gives 40 explosions in 100 tests with a mass of 10 kg falling from 3 m. At a density of 0.9 g/cm³ it can be detonated quite easily with a No. 8 detonator. In a steel tube with a diameter of 30 mm it can be detonated by a booster at more than 3000 m/s at densities of 1 and 1.1 g/cm³. It has a c.p.u (see 14.3.2) of 100, and is therefore a 'powerful' explosive even though its sensitivity is quite poor.

It is manufactured industrially as a hot, aqueous, 86–87% solution by saturating an 80% solution of nitric acid with methylamine. When this solution is transferred to transport containers, it partially crystallises at around 42°C and becomes a magma of crystals and saturated solution containing 60% nitrate. Tests carried out in 1968 by American producers led to the conclusion that the hot solution and the partially crystallised magma are not sensitive to a No. 8 detonator. When barrels containing the product are exposed to fire, they burst after a certain length of time, and then when the heat has expelled enough water, the substance burns calmly in air.

However, this hot solution did explode on 6 August 1974 in Wenatchee in a stainless steel rail tanker with a wall 13 mm thick containing 38 000 litres. The tanker was the last of a five-carriage train parked on a siding which was struck by several carriages sent along the same track. An orange-coloured flame and a column of grey smoke were seen rising from some distance away, and then some fifteen to twenty seconds later there was a detonation which blasted a hole in the ground and threw metal debris over a kilometre away. Two people were killed and over a hundred were injured. Although the cause of the accident cannot be stated for certain, it may have been one of the following:

1° Methylammonium nitrate in the evacuation pipe and valve at the foot of the tank was subjected to impact and intense friction by the collision.

2° The impact threw the semi-liquid mass in surges from one end to the other, causing high pressure waves, since, in tests conducted after the accident, a (gauge) pressure of more than 6 bars was measured in a similar carriage. Gas bubbles may have been formed by cavitation and subjected to violent compression, so creating hot spots.

Between 1969 and 1974, the substance was transported over forty times in tankers without incident. The following are some of the lessons to be learnt from the accident in Wenatchee:

(a) In a container with a strong wall a deflagration in methylammonium nitrate quickly gives way to a detonation.

(b) Since the crystals are more sensitive than the solution, their presence even in small amounts should be taken into account when choosing transport conditions.

(c) In a very large mass, the dynamic phenomena produced by an impact (or by sudden braking) on a vehicle have an order of magnitude different from those which are found in a moderate mass such as the contents of a drum.

Since this accident, methylammonium nitrate in an 86% solution is no longer transported in railway tankers in the United States, but only in polyethylene containers placed inside an outer protective covering.

30.2.4 Amine nitrates and perchlorates

Primary and secondary aliphatic amine nitrates tend to be very hygroscopic. In the dry state only the nitrates of monomethylamine, dimethylamine, and ethylamine are explosive. Tetramethylammonium nitrate $(CH_3)_4N.NO_3$ is not. Some heterocyclic bases such as piperazine and morpholine give nitrates which deflagrate when heated.

Nitrogen bases with a negative heat of formation give particularly explosive nitrates. A concentrated aqueous solution of 2-aminothiazole nitrate is liable to decompose explosively.

Sodium nitrite or any other metal nitrite must not be allowed into contact with an amine salt (nitrate, chloride, etc.) since amine nitrite would be formed, a salt even less stable than ammonium nitrite.

Most of the perchlorates formed by amines are more or less hygroscopic. *Methylammonium perchlorate* occurs as white crystals with a specific gravity of 1.63 g/cm³ which are highly soluble in water. It is extremely sensitive to impact and initiation and, in the lead block test, is close to cyclonite in its power. In the Dutch test (see 16.1.3) it burns very strongly at around 260°C.

Generally speaking, even when amine perchlorates are low-strength, they are quite sensitive to impact and friction. In this respect, *pyridinium perchlorate* $C_5H_5NH.ClO_4$ deserves a special mention.

Explosions have been reported on a number of occasions during the purification of pyridine using the method described in 1926 by Arndt and Nachwey, which involves the perchlorate of this base as an intermediate product. In one particularly serious explosion in Paris in 1948 a chemist was killed in a university laboratory. It seems to have happened during the transfer of dry perchlorate from one container to another. This dry perchlorate occurs as non-hygroscopic crystals which melt at 298°C, and which, in the Dutch test, deflagrate at around 320°C with a loud noise. Moureu and Munsch [8] concluded from an experimental study that this perchlorate, although undoubtedly explosive, should not be classified with the most sensitive explosives which present very great risks in handling. They believe that the 1948 explosion may have been caused by the presence as an impurity of ammonium chlorate, which is known to be very sensitive. Kuhn and Otting [9] note that the decomposition of pyridine perchlorate is catalysed by the presence of certain ions (Cu^{2+}, Zn^{2+}). In any event, one can only advise against purifying pyridine by the above-quoted method, especially since there are other, risk-free, methods available.

Pyridinium dichromate $(C_5H_5NH)_2Cr_2O_7$, a salt with a beautiful orange colour which melts at 145°C, seems to present fewer dangers than the perchlorate of the same base. It has been proposed in organic chemistry as a gentle oxidising agent in an aprotic medium [42]. However, there is a risk of explosion if certain precautions are not taken in preparing it [51]: chromium trioxide must first be completely dissolved in water and then pyridine must be added slowly, with the temperature not being allowed to rise above 25°C.

Amine permanganates are no less dangerous than ammonium permanganate

(see 30.2.1).   There have been reports of explosion during handling of
tetrabutylammonium [41] and benzyltriethylammonium [43] perchlorates.

Urea is not an amine but an amide.   Its nitrate, which has the formula
$CO(NH_2)_3.HNO_3$, is a white crystalline powder which is used in the dairy
industry to clean machines and equipment, since it liberates nitric acid in
the presence of water.   It is an explosive substance [40], although not
sensitive to impact, but it can be detonated more easily than ammonium
nitrate.   Guanidinium nitrate is less sensitive than urea nitrate.

It is clear from the above observations that caution is needed in any
operation in which an amine or a nitrogen-containing substance is in the
presence of an oxidising salt or acid, especially a perchlorate.

30.3 EXPLOSIVE SALTS WITH LIGANDS TO THE CATION

30.3.1 Explosive salts containing a cation with ligands

Among the very many coordination compounds are salts with an oxidising
anion (nitrate, chlorate, perchlorate, etc.) and a cation containing
combustible ligands.   Such compounds are often explosives which are sometimes highly sensitive.   One of the oldest known is tetrammine copper (II)
nitrate, formerly known as ammonium copper nitrate or cuprammonium nitrate

$$[Cu(NH_3)_4](NO_3)_2$$

the explosive properties of which were studied in 1888 by Mallard and Le
Chatelier [10].   This salt, which takes the form of dark-blue crystals
which melt at $210°C$ and already begin to decompose at that temperature,
then deflagrates vigorously at around $270°C$, leaving a black residue of
copper oxide.   It can be exploded by the falling weight or ignited by a
detonator of mercury fulminate.   Nitrous fumes are amongst the explosion
products.   It was later studied by Bassett and Durrant [11] together with
the two nitrites

$$[Cu(NH_3)_2](NO_2)_2$$

and

$$[Cu(NH_3)_4](NO_2)_2$$

Many other similar compounds have been studied, including the chlorates
of tetrammine copper (II) and of various tetralkylamine coppers (II), which
are highly sensitive to impact and which deflagrate at temperatures between
94 and $174°C$ [12], and hexammine chromium (II) permanganate

$$[Cr(NH_3)_6](MnO_4)_2$$

as well as hexammine chromium (III) perchlorate

$$[Cr(NH_3)_6](ClO_4)_3,$$

which is reported by Pennington to have injured a researcher who was mixing
crystals of the substance with a glass rod.

Hydrazine as a ligand in a complex cation also forms very sensitive

salts, such as
- Hoffmann and Marburg's [13] hydrazine copper (II) nitrate,
- Franzen and Mayer's [14] trihydrazine nickel (II) nitrate

$$[Ni(N_2H_4)_3](NO_3)_2,$$

- the nitrates of similar ions of zinc, cadmium, and cobalt with the ligand hydrazine, the explosive properties of which have been studied by Médard and Barlot [15]. The nickel compound gave rise to a spontaneous explosion [16].

The complex salts $LiClO_4.2N_2H_4$ and $NaClO_4.N_2H_4$ explode when one tries to crush them in a mortar.

Friederich [17] has studied similar complex chlorates and perchlorates. No applications have been found for them because they are generally too sensitive.

A group of seventeen similar complex salts containing tetrammine copper nitrate, which has just been discussed, and ammonium hexanitrocobaltate (III), in which it is the anion which contains the oxidising ligand, have been studied by Tomlinson et al. [18], who measured their deflagration temperatures, which fall between 265 and 360°C, and their sensitivity to impact. One of the most sensitive of these salts is hexammine cobalt nitrate (III).

Some picrates seem to be extremely sensitive. Thus, the bright yellow precipitate which picric acid gives with a basic solution of lead acetate and which is probably a basic picrate is, according to Carey, even more sensitive to impact than mercury fulminate.

Great care must be taken when preparing and handling such salts of complex ions since it takes very little to explode some of them. For example, dihydrazine nickel (II) perchlorate

$$[Ni(N_2H_4)_2](ClO_4)_2$$

can explode in water on simple contact with a glass stirring rod [19].

Amongst these complex salts are those containing pyridine (Pyr) which have been prepared by Sinha and Ray [20]:

$$[CuPyr_4](ClO_4)_2 \qquad [AgPyr_4](ClO_4)$$
$$[CuPyr_6](ClO_4)_2 \qquad [MnPyr_8](ClO_4)_2.$$

Some of them are explosive.

30.3.2 Salts forming explosive molecular combinations

A salt with an oxidising anion, such as a nitrate or a perchlorate, may quite frequently, when crystallised out of a solution into an organic solvent, separate out as an explosive addition compound (molecular combination). The chemical literature mentions quite a number of such compounds formed by methanol or some other alcohol, acetamide, methyl cyanide (acetonitrile), etc. The following are some examples:

1. It has been known for a long time that the combination formed by urea with sodium nitrate and water $CO(NH_2)_2.NaNO_3.H_2O$ deflagrates when it is heated. This is also true of the compound $6CO(NH_2)_2.Ca(NO_3)_2$.

2. Calcium nitrate bismethanol $Ca(NO_3)_2.2CH_3OH$ and calcium methyl-

cyanide nitrate $Ca(NO_3)_2 \cdot CH_3CN$, the last of which was discovered by Naumann [45].

The hard mass formed by the reaction of equimolar quantities of calcium nitrate and ethanediol (ordinary glycol) has been proposed for use as a blasting explosive.

3° The addition compounds of benzonitrile with nitrates, discovered by Guntz and Martin [46] in 1910

$$4Cu(NO_3)_2 \cdot C_6H_5CN$$
$$2Mn(NO_3)_2 \cdot C_6H_5CN.$$

4° The crystalline compound prepared by Lund [47]

$$AgClO_4 \cdot 3CH_3CN.$$

5° The various addition compounds of dimethyl sulphoxide $(CH_3)_2SO$ with perchlorates.

The precise composition of these substances is not very well known. Some of them may not be simple juxtaposition compounds but coordinate compounds like those in the previous section. Most of them are explosive, although the nitrates are less sensitive than the perchlorates. Writing about tropylium perchlorate, which has caused several accidents, Barltrop [48] quite rightly recommends that the greatest precautions should be taken when handling non-metallic perchlorates. They are often liable to explode under the effect of a very weak mechanical action. This is the case with the perchlorates of thianthrene and perylene [52].

30.4 THE SALTS OF AROMATIC NITRO-COMPOUNDS

30.4.1 The nature of the salts of aromatic nitro-compounds

In the first place aromatic nitro acids, like the nitrobenzoic acids, give salts which are no less explosive than the acid itself. Nitrophenols, the acidity of which increases with the number of NO_2 groups they contain, form explosive salts of which the best known are the picrates. In the aromatic nitroamines the amino or imino group also becomes acidic and these amines form explosive salts.

30.4.2 Metallic picrates

Picric acid displaces the carbon dioxide in carbonates. This reaction occurs readily in the presence of water and thus usually gives a hydrated picrate (for example, zinc picrate with $6H_2O$, copper picrate with $3H_2O$, etc.). These picrates may exist at varying degrees of hydration, and this explains the discrepancies to be seen in the results given by different authors of tests of sensitivity to impact. However, some picrates, such as potassium and silver picrate, occur only in the anhydrous form.

All metallic picrates are explosive. Those of heavy metals, such as anhydrous or $1H_2O$ lead picrate, have the properties of primary explosives (see Carey [49]). The picrates of alkali metals are made to deflagrate very strongly by a flame, and in a large mass this deflagration may turn into a detonation.

One of the most recent studies of picrates was made by Hopper [21], who found that the deflagration temperatures with abrupt heating (with a delay of 5 seconds) range between 295 and 390°C. Sensitivity to impact, measured in an apparatus similar to that of Kast (see 15.2.5.4), varies considerably from one picrate to another. For example, it is 2 joules for the anhydrous nickel picrate and 13 joules for the hydrate

$$Ni[OC_6H_2(NO_2)_3]_2.6H_2O.$$

With the exception of aluminium and tin, all the common metals are attacked by picric acid with the formation of picrates, and this has been known as a source of danger to manufacturers of picric acid for over a century, since the layer of picrate formed is liable to deflagrate under the effect of an impact, friction, or a rise in temperature (in case of a fire in the vicinity). Lead and all its compounds are strictly prohibited in workshops manufacturing or treating picric acid.

In 1901, Dupré [22] reported experiments showing that lead, calcium, or zinc picrates formed *in situ* may detonate molten picric acid. We know of explosions in which a fire in picric acid has caused molten lead from the roof to fall into the acid and form lead picrate which has then detonated the picric acid. Calcium picrate may also act as a detonator, especially when the picric acid is confined. This is believed to be the cause of the accident which destroyed a picric acid factory in La Pallice on 1 May 1916. The fire, which began in a sifting workshop, spread to a store of picric acid in barrels. Workers fought the blaze for fifteen to twenty minutes, but then picric acid melted by the heat of the fire flowed onto the badly cracked calcareous ground and seeped into the cracks, forming calcium picrate which detonated almost 200 tons of picric acid, killing 170 people. It was also calcium picrate which caused an explosion with detonation of 5 tons of picric acid in Huddersfield in 1900.

Such accidents demonstrate that workshops manufacturing or treating picric acid should be built on an impermeable floor of concrete covered, if need be, with asphalt, and that no compound which is attacked by picric acid should be allowed into the workshop. Equipment, such as tubular dryers, should be made of aluminium or stainless steel. Any iron, copper, or zinc parts in the building should be protected from picric acid dust by a coat of lead-free paint.

30.4.3 Organic picrates

Amines and basic heterocyclic nitrogen compounds readily form picrates which are usually not very soluble in cold water. This property is put to use in laboratories or in the organic chemical industry to separate out and purify nitrogen bases, but these organic picrates are explosive, although not very sensitive, and must consequently be treated with caution.

One example is imidazoline-3,Δ3-hydroxymethyl picrate

$$C_6H_2(OH)(NO_2)_3 . N - C - CH_2OH$$
$$\qquad\qquad\qquad\qquad || \quad ||$$
$$\qquad\qquad\qquad\quad CH \quad CH$$
$$\qquad\qquad\qquad\qquad \backslash \; /$$
$$\qquad\qquad\qquad\qquad NH$$

which has the following properties [23]:
- heat of combustion (at constant volume) 14 600 kJ/kg
- heat of formation F_v = 427 kJ/mol
- heat of explosion app. 2400 kJ/mol
- detonation velocity at a diameter of 60 mm:
     3570 m/s at a density of 0.9
     6000 m/s at a density of 1.5.

30.4.4 Explosive salts of nitrophenols

2,4,6-trinitroresorcinol (commonly called styphnic acid) gives salts which
are no less dangerous than the picrates. Indeed, lead styphnate is one of
the components in mixtures used as priming explosives.

Dinitrophenols also form explosive salts which may be detonated by a
strong primer (see 14.4.10). Sodium dinitrophenolate, which crystallises
with $1H_2O$, has a sensitivity to impact comparable to that of picric acid.
Dinitrocresolates are also explosive. The ammonium salts of nitrophenols
burn at a moderate rate, as do the nitrophenols themselves, unlike the
salts of metals (alkali metals or otherwise), which deflagrate with extreme
vigour.

Special mention should be made of ferrous picramate: if a small amount
of water is added to an intimate mixture of picric acid and iron filings,
there is an immediate, strong reaction and the products formed, which are
soluble in acetone, contain, in addition to picramic acid formed by
reduction of picric acid:
(a) ferrous picramate, a brown substance which undergoes a fizzing
deflagration at around 280°C and which is readily ignited by friction;
(b) a dark-coloured substance which may be an iron salt of nitrosodinitro-
phenol.
These substances are dangerous because they deflagrate so readily under the
effect of friction.

30.4.5 The salts of hexanitrodiphenylamine

Applications have been found for the very poor solubility in water of the
potassium salt of hexanitrodiphenylamine (dipicrylamine), a red substance
already mentioned in 26.4.8: the property has been used as the basis for a
process for extracting potassium from the mother liquors of salt marshes.
Forty years ago, a very powerful explosion was caused in one of these
factories when a blowpipe was used to repair a pipe without realising that
it still contained a small quantity of the salt in question.

The ammonium salt $NH_4N[C_6H_2(NO_2)_3]_2$ forms dark-red needles and has been
used a dye (Aurantia yellow).

Most salts of dipicrylamine are readily formed by the action of the
latter on a carbonate or a hydroxide. Some of these salts are hydrated:
for example, strontium salt with $2H_2O$. With the exception of the ammonium
and the magnesium salt, they are more sensitive to impact than hexanitrodiphenylamine itself, and are comparable from this point of view to the
corresponding picrates. The lead salt, which is one of the most sensitive,
has a deflagration temperature of around 195°C.

30.5 AZIDES AND FULMINATES

30.5.1 Azides

Azides are the salts of hydrazoic acid (see 29.4.1), but they have better stability than the latter since they contain the N_3^- anion which has a symmetrical structure†, unlike that of the N_3 group present in hydrazoic acid. Nevertheless, almost all the metallic azides are explosive and, in the anhydrous form‡ often have high sensitivity.

The azides of Cu (I), Ag, and Pb have long been known as explosives, and indeed lead azide PbN_6 is used in mine detonators and has now replaced mercury fulminate. Although these azides are less sensitive to heat than fulminates, their deflagration temperatures (see 16.1.2) being 460°C for AgN_3 and 340 for PbN_6, they are, by contrast, more sensitive to friction and impact, the most sensitive being, apparently, copper azide. A very weak mechanical action will frequently cause azides to explode, as a researcher discovered around 1900 when he was injured by an explosion after lightly touching fine crystals of mercury azide $Hg_2(N_3)_2$ in a vessel with a platinum wire. According to a later report, this azide is even liable to explode spontaneously [53]. Large crystals are sometimes more sensitive to mechanical actions, whilst needle-shaped crystals of lead azide several millimetres long explode when the tip is broken. It has also been reported that when this azide is recrystallised, it may detonate spontaneously in water.

Even when they have fixed several ammonia molecules by forming a coordinate ion, some azides, such as hexammine cobalt (III), are still highly sensitive to impact.

Sodium and potassium azide decompose calmly into metal and nitrogen when heated to around 300°C. They are insensitive to friction and impact, as also to excitation by a strong booster of secondary explosive. Lithium azide and alkaline-earth azides have only moderate explosive properties. Calcium azide, which is formed endothermically, is more explosive than the exothermic azides of barium and strontium. The azide BaN_6, which is used in the manufacture of oxide filaments for triode valves, gives rise to the nitride when it explodes

$$3BaN_6 \rightarrow Ba_3N_2 + 8N_2.$$

This reaction, which liberates gases and releases 285 kJ, has all the properties of an explosive reaction. With calcium azide the comparable decomposition liberates 560 kJ, which explains why explosions of CaN_6 are much more violent than those of BaN_6. Haid, who has made a study of these alkaline-earth azides [25], calculates that the addition of 10% water to barium azide lowers its sensitivity enough for it to be transported as a simple flammable solid.

---

† The azide ion is a resonance hybrid between $(N \equiv N \rightarrow N)^-$ and $(N \leftarrow N \equiv N)^-$.

‡ Some azides occur in the hydrated form (for example, $LiN_3.H_2O$, $BaN_6.H_2O$, and $CaN_6.1.5H_2O$). Some authors have sometimes neglected to say whether their tests were made on an anhydrous or a hydrated azide, which explains the discrepancies between the published results.

Non-explosive sodium azide is used in a reaction with halogenated compounds to make substances containing the azido group N_3 which are used as intermediate products in a variety of syntheses (in particular in the pharmaceutical industry). During the reaction, which is usually carried out in a solution of dimethylformamide, care must be taken to keep the apparatus and the reagents used perfectly free of heavy metals (Pb, Hg, Ag, etc.) or of cadmium, otherwise the highly explosive azides described above may be formed. Sodium azide reacts readily with non-metallic halogenated compounds such as the chlorides of silicon and boron to give the explosive azides $Si(N_3)_4$ and $B(N_3)_3$. Similarly, methylchlorosilanes readily give azide compounds, some of which, like $(CH_3)Si(N_3)_3$, explode below 100°C.

Ammonium azide $NH_4.N_3$, which readily forms long crystals, is, like hydrazinium azide $N_2H_5.N_3$, less sensitive to impact than metal azides, giving 50% explosions in the Sevran drop-weight test for impact energies of 16 to 20 joules. It should be known that if ammonium azide is stored in a desiccator above P_2O_5 or $CaCl_2$ or any other drying agent which is capable of absorbing ammonia but not hydrazoic acid in the vapour state, the latter may accumulate in appreciable quantities in the gas phase and cause an explosion.

Addition compounds of hydrazoic acid with amines are ionic compounds like the azides of alkali metals. Cirulis and Straumann [50], who have made a dozen amine azides, say that they have no explosive properties, and yet it would seem from the thermochemical data available that if a large detonator is used with methylammonium azide $(CH_3 - NH_3)(N_3)$ under strong confinement, the substance can be detonated. Substitution compounds in which hydrogen is replaced by the N_3 azido group are, by contrast, easy to explode (see 29.4.2).

30.5.2 Fulminates

The salts of fulminic acid $C = N - OH$ are well known for their explosive properties. Even sodium fulminate may explode. What is less well known is the fact that fulminates can be formed quite easily whenever ethanol (or any other organic C_2 substance, such as acetaldehyde) is in the presence of nitric acid and a metallic salt. The following accident has been reported, for example: silver nitrate crystals obtained from an acid solution were neutralised by washing with ethyl alcohol; shortly after, the mass, still wet with alcohol, exploded when an attempt was made to pick it up with a porcelain spatula because silver fulminate had formed. The accident would never have happened if propyl alcohol had been used instead of ethyl alcohol.

There is also a risk of fulminate forming acinitromethane (see 26.2.5).

30.6 EXPLOSIVE ACETYLIDES

30.6.1 The complexity of metal compounds derived from acetylene

It has been known for over a century that acetylene in aqueous solutions of salts of heavy metals (especially Cu, Ag, and Hg) precipitates explosive substances called acetylides. The simplest of these compounds, which have formulae such as Cu_2C_2 or Ag_2C_2, are decomposed by strong or medium acids with release of acetylene, and may be considered as substitution compounds in which a metal replaces the hydrogen in acetylene, which is thus a weak acid.

Calcium carbide, whose crystals have a structure similar to those of NaCl, contains, as X-ray analysis has shown, Ca^{2+} and $(C \equiv C)^{2-}$ ions. It can be classified with the acetylides.

However, the salts of heavy metals may form combinations with acetylene which are not simple binary compounds of a metal and carbon. They have a composition which is frequently quite complex and a structure which is sometimes not known for certain. Of these complex acetylene substances many have explosive properties. Acetylene compounds of copper are found in the chemical industry, where they are used to catalyse various reactions, such as the dimerisation of acetylene to vinyl acetylene, an intermediate product in the manufacture of neoprene; on the other hand, if any should form accidentally in factories in which acetylene is being used, they may cause an explosion. Compounds of silver lend themselves to analytical applications (titration of C_2H_2), whilst compounds of mercury should be known because of the accidents they may cause. Gold, which is found with copper and silver in group 1B of the periodic table of elements, also forms an explosive gold acetylide Au_2C_2 which has been known for a long time. It would be wrong to believe, therefore, that, because it does not normally decompose, gold (in leaf form, for example) can be used in apparatuses treating acetylene.

30.6.2 Acetylene compounds of silver

There are fewer silver compounds than there are copper compounds, and their composition is better known. Those which are obtained from solutions of silver nitrate are a good example of the variations in explosive properties with chemical composition.

Acetylene bubbling in an ammoniacal solution of silver nitrate (with a low Ag content) precipitates a yellow substance which becomes white under the effect of an excess of acetylene. This is the acetylide Ag_2C_2. In a neutral or acid solution of silver nitrate containing about 10% $AgNO_3$, acetylene precipitates a white compound with the formula $Ag_3C_2NO_3$ which is often considered as a molecular combination $Ag_2C_2.AgNO_3$. In an acid solution high in silver nitrate the substance which is precipitated [27] has the formula $Ag_2C_2.6AgNO_3$. The equilibria to which these three compounds† may give rise with solutions of silver have been studied in detail by Vestin [28]. They have very different explosive properties (Table 30.2).

The acetylide Ag_2C_2 decomposes suddenly on impact in the dry state in air or even in the wet state in water, but the explosion has only minor effects. If the dry acetylide is subjected, as was done by Eggert and Schimank [29], to the action of a white-hot wire *in a vacuum*, it decomposes with a negligible explosive effect because, although the products of the explosion, carbon and silver, are raised to 2220°K, the heat of explosion is such that only a very small part of the silver produced is volatilised. In air the explosion is slightly stronger because the air trapped between

---

† In 1895, Willgerodt described another explosive compound with the formula $AgC \equiv CH.AgNO_3$.

the crystals is involved in the explosion. Thus, the acetylide Ag_2C_2 is a pseudo-explosive (see the last paragraph of 1.1). The compound $Ag_2C_2.AgNO_3$ is detonated readily by an impact or a flame with serious effects which are seen in both a vacuum and in air:

$$Ag_3C_2NO_3 = CO_2 + CO + 1/2N_2 + 3Ag,$$

since the reaction creates large quantities of gases. It has the nature of a primary explosive. As for $Ag_2C_2.6AgNO_3$, it has no explosive properties and decomposes calmly when heated.

A large number of complex compounds similar to those of silver nitrate can be obtained quite easily, for example,

$$Ag_2C_2.AgCl \qquad Ag_2C_2.Ag_2SO_4.$$

Many of them are sensitive to impact or a flame.

30.6.3 The dangers of silver in the presence of acetylene

The decomposition of the acetylide Ag_2C_2 has such weak mechanical effects that if it occurs in an acetylene atmosphere it does not detonate it. But the products of the decomposition of the acetylide are at a sufficiently high temperature to initiate decomposition of the acetylene, which will either propagate or remain restricted to the vicinity of the heat source, depending on the pressure. Thus, silver and its alloys or compounds should be banned from apparatuses containing or treating acetylene. However, it is acceptable to use silver brazing, called cold brazing[†], to assemble pipes or parts used with acetylene at a (gauge) pressure of no more than 1.5 bars.

Table 30.2

Silver acetylides

	Ag_2C_2	$Ag_2C_2.AgNO_3$	$Ag_2C_2.6AgNO_3$
Heat of formation kJ/mol	− 305	− 218	+ 460
Calorific value Q_v kJ/kg	1 250	1 890	non-explosive; decomposition
Explosion temperature T_v °K	2 220	2 220	to CO_2, NO, NO_2, Ag is
Gas volume at N.T.P. V_0 dm³/kg	23	214	endothermic
Decomposition temperature	150°C (a)	240°C (b)	350°C (c)

(a) Deflagration;   (b) Detonation;   (c) Non-explosive decomposition

† One such type of brazing which is used quite frequently is a quaternary alloy Ag–Cu–Zn–Cd containing 42% silver and 20% copper.

The following accident (1964) proves how rapidly an explosive compound of acetylene can form: in a factory of dissolved acetylene a test paper of silver nitrate was used after purification to check that impurities (PH_3, AsH_3, etc.), which turn the paper black, had been eliminated. The paper was prepared just before use by depositing on a strip of filter paper two drops of a 10% solution of $AgNO_3$. The solution was kept in a 200 ml glass flask closed by a metal screw cap. One day the shift foreman prepared the test paper and then forgot to re-cap the flask of nitrate solution and put it back in the cupboard in which it was normally kept. Eight hours later, after a change of shift, the new foreman, seeing the flask open, picked it up and tried to re-cap it. An explosion occurred and glass splinters from the flask lacerated the operative's left hand. Clearly, the friction of the cap on the neck had exploded the $Ag_3C_2NO_3$ compound which had formed on the wet wall and in the solution as a result of the action of acetylene, which is nearly always present (at rates of 0.00005 to 0.005%) in the air in workshops where acetylene is manufactured.

30.6.4 Acetylene compounds of mercury

The study of compounds created by the action of acetylene on the salts of mercury is complicated by the fact that these salts catalyse the hydration of acetylene into acetaldehyde. Also, amongst the substances obtained are some which are derivatives of $CH_3.CHO$, and in addition vinyl compounds may be formed.

Berthelot mentions a mercury acetylide as early as 1866, and in 1893 Keiser established that its formula was, in fact, HgC_2. It is a highly explosive yellow substance which is precipitated by the action of acetylene on a solution of mercury salt. With the alkaline solution of potassium tetraiodomercurate (II) (Nessler's reagent) it precipitates a complex white substance $HgC_2.HgI$. A hydrate, $3HgC_2.H_2O$, which is also explosive, is obtained by the action of C_2H_2 on an ammoniacal solution of mercuric oxide.

From the action of acetylene on a solution of mercuric chloride which had been acidified by ClH, Biginelli in 1896 obtained white crystals which are hardly soluble in water and which melt at 129–130°C. Originally thought to be an addition compound $HgCl_2.C_2H_2$, Biginelli's compound was later found to be a chlorovinyl mercury chloride

$(Hg - CH = CHCl)^+Cl^-$,

which is found in two stereoisomer forms (*cis* and *trans* with different melting points). Treated with an alkali, Biginelli's compound decomposes to give the hydrated mercury acetylide.

Acetylene precipitates a white substance in a neutral aqueous solution of mercury chloride which is considered to be a derivative of acetaldehyde

$(HgCl)_3C - CHO$.

Many other often quite complex compounds, some of which are explosive, are formed by the reaction of C_2H_2 with solutions of mercury salts of organic acids.

A hydrate of mercury acetylide Hg_2C_2,H_2O forms a grey precipitate when a suspension of mercury acetate in water is saturated with acetylene [30]. It is an explosive substance.

It should be noted that acetylides of mercury, like those of silver, are formed in a neutral or alkaline solution.

30.6.5 The dangers of mercury in the presence of acetylene

Because explosive compounds of acetylene and mercury are formed so readily, the metal should be banned from buildings and equipment in which acetylene is treated.

Explosions which remained unexplained until 1958 occurred in factories making dissolved acetylene in which the raw gas was purified by a purifying mass which contained a small amount of mercury salt (see 28.2.4). If the process of purification is carried out correctly, no dangerous substances can form, but if it is done wrongly, then mercury is liberated and may form an explosive acetylide. The purifying substances involved[†] have a ferric chloride or oxychloride base with copper sulphate and mercury chloride added. The role of the latter in the oxidation reaction of phosphine by ferric chloride

$$PH_3 + 8FeCl_3 + 4H_2O \rightarrow PO_4H_3 + 8FeCl + 8HCl$$

is catalytic, probably passing through an intermediate phosphomercury complex. As for the copper sulphate, it is intended to facilitate the regeneration[‡] in air of the purifying substance. The solution of these salts is absorbed by kieselguhr. The substance also contains a small amount of manganese dioxide to prevent the release of chlorine. It is thus a complex mixture whose liquid phase contains Fe^{3+}, Cu^{2+}, Hg^{2+}, H^+, Cl^-, and $(SO_4)^{2-}$ ions. Its pH is of the order of 1.5.

Without going into detail about the reactions which take place between acetylene impurities and the constituents of the purifying substance, we may say that phosphine in the latter oxidises first at the expense of the ferric ions. When these have been reduced, mercury chloride is reduced

$$PH_3 + 3HgCl_2 + 3H_2O \rightarrow PO_3H_3 + 6HCl + 3Hg.$$

Finally, when the ferric and mercury ions are exhausted, cupric ions come into play and are returned to the cuprous state or even to the state of metallic copper.

Thus, if a purifying substance is used for too long, to the point where its ferric salts are exhausted, mercury is released into the mass and the gas flowing through it carries off mercury vapour at levels which depend on

---

† Purifying substances of this kind, which have a variety of brand names (Siotol, Catalysol, Regenetal, etc.) come in powdered form because they are composed of 40 to 50% absorbing silica (kieselguhr) which is made to absorb 50 to 60% of an aqueous solution containing:
    30 to 40% ferric chloride
    10 to 18% copper sulphate
    1 to 3% mercury chloride
    0.7 to 1.5% manganese salt.
‡ This regeneration in air returns ferrous chloride to the state of ferric chloride.

the vapour pressure of the metal and which will be 1.5 mg/m³ and 3.4 mg/m³ at 20 and 30°C respectively.

Acetylene saturated with mercury vapour loses most of the vapour by condensation when the acetylene is compressed and cooled, which explains why droplets of mercury have been found in acetylene compressors, as well as in the pipes leading away from them and in the oil-separator and drying equipment downstream of the compressors. In some cases even the internal wall of the purifier above the purifying agent has been found to be covered with a lead-grey substance which turned out to be microglobules of mercury which had condensed onto a wall colder than the purifying agent they came from.

This mercury in the high-pressure parts of a factory making dissolved acetylene occurs in a neutral or even alkaline medium, since it was often the case that the oil-separators were cleaned internally by washing with caustic soda and not then thoroughly rinsed. Moreover, the mere presence of rust on the internal walls of the cylinder stack used for oil-separation and drying guarantees a high pH. In such conditions mercury reacts with acetylene to form an acetylide.

Explosions have occurred during manipulation of the outlet valve on dryers and oil-separators, initiated by friction on mercury acetylide. The presence of this acetylide has even been indicated by a metal key, wetted with cleaning liquid and scraped against cement, giving off a large number of sparks caused by deflagration of Hg_2C_2 particles and glowing greenish-white in the darkness.

The consequences for safety of the above observations are:
1° The purifying agent containing ferric chloride and mercury chloride should not be used to exhaustion but replaced or regenerated before the mercury chloride is reduced.
2° An alkaline detergent should not be used to wash apparatuses which treat acetylene at high pressure.

30.6.6 Acetylene compounds of copper

Very many substances are formed by the action of acetylene on compounds of copper, since, besides C_2H_2 substitution compounds which may themselves be combined with copper salts, there exist compounds formed by the addition of C_2H_2 to copper salts. Moreover, the dismutation reaction

$$2Cu (I) = Cu (II) + Cu$$

takes place whenever a copper salt is in the presence of acetylene. The compounds formed, most of which decompose to varying degrees in air, are often obtained as a mixture with the decomposition products of acetylene. Consequently, although a great deal of experimental work has been carried out over the last hundred years, our knowledge of the exact nature of many of these copper acetylene compounds is still imperfect. From the practical point of view of the dangers they pose, the most useful results come from research by Perraudin [31] on the one hand and Feitknecht and Hugi-Carmes [32] on the other. In particular the two Swiss authors have identified the compounds encountered by X-ray diagrams, determined the percentages of copper, carbon of the C ≡ C grouping, residual carbon†, and chlorine where appropriate, and indicated the method by which they are obtained and what their decomposition temperatures are.

True copper acetylide is precipitated by the action of acetylene on an ammonium solution of copper chloride. Authors who have studied it give it the formula $Cu_2C_2.H_2O$, with the exception of Vestin [28] who gives it the formula Cu_2C_2 (anhydrous). It is obtained in the pure state by the action of C_2H_2 in the absence of air, which gives a yellow acetylide, but it is gradually decomposed by oxygen in the air, forming the oxide Cu_2O and graphite carbon, so that it turns reddish-brown. The freshly prepared acetylide is explosive and quite sensitive, and the decomposed substance is still explosive. There are considerable variations in the deflagration temperature: for a recently prepared sample it is usually close to 100°C, but rises to 180°C when the substance has decomposed in moist air.

This copper acetylide was once used in Great Britain to make ignition caps for detonators. When it is good quality, it ignites at around 180°C with a hot flame, but when it has been too badly decomposed by oxidation, giving it a dark hue, contact with an incandescent wire gives only a spray of weak sparks.

With hydrochloric solutions of copper chloride the precipitate, which may be reddish-brown or purple, is the compound $Cu_2C_2.CuCl$, but the action of acetylene on a suspension of CuCl in an alcohol containing HCl gives colourless compounds which are practically non-explosive

$$C_2H_2(CuCl)_2 \quad \text{and} \quad C_2H_2(CuCl)_3$$

which are decomposed by water with formation of the acetylide Cu_2C_2.

In solutions of copper salts the precipitates are black, explosive substances which were thought by early authors to be a copper acetylide (analysis showed a Cu:C ratio close to 1:2). We now know, however, that they are mixtures of copper acetylide with carbon or with substances which are very rich in carbon. There is no cupric acetylide CuC_2; copper is always bonded to the C ≡ C group in the form of Cu (I). In a solution of copper salt Cu (II) reduces to Cu (I) with simultaneous co-precipitation of amorphous carbon or of highly condensed substances. The products thus obtained are black, or grey with a metallic sheen, and are highly sensitive explosives. As both Perraudin [31] and Brameld and his associates [33] found, these products explode violently in the solution in which they have formed on simple contact with a glass rod.

The reaction between dry acetylene and dry copper oxide is more or less rapid depending on the degree of fineness of the Cu_2O. The reaction

$$Cu_2O + C_2H_2 = Cu_2C_2.H_2O$$

is always accompanied by some decomposition of the acetylene, so that the product is black and contains residual carbon. After explosion this black product leaves a mixture of cuprous oxide, metallic copper, and amorphous

---

† Dissolving an acetylene compound of copper in a solution of KCN liberates carbon of the C ≡ C groups as C_2H_2, turns copper into a soluble cyanate complex, and leaves carbon which is not in the C ≡ C form as an insoluble residue.

carbon.

It can be seen that we are dealing with many, varied, and complex substances. We cannot talk of 'copper acetylide' but only of acetylene compounds of copper. One very interesting observation by Feitknecht and Hugi–Carmes is that in some cases, when a decomposition product in air of an acetylene compound of copper chloride is placed back in contact with acetylene, it deflagrates spontaneously.

30.6.7 The action of acetylene on copper and its alloys

There can be no doubt that in many circumstances dangerous compounds are formed by the action of acetylene on a copper wall. The following are two examples which occurred between 1950 and 1965:

1° During dismantling of an apparatus for the low–temperature treatment of gases containing small amounts of acetylene, green deposits were found on a tube stack. They were a carbonate containing acetylene compounds and they exploded with a flame and a sharp noise when hit with a hammer or rubbed with a wire brush.

2° When an electrician working on a junction box attempted to scrape a greenish deposit from some cables, there was an explosion which hurled a metal splinter into his eye. The inquiry showed that long exposure to air containing some acetylene had led to the formation of an acetylide.

It is interesting to recall that as long ago as 1860 Nickles [38] had drawn attention to the risk of accidental formation of dangerous acetylene compounds when a copper pipe carries badly purified lighting gas (coal gas) containing acetylene and ammonia. He recalled that in 1839 in New York, when a worker blew into a pipe he was dismantling which had been in service for a long time and was partly blocked by a deposit of naphthalene, he was killed instantly by a 'terrible explosion'. Tests on the blackish crust extracted from a similar pipe showed that it could be exploded by rubbing it with an iron wire. Torrey realised that the explosive substance in question does not form when the gas has been carefully cleaned of ammonia traces. Nowadays, when the gas is manufactured by pyrogenation of coal, it is so well purified that it is free of ammonia, and copper can be used in the distribution network even though it contains traces of acetylene.

Researchers are in agreement on one point: in the absence of moisture acetylene has no effect on clean copper, on copper covered with a film of copper oxide, or on copper alloys from ordinary temperature up to around 200°C. The same is still true at low temperatures for dry acetylene which contains a small amount of ammonia, but in practice acetylene is always more or less moist. On the other hand, copper metals on which acetylene may act often have their surface covered with corrosion products such as copper carbonate. In both new and old pressure gauge tubes Feitknecht and Hugi–Carmes frequently found deposits of the basic chloride $3Cu(OH)_2.CuCl_2$ formed by the action of brazing flux when the flexible pressure gauge tube is fixed to the block carrying the threaded rod. Such ion compounds react readily with acetylene to give compounds of which some are explosive. Moreover, it should be noted that it is not just the ionised copper which is attacked, since acetylene acting on a mixture of powdered copper and copper chloride reacts very rapidly with all the free copper to form essentially the simple acetylide Cu_2C_2. In the presence of chloride free copper is attacked rather than the chloride.

Following an explosion in Odense (Denmark) in 1938 during testing of a pressure-reducing valve which had just been repaired, tests were carried out [36] on brass with the same composition as that of the pressure gauge tube in which the explosion had occurred. They led to the conclusion that the explosion had started at two points in the tube where the brass had been subjected to prior corrosion on which acetylene had formed an explosive acetylene compound. The tests showed that crystallised copper nitrate deposited on a glass plate is not itself attacked by acetylene, but that it is attacked if it is in contact with brass.

Brameld and his associates [33] have studied the action of acetylene on various bronzes and brasses and found that, even on some alloys containing no more than 50% copper, explosive acetylene compounds may be formed, and that the formation of such compounds is greatly assisted by the presence of a small amount of air and oxygen.

By contrast, cupro-aluminiums with 90% copper can be left exposed to impure acetylene without the metal being attacked, although tombac (brass with 20% zinc) is attacked rapidly, as a Swedish factory discovered forty years ago as a result of an unfortunate experience.

Perraudin [31] examined more than one hundred pressure gauge tubes which had been used with acetylene, collecting the deposits which had formed on them for experimental study. His conclusion was that 'Whereas some samples of pure copper or of phosphor bronze containing 93% copper harboured dangerous acetylene compounds, brass with 70% copper and above all nickel silver with 62% copper and 18% nickel showed no compounds giving rise to decomposition by mechanical or thermal impact.'

It has often been pointed out that explosive acetylene compounds of copper which may be formed are decomposed by moisture and that if they are left exposed to the air for long enough they undergo changes which turn them into harmless substances. In actual fact, the transformation is quite a slow process and dangerous deposits can remain dangerous for a very long time.

Voigtsberger [34] has studied the compounds which may be formed on copper metals by the action of acetylene, but in conditions very different from those encountered in practice. He concluded that the copper content of the alloy has only a limited influence on the formation of dangerous acetylene compounds, although acetylene is all the more likely to be ignited by the deflagration of these compounds as the alloy is richer in copper. Hill [35], whose experimental results agree with those of Brameld, Feitknecht, and Perraudin, discusses their importance from a realistic point of view and concludes that everything that has been said about copper acetylides as a cause of igniting acetylene is pure mythology, but this seems to us to be too optimistic an attitude. There can be no doubt that if a small amount of copper acetylene is subjected to impact, friction, or heating, as may happen when using a pressure gauge or manipulating a valve, its explosive decomposition produces a hot spot which may cause any compressed acetylene gas present to explode. It is reasonable, therefore, to ban from acetylene workshops Bourdon pressure gauges with a flexible tube made of copper alloy, since perfectly good pressure gauges are made which have a carbon steel or stainless steel tube. Copper-rich alloys should also be banned except where thorough experiment has established that these alloys are resistant to corrosion by acetylene. In France, as also in the U.K., brass with more than 70% copper is banned, and there is no reason to reduce this figure, given that millions of dissolved-acetylene cylinders are fitted with a brass valve containing 66% copper which seem to have caused no accidents.

All the various tests described above clearly highlight the important part played in the formation of dangerous acetylene compounds by the local presence, even on a surface of no more than one square millimetre, of a copper salt on metal or a copper alloy, which is why an apparatus exposed to the action of acetylene – either normally or potentially – must, after all manufacture or repair work, be carefully inspected and cleaned of all traces of salt compound such as those left by brazing, for example.

The dangers posed by copper acetylides have been no obstacle to their use in large quantities as catalysts in the reaction to form 1,4–butyne diol from C_2H_2 and formaldehyde in a compressed aqueous solution at around 100°C. The prime safety condition is to keep the acetylide moist at all times, which means that when, after several months' use, the activity of the catalyst has diminished and the reaction tower has to be emptied, the catalyst is drowned with jets of compressed water. To avoid having to handle the acetylide on start–up, it is formed *in situ* by the action of acetylene on silica gel soaked in copper nitrate.

30.7 VARIOUS EXPLOSIVE SALTS

With the azides, acetylides, and picrates described above, we have examined some highly explosive salts of heavy metals. There are many others, and some even have an anion which contains no explosophore group, in which case the explosive property is due to the relatively low heat of formation making an exothermic decomposition possible (see 2.3). For example, silver oxalate explodes according to the equation

$$Ag_2C_2O_4 \rightarrow 2Ag(cr) + 2CO_2 + 29 \text{ kcal (cst. vol.),}$$

with the temperature reached being lower than the melting point of silver. Mercury oxalate has a very low calorific value (400 kJ/kg) but presents a sensitivity to impact comparable to that of P.E.T.N. and mercury fulminate.

Silver cyanate Ag(NCO) is not explosive, contrary to what was written about it even in quite recent times. Indeed, we know of no explosive metal cyanate.

Special precautions should be taken with the many complex salts formed by mercury with a wide variety of acids and other substances, such as the orange–coloured compound obtained in 1898 by Deniges who ascribed to it the formula

$$NO_3 \cdot Hg - C_4H_8 - Hg - Hg - NO_3.$$

Mercury and mercury salts should not be allowed to act in a reactive medium without thinking of the possibility that such dangerous substances may be formed.

BIBLIOGRAPHICAL REFERENCES

[1]   Aufschläger, R. (1924) *Z. ges. Sch. Sprengst.* 19 121
[2]   Smith, G. F. (1951) *Ch. Eng. News* 29 1770
[3]   Shidlovskii *et al.* (1968) *Doklady*, p. 415
[4]   Bircumshaw, L. L & Taylor, F. M. (1950) *J. Ch. Soc.*, p. 3674
[5]   Taylor, D. (1955) *J. Ch. Soc.*, p. 1033

[6]   Médard, L. (1952) *Mém. Poudres* **34** 147
[7]   Le Roux, A. (1952) *Mém. Poudres* **34** 129
[8]   Moureu, H. & Munsch, H. (1951) *Arch. maladies prof.* **12** 157
[9]   Kuhn, R. & Ottig. W. (1950) *Chem. Ztg.* **74** 139
[10] Mallard, E. & Le Chatelier, H. (1884-9) *Mém. Poudres* **2** 497
[11] Bassett, H. & Durrant, R. G. (1922) *J. Chem. Soc.* **121** 2630
[12] Amiel, J. (1934) *Compt. Rend.* **199** 51
[13] Hoffmann, K. A. & Marburg (1899) *Ann.* **305** 221
[14] Franzen, H. & von Mayer, O. (1908) *Z. anorg. Chem.* **60** 247
[15] Médard, L. & Barlot, J. (1952) *Mém. Poudres* **34** 159
[16] Ellern, H. & Olander, D. E. (1955) *J. Chem. Educ.* **32** 24
[17] Friederich, W. & Verwoost, P. (1926) *Z. ges. Sch. Sprengst.* **21** 49
[18] Tomlinson, W. R., Ottoson, K. G. & Audrieth, L. F. (1944) *J. Am. Ch. Soc.* **71** 375
[19] Maissen, B. & Schwarzenbach, G. (1951) *Helv. Chim. Acta* **34** 2084
[20] Sinha, P. & Ray, R. C. (1943) *J. Indian Ch. Soc.* **20** 32
[21] Hopper, J. D. (1938) *J. Franklin Inst.* **225** 219
[22] Dupré, A. (1901) *Mém. Poudres* **11** 92
[23] Médard, L. (1953) *Lab. C.S.E.*
[24] Bassière, M. (1930) *Compt. Rend.* **208** 659
[25] Haid, A. (1929) *C.T.R. Bericht VIII*, p. 102
[26] Tully, J. P. (1941) *News Edit.* (Am. Ch. Soc.) **19** 250
[27] Shaw, J. A. & Fisher, L. (January 1949) *Br. pats.* 616.381 and 616.315
[28] Vestin, R. (1954) *Svensk. Kem. Tidskr.* **66** 65
[29] Eggert, J. & Schimank, H. (1918) *Ber.* **51** 454
[30] Burckardt, E. & Travers, M. W. (1902) *J. Chem. Soc.* **81** 1270
[31] Perraudin, R. (1955) Thesis, Paris; (May 1958) *Cuivre et laiton*, No. 43, 33
[32] Feitknecht, W. & Hugi-Carmes, H. (1957) *Schweizer Arch. Angew. Wiss.-u-Technik* **23** 328
[33] Brameld, V. F., Clark, N. T. & Seyfang, A. P. (1947) *J. Soc. Ch. Ind.* **66** 346
[34] Voigtsberger, P. (1965) *Arbeitschutz*, p. 135
[35] Hill, F. W. (1968) *Metall* **22** 153
[36] Hoeg, E. (1938-9) *Beretn. om Statsproveanst. Virksomhed I - Finansaaret.*, p. 6
[37] Millon, E. (1847) *Ann. de chim.* [3] **19** 255
[38] Nickles, J. (1860) *J. Pharm. et Chim.* **38** 79
[39] Pawlikowski, S. & Baginska, J. (1957) *Przemysl Chem.* **13** 338
[40] Médard, L. (1951) *Mémorial Poudres* **33** 113
[41] Morris, J. A. & Mills, D. C. (1978) *Chemistry in Britain* **14** 326
[42] Corey, E. J. & Schmidt, G. (1979) *Tetrahedron Letters* No. 5, 399
[43] Graefe, J. (1983) *Angew. Chem. Intern. Ed.* **22** 625
[44] Pennington, D. E. (1982) *Chem. Eng. News* **60** No. 33, 55
[45] Naumann, A. (1914) *Ber.* **47** 250
[46] Guntz, A. & Martin, F. (1910) *Bull. Soc. Chim.* [4] **7** 313
[47] Lund, H. (1957) *Acta Chem. Scandin.* **11** 491
[48] Barltrop, J. (1980) *Chemistry in Britain* **16** 452
[49] Garey, H. E. (1979) *Chem. Eng. News* **57** 51
[50] Cirulis, A. & Straumanis, M. (1942) *J. Prakt. Chem.* **161** 65
[51] Salmon, J. (1982) *Chemistry in Britain* **18** No. 10, 703
[52] Davia *et al.* (1985) *J. Chem. Soc. Perkin Trans.* 2 135
[53] Yao N. & Huang, H. (1985) *C.A.*, **102** 134423 y

31

Hydrogen and the hydrides

31.1 HYDROGEN GAS

31.1.1 General properties of hydrogen

Ordinary hydrogen (atomic weight 1.008) found in nature is a mixture of two isotopes, light hydrogen or protium (H = 1) and heavy hydrogen or deuterium (D = 2), but this has practically no consequences for safety, even though deuterium has flammability limits slightly different from those of ordinary hydrogen, as can be seen from Table 8.5. The low molar mass of hydrogen produces various properties:

1° This gas, which is diatomic at ordinary temperature, has a density of 0.07 in relation to air. It is the lightest of all the gases.

2° It is less viscous at ordinary temperature than all other gases and so easily crosses porous walls and escapes very easily through the slightest crack. It can thus escape from an apparatus or circuit which would be leakproof to air or any other gas.

3° Its diffusion coefficient is higher than that of other gases at the same temperature, but the accident described in 10.1.4 shows that one cannot rely too heavily on this property to eliminate the gas from a container.

4° Being diatomic, hydrogen gas has a ratio γ of its two specific heats very close to 1.4 like oxygen or nitrogen, which means that it is heated neither more nor less than these gases by isentropic adiabatic compression (see 7.5). For example, from an initial temperature of 18°C, a compression of 1 to 10 bars raises it to 288°C.

At ordinary temperatures the Joule–Thomson coefficient of isenthalpic expansion of hydrogen gas is negative, unlike other gases, so that when hydrogen expands without forming a high-speed jet, it heats up slightly rather than cooling. However, this effect is weak (20°C approximately for an expansion from 200 bars to 1 bar) and the phenomenon does not usually have any consequences for safety.

The dangers associated with hydrogen arise mainly from the ease with which mixtures with air or oxygen ignite. Its minimum ignition energy by a spark is very low (see 10.3.7). A pure hydrogen flame is hardly luminous and becomes visible only if dust is present in the flame. Consequently, leaks of burning hydrogen may easily go unnoticed in the early stages.

31.1.2 The nature of explosions caused by hydrogen

The flame speed of hydrogen–air mixtures is very high (see Table 6.2), so that explosions *in a closed vessel* of mixtures containing hydrogen develop in a much shorter time than do explosions of other gases and cause more damage to weak containers. Dangerous mixtures containing hydrogen may form in many circumstances (see 31.1.3 and 31.1.4). They have been, and still are, the cause of frequent explosions.

If an air–hydrogen mixture such as is formed by a spillage of liquid hydrogen on the ground is ignited by a flame or a spark *in the open air*, it deflagrates with a flame speed which depends on the concentration but will not normally be higher than 10 m/s. The pressure waves which are formed in the atmosphere are weak, although a noise of varying degrees of loudness is heard when ignition is initiated.

Tests to detonate air–hydrogen mixtures in the open air have given only negative results, except when a large mass of condensed explosive was used as a detonator, and even in that case the results are by no means easy to interpret. However, partial confinement, such as may occur in the angle formed by two perpendicular walls, may allow a detonation to evolve, which is why it is better not to surround liquid hydrogen tanks with barricades.

31.1.3 Accidental formation of an oxyhydrogen mixture.

Oxygen–hydrogen mixtures may form accidentally when hydrogen is produced by electrolysis of an aqueous solution (generally a potash solution). This may happen if the diaphragm of an electrolytic cell is not air-tight and so allows oxygen from the anode compartment to enter the cathode compartment.

The following is another type of accident which has occurred on several occasions: after shutting down the apparatus for maintenance, a mistake was made in re-connecting the three inlet cables A, A', and A'' and the three outlet cables B, B', and B'' to the three electrolytic cells. Instead of the cables being connected A.B, A'.B', and A''.B'' respectively, they were connected as AB', A'B'', and BA'', with the result that in the last of the cells the compartment which should have been the cathode became the anode and the oxygen produced there was piped to the factory gasometer along with hydrogen from the two other cathode compartments, so forming an explosive gas (mixture $2H_2 + O_2$). This explosive mixture was sucked into a compressor where it exploded and caused considerable damage.

Thus, when electrolysers are dismantled for repair or maintenance, the electrical connexions must be checked very carefully. Indeed, such checks are necessary for all electrical apparatuses. Accidents have been caused by the faulty connecting of three triphase current cables in an engine operating a centrifugal pump. The motor went into reverse and instead of sucking in the liquid to be transferred, expelled it, so causing an accident.

31.1.4 Accidental formation of air–hydrogen mixtures

Air–hydrogen mixtures may form accidentally in very varied circumstances. They have caused many explosions. The most frequent conditions are the following:

1° *Acids attacking metals.* The following are a few cases out of many:
In June 1920 in the United States [1], lightning struck a 200 ton tank containing an 89% solution of sulphuric acid, causing an explosion in the gas phase formed by a mixture of air and hydrogen. The pressure created caused considerable distortion to the tank and burst the pipes in several places.

In October 1922, compressed air was blown down a dip tube to empty a nitrosulphuric mixture from a railway tanker. There was an immediate explosion which left two people dead and caused severe damage.

In December 1962, cracks in the internal coating of ebonite in a steel tank used to store hydrochloric acid (a 20% aqueous solution) brought the surface of the metal into contact with the acid locally, causing a slight release of hydrogen which mixed with the air in the upper part of the tank. Subsequently, when an angle iron above the tank was being cut with a blowpipe, a spark (white-hot Fe_3O_4) fell through a vent into the tank and exploded the air–hydrogen mixture, blowing off the top part of the tank and injuring the workers.

In April 1964, when a large vertical cylindrical steel tank was being filled with a 92% solution of sulphuric acid, there was an explosion which blew off part of the domed roof and buckled the walls and bottom. It was established at the inquiry that moist air had seeped into the tank and locally diluted the surface of the acid, attacking the steel and releasing hydrogen. According to the inquiry, there had been no mechanical, thermal, or electrostatic spark, so it may be asked if the explosion was not perhaps caused by a voltaic spark (see 10.4). The tank was resting on lead–capped iron and was very large (270 m³).

A stainless steel tank containing phosphoric acid was accidentally contaminated by chlorides, and although the concentration of the latter was no more than a few millionths, it was enough to corrode the tank and give off hydrogen. An explosion was triggered by the level indicator system.

There have often been explosions when metal drums or empty tanks which have been used to store sulphuric acid are cut with a chisel or a blowpipe. No work should be carried out on such a container until it has been first completely filled with water.

2° *The reaction of aluminium* (or an aluminium–based alloy) *with water* or soda. When aluminium is not superficially oxidised, it gradually reacts with water to release hydrogen, with the quantity of gas released being in direct proportion to the surface area of the metal, as is the case with powdered or flaked aluminium. The metal is gradually heated up during the process, so accelerating the chemical reaction.

The following is a description of a remarkable accident which happened in 1962. A hydraulic pressure test had been conducted on a cold exchanger with a capacity of 17 m³ made of a stainless steel shell containing stacks of corrugated aluminium rolls (A4 quality). There were 16 tons of the metal in the apparatus. The test had used water from the mains in a Paris suburb, after which the water was drained off and the apparatus filled with nitrogen at atmospheric pressure and closed. On the following day the wall of the apparatus was found to be hot (around 50 to 60°C) and the pressure inside the apparatus was 6.5 bars. A valve was opened and a gas that was

very rich in hydrogen was drawn off. It was rapidly realised that after
emptying, the aluminium filler still contained more than 250 litres of
water which wetted it and with which it had reacted during the night to
form more than 60 m³ of hydrogen.

In this incident the reaction between the water and the aluminium was
helped
(a) by the existence of an electric couple between the stainless steel hull
and the aluminium filler (about 0.85 V);
(b) by impurities held in inclusion in the A4-quality aluminium, especially
copper, and by the presence of chlorine in the water;
(c) by the cracks created by the forming of the corrugated strip.

The explosion which occurred in Pasadena (Texas) in January 1973 in a
large-diameter pipe that had been rinsed with soda was caused by the
presence in the pipe of aluminium residues which reacted with the soda to
release hydrogen.

A similar accident occurred in France around 1958 after an apparatus
had been washed with soda to cleanse it of nitric oxide gums (see 27.1.2).
It was forgotten that some parts of the complex apparatus were made of an
aluminium alloy, and as a result an air-hydrogen mixture was formed.

When aluminium is amalgamated, it reacts very readily with liquid water
or water vapour from a moist atmosphere to liberate hydrogen. This was the
cause of an explosion in an aluminium apparatus fitted with a small mercury
manometer (a simple U tube). Mercury got into the apparatus when it was
accidentally depressurised and triggered a process leading to the formation
of an air-hydrogen mixture.

Mention should also be made of the explosion in 1950 which left one
person dead and several injured during a fire in an aluminium waste depot,
because the burning pile had been doused with water.

3$^{\bullet}$ *Reaction of a metal with water.* Most metals which are unaffected by
water at temperatures below 100°C are liable, when the temperature is high
enough, to decompose even pure water and liberate hydrogen. Thus, the
reaction of zirconium with compressed water vapour at around 1000°C, which
is a strongly exothermic reaction (more than 290 kJ per mole of hydrogen
produced), aggravated the situation considerably [9] during the accident at
the nuclear power station at Three Mile Island in 1979.

31.1.5 The apparently spontaneous ignition of hydrogen gas

When a metal cylinder containing compressed hydrogen bursts accidentally,
the gas very frequently ignites on contact with air. One probable cause of
this ignition is the production of hot spots on the crack in the metal (see
10.2.1), but other ignition mechanisms may also be involved, such as the
heating of the air by a shock wave (see 12.14b) or sometimes electric
phenomena, which are the cause of hydrogen igniting when a leak occurs
without metal breaking. This type of ignition was a common occurrence in
the early decades of the century when hydrogen was used to inflate balloons
or dirigibles. Nusselt [2] concluded from a study that hydrogen which is
perfectly free of dust does not ignite on emerging from a pipe or escaping
from a leaking joint into the air, but that, as a general rule, ignition
does occur if there are particles of dust in the gas. Such dusts can be
very varied in nature, and in particular may be incombustible dusts such as
ferric oxide. In the darkness a pale blue glow is visible just before the
hydrogen ignites, but ignition does not occur if the electrostatic cloud is

discharged as soon as it flows into the air by a metal rod connected to the gas duct.

Ignition may also be caused by the presence of fine droplets of water in the gas. Consequently, when a mixture of oxygen and hydrogen has to be prepared in the laboratory, very dry gases must be used, of the type now supplied by the gas industry, and any dust should be removed.

31.1.6 Safety measures in the manufacture and use of hydrogen gas

In workshops manufacturing hydrogen by electrolysis, push buttons to cut the current should be fitted in a number of places both inside and outside the building. The same precaution applies to workshops in which hydrogen is compressed and loaded into containers. Hydrogen compressors should be protected against the risk of air entering by means of a manostat fitted upstream of the intake valve which automatically stops the compressor motor when the gauge pressure of the hydrogen falls below a certain threshold of something like 20 millibars. It is also advisable to fit a continuous hydrogen analyser on the delivery pipe of the first stage of compression.

The regulations governing classified installations will stipulate safety measures to be taken in the compression of hydrogen and the storage of compressed hydrogen.

The main safety measures to be taken when using hydrogen are to prevent leaks and to ensure that any which do occur cannot result in the formation of explosive mixtures with air.

Wherever possible, equipment using hydrogen will be set up in the open air or in a building open on several sides. In a four-sided building there must be an adequate number of doors and windows, and it is best, when the ambient temperature permits, to work with the doors open. There should be good ventilation, and in particular there should be enough openings in the upper part of the roof to evacuate any hydrogen floating upwards.

Hydrogen detectors (explosimeters) can be used in workshops to measure the concentration of gas at floor-level and halfway up the building.

In factories where there is a separate control room for the staff, no pipe should carry hydrogen through it, and the room should be kept at a slightly higher pressure than atmospheric so that air containing hydrogen cannot enter.

Before start-up and close-down containers and circuits housing hydrogen should be purged with dry nitrogen, but the jet of gas used should not be violent. However, with very strong, low-volume containers such as flexible connecting pipes the initial purge can be carried out with a weak stream of hydrogen itself.

Equipment should be checked for air-tightness before opening valves on distribution pipes or valves on cylinders. The latter should always be opened slowly but to their full extent, and the cylinder should be fitted with a pressure-reducing valve.

If hydrogen is found to be leaking around the stem of the valve when the latter is opened, it should be closed again and the cylinder returned to the supplier. If a cylinder valve is leaking even when closed, the cylinder should be carried out into the open air and left at a suitable distance.

Carbon steels subjected to the action of compressed hydrogen are prone to stress corrosion cracking. So all apparatuses working at high pressure must be checked for this.

31.2 LIQUID HYDROGEN

31.2.1 Orthohydrogen and parahydrogen

Depending on whether the two nuclei of the H_2 molecule spin in the same or
opposite directions, the molecule is that of orthohydrogen or parahydrogen.
In ordinary hydrogen these two forms are in equilibrium with one another,
and in hydrogen gas at ordinary temperature there is 75% ortho- and 25%
para-hydrogen. When the temperature falls, equilibrium requires that there
should be more and more parahydrogen. The existence of these two forms of
the hydrogen molecule has no practical consequences as far as hydrogen gas
is concerned, but they play an important part when liquid hydrogen is being
made.

If ordinary hydrogen is liquefied rapidly, a liquid is obtained at
around 20°K which still contains 75% orthohydrogen but in which, at this
low temperature, the two forms are no longer in equilibrium. The ortho
variety is gradually transformed into the para variety until a mixture is
obtained containing only 0.2% orthohydrogen. This liquid mixture in which
both forms are in equilibrium is called 'converted liquid hydrogen', or
sometimes 'parahydrogen' because it consists almost entirely of the para
variety, or 'e-hydrogen' (the letter 'e' standing for a mixture in
equilibrium).

The transformation of orthohydrogen into parahydrogen is exothermic,
and the amount of heat released, equivalent to almost 710 J/g at around
20°K, is greater than the heat of vaporisation of hydrogen. Consequently,
if normal (75% ortho) liquid hydrogen is in a container which is in contact
with the atmosphere, the liquid gradually evaporates, even if the container
is such that no heat can enter from the outside. If the liquid is in a
closed vessel the effect of vaporisation is to raise the pressure.

Handling or storing unconverted liquid hydrogen is both inconvenient
and dangerous. Fortunately, it can be converted in hydrogen liquefaction
apparatuses by passing it over catalysts such as ferric oxide, and in
practice it is always converted liquid hydrogen which is handled.

The following are some of the physical properties of converted liquid
hydrogen (with 99.8% para):

Critical temperature	33.97°K (− 240°C)
Critical pressure	13.1 bars
Critical density	0.031 4 g/cm³
Normal boiling point	20.27°K (− 252.9°C)
Triple temperature point	13.8°K (− 259.4°C)
Triple pressure point	0.069 bars.

The vapour pressure reaches 1.7 bars at 22°K and 12.5 bars at 32°K. One
litre of liquid hydrogen at its normal b.p. has a mass of 0.0708 kg and
gives on vaporising 763 litres of gas at 15°C and 1 atm.

The properties of 'normal' hydrogen are only slightly different from
those of converted hydrogen. All gases except helium solidify at the
temperature of liquid hydrogen.

Vaporised hydrogen at its b.p. of 20°K has a specific gravity higher
than that of air at ordinary temperature, so that when liquid hydrogen is
spilled on the ground, a heavy cloud is formed which is carried along by
the wind and which is visible because it condenses moisture out of the air.
However, this cold cloud heats up quite rapidly and the less dense gas then

rises in the air.

31.2.2 The dangers of liquid hydrogen

Large quantities of liquid hydrogen are used at rocket launching sites and in cryogenics laboratories. It is also used in the filling of some 'bubble chambers'.

Liquid hydrogen poses all the dangers associated with the gas since it vaporises readily. In addition, it causes accidents for the following reasons:

1˙ The liquid severely burns skin because of its very low temperature. Burns are also caused by contact with a pipe carrying the liquid.

2˙ Many substances, including most lubricants, become fragile or friable at the temperature of liquid hydrogen.

3˙ The solidification of nitrogen or air at temperatures below 60˙K may block pipes or prevent parts from working.

4˙ Any contamination of liquid hydrogen by oxygen may cause accidents, in particular in small apparatuses for re-liquefying hydrogen gas from 'bubble chambers'. These are apparatuses of quite simple design whose main part is a needle valve in which expansion allows the compressed gas to be cooled and liquefied. If crystals of oxygen are present in the hydrogen being treated, they may become electrostatically charged and cause an explosion by reacting with the hydrogen. Even if the apparatus is not damaged, the phenomenon is unpleasant for the person operating the expansion valve.

Contrary to what happens with compressed hydrogen gas, the rupture of a container housing liquid hydrogen is not usually followed by ignition (on condition, of course, that there is no flame or spark in the vicinity). The liquid spills onto the floor and produces a clearly visible white mist. This has happened on several occasions:

(a) In 1955 in Great Malvern (Great Britain) a tank of compressed† liquid hydrogen burst because it was not strong enough and spilled its contents, but there was no ignition.

(b) In January 1967, an experiment was conducted which consisted in raising the pressure to bursting point in a tank containing 300 litres of liquid hydrogen. The welding joins gave way at about 16 bars, with immediate and total evacuation of the liquid, but there was no spontaneous ignition.

(c) In June 1967, in a research centre near Paris, a small explosion in the vicinity burst a tank containing 2000 litres of liquid hydrogen, emptying the contents but without ignition.

31.2.3 Safety measures in the use of liquid hydrogen

When using liquid hydrogen, the safety measures to be taken are dictated mainly by the following concerns:

1˙ Air must not be able to get into tanks and apparatuses, so the pressure should be kept above atmospheric.

---

† Liquid hydrogen is rarely stored at a pressure of more than 10 bars, whereas hydrogen gas is often used at 30 bars and is stored in cylinders at 150 bars.

2* Any blockage by nitrogen or oxygen crystals should be avoided in pipes of which one section may be at the temperature of liquid hydrogen and which are used either for purging or for evacuation.

The safety measures taken with hydrogen gas, especially those for ventilating workshops, should also be applied to liquid hydrogen.

In factories using large quantities of liquid hydrogen, each particular case requires an appropriate design of apparatus, the fitting of a suitable and frequently complex set of safety devices, and the strict application of quite a large number of detailed procedures and safety instructions.

Even in laboratories where the amount handled is of the order of 1 to 2 kg (or 10 to 30 litres), a large number of precautions are still necessary, of which we shall mention just one: liquid hydrogen should never be poured from one container into another in the presence of air. Instead, it should be transferred by means of a siphon which uses the pressure of hydrogen or helium gas to force the liquid along a dip tube, and this equipment should be electrically earthed. The transfer should be carried out slowly and the receptacle should never be filled to more than 85%.

When using liquid hydrogen, there are normally small quantities of unused gas to be disposed of. If the amounts involved are very small, they can simply be released into the atmosphere through a pipe rising to a sufficient height, but if larger quantities are to be treated, they must be burned in a flare. A case is known in which a large quantity released into the atmosphere was blown down by the wind onto a building 200 m away and caused an explosion.

If no more than a few litres of liquid hydrogen have to be disposed of, it can be done by pouring it onto the ground far away from any building.

31.3 HYDRIDES

31.3.1 Explosive gaseous hydrides

The heats of formation of gaseous hydrides, other than those such as hydrogen chloride which are very stable, were for a long time known either incompletely or only with a great degree of uncertainty. We owe precise measurements to Gunn and his associates [4] who obtained them in a highly ingenious way by explosively decomposing hydrides in the gaseous state in a calorimeter. These experiments constitute an important contribution to the evaluation of the explosive (or non-explosive) nature of the substances in question.

Gunn observed that gaseous *stibine* SbH_3 at ordinary pressure, and *a fortiori* at higher pressures, is decomposed completely and explosively when ignited with an incandescent platinum wire, whilst gaseous arsine AsH_3 in the same conditions undergoes only insignificant decomposition in zones close to the metal. However, a mixture of one mole of arsine and two moles of stibine explodes completely when ignited in the same way at a pressure of 1.5 bars. This allows the heat of formation of AsH_3 to be determined, after measuring that of SbH_3. In the same way, by mixing them with SbH_3, Gunn was able to decompose completely into their elements phosphine PH_3, diphosphine P_2H_4, silane SiH_4, disilane Si_2H_6, germane GeH_4, and diborane B_2H_6. A platinum wire will also explode hydrogen telluride H_2Te, digermane Ge_2H_6, and stannane SnH_4. The latter explodes even more violently than stibine. Finally, the heat of explosion of hydrogen selenide H_2Se is obtained by mixing it with hydrogen telluride H_2Te.

By taking the most likely decomposition equations, one can calculate the explosion temperature at constant volume (T_v) and the pressure rise factor (π) of these gases using the method described in Chapter 5. Table 31.1 shows that for those gases which explode the violence of the explosion is related to the value of the factor π. On the other hand, it is only when the theoretical temperature T_v given by calculation is greater than 900°K that explosion occurs with the ignition source and the experimental pressures, which were only slightly above atmospheric, used by Gunn.

Table 31.1

Explosion properties of gaseous hydrides

Hydride		Calorific value (kJ/mol)	Explosion temperature (cst. vol.) (°K)	Pressure rise factor (π)
Stibine	SbH_3	1 200	1 800	10
Arsine	AsH_3	886	1 010	6
Silane	SiH_4	1 030	800	5.5
Disilane	Si_2H_6	1 188	950	10
Germane	GeH_4	1 218	1 400	9.6
Stannane	SnH_4	1 368	2 200	15
Diborane	B_2H_6	1 314	620	6.4
Hydrogen telluride		770	1 700	7
	H_2Te			

The hydrides of the heaviest elements (hydrogen telluride, stibine, stannane, digermane) are strongly endothermic substances with pronounced explosive properties, and are therefore not manufactured industrially, but phosphine, arsine, and silane are manufactured by industry and are used as doping gases in the manufacture of semiconductors.

On the subject of *arsine*, one treatise [5] tells us that 'because arsine is endothermic (Berthelot) was able to detonate it with mercury fulminate'. Berthelot [6] experimented on arsine only in the gaseous state at atmospheric pressure and was unable to explode it either with a hot wire, like Gunn, or with an electric spark. He concluded that arsine could be exploded only after experiments using a primer of mercury fulminate. But in experiments [7] in which primers of varying amounts of fulminate (0.1–0.2 to 0.4 g) were detonated in 0.3 litres of arsine at atmospheric pressure, analysis showed that the amount of decomposed arsine increased with that of the primer (13% – 44% – 84% respectively). Clearly, arsine is decomposed by the heat of the gases released by the fulminate in a region with a volume roughly proportional to the quantity of heat supplied, but the explosion does not propagate. Liquid arsine housed in a thick steel tube 30 mm in diameter and excited against one end by 50 g of compressed P.E.T.N. did not detonate [7].

In other experiments [8], arsine was put in an air-tight metal cylinder in such a quantity that at a temperature of 10°C the liquid phase took up about 3/10 and the gas phase 7/10 of the internal volume of 1 litre. The pressure was about 9 bars. A spark plug was fitted in the upper part of the cylinder in the space filled by the gas phase with its two electrodes connected by a tungsten wire 0.5 cm long and 0.3 mm in diameter. Applying a voltage of 240 volts rapidly brought the wire to a temperature (3400°C) at which it melted, giving off only one calorie. Thermocouples placed on the outside against the wall of the cylinder detected no temperature rise. A manometer connected to the cylinder by a long tube recorded a pressure rise of 0.25 bars. From these results it can be easily calculated that only 1.5% of the gaseous arsine decomposed. In a similar experiment in which the tungsten wire was plunged into the liquid phase, there was no temperature or pressure rise.

It cannot be stated categorically that at pressures higher than 40 bars (over 75°C) a sufficiently strong ignition source will not explode gaseous arsine, but it can be concluded from the tests that in ordinary handling conditions arsine is not liable to explode.

Silane SiH_4 is thermodynamically more stable than most other doping gases and decomposes only at red-heat. It ignites spontaneously in air in normal conditions when moisture is present but not in perfectly dry air. It reacts very strongly with chlorine and bromine.

Although *germane* GeH_4 is less stable, it can still be handled.

31.3.2 Boranes

Of the dozen known compounds of boron and hydrogen the only ones with any industrial importance are diborane B_2H_6, 9-pentaborane B_5H_9, and 14-decaborane $B_{10}H_{14}$. They are substances which ignite very readily. Their spontaneous ignition temperature can be considerably lowered by the presence of a small amount of impurity. Pentaborane and decaborane can thus become spontaneously ignitible in air at atmospheric pressure at temperatures of around 15–20°C. These last two boranes are not explosive, but they are powerful reducing agents which, in a mixture with oxidising substances, form sensitive explosives. It is therefore important when handling them to prevent them from being contaminated by foreign bodies. They are also highly toxic like diborane.

Diborane decomposes slowly into hydrogen and higher boranes at ordinary temperature. Therefore, if it is to be stored properly, the containers in which it is housed should be kept at a low temperature (in dry ice, for example). Its lower flammability limit in air is 0.9% and its upper limit is around 95% but may rise to 98–99% since it depends to a large extent on the temperature. The lower limiting flammability pressure is reached at 3 mm of mercury for about 15% of B_2H_6 in air.

Air-diborane mixtures not only ignite easily, but also pass very easily from deflagration to detonation. The latter has a velocity of the order of 2500 to 3000 m/s.

No experiments have been published on the ignition of pure diborane, but it can be assumed from theoretical calculations (see Table 31.1) that it may explode in the gaseous state at a high enough pressure.

Diborane in metal cylinders is liquid below 16.7°C. Its orthobaric density is 0.25 g/cm³ at around + 10°C. Containers are normally filled at a rate of between 0.15 and 0.25 kg/l depending on the test pressure of the container.

For many purposes diborane is used diluted with hydrogen, nitrogen, or argon.   It must not be diluted with CO_2, which reacts with it in certain conditions.

Liquid *pentaborane* is relatively more stable than diborane.   The lower flammability limit of its vapour† in air is about 0.4%.   In the pure state its spontaneous ignition temperature in air is 35–40°C.

Decaborane, the most stable of the volatile hydrides of boron, is a solid which withstands contact with air without decomposing, even at 60°C. Its spontaneous ignition temperature is about 140°C.

BIBLIOGRAPHICAL REFERENCES

[1]   de Wolf, P. (1921) *Chem. Met. Eng.* 25 336
[2]   Nusselt, W. (1922) *Z. Ver. dtsch. Ing.* (V.D.I.) 66 203
[3]   Thurel, G. (1967) Centre d'Etudes Cryogéniques de Sassenage, note
       dated 24 January
[4]   Gunn, S. R. *et al.* (1960) *J. phys. Chem.* 64 1334;   (1961) 65 779 and
       2173;   (1964) 68 949
[5]   Dolique (1958) in *Nouveau Traité de Chimie Minérale.*   Vol. XI
[6]   Berthelot, M. (1882) *Ann. chimie et phys.* [5] 27 192
[7]   Médard, L. (1940) *Lab. C.S.E.*
[8]   Allamagny, P. (1968) *Lab. Soc. Air Liquide*
[9]   Schneider, A. (1981) *Loss Prevention* 14 96

---

† For mixtures at the lower limit the heat of explosion is 17.1 and 16.3 kJ/mol for diborane and pentaborane respectively in a mixture with air. These values, which are much lower than the 45 to 50 kJ/mol characteristic of common gases (see 8.3.3), are related to the great ease with which these boranes ignite.

32

Various types of explosion

32.1 EXPLOSIONS OF CHEMICAL ORIGIN

32.1.1 Unexpected cases of explosive definite compounds

There are many other explosive compounds than those described in Chapters
18 to 31. Indeed, substances which are quite rightly considered to be
non-explosive in normal handling conditions may become unwanted explosives
in particular conditions of temperature and pressure. This is the case
with carbon disulphide whose vapour in the absence of oxygen and atmospheric pressure is not explosive but may deflagrate at 140°C and 4 bars.
This is explained by the fact that under pressure at temperatures between
500 and 900°C a high percentage of sulphur vapour occurs in the form of S_8
molecules whose heat of formation *in relation to an S atom* is, as an
absolute value, less than that of the diatomic molecule S_2, since calculation, which can only be approximate, suggests a calorific value of
between 502 and 590 kJ/kg for the explosion of carbon disulphide vapour by
a dissociation reaction at 4 bars.

Some organometallic compounds have only a limited range of stability
around ordinary temperature and are liable to explode at a slightly higher
temperature, during distillation for example, even at reduced pressure.

32.1.2 Explosive chemical reactions

A large number of exothermic chemical reactions may become explosive when
they take place in conditions which do not allow the heat released to
dissipate, either because the reaction directly creates gases, or because
it takes place in liquids which vaporise. Sometimes the dangerous reaction
is not that of the two substances which are supposed to react together, but

a reaction between one of them and the solvent used as the reactive medium.
For example, dimethyl sulphoxide $OS(CH_3)_2$, which is a convenient medium for
reacting two substances in a liquid phase because of its good ability to
dissolve many substances, may lead to explosions with inorganic or organic
acid halides.   Allan, Moks, and Nelson [1] have warned of the dangers of
dimethyl sulphoxide when one of the reactants has an acidic reaction. They
believe this causes the sulphoxide to form formaldehyde which then rapidly
polymerises exothermically.

There are many pairs of substances which may when mixed, and sometimes
by simply being brought into contact, react explosively when subjected to
appropriate excitation. Chapters 17, 18, and 19 described oxidising agents
which may combine with combustible substances to form explosives, but many
other dangerous chemical systems exist.   Whenever a laboratory chemist
studies an unknown reaction, he should consult a pamphlet [2] on dangerous
chemical reactions published by the National Fire Protection Association
which lists in alphabetical order two thousand pairs of substances which
have been reported to be capable of giving a violent, usually explosive,
reaction.   This compilation does not give precise indications about the
conditions in which the dangerous reaction occurs;   its aim is quite simply
to draw the attention of researchers to possible risks, leaving it to the
individual to carry out more thorough research in the chemical literature
or to conduct experimental research, with the necessary degree of caution,
to establish the conditions in which a reaction may be safely carried out.

Concerning pairs of incompatible substances, it should be remembered
that many accidents occur in laboratories because of residues thrown into
dustbins where they may react dangerously together. Laboratory researchers
should always make sure that residues are rendered harmless before they are
thrown away.

Similarly, in a workshop using raw materials which react violently with
either acids or bases, care should be taken to ensure that they are never
in the presence, even in small quantities, of such incompatible substances.
An accident has been reported of an assistant, who had no means of knowing
about such incompatibilities, putting an uncleaned bucket which had held
sulphuric acid in an apparatus containing a liquid which polymerises very
strongly under the action of this acid.

32.1.3 Reactions of halogenated hydrocarbons with some metals

When Staudinger tried in 1922 to dry chloroform completely by stirring it
in contact with sodium wires, he observed an explosion which led him to
make a study [3] of the action of alkali and alkaline-earth metals on
halogenated hydrocarbons. He was able to initiate an explosive reaction by
impact: an explosion accompanied by a flash of light and a loud noise can
be produced simply by dropping a bulb containing a small piece of potassium
and 1 cm³ of carbon tetrachloride from a height of one metre. The reaction
involved seems to be

$$4K + CCl_4 \rightarrow C + 4KCl.$$

For a given metal it is the most highly chlorinated compounds which
react most strongly, but even methyl chloride CH_3Cl gives rise to an
explosive reaction with potassium at ordinary temperature. The reactions
are especially strong if the metal is in the liquid state, as is molten

potassium (m.p. 62.5°C), or the alloy K – Na, or an amalgam of alkali metal. These systems are extraordinarily sensitive to mechanical stimuli since, according to Staudinger, the impact energy which causes an explosion is about one hundred times smaller than that which is needed to explode mercury fulminate. Temperatures between 0 and 100°C have hardly any effect on the initiation of the explosive reaction unless the melting point of the metal in question falls within that range.

Reactions are also very strong with brominated compounds and with methyl iodide, and violent reactions have subsequently also been observed with chlorofluorinated hydrocarbons (with the trade names of foranes, freons, etc.).

We owe to Lenze and Metz [4] the quantitative study of these explosive systems. The main results are:

(a) Some halogenated compounds explode at ordinary temperature on simple contact with solid potassium after a certain contact time. Examples of such substances are 1,1,2,2-tetrachloroethane, pentachloroethane, and carbon tetrabromide.

(b) Other compounds at ordinary temperature require an impact to give rise to an explosion with potassium.

(c) Chlorinated or brominated compounds of ethane are, from this point of view, no less reactive than those of methane, but chlorinated aromatic hydrocarbons on the benzene nucleus are less so.

(d) The different metals studied can be classified, in relation to carbon tetrachloride, by ascending order of sensitivity to impact as follows:

Ca – Li – Sr – Na – Ba – K.

(e) In tests in the lead block (see 14.3.2) with a No. 8 detonator, Lenze and Metz obtained expansions which, adjusted to 10 g, range, depending on the mixture, from 50 to 180 cm³, with the highest values being obtained not with mixtures containing the same number of atoms of alkali metal and atoms of chlorine, but with mixtures containing an excess of chlorinated compounds, since that increases the gas volume of the explosion products.

Explosions have occurred in industry in operations which bring into contact an alkali or alkaline-earth metal and an halogenated compound. We may quote the accident in Berlin in 1928 when barium stored in mineral oil was being degreased by washing with carbon tetrachloride. In 1967, a big explosion in the United States which killed two people was caused by a mixture of fine barium crystals with 1,1,2-trichlorotrifluoroethane (refrigerant R.113).

Cueilleron [5] found that explosive reactions are initiated by an impact on mixtures of potassium with many inorganic halides such as those of Cu (I), Cu (II), Zn, Cd, Pb, Hg (I), Hg (II), Sn (II), and Sn (IV). The reaction is particularly violent with the chlorides and bromides of cobalt, nickel, and iron (ferric). Sodium reacts in a similar way to potassium, although less violently.

The explosive reaction of the liquid sodium-potassium alloy is not limited to halogenated compounds but also, according to Staudinger [6], occurs with dry ice (solid CO_2), silver oxide, carbon disulphide, and even nitro-compounds such as mononitrobenzene. Very little is known about reactions of this kind. Senderens [7] reports that sodium or potassium in the molten state decomposes mercury oxide explosively.

It clearly follows from the above observations that:
– the widespread use in laboratories of sodium wire to dry a solvent may

pose risks with chlorinated solvents;
- and that in laboratory or workshop operations in which an alkali or alkaline-earth metal is reacted, an halogenated solvent should not be used as a reactive medium.

In addition to the above metals, two other highly oxidisable metals, magnesium and above all aluminium, are liable to react dangerously with halogenated compounds. A study by Clogston [8] has shown that a system combining powdered aluminium with methyl chloride, carbon tetrachloride, or pentachloroethane may explode. In particular, it should be noted that the action at ordinary temperature of methyl chloride vapour on aluminium, especially if a small amount of the chloride $AlCl_3$ is present, produces trimethyl aluminium $Al(CH_3)_3$, a substance which ignites spontaneously in air. Magnesium powder also reacts with the chlorinated compounds studied, although much more slowly than aluminium.

On various occasions, accidental explosions, some of which were very serious [9], have been caused by carbon tetrachloride and aluminium, but the other chlorinated compounds of methane may react. In laboratory tests dichloromethane CH_2Cl_2 at around 100°C and about 2 bars reacts explosively with divided aluminium. In industrial apparatuses containing large masses explosions are much more violent than those observed in laboratory tests. The effects depend on the quantity of heat released as well as the volume of gases created by the reaction, and in this respect it should be observed that dichloromethane and trichloromethane (chloroform) must, because of the hydrogen they contain, give rise to much larger emissions of gas than carbon tetrachloride. It can thus be understood why strongly exothermic reactions between aluminium and dichlorodifluoromethane (refrigerant R 12) were not explosive in nature, since the products of the reaction between the metal and refrigerant R 12 consisted of the solids carbon, aluminium chloride, and aluminium fluoride. Such reactions have occurred in the centrifugal compressors of refrigerating plants using the refrigerant R 12 since the rotor is made of aluminium. An accident of this kind which happened in 1970 has been described by Schwab [10]. After the compressor was dismantled, black soot was found in it. The whole aluminium section of the first stage had disappeared, and a small amount of solidified aluminium was found in a branch pipe. The reaction between agent R 12 and the aluminium must have begun at a point on the rotor where a fragment of carbon steel from a broken blade upstream had struck it and created a hot spot. Although the system composed of aluminium and gaseous dichloro-difluoromethane reacts very rapidly and releases more than 4600 kJ/kg, it does not constitute a pseudo-explosive (see 1.1.1) because, far from giving off gases, its reaction actually results in a decrease in the gas volume. It does not, therefore, produce a rise in pressure as an explosive would do.

Explosions have sometimes occurred when aluminium parts are treated with hot trichloroethylene to degrease them. A paper on this subject has been published by Metz and Roedig [11].

32.1.4 The role of impurities in certain explosive reactions

The catalytic action of some substances on decomposition reactions has been mentioned on various occasions. Amongst these undesirable catalysts, rust and ferric salts which form deposits on the walls of apparatuses are often found in steel apparatuses. They may cause hydrogen peroxide (see 20.2.7) or organic peroxides (see 21.1.3) to explode, and various substances such as ethylene oxide to polymerise explosively, as well as producing explosive decomposition reactions in various substances such as benzyl chloride $C_6H_5 - CH_2Cl$.

Some impurities are active at very low levels and may considerably increase the rate of a reaction to the point where it becomes explosive, whereas the same reaction with pure substances takes place calmly. An example of this is provided by the pyrolysis of maleic anhydride, which was referred to in 2.12. The following two accidents have been reported:

(a) In 1960, in a factory in Louisiana, an apparatus was being cleaned with caustic soda. Because one of the valves was not water-tight in the off position, a small amount of soda got into a 3 m³ stainless steel apparatus containing maleic anhydride. The heat of hydration and neutralisation of the anhydride triggered exothermic reactions accompanied by an emission of gas. The contents exploded and two people were killed by flying metal splinters.

(b) In 1963, in a French factory, raw maleic anhydride was being distilled at reduced pressure (0.2 bars absolute) in a plate–column 3 m in diameter and 10 m high. Normally, the temperature in the boiler at the foot of the column is 165°C. Several hours after distillation had begun it was noticed that the temperature in the column was rising, slowly at first and then more and more rapidly, until it was over 260°C three hours later. At that moment the pressure in the column was higher than atmospheric. The safety valves opened and let out violent jets of white vapour, and then the column exploded, with one fragment weighing over a ton landing 200 m away. This explosion inside the apparatus was very quickly followed by an explosion (called a secondary explosion) in the mixture in air of the gases and vapours from the broken apparatus. Observers some distance away clearly saw a huge ball of fire.

In both of these accidents maleic anhydride decomposed explosively. This decomposition is catalysed by the ions of alkali metals as explained in the following:

Many organic acids may easily lose a mole of carbon dioxide. This decarboxylation can be obtained by heating the acid alone or in the presence of a decarboxylating agent such as lime. Diacids as well as their anhydrides may undergo this reaction even more readily than monoacids, giving, in addition to CO_2, more or less complex products. Most of these decarboxylation reactions are endothermic and are therefore not explosive, but this is not the case with the decarboxylation of maleic anhydride[†], which, when carried out at around 400°C with the help of water vapour,

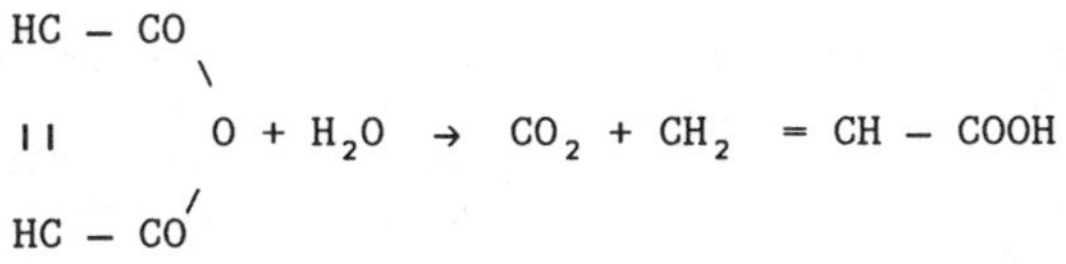

$$
\begin{array}{l}
HC - CO \\
\quad\quad\quad \backslash \\
\| \quad\quad\quad O + H_2O \rightarrow CO_2 + CH_2 = CH - COOH \\
\quad\quad\quad / \\
HC - CO
\end{array}
$$

[†] The heats of formation at constant pressure of solid maleic anhydride and succinic anhydride are 460 and 598 kJ/mol respectively. The chemical energy of the former is thus higher than that of the latter by 138 kJ, a fact which explains why the decarboxylation of succinic anhydride is endothermic, unlike that of maleic anhydride.

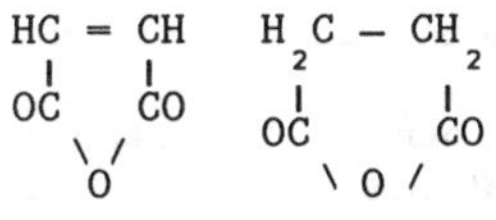

$$
\begin{array}{ll}
HC = CH & H_2C - CH_2 \\
| \quad\quad | & | \quad\quad\quad | \\
OC \quad CO & OC \quad\quad CO \\
\backslash \, / & \backslash \,\, O \,\, / \\
O &
\end{array}
$$

releases 75 kJ/mol.

Various authors, including Rittenberg and Ponticorvo [12], have shown that small quantities of tertiary amines, strong bases, and even salts of sodium catalyse the decomposition of maleic anhydride. If 1 g of sodium chloride is added to 100 g of anhydride and the mixture is boiled in a reflux condenser, the initial temperature of 200°C, which is the normal boiling point of maleic anhydride, gradually rises and around 215°C is accompanied by a large emission of gas. In this laboratory experiment conducted at atmospheric pressure on a small mass the heat evacuated from the apparatus may be the same as that given off by the decomposition reaction and may thus limit the temperature rise and the rate of the reaction. The situation is quite different in industrial distillation columns or evaporators which are insulated and contain tons of the substance. Vogler and his associates [13] made a quantitative study in a differential thermal analysis apparatus of the action of various sodium salts on the decomposition of maleic anhydride. When the latter is pure, heat release is scarcely detectable below 200°C but begins at 145°C if 0.3% sodium ions are added in carbonate form. It obeys the Arrhenius law (equation 3.11). The presence of 0.01% sodium ions increases by 20 to 30 times the amount of heat released per minute per kilogramme of heated molten substance, and the fact that the phenomenon obeys Arrhenius' law implies that it must lead to an explosion when heat dissipation is no longer sufficient.

After the 1963 accident it was established that there were on average 0.008% alkaline ions in the raw product before distillation but 0.2% in deposits on the boiler wall, which is where the centre of the explosive decomposition was located. Various considerations lead to the conclusion that the reactions consisted of

(a) decarboxylation liberating about 750 kJ/kg and some 100 dm³ of gas per kilogramme of decomposed substance;

(b) a polymerisation of the vinyl type, in other words a polymerisation giving

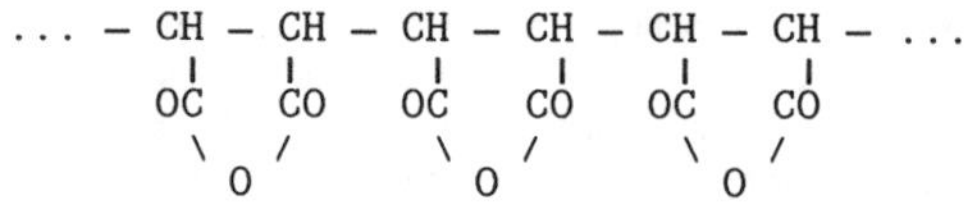

```
... - CH - CH - CH - CH - CH - CH - ...
       |    |    |    |    |    |
       OC   CO   OC   CO   OC   CO
        \  /      \  /      \  /
         O          O         O
```

which produces no gas but releases about 140 kcal/kg;

(c) complex exothermic degradations giving gases and leaving a sooty residue.

Three points should be noted:

1° The contamination of the substance by alkali metal ions was caused by small leaks of the heat transfer salt mixture (see 17.1.4) into the reactor in which benzene vapour is oxidised to maleic anhydride. These extremely small leaks had no effect on the working of the reactor; their harmfulness became apparent only in a later stage of manufacture.

2° An induction period of several hours elapsed between the beginning of heating and the explosion.

3° The release of heat from the substance during decomposition certainly did not exceed 200 kcal/kg, which contradicts the statement reported in the third paragraph of 2.11 and confirms the conclusion reached at the end of 2.11.

Maleic anhydride is only one example amongst many others of organic substances whose reaction is quite safe when the substance is pure but which becomes explosive in the presence of certain impurities which behave as catalysts in low quantities. Thus, a study [[22] has been published of the explosion in a factory in 1976 of an autoclave in which hydrogen was being used to reduce 3,4–dichloronitrobenzene to 3,4–dichloroaniline. The inquiry proved that the presence in minute quantities of nitrate ions had considerably modified the evolution of this hydrogenation reaction.

Consequently, when conducting an initial study in the laboratory of a reaction which is later to be carried out on an industrial scale, it is vital to analyse the potential action of impurities which can be reasonably considered to be present in the commercial products to be used.

32.2 EXPLOSIONS WITH A PHYSICAL CAUSE

32.2.1 Pneumatic explosions

When a fluid in an apparatus exerts on the internal wall a pressure higher than the atmospheric pressure applied to the outside, the container is said to be *pressurised*. If it is not strong enough, it may burst. The effects of such a rupture vary according to the nature of the fluid contents:

1˙ If the fluid is a liquid of low volatility, in other words a liquid whose saturating vapour pressure at the temperature prevailing inside the apparatus is lower than atmospheric pressure, then a rupture leads to only a small amount of vaporisation and the temperature of the liquid changes hardly at all. But if the pressure rises and the rupture produces only a small opening, then the liquid will be expelled at high velocity. During hydraulic tests under pressure using water at ordinary temperature, metal tanks have burst along a defective welding join, throwing out a kind of liquid blade which has caused profound ecchymosis of the thorax or fatal lesions of the abdominal viscera to nearby observers. Consequently, a hydraulic pressure test, particularly on a large–volume container at high pressure, must be carried out with great care.

2˙ If the fluid content is a liquid at a temperature at which its vapour pressure is higher than the pressure of the outside medium, a burst in the container will expel the liquid with at least partial vaporisation. Sometimes the expansion cools the fluid to some extent, leaving some of it in liquid form at a very low temperature. When the compressed fluid is very hot, like the water in a steam boiler when it is in operation, the entire contents are expelled as vapour. At the moment of rupture a shock wave is transmitted to the ambient medium and if the container fragments, splinters will be thrown off with considerable momentum.

3˙ If the fluid is a compressed gas, it is expelled at high velocity through the opening, cooling down at the same time. A shock wave is also created and fragments may be thrown over some distance.

Cases 2 and 3 are a *pneumatic explosion*, a phenomenon in which a large quantity of gas is released in a very short space of time. Explosions of a chemical nature are exothermic and give gases at very high temperatures, but pneumatic explosions are endothermic and may give relatively very cold gases between 50 and 60˙C below the ambient temperature.

The pressure does not have to be very high for a pneumatic explosion to be dangerous, and such an explosion may even occur in the most banal of circumstances: for example, a person using the end of a fork to remove the cap from a bottle of non–alcoholic fizzy drink that had not been kept cool had one eye badly damaged when the cap was expelled at high speed. There

have also been cases of people blinded in one eye by corks from champagne
bottles, and explosions have been reported [14] of bottles of beer.   In
this respect, it should be noted that glass containers are not very safe.
Bottles tested to 30 bars have been shattered shortly after by a pressure
of 3 bars, probably because there were already cracks in the glass.

32.2.2 Pressure vessels

Apparatuses or constructions of any kind are called pressure vessels when
they are designed to use, store, or transport compressed fluids.   Such
apparatuses are governed in all industrialised countries by regulations
covering construction, maintenance, inspection (including internal and
external examination and regular repeating of the initial hydraulic test),
and use.   Both producers and users of such apparatuses must study these
regulations minutely, and they must be well known to the engineers in a
factory whose responsibility it is to maintain the equipment.   In factories
in the chemical industry in particular special attention should be paid to
apparatuses exposed to internal or external corrosion by normal operation
or because of environmental factors.

The papers written by Servant [15] and de Torquat [16] contain valuable
information on the safety of pressure vessels, while the protection from
fire of large pressurised tanks has been studied in a highly pertinent
paper by Kletz [17].

When building apparatuses and the connected pipes and valves, account
must be taken of the temperature and pressure conditions to which they are
to be subjected both in normal running and on start-up and shut-down, and
even to highly unlikely but still foreseeable anomalies of operation.   In
particular, the nature of metals and steels used must be chosen in relation
to these conditions.   Indeed, this is also true of apparatuses which work
at close to atmospheric pressure.   It should not be forgotten that ordinary
carbon steels become brittle at temperatures just below $0°C$.   The explosion
which occurred in a factory in the Netherlands in 1975 and which left
fourteen people dead [23] was caused by the brittle fracture at around $0°C$
of part of a pipe which led to a large leak of propylene which mixed with
air and exploded two minutes later on contact with a hot oven.

32.2.3 Accidental pressurisation of a container

Pneumatic explosions may occur not only in pressurised apparatuses but also
in other equipment which has been pressurised either deliberately by an
operator who does not know that in doing so he is contravening regulations,
as happened with an ordinary metal drum which had been equipped to work as
an acid-egg, or more frequently by mistake.   The latter case may arise, for
example, when the evaporation pipe on an ordinary tank for storing liquid
becomes blocked by water trapped at a low point freezing over in winter.
Another, unfortunately quite frequent, type of accident is the one which
happens when a hollow part to be repaired is heated without realising that
it may not be empty.   The ball of a ball-cock into which water has leaked
and then become trapped because the opening has closed for some reason will
explode and throw out lethal splinters when placed on a forge fire.   A
closed part should never be heated until it has first been opened or pierced.

The accidental pressurising of a container may be caused by slow chemical reactions giving off gases. Cases of this type are frequent in the chemical industry. The following are just a few examples:

(a) Sulphamic acid, which is used as a cleaning agent, slowly attacks the metal when stored in iron containers. The hydrogen released creates a pressure which ultimately shatters the container.

(b) In hermetic containers housing calcium hypochlorite the pressure builds up gradually until the container is shattered.

(c) A drum which had held dimethyl sulphate was left open to the air for some time and then closed again. Moisture from the atmosphere which had entered the container hydrolysed the ester to give sulphuric acid which attacked the metal and caused the pressure to rise.

(d) Around 1973, a metal drum containing isopropyl chloroformate sent from France exploded several weeks later in Great Britain because of a release of gas inside.

(e) In 1949, a drum of brewer's yeast exploded on a Paris street because of a build-up of carbon dioxide inside it.

32.2.4 Implosions

An *implosion* is the violent crushing or shattering of a container with an internal pressure lower than the pressure applied on it from the outside.

One remarkable case of implosion was that which damaged railway tankers carrying butane in Neufchateau in January 1976. During a particularly cold night the pressure inside the tankers dropped to below atmospheric and the tankers, which were 3 m in diameter and very long, were crushed in the middle.

Another case is that of a tank containing molten naphthalene which was being pumped into another apparatus. The vent pipe, which would normally have allowed air into the tank as it was being emptied, was blocked by a sublimate of naphthalene. The pressure in the tank fell low enough to cause the walls to cave in.

On more than one occasion, pumping water into a large ammonia tank emptied of liquid but containing NH_3 gas has caused the gas to dissolve almost instantaneously, leading to loss of pressure and implosion.

There are frequent implosions of glass equipment in laboratories with dangerous splinters being hurled over some distance. An empty bell-jar with even the slightest apparent defect should not be used. A case has also been reported of a large 5-litre conical flask being filled with warm distilled water and then corked so hermetically that cooling condensed the water vapour and led to a fall in internal pressure. The implosion cracked a bench tile and hurled large splinters across the room.

32.2.5 Gas cylinders

Amongst pressure vessels, gas cylinders deserve a special mention, not only because there are so many of them in industry, but also because they cause accidents which happen as a result of negligence or ignorance on the part of the user. The following are some probable causes:

1° Lack of care, maintenance, or inspection, which allows *internal corrosion* to weaken the wall dangerously. In this respect, it should be remembered that most compressed or liquefied gases are not corrosive with ordinary steels when they are very pure, but that they become more or less so when they contain certain impurities, of which the most common is water. Weighing an empty cylinder can give some idea of the degree of corrosion which may have taken place inside. Any loss of weight compared with the tare stamped on the cylinder is obviously proof of corrosion unless some integral part of the cylinder (valve, foot-ring) has been changed without altering the stamped tare. Surplus weight is also a sign of corrosion because it comes from the transformation of a layer of metal on the internal wall into an oxide, a chloride, or some other compound which has stuck to the wall. If the empty weight is the same as the tare, one can only *assume* that there has been no corrosion, since oxides may have formed and then been partly or wholly flushed out during cleaning.

2˙ Weakening of the wall by *external corrosion*, since cylinders are often used in a humid and polluted, and therefore corrosive, environment. The base of the cylinder or the parts of the shell hidden by the foot-ring are most affected by this kind of corrosion, which is why the foot-ring should be removed when the cylinder is due for external inspection.

3˙ *Excessive filling* of a liquefied gas cylinder. According to the regulations governing the transport of dangerous materials, at the maximum allowable temperature, which is set rather arbitrarily in France at 50˙C, a minimum volume of 3% of the total (or 5% in the case of a toxic gas) must be left in the cylinder for the gas phase. This ullage is deemed necessary to allow for errors of weighing during filling or errors of tare. For the regulation filling margin to be observed, account must be taken during filling of the temperature of the liquid. Liquefied gases dilate quite appreciably when the temperature rises. For example, when the temperature rises from 10 to 40˙C, the relative increase in volume is

> 5% for nitrogen dioxide,
> 7.5% for ammonia,
> 11.5% for propene.

Where gases have a critical temperature close to ordinary temperature, the filling ratio depends on the test pressure of the cylinder. For example, for carbon dioxide (critical temperature 31˙C) it is equal to 0.75 kg per litre for containers which have been tested at 250 bars, which is customary for this gas.

4˙ *Exposing the cylinder to a source of heat*. When it is placed too close to a source of heat, the pressure of the contents of a gas cylinder may rise to an excessively high value. On the other hand, every year fires which break out during the night in garages or other small establishments cause explosions of cylinders of compressed oxygen or dissolved acetylene which are used with welding equipment and which are left among combustible materials rather than being moved away.

Some users try to increase the output of gas from a liquefied gas cylinder by heating it with electric resistors or steam. This is a very dangerous practice which has caused a large number of accidents. At the very most one can stand a cylinder in a water bath at a temperature of no more than 40˙C.

In some countries, including the United States, cylinders of compressed gas are fitted with fusible plugs which can be melted by heat and which are relied on to prevent the cylinder from exploding if it is caught in a fire. These fusible plugs consist of small threaded cylinders which are screwed into an opening in the wall of the container. The outer surface has a hollow part into which is poured an alloy with a low melting point. One commonly used alloy has the composition

bismuth	50
lead	25
tin	12.5
cadmium	12.4.

It melts at 70°C. On movable cylinders they are generally placed on top of the dome, whilst in the case of cylinders with a concave base, such as the 800 litre cylinders for chlorine, they are placed on the end which is not fitted with the valve.

Fusible plugs are prone to various sources of damage and deterioration: (a) handling the containers and the jolts they undergo during transport may slightly unseat the fusible part from its housing; (b) slow changes in the structure of the alloy (redistribution of phases) may cause it to contract, giving a slight leak; (c) the alloy may also be chemically altered by the fluid contained in the cylinder.

Consequently, only limited confidence can be placed in the proper working of these fusible plugs which, if they are not replaced at frequent intervals, give rise to leaks which may cause accidents. In addition, experience has shown that on cylinders of dissolved acetylene these plugs do not prevent a cylinder which is the seat of an internal decomposition from exploding if the porous substance used is not of good quality. In Europe regulations do not require the use of such plugs and producers believe, quite rightly, that their disadvantages far outweigh any advantages they may have.

32.2.6 Cases of explosive vaporisation

Some liquids which are pure and free from solid matter in suspension are subject to the phenomenon of delayed boiling: they can be raised at atmospheric pressure to a temperature higher than their normal boiling point without boiling occurring. Such superheating without boiling can be stopped by introducing into the liquid a porous substance which supplies a small amount of gas, so allowing vapour bubbles to form. Boiling initiated in this way is, like normal boiling, nucleated boiling, but it is violent and may have a certain explosive nature. In addition, for each liquid and each pressure there is a degree of superheating which cannot be surpassed, since, when it is reached, the liquid vaporises instantaneously at every point. It is an homogeneous explosion which increases the pressure abruptly.

Such an explosive vaporisation was observed in experiments which involved dropping into the sea quantities of between 20 and 500 litres of cold (around - 150°C) liquefied natural gas. They are described in a paper by Burgess et al., although it was Katz and Sliepcevich [19] who linked these explosions with the phenomenon of delayed boiling.

Similar in nature to these phenomena are cases of explosions which have occurred in containers of liquid hydrogen in which the pressure was reduced by pumping off the gas phase. Consider an isotherm of hydrogen LABG on a Clapeyron diagram (Fig. 32.1). If we start with the liquid at the pressure represented by point P and reduce it, when point A on the saturation curve

SCR is reached, the hydrogen should vaporise at constant pressure according to AB, but it is possible to reduce the liquid to a lower pressure at a point on the arc AM_1 of the unstable section of the Van der Waals isotherm. The same is also true if we begin with a liquid in the presence of its saturating vapour at point A. The locus of the minima M_1 and maxima M_2 of the isotherms is a curve ICJ which defines a region of total instability of the fluid. Between this curve and the saturation curve is a metastable region. If the reduction in pressure has allowed the point M_1 to be reached, the liquid hydrogen then undergoes an explosive vaporisation. Such explosions can be prevented by stirring the liquid or encouraging the formation of nuclei of bubbles.

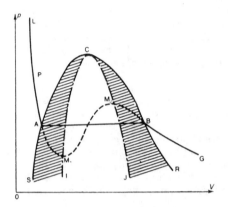

Fig. 32.1 – Diagram of unstable states leading to explosive vaporisation. C: critical point; inside the curve ICJ: total instability range; the section IC of the curve ICJ represents all states in which a true explosive vaporisation occurs; the hatched surface is the range of metastable states; in the left part, between IC and SG, violent boiling may occur.

32.3 NICKEL CARBONYL

It may be a kind of explosive vaporisation, similar to those described in the previous paragraph, which is seen when somewhat sudden heating is applied to nickel carbonyl $Ni(CO)_4$ in which carbon monoxide from its dissociation has remained dissolved in the supersaturated state. But this compound, a liquid which boils at 43°C and which has a vapour pressure of around 0.4 bars at ordinary temperature, is also liable to undergo chemical explosion, albeit of very moderate strength, when heated strongly at a point. From its heat of formation, which is

F_p = 638 kJ/mol in the liquid state
F_p = 610 kJ/mol in the gaseous state,

calculation shows that the explosion, which has the approximate equation

$$Ni(CO)_4 = Ni + 1.5C + CO + 1.5CO_2,$$

gives products raised to about 750°C. As an explosive, the calorific value of nickel carbonyl, which is of the order of 600 kJ/kg, is lower than that of benzoyl peroxide. This kind of low-strength explosion had been observed by Mond in 1891 and by Berthelot [20], who noted the formation of large quantities of carbon black in the explosion products†. Gilliland and Blanchard [21] confirmed that if the vapour given off by the substance at ordinary temperature comes into contact with a hot solid surface, it will explode weakly with formation of a deposit of black soot.

Nickel carbonyl reacts very strongly with many substances, and may then give rise to strong explosions.

BIBLIOGRAPHICAL REFERENCES

[1]   Allan, G. G., Moks, E. & Nelson, E. N. (1967) *Chem. and Ind.*, p. 1706
[2]   N.F.P.A. (1975) *Manual of Hazardous Chemical Reactions*, No. 491 M. Boston
[3]   Staudinger, H. (1922) *Angew. Chemie* 35 657
[4]   Lenze, F. & Metz, L. (1932) *Z. ges. Sch. Sprengst.* 27 255
[5]   Cueilleron, J. (1945) *Bull. Soc. Chim.* [5] 12 88
[6]   Staudinger, H. (1925) *Z. Elektroch.* 31 549
[7]   Senderens, J. B. (1891) *Bull. Soc. Chim.* [3] 6 802
[8]   Clogston, C. C. (1945) *Underwriters Bull. Research* 34 5; cf. (1946) *C.A.* 40 209, and (1950) *Chem. Age* 63 155
[9]   Lindeijer, E. W. (1950) *Chem. Weekblad* 46 571
[10]   Schwab, R. F. (1971) *Loss Prevention* 5 111
[11]   Metz, L. & Roedig (1949) *Chem. Ing. Technik*, p. 191
[12]   Rittenberg, D. & Ponticorvo, L. (1960) *Proc. Nat. Acad. Sci. U.S.* 46 822
[13]   Vogler, C. E., Cecil, O. B. & Koerner, W. E. (1963) *J. Chem. Eng. Data* 8 620
[14]   Raux, J. (1939) *Brasserie et Malterie* 3 25
[15]   Servant, J. (1968) *Arts et manufactures*
[16]   de Torquat, C. (1973) *Annales des Mines*, p. 97
[17]   Kletz, T. (August 1977) *Hydrocarbon Processing*, p. 98
[18]   Burgess, D. S., Murhpy, J. N. & Zabetakis, M. G. (1970) Bureau of Mines *Rep. Inv. 7448*
[19]   Katz, D. L. & Sliepcevich, C. M. (1971) *Hydrocarbon Processing*, p. 240
[20]   Berthelot, M. (1891) *Compt. Rend.* 112 1343
[21]   Gilliland, W. L. & Blanchard, A. A. (1946) *Inorganic Syntheses* 2 234
[22]   Tong, W. R. et al. (1977) *Loss Prevention* 11 71
[23]   Van Eijnatten, A. L. M. (1977) *Loss Prevention*, 11 836

---

† Berthelot wrongly gave the decomposition equation as $Ni(CO)_4 = Ni + 2C + 2CO_2$, which was reproduced by Gilliland and Blanchard in 1946, even though an explosion with this equation would be stronger than the one observed.

Index

NB – Not all chemical substances referred to in the text are included in this index, and for those which are, the list of page numbers supplied is not exhaustive.

ELLIS HORWOOD SERIES IN
APPLIED SCIENCE AND INDUSTRIAL TECHNOLOGY

Series Editor: Dr D. H. SHARP, OBE, former General Secretary, Society of Chemical Industry; formerly General Secretary, Institution of Chemical Engineers; and former Technical Director, Confederation of British Industry.

REFRACTORIES TECHNOLOGY
C. STOREY, Consultant, Durham; former General Manager, Refractories, British Steel Corporation
COATINGS AND SURFACE TREATMENT FOR CORROSION AND WEAR RESISTANCE
K. N. STRAFFORD and P. K. DATTA, School of Material Engineering, Newcastle upon Tyne Polytechnic, and C. G. GOOGAN, Global Corrosion Consultants Limited, Telford
MODERN BATTERY TECHNOLOGY
C. D. S. TUCK, Alcan International Ltd, Oxon
FIRE AND EXPLOSION PROTECTION: A System Approach
D. TUHTAR, Institute of Fire and Explosion Protection, Yugoslavia
PERFUMERY TECHNOLOGY 2nd Edition
F. V. WELLS, Consultant Perfumer and former Editor of *Soap, Perfumery and Cosmetics,* and
M. BILLOT, former Chief Perfumer to Houbigant-Cheramy, Paris, Président d'Honneur de la Société Technique des Parfumeurs de la France
THE MANUFACTURE OF SOAPS, OTHER DETERGENTS AND GLYCERINE
E. WOOLLATT, Consultant, formerly Unilever plc